INSTRUCTOR'S SOLUTIONS MANUAL

JAY R. SCHAFFER
University of Northern Colorado

ELEMENTARY STATISTICS: PICTURING THE WORLD

FIFTH EDITION

Ron Larson
The Pennsylvania State University
The Behrend College

Betsy Farber
Bucks County Community College

Prentice Hall
is an imprint of

PEARSON

The author and publisher of this book have used their best efforts in preparing this book. These efforts include the development, research, and testing of the theories and programs to determine their effectiveness. The author and publisher make no warranty of any kind, expressed or implied, with regard to these programs or the documentation contained in this book. The author and publisher shall not be liable in any event for incidental or consequential damages in connection with, or arising out of, the furnishing, performance, or use of these programs.

Reproduced by Pearson Prentice Hall from electronic files supplied by the author.

ISBN-13: 978-0-321-69366-2
ISBN-10: 0-321-69366-3

1 2 3 4 5 6 BRR 15 14 13 12 11

Prentice Hall
is an imprint of

www.pearsonhighered.com

CONTENTS

CONTENTS

Chapter 1	Introduction to Statistics	1
Chapter 2	Descriptive Statistics	15
Chapter 3	Probability	103
Chapter 4	Discrete Probability Distributions	137
Chapter 5	Normal Probability Distributions	173
Chapter 6	Confidence Intervals	223
Chapter 7	Hypothesis Testing with One Sample	257
Chapter 8	Hypothesis Testing with Two Samples	303
Chapter 9	Correlation and Regression	353
Chapter 10	Chi-Square Tests and the *F*-Distribution	401
Chapter 11	Nonparametric Tests	453
Appendix A	Alternative Presentation of the Standard Normal Distribution	507
Appendix C	Normal Probability Plots and Their Graphs	508
Activities		509
Case Studies		513
Uses and Abuses		531
Real Statistics–Real Decisions		535
Technologies		545

CHAPTER

1

1.1 AN OVERVIEW OF STATISTICS

1.1 Try It Yourself Solutions

1a. The population consists of the prices per gallon of regular gasoline at all gasoline stations in the United States. The sample consists of the prices per gallon of regular gasoline at the 900 surveyed stations.

 b. The data set consists of the 900 prices.

2a. Because the numerical measure of $2,655,395,194 is based on the entire collection of player's salaries, it is from a population.

 b. Because the numerical measure is a characteristic of a population, it is a parameter.

3a. Descriptive statistics involve the statement "76% of women and 60% of men had a physical examination within the previous year."

 b. An inference drawn from the study is that a higher percentage of women had a physical examination within the previous year.

1.1 EXERCISE SOLUTIONS

1. A sample is a subset of a population.

2. It is usually impractical (too expensive and time consuming) to obtain all the population data.

3. A parameter is a numerical description of a population characteristic. A statistic is a numerical description of a sample characteristic.

4. Descriptive statistics and inferential statistics

5. False. A statistic is a numerical measure that describes a sample characteristic.

6. True

7. True

8. False. Inferential statistics involves using a sample to draw conclusions about a population.

9. False. A population is the collection of *all* outcomes, responses, measurements, or counts that are of interest.

10. False. A statistic can differ from sample to sample.

11. The data set is a population because it is a collection of the heights of all the players on a school's basketball team.

12. The data set is a population because it is a collection of the energy collected from all the wind turbines on the wind farm.

13. The data set is a sample because the collection of the 500 spectators is a subset within the population of the stadium's 42,000 spectators.

14. The data set is a population because it is a collection of the annual salaries of all pharmacists at a pharmacy.

15. Sample, because the collection of the 20 patients is a subset within the population

16. The data set is a population since it is a collection of the number of televisions in all U.S. households.

17. Population, because it is a collection of all golfers' scores in the tournament

18. Sample, because only the age of every third person entering the clothing store is recorded

19. Population, because it is a collection of all the U.S. presidents' political parties

20. Sample, because the collection of the 10 soil contamination levels is a subset in the population

21. Population: Party of registered voters in Warren County

Sample: Party of Warren County voters responding to online survey

22. Population: All students who donate at a blood drive

Sample: The students who donate and have type O^+ blood

23. Population: Ages of adults in the United States who own cellular phones

Sample: Ages of adults in the United States who own Samsung cellular phones

24. Population: Income of all homeowners in Texas

Sample: Income of homeowners in Texas with mortgages

25. Population: Collection of all adults in the United States

Sample: Collection of 1000 adults surveyed

26. Population: Collection of all infants in Italy

Sample: Collection of 33,043 infants in the study

27. Population: Collection of all adults in the U.S.

    Sample: Collection of 1442 adults surveyed

28. Population: Collection of all people

    Sample: Collection of 1600 people surveyed

29. Population: Collection of all registered voters

    Sample: Collection of 800 registered voters surveyed

30. Population: Collection of all students at a college

    Sample: Collection of 496 students surveyed

31. Population: Collection of all women in the U.S.

    Sample: Collection of the 546 U.S. women surveyed

32. Population: Collection of all U.S. vacationers

    Sample: Collection of the 791 vacationers surveyed

33. Population: Collection of all Fortune magazine's top 100 companies to work for

    Sample: Collection of the 85 companies who responded to the questionnaire

34. Population: Collection of all light bulbs from the day's production

    Sample: Collection of the 20 light bulbs selected from the day's production

35. Statistic. The value $68,000 is a numerical description of a sample of annual salaries.

36. Statistic. 43% is a numerical description of a sample of high school students.

37. Parameter. The 62 surviving passengers out of 97 total passengers is a numerical description of all of the passengers of the Hindenburg that survived.

38. Parameter. 52% is a numerical description of the total number of governors.

39. Statistic. 8% is a numerical description of a sample of computer users.

40. Parameter. 12% is a numerical description of all new magazines.

41. Statistic. 44% is a numerical description of a sample of all people.

42. Parameter. 21.0 is a numerical description of ACT scores for all graduates.

43. The statement "56% are the primary investors in their household" is an application of descriptive statistics.

An inference drawn from the sample is that an association exists between U.S. women and being the primary investor in their household.

44. The statement "spending at least $2000 for their next vacation" is an example of descriptive statistics.

An inference drawn from the sample is that United States vacationers are associated with spending more than $2000 for their next vacation.

45. Answers will vary.

46. (a) The volunteers in the study represent the sample.

   (b) The population is the collection of all individuals who completed the math test.

   (c) The statement "three times more likely to answer correctly" is an application of descriptive statistics.

   (d) An inference drawn from the sample is that individuals who are not sleep deprived will be three times more likely to answer math questions correctly than individuals who are sleep deprived.

47. (a) An inference drawn from the sample is that senior citizens who live in Florida have better memory than senior citizens who do not live in Florida.

   (b) It implies that if you live in Florida, you will have better memory.

48. (a) An inference drawn from the sample is that the obesity rate among boys ages 2 to 19 is increasing.

   (b) It implies the same trend will continue in future years.

49. Answers will vary.

1.2 DATA CLASSIFICATION

1.2 Try It Yourself Solutions

1a. One data set contains names of cities and the other contains city populations.

   b. City: Nonnumerical
   Population: Numerical

   c. City: Qualitative
   Population: Quantitative

2a. (1) The final standings represent a ranking of basketball teams.

   (2) The collection of phone numbers represents labels. No mathematical computations can be made.

 b. (1) Ordinal, because the data can be put in order

   (2) Nominal, because you cannot make calculations on the data

3a. (1) The data set is the collection of body temperatures.

   (2) The data set is the collection of heart rates.

 b. (1) Interval, because the data can be ordered and meaningful differences can be calculated, but it does not make sense writing a ratio using the temperatures

   (2) Ratio, because the data can be ordered, can be written as a ratio, you can calculate meaningful differences, and the data set contains an inherent zero

1.2 EXERCISE SOLUTIONS

1. Nominal and ordinal

2. Ordinal, interval, and ratio

3. False. Data at the ordinal level can be qualitative or quantitative.

4. False. For data at the interval level, you can calculate meaningful differences between data entries. You cannot calculate meaningful differences at the nominal or ordinal level.

5. False. More types of calculations can be performed with data at the interval level than with data at the nominal level.

6. False. Data at the ratio level can be placed in a meaningful order.

7. Qualitative, because telephone numbers are merely labels

8. Quantitative, because the heights of hot air balloons are a numerical measure

9. Quantitative, because the body temperatures of patients is a numerical measure.

10. Qualitative, because the eye colors are merely labels

11. Quantitative, because the lengths of songs on an MP3 player are numerical measures

12. Quantitative, because the carrying capacities of pickups are numerical measures

13. Qualitative, because the player numbers are merely labels

14. Qualitative, because student ID numbers are merely labels

15. Quantitative, because weights of infants are a numerical measure

16. Qualitative, because species of trees are merely labels

17. Qualitative, because the poll results are merely responses

18. Quantitative, because wait times at a grocery store are a numerical measure

19. Qualitative. Ordinal. Data can be arranged in order, but differences between data entries make no sense.

20. Qualitative. Nominal. No mathematical computations can be made and data are categorized using names.

21. Qualitative. Nominal. No mathematical computations can be made and data are categorized using names.

22. Quantitative. Ratio. A ratio of two data values can be formed so one data value can be expressed as a multiple of another.

23. Qualitative. Ordinal. The data can be arranged in order, but differences between data entries are not meaningful.

24. Quantitative. Ratio. The ratio of two data values can be formed so one data value can be expressed as a multiple of another.

25. Ordinal

26. Ratio

27. Nominal

28. Ratio

29. (a) Interval   (b) Nominal   (c) Ratio   (d) Ordinal

30. (a) Interval   (b) Nominal   (c) Interval   (d) Ratio

31. An inherent zero is a zero that implies "none." Answers will vary.

32. Answers will vary.

1.3 DATA COLLECTION AND EXPERIMENTAL DESIGN

1.3 Try It Yourself Solutions

1a. (1) Focus: Effect of exercise on relieving depression

    (2) Focus: Success of graduates

  b. (1) Population: Collection of all people with depression

  (2) Population: Collection of all university graduates at this large university

  c. (1) Experiment

  (2) Survey

2a. There is no way to tell why people quit smoking. They could have quit smoking either from the gum or from watching the DVD.

  b. Two experiments could be done; one using the gum and the other using the DVD.

3a. Example: start with the first digits 92630782 …

  b. 92 | 63 | 07 | 82 | 40 | 19 | 26

  c. 63, 7, 40, 19, 26

4a. (1) The sample was selected by only using the students in a randomly chosen class. Cluster sampling

  (2) The sample was selected by numbering each student in the school, randomly choosing a starting number, and selecting students at regular intervals from the starting number. Systematic sampling

  b. (1) The sample may be biased because some classes may be more familiar with stem cell research than other classes and have stronger opinions.

  (2) The sample may be biased if there is any regularly occurring pattern in the data.

1.3 EXERCISE SOLUTIONS

1. In an experiment, a treatment is applied to part of a population and responses are observed. In an observational study, a researcher measures characteristics of interest of part of a population but does not change existing conditions.

2. A census includes the entire population; a sample includes only a portion of the population.

3. In a random sample, every member of the population has an equal chance of being selected. In a simple random sample, every possible sample of the same size has an equal chance of being selected.

4. Replication is the repetition of an experiment using a large group of subjects. It is important because it gives validity to the results.

5. True

6. False. A double-blind experiment is used to decrease the placebo effect.

7. False. Using stratified sampling guarantees that members of each group within a population will be sampled.

8. False. A census is a count of an entire population.

9. False. To select a systematic sample, a population is ordered in some way and then members of the population are selected at regular intervals.

10. True

11. Use a census because all the patients are accessible and the number of patients is not too large.

12. Perform an observational study because you want to observe and record motorcycle helmet usage.

13. In this study, you want to measure the effect of a treatment (using a fat substitute) on the human digestive system. So, you would want to perform an experiment.

14. It would be nearly impossible to ask every customer whether he or she would still buy a product with a warning label. So, you should use a survey to collect these data.

15. Because it is impractical to create this situation, you would want to use a simulation.

16. Perform an observational study because you want to observe and record how often people wash their hands in public restrooms.

17. (a) The experimental units are the 30–35 year old females being given the treatment. One treatment is used.

    (b) A problem with the design is that there may be some bias on the part of the researchers if he or she knows which patients were given the real drug. A way to eliminate this problem would be to make the study into a double-blind experiment.

    (c) The study would be a double-blind study if the researcher did not know which patients received the real drug or the placebo.

18. (a) The experimental units are the 80 people with early signs of arthritis. One treatment is used.

    (b) A problem with the design is that the sample size is small. The experiment could be replicated to increase validity.

    (c) In a placebo-controlled double-blind experiment, neither the subject nor the experimenter knows whether the subject is receiving a treatment or a placebo. The experimenter is informed after all the data have been collected.

    (d) The group could be randomly split into 20 males or 20 females in each treatment group.

19. Each U.S. telephone number has an equal chance of being dialed and all samples of 1400 phone numbers have an equal chance of being selected, so this is a simple random sample. Telephone sampling only samples those individuals who have telephones, are available, and are willing to respond, so this is a possible source of bias.

20. Because the persons are divided into strata (rural and urban), and a sample is selected from each stratum, this is a stratified sample.

21. Because the students were chosen due to their convenience of location (leaving the library), this is a convenience sample. Bias may enter into the sample because the students sampled may not be representative of the population of students. For example, there may be an association between time spent at the library and drinking habits.

22. Because the disaster area was divided into grids and thirty grids were then entirely selected, this is a cluster sample. Certain grids may have been much more severely damaged than others, so this is a possible source of bias.

23. Simple random sampling is used because each customer has an equal chance of being contacted, and all samples of 580 customers have an equal chance of being selected.

24. Systematic sampling is used because every tenth person entering the shopping mall is sampled. It is possible for bias to enter the sample if, for some reason, there is a regular pattern to people entering the shopping mall.

25. Because a sample is taken from each one-acre subplot (stratum), this is a stratified sample.

26. Each telephone has an equal chance of being dialed and all samples of 1012 phone numbers have an equal chance of being selected, so this is a simple random sample. Telephone sampling only samples those individuals who have telephones and are willing to respond, so this is a possible source of bias.

27. Answers will vary.

28. Answers will vary.

29. Answers will vary.

30. Answers will vary.

31. Census, because it is relatively easy to obtain the ages of the 115 residents

32. Sampling, because the population of subscribers is too large to easily record their favorite movie type. Random sampling would be advised since it would be too easy to randomly select subscribers then record their favorite movie type.

33. Question is biased because it already suggests that eating whole-grain foods is good for you. The question might be rewritten as "How does eating whole-grain foods affect your health?"

34. Question is biased because it already suggests that text messaging while driving increases the risk of a crash. The question might be rewritten as "Does text messaging while driving increase the risk of a crash?"

35. Question is unbiased because it does not imply how much exercise is good or bad.

36. Question is biased because it already suggests that the media has a negative effect on teen girls' dieting habits. The question might be rewritten as "Do you think the media has an effect on teen girls' dieting habits?"

37. The households sampled represent various locations, ethnic groups, and income brackets. Each of these variables is considered a stratum.

38. Stratified sampling ensures that each segment of the population is represented.

(a) Answers will vary.

(b) Answers will vary.

(c) Answers will vary.

(d) Answers will vary.

39. Observational studies may be referred to as natural experiments because they involve observing naturally occurring events that are not influenced by the study.

40. Open Question
Advantage: Allows respondent to express some depth and shades of meaning in the answer
Disadvantage: Not easily quantified and difficult to compare surveys

Closed Question
Advantage: Easy to analyze results
Disadvantage: May not provide appropriate alternatives and may influence the opinion of the respondent

41. (a) Advantage: Usually results in a savings in the survey cost

(b) Disadvantage: There tends to be a lower response rate and this can introduce a bias into the sample.
Sampling Technique: Convenience sampling

42. Answers will vary.

43. If blinding is not used, then the placebo effect is more likely to occur.

44. The Hawthorne effect occurs when a subject changes behavior because he or she is in an experiment. However, the placebo effect occurs when a subject reacts favorably to a placebo he or she has been given.

45. Both a randomized block design and a stratified sample split their members into groups based on similar characteristics.

CHAPTER 1 REVIEW EXERCISE SOLUTIONS

1. Population: Collection of all U.S. adults

   Sample: Collection of the 1000 U.S. adults that were sampled

2. Population: Collection of all nurses in San Francisco area

   Sample: Collection of 38 nurses in San Francisco area that were sampled

3. Population: Collection of all credit cards

   Sample: Collection of 39 credit cards that were sampled

4. Population: Collection of all physicians in the U.S.

   Sample: Collection of 1205 physicians that were sampled

5. The team payroll is a parameter since it is a numerical description of a population (entire baseball team) characteristic.

6. Since 42% is describing a characteristic of the sample, this is a statistic.

7. Since "10 students" is describing a characteristic of a population of math majors, it is a parameter.

8. Since 50% is describing a characteristic of a sample of U.S. adults who say they oppose drilling for oil and gas in the Arctic National Wildlife Refuge, this is a statistic.

9. The average APR of 12.83% charged by credit cards is representative of the descriptive branch of statistics. An inference drawn from the sample is that all credit cards charge an APR of 12.83%.

10. 60% of all physicians surveyed consider leaving the practice of medicine because they are discouraged over the state of U.S. healthcare is representative of the descriptive branch of statistics. An inference drawn from the sample is that 60% of all physicians surveyed consider leaving the practice of medicine because they are discouraged over the state of U.S. healthcare.

11. Quantitative, because monthly salaries are numerical measurements

12. Qualitative, because Social Security numbers are merely labels for employees

13. Quantitative, because ages are numerical measurements

14. Qualitative, because zip codes are merely labels for the customers

15. Quantitative, because revenues are numerical measures

16. Qualitative, because marital statuses are attributes

17. Interval. It makes no sense saying that 100 degrees is twice as hot as 50 degrees.

18. Ordinal. The data are qualitative but could be arranged in order of severity.

19. Nominal. The data are qualitative and cannot be arranged in a meaningful order.

20. Ratio. The data are numerical, and it makes sense saying that one amount is twice as large as another amount.

21. Because CEOs keep accurate records of charitable donations, you could take a census.

22. Because it is impractical to create this situation, you would want to perform a simulation.

23. Perform an experiment because you want to measure the effect of training from animal shelters on inmates.

24. Because it would be nearly impossible to ask every college professor about teaching classes online, you should take a survey to collect the data.

25. The subjects could be split into male and female and then be randomly assigned to each of the five treatment groups.

26. Number the volunteers and then use a random number generator to assign subjects to one of the treatment groups or the control group.

27. Answers will vary.

28. Sample. Take a survey, because asking all students at the university about their favorite spring break destinations would be nearly impossible.

29. Because random telephone numbers were generated and called, this is a simple random sample.

30. Because the student sampled a convenient group of friends, this is a convenience sample.

31. Because each community is considered a cluster and every pregnant woman in a selected community is surveyed, this is a cluster sample.

32. Because every third car is stopped, this is a systematic sample.

33. Because grade levels are considered strata and 25 students are sampled from each stratum, this is a stratified sample.

34. Because of the convenience of surveying people waiting for their baggage, this is a convenience sample.

35. Telephone sampling only samples individuals who have telephones, are available, and are willing to respond.

36. Due to the convenience sample taken, the study may be biased toward the opinions of the student's friends.

37. The selected communities may not be representative of the entire area.

38. It may be difficult for the law enforcement official to stop every third car.

CHAPTER 1 QUIZ SOLUTIONS

1. Population: Collection of all men

    Sample: Collection of 20,000 men in study

2. (a) Statistic. 19% is a characteristic of a sample of Internet users.

    (b) Parameter. 90% is a characteristic of the entire Board of Trustees (population).

    (c) Statistic. 55% is a characteristic of a sample of chief financial officers and senior comptrollers.

3. (a) Qualitative, since debit card pin numbers are merely labels.

    (b) Quantitative, since a final score is a numerical measure.

4. (a) Ordinal. Badge numbers may be ordered numerically according to seniority of service, but no mathematical computations can be made.

    (b) Ratio. It makes sense to say that the horsepower of one car was twice as many as another car.

    (c) Ordinal, because data can be arranged in order but the differences between data entries make no sense

    (d) Interval, because meaningful differences between entries can be calculated, but a zero entry is not an inherent zero.

5. (a) In this study, you want to measure the effect of a treatment (low dietary intake of vitamin C and iron) on lead levels in adults. You want to perform an experiment.

    (b) Because it would be difficult to survey every individual within 500 miles of your home, sampling should be used.

6. Randomized Block Design

7. (a) Because people were chosen due to their convenience of location (on the campground), this is a convenience sample.

    (b) Because every tenth part is selected from an assembly line, this is a systematic sample.

    (c) Stratified sample because the population is first stratified and then a sample is collected from each stratum

8. Convenience

CHAPTER 2

Descriptive Statistics

2.1 FREQUENCY DISTRIBUTIONS AND THEIR GRAPHS

2.1 Try It Yourself Solutions

1a. The number of classes is 8.

b. Min = 35, Max = 89, Class width = $\dfrac{\text{Range}}{\text{Number of classes}} = \dfrac{89-35}{8} = 6.75 \Rightarrow 7$

c.

Lower limit	Upper limit
35	41
42	48
49	55
56	62
63	69
70	76
77	83
84	90

d. See part (e).

e.

Class	Frequency, f
35-41	2
42-48	5
49-55	7
56-62	7
63-69	10
70-76	5
77-83	8
84-90	6

2a. See part (b).

b.

Class	Frequency, f	Midpoint	Relative frequency	Cumulative frequency
35-41	2	38	0.04	2
42-48	5	45	0.10	7
49-55	7	52	0.14	14
56-62	7	59	0.14	21
63-69	10	66	0.20	31
70-76	5	73	0.10	36
77-83	8	80	0.16	44
84-90	6	87	0.12	50
	$\sum f = 50$		$\sum \frac{f}{n} = 1$	

c. 72% of the 50 richest people are older than 55.
4% of the 50 richest people are younger than 42.
The most common age bracket for the 50 richest people is 63-69.

3a.

Class Boundaries
34.5-41.5
41.5-48.5
48.5-55.5
55.5-62.5
62.5-69.5
69.5-76.5
76.5-83.5
83.5-90.5

b. Use class midpoints for the horizontal scale and frequency for the vertical scale. (Class boundaries can also be used for the horizontal scale.)

c.

d. 72% of the 50 richest people are older than 55.
4% of the 50 richest people are younger than 42.
The most common age bracket for the 50 richest people is 63-69.

4a. Use class midpoints for the horizontal scale and frequency for the vertical scale. (Class boundaries can also be used for the horizontal scale.)

b. See part (c).

c.

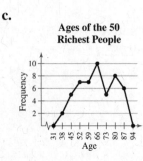

d. The frequency of ages increases up to 66 and then decreases.

5abc.

Ages of the 50 Richest People

6a. Use upper class boundaries for the horizontal scale and cumulative frequency for the vertical scale.

b. See part (c).

c.

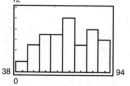

Ages of the 50 Richest People

d. Approximately 40 of the 50 richest people are 80 years or younger.

e. Answers will vary.

7ab.

2.1 EXERCISE SOLUTIONS

1. Organizing the data into a frequency distribution may make patterns within the data more evident. Sometimes it is easier to identify patterns of a data set by looking at a graph of the frequency distribution.

2. If there are too few or too many classes, it may be difficult to detect patterns because the data are too condensed or too spread out.

3. Class limits determine which numbers can belong to that class.
Class boundaries are the numbers that separate classes without forming gaps between them.

4. Relative frequency of a class is the portion or percentage of the data that falls in that class. Cumulative frequency of a class is the sum of the frequencies of that class and all previous classes.

5. The sum of the relative frequencies must be 1 or 100% because it is the sum of all portions or percentages of the data.

6. A frequency polygon displays relative frequencies whereas an ogive displays cumulative frequencies.

7. False. Class width is the difference between the lower (or upper limits) of consecutive classes.

8. True

9. False. An ogive is a graph that displays cumulative frequencies.

10. True

11. Class width $= \dfrac{\text{Range}}{\text{Number of classes}} = \dfrac{64-9}{7} \approx 7.9 \Rightarrow 8$
Lower class limits: 9, 17, 25, 33, 41, 49, 57
Upper class limits: 16, 24, 32, 40, 48, 56, 64

12. Class width $= \dfrac{\text{Range}}{\text{Number of classes}} = \dfrac{88-12}{6} \approx 12.7 \Rightarrow 13$
Lower class limits: 12, 25, 38, 51, 64, 77
Upper class limits: 24, 37, 50, 63, 76, 89

13. Class width $= \dfrac{\text{Range}}{\text{Number of classes}} = \dfrac{135-17}{8} = 14.75 \Rightarrow 15$
Lower class limits: 17, 32, 47, 62, 77, 92, 107, 122
Upper class limits: 31, 46, 61, 76, 91, 106, 121, 136

14. Class width $= \dfrac{\text{Range}}{\text{Number of classes}} = \dfrac{247-54}{10} = 19.3 \Rightarrow 20$
Lower class limits: 54, 74, 94, 114, 134, 154, 174, 194, 214, 234
Upper class limits: 73, 93, 113, 133, 153, 173, 193, 213, 233, 253

15a. Class width $= 31 - 20 = 11$

b. and c.

Class	Frequency, f	Midpoint	Class boundaries
20-30	19	25	19.5-30.5
31-41	43	36	30.5-41.5
42-52	68	47	41.5-52.5
53-63	69	58	52.5-63.5
64-74	74	69	63.5-74.5
75-85	68	80	74.5-85.5
86-96	24	91	85.5-96.5

16a. Class width $= 10 - 0 = 10$

b. and c.

Class	Frequency, f	Midpoint	Class boundaries
0-9	188	4.5	-0.5-9.5
10-19	372	14.5	9.5-19.5
20-29	264	24.5	19.5-29.5
30-39	205	34.5	29.5-39.5
40-49	83	44.5	39.5-49.5
50-59	76	54.5	49.5-59.5
60-69	32	64.5	59.5-69.5

17.

Class	Frequency, f	Midpoint	Relative frequency	Cumulative frequency
20-30	19	25	0.05	19
31-41	43	36	0.12	62
42-52	68	47	0.19	130
53-63	69	58	0.19	199
64-74	74	69	0.20	273
75-85	68	80	0.19	341
86-96	24	91	0.07	365
	$\sum f = 365$		$\sum \dfrac{f}{n} \approx 1$	

18.

Class	Frequency, f	Midpoint	Relative frequency	Cumulative frequency
0-9	188	4.5	0.15	188
10-19	372	14.5	0.30	560
20-29	264	24.5	0.22	824
30-39	205	34.5	0.17	1029
40-49	83	44.5	0.07	1112
50-59	76	54.5	0.06	1188
60-69	32	64.5	0.03	1220
	$\sum f = 1220$		$\sum \dfrac{f}{n} = 1$	

19a. Number of classes = 7 **b.** Least frequency ≈ 10
   c. Greatest frequency ≈ 300 **d.** Class width = 10

20a. Number of classes = 7 **b.** Least frequency ≈ 100
   c. Greatest frequency ≈ 900 **d.** Class width = 5

21a. 50 **b.** 22.5-23.5 pounds

22a. 50 **b.** 64-66 inches

23a. 42 **b.** 29.5 pounds
  c. 35 **d.** 2
24a. 48 **b.** 66 inches
  c. 20 **d.** 6

25a. Class with greatest relative frequency: 8-9 inches
     Class with least relative frequency: 17-18 inches

  b. Greatest relative frequency ≈ 0.195
     Least relative frequency ≈ 0.005

  c. Approximately 0.015

26a. Class with greatest relative frequency: 19-20 minutes
     Class with least relative frequency: 21-22 minutes

  b. Greatest relative frequency ≈ 40%
     Least relative frequency ≈ 2%

  c. Approximately 33%

27. Class with greatest frequency: 29.5-32.5
   Classes with least frequency: 11.5-14.5 and 38.5-41.5

28. Class with greatest frequency: 7.75-8.25
   Class with least frequency: 6.25-6.75

29. Class width = $\dfrac{\text{Range}}{\text{Number of classes}} = \dfrac{39-0}{5} = 7.8 \Rightarrow 8$

Class	Frequency, f	Midpoint	Relative frequency	Cumulative frequency
0-7	8	3.5	0.32	8
8-15	8	11.5	0.32	16
16-23	3	19.5	0.12	19
24-31	3	27.5	0.12	22
32-39	3	35.5	0.12	25
	$\sum f = 25$		$\sum \dfrac{f}{n} = 1$	

Classes with greatest frequency: 0-7, 8-15
Classes with least frequency: 16-23, 24-31, 32-39

30. Class width = $\dfrac{\text{Range}}{\text{Number of classes}} = \dfrac{530 - 30}{6} \approx 83.3 \Rightarrow 84$

Class	Frequency, f	Midpoint	Relative frequency	Cumulative frequency
30-113	5	71.5	0.1724	5
114-197	7	155.5	0.2414	12
198-281	8	239.5	0.2759	20
282-365	2	323.5	0.0690	22
366-449	3	407.5	0.1034	25
450-533	4	491.5	0.1379	29
	$\sum f = 29$		$\sum \dfrac{f}{n} = 1$	

Class with greatest frequency: 198-281
Class with least frequency: 282-365

31. Class width = $\dfrac{\text{Range}}{\text{Number of classes}} = \dfrac{7119 - 1000}{6} \approx 1019.83 \Rightarrow 1020$

Class	Frequency, f	Midpoint	Relative frequency	Cumulative frequency
1000-2019	12	1509.5	0.5455	12
2020-3039	3	2529.5	0.1364	15
3040-4059	2	3549.5	0.0909	17
4060-5079	3	4569.5	0.1364	20
5080-6099	1	5589.5	0.0455	21
6100-7119	1	6609.5	0.0455	22
	$\sum f = 22$		$\sum \dfrac{f}{n} \approx 1$	

July Sales for Representatives

The graph shows that most of the sales representatives at the company sold between $1000 and $2019. (Answers will vary.)

32. Class width = $\dfrac{\text{Range}}{\text{Number of classes}} = \dfrac{51 - 32}{5} = 3.8 \Rightarrow 4$

Class	Frequency, f	Midpoint	Relative frequency	Cumulative frequency
32-35	3	33.5	0.1250	3
36-39	9	37.5	0.3750	12
40-43	8	41.5	0.3333	20
44-47	3	45.5	0.1250	23
48-51	1	49.5	0.0417	24
	$\sum f = 24$		$\sum \dfrac{f}{n} = 1$	

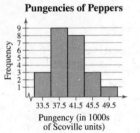

Pungencies of Peppers

Pungency (in 1000s of Scoville units)

The graph shows that most of the pungencies of the peppers were between 36 and 43 Scoville units. (Answers will vary.)

33. Class width = $\dfrac{\text{Range}}{\text{Number of classes}} = \dfrac{514-291}{8} = 27.875 \Rightarrow 28$

Class	Frequency, f	Midpoint	Relative frequency	Cumulative frequency
291-318	5	304.5	0.1667	5
319-346	4	332.5	0.1333	9
347-374	3	360.5	0.1000	12
375-402	5	388.5	0.1667	17
403-430	6	416.5	0.2000	23
431-458	4	444.5	0.1333	27
459-486	1	472.5	0.0333	28
487-514	2	500.5	0.0667	30
	$\sum f = 30$		$\sum \dfrac{f}{n} = 1$	

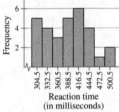

Reaction Times for Females

Reaction time (in milliseconds)

The graph shows that the most frequent reaction times were between 403 and 430 milliseconds. (Answers will vary.)

34. Class width = $\dfrac{\text{Range}}{\text{Number of classes}} = \dfrac{2888-2456}{5} = 86.4 \Rightarrow 87$

Class	Frequency, f	Midpoint	Relative frequency	Cumulative frequency
2456-2542	7	2499	0.28	7
2543-2629	3	2586	0.12	10
2630-2716	2	2673	0.08	12
2717-2803	4	2760	0.16	16
2804-2890	9	2847	0.36	25
	$\sum f = 25$		$\sum \dfrac{f}{n} = 1$	

Pressure at Fracture Time

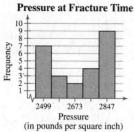

The graph shows that the most common pressures at fracture time were between 2804 and 2890 pounds per square inch. (Answers will vary.)

35. Class width = $\dfrac{\text{Range}}{\text{Number of classes}} = \dfrac{55-24}{5} = 6.2 \Rightarrow 7$

Class	Frequency, f	Midpoint	Relative frequency	Cumulative frequency
24-30	9	27	0.30	9
31-37	8	34	0.27	17
38-44	10	41	0.33	27
45-51	2	48	0.07	29
52-58	1	55	0.03	30
	$\sum f = 30$		$\sum \dfrac{f}{n} = 1$	

Gasoline Consumption

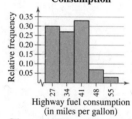

Class with greatest relative frequency: 38-44
Class with least relative frequency: 52-58

36. Class width = $\dfrac{\text{Range}}{\text{Number of classes}} = \dfrac{80-10}{5} = 14 \Rightarrow 15$

Class	Frequency, f	Midpoint	Relative frequency	Cumulative frequency
10-24	11	17	0.3438	11
25-39	9	32	0.2813	20
40-54	6	47	0.1875	26
55-69	2	62	0.0625	28
70-84	4	77	0.1250	32
	$\sum f = 32$		$\sum \dfrac{f}{n} \approx 1$	

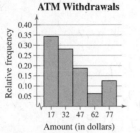

ATM Withdrawals

Class with greatest relative frequency: 10-24
Class with least relative frequency: 55-69

37. Class width $= \dfrac{\text{Range}}{\text{Number of classes}} = \dfrac{462 - 138}{5} = 64.8 \Rightarrow 65$

Class	Frequency, f	Midpoint	Relative frequency	Cumulative frequency
138-202	12	170	0.46	12
203-267	6	235	0.23	18
268-332	4	300	0.15	22
333-397	1	365	0.04	23
398-462	3	430	0.12	26
	$\sum f = 26$		$\sum \dfrac{f}{n} = 1$	

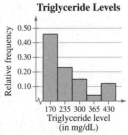

Triglyceride Levels

Class with greatest relative frequency: 138-202
Class with least relative frequency: 333-397

38. Class width $= \dfrac{\text{Range}}{\text{Number of classes}} = \dfrac{14 - 6}{5} = 1.6 \Rightarrow 2$

Class	Frequency, f	Midpoint	Relative frequency	Cumulative frequency
6-7	3	6.5	0.12	3
8-9	10	8.5	0.38	13
10-11	6	10.5	0.23	19
12-13	6	12.5	0.23	25
14-15	1	14.5	0.04	26
	$\sum f = 26$		$\sum \dfrac{f}{n} = 1$	

Years of Service

Class with greatest relative frequency: 8-9
Class with least relative frequency: 14-15

39. Class width = $\dfrac{\text{Range}}{\text{Number of classes}} = \dfrac{73-52}{6} = 3.5 \Rightarrow 4$

Class	Frequency, f	Relative frequency	Cumulative frequency
52-55	3	0.125	3
56-59	3	0.125	6
60-63	9	0.375	15
64-67	4	0.167	19
68-71	4	0.167	23
72-75	1	0.042	24
	$\sum f = 24$	$\sum \dfrac{f}{n} \approx 1$	

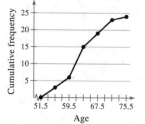

Retirement Ages

Location of the greatest increase in frequency: 60-63

40. Class width = $\dfrac{\text{Range}}{\text{Number of classes}} = \dfrac{57-16}{6} \approx 6.83 \Rightarrow 7$

Class	Frequency, f	Relative frequency	Cumulative frequency
16-22	2	0.10	2
23-29	3	0.15	5
30-36	8	0.40	13
37-43	5	0.25	18
44-50	0	0.00	18
51-57	2	0.10	20
	$\sum f = 20$	$\sum \dfrac{f}{n} = 1$	

Daily Saturated Fat Intake

Location of the greatest increase in frequency: 30-36

41. Class width = $\dfrac{\text{Range}}{\text{Number of classes}} = \dfrac{98-47}{5} = 10.2 \Rightarrow 11$

Class	Frequency, f	Midpoint	Relative frequency	Cumulative frequency
47-57	1	52	0.05	1
58-68	1	63	0.05	2
69-79	5	74	0.25	7
80-90	8	85	0.40	15
91-101	5	96	0.25	20
	$\sum f = 20$		$\sum \dfrac{f}{N} = 1$	

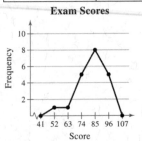

Exam Scores

The graph shows that the most frequent exam scores were between 80 and 90. (Answers will vary.)

42. Class width = $\dfrac{\text{Range}}{\text{Number of classes}} = \dfrac{15-0}{6} = 2.5 \Rightarrow 3$

Class	Frequency, f	Midpoint	Relative frequency	Cumulative frequency
0-2	17	1	0.3953	17
3-5	17	4	0.3953	34
6-8	7	7	0.1628	41
9-11	1	10	0.0233	42
12-14	0	13	0.0000	42
15-17	1	16	0.0233	43
	$\sum f = 43$		$\sum \dfrac{f}{N} = 1$	

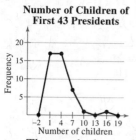

Number of Children of First 43 Presidents

The graph shows that most of the first 43 presidents had fewer than 6 children. (Answers will vary.)

43a. Class width = $\dfrac{\text{Range}}{\text{Number of classes}} = \dfrac{120-65}{6} \approx 9.2 \Rightarrow 10$

Class	Frequency, f	Midpoint	Relative frequency	Cumulative frequency
65-74	4	69.5	0.17	4
75-84	7	79.5	0.29	11
85-94	4	89.5	0.17	15
95-104	5	99.5	0.21	20
105-114	3	109.5	0.13	23
115-124	1	119.5	0.04	24
	$\sum f = 24$		$\sum \dfrac{f}{N} \approx 1$	

b.

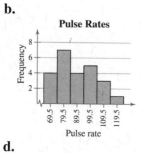

c.

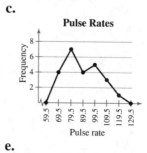

d.

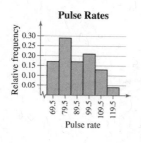

e.

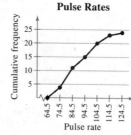

44a.   Class width = $\dfrac{\text{Range}}{\text{Number of classes}} = \dfrac{378-7}{8} = 46.375 \Rightarrow 47$

Class	Frequency, f	Midpoint	Relative frequency	Cumulative frequency
7-53	22	30	0.44	22
54-100	16	77	0.32	38
101-147	6	124	0.12	44
148-194	2	171	0.04	46
195-241	2	218	0.04	48
242-288	0	265	0	48
289-335	0	312	0	48
336-382	2	359	0.04	50
	$\sum f = 50$		$\sum \dfrac{f}{N} = 1$	

b.

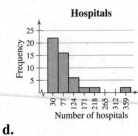

c.

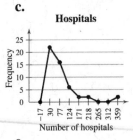

d.

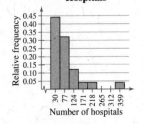

e.

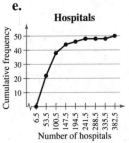

45.

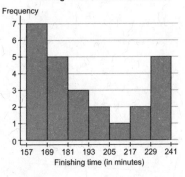

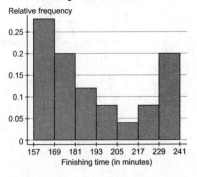

46.

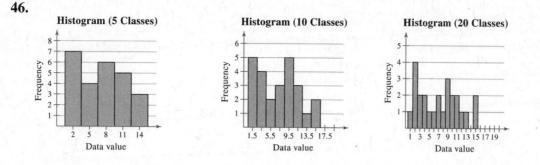

In general, a greater number of classes better preserves the actual values of the data set but is not as helpful for observing general trends and making conclusions. In choosing the number of classes, an important consideration is the size of the data set. For instance, you would not want to use 20 classes if your data set contained 20 entries. In this particular example, as the number of classes increases, the histogram shows more fluctuation. The histograms with 10 and 20 classes have classes with zero frequencies. Not much is gained by using more than five classes. Therefore, it appears that five classes would be best.

47a. Class width $= \dfrac{\text{Range}}{\text{Number of classes}} = \dfrac{104-61}{8} = 5.375 \Rightarrow 6$

Class	Frequency, f	Midpoint	Relative frequency
61-66	1	63.5	0.0333
67-72	3	69.5	0.1000
73-78	6	75.5	0.2000
79-84	10	81.5	0.3333
85-90	5	87.5	0.1667
91-96	2	93.5	0.0667
97-102	2	99.5	0.0667
103-108	1	105.5	0.0333
	$\sum f = 30$		$\sum \dfrac{f}{N} = 1$

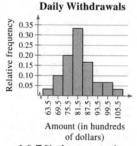

b. 16.7%, because the sum of the relative frequencies for the last three classes is 0.167.

c. $9600, because the sum of the relative frequencies for the last two classes is 0.10.

48a. Class width = $\dfrac{\text{Range}}{\text{Number of classes}} = \dfrac{2250 - 976}{10} = 127.4 \Rightarrow 128$

Class	Frequency, f	Relative frequency
976-1103	1	0.02
1104-1231	1	0.02
1232-1359	4	0.08
1360-1487	6	0.12
1488-1615	7	0.14
1616-1743	9	0.18
1744-1871	6	0.12
1872-1999	8	0.16
2000-2127	5	0.10
2128-2255	3	0.06
	$\sum f = 50$	$\sum \dfrac{f}{N} = 1$

SAT Scores

b. 62%, because the sum of the relative frequencies of the class starting with 1616 and all classes with higher scores is 0.62.

c. A score of 1360 or above, because the sum of the relative frequencies of the class starting with 1360 and all classes with higher scores is 0.88.

2.2 MORE GRAPHS AND DISPLAYS

2.2 Try It Yourself Solutions

1a.
```
3|
4|
5|
6|
7|
8|
```

b.
```
3|6  5                              Key 3|6 = 36
4|9  7  6  4  3  2
5|9  8  7  6  4  4  3  3  1  1
6|9  9  8  7  6  6  5  5  4  3  1  1  0
7|8  8  7  6  3  3  3  2
8|9  9  7  6  6  5  3  3  2  1  0
```

c.
```
3|5  6                              Key 3|5 = 35
4|2  3  4  6  7  9
5|1  1  3  3  4  4  6  7  8  9
6|0  1  1  3  4  5  5  6  6  7  8  9  9
7|2  3  3  3  6  7  8  8
8|0  1  2  3  3  5  6  6  7  9  9
```

d. More than 50% of the 50 richest people are older than 60. (Answers will vary.)

2a, b.

```
3|                      Key  3|5 = 35
3|5  6
4|2  3  4
4|6  7  9
5|1  1  3  3  4  4
5|6  7  8  9
6|0  1  1  3  4
6|5  5  6  6  7  8  9  9
7|2  3  3  3
7|6  7  8  8
8|0  1  2  3  3
8|5  6  6  7  9  9
```

c. Most of the 50 richest people are older than 60. (Answers will vary.)

3a. Use the age for the horizontal axis.

   b.

**Ages of the 50
Richest People**

c. A large percentage of the ages are over 60. (Answers will vary.)

4a.

Type of Degree	f	Relative Frequency	Angle
Associate's	455	0.23	82.8°
Bachelor's	1052	0.54	194.4°
Master's	325	0.17	61.2°
First Professional	71	0.04	14.4°
Doctoral	38	0.02	7.2°
	$\sum f = 50$	$\sum \dfrac{f}{N} = 1$	$\sum = 360°$

b.

**Earned Degrees
Conferred in 1990**

Doctoral 2% — First professional 4% — Master's 17% — Bachelor's 54% — Associate's 23%

c. From 1990 to 2007, as percentages of total degrees conferred, associate's degrees increased by 1%, bachelor's degrees decreased by 3%, master's degrees increased by 3%, first professional degrees decreased by 1%, and doctoral degrees remained unchanged.

5a.

Cause	Frequency, f
Auto Dealers	14,668
Auto Repair	9,728
Home Furnishing	7,792
Computer Sales	5,733
Dry Cleaning	4,649

b.

c. It appears that the auto industry (dealers and repair shops) account for the largest portion of complaints filed at the BBB. (Answers will very.)

6a, b.

c. It appears that the longer an employee is with the company, the larger the employee's salary will be.

7a, b.

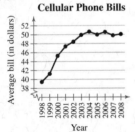

c. The average bill increased from 1998 to 2004, then it hovered around $50.00 from 2004 to 2008.

2.2 EXERCISE SOLUTIONS

1. Quantitative: stem-and-leaf plot, dot plot, histogram, time series chart, scatter plot.
Qualitative: pie chart, Pareto chart

2. Unlike the histogram, the stem-and-leaf plot still contains the original data values. However, some data are difficult to organize in a stem-and-leaf plot.

3. Both the stem-and-leaf plot and the dot plot allow you to see how data are distributed, determine specific data entries, and identify unusual data values.

4. In a Pareto chart, the height of each bar represents frequency or relative frequency and the bars are positioned in order of decreasing height with the tallest bar positioned at the left.

5. b   6. d   7. a   8. c

9. 27, 32, 41, 43, 43, 44, 47, 47, 48, 50, 51, 51, 52, 53, 53, 53, 54, 54, 54, 54, 55, 56, 56, 58, 59, 68, 68, 68, 73, 78, 78, 85
   Max: 85   Min: 27

10. 12.9, 13.3, 13.6, 13.7, 13.7, 14.1, 14.1, 14.1, 14.1, 14.3, 14.4, 14.4, 14.6, 14.9, 14.9, 15.0, 15.0, 15.0, 15.1, 15.2, 15.4, 15.6, 15.7, 15.8, 15.8, 15.8, 15.9, 16.1, 16.6, 16.7
    Max: 16.7   Min: 12.9

11. 13, 13, 14, 14, 14, 15, 15, 15, 15, 15, 16, 17, 17, 18, 19
    Max: 19   Min: 13

12. 214, 214, 214, 216, 216, 217, 218, 218, 220, 221, 223, 224, 225, 225, 227, 228, 228, 228, 228, 230, 230, 231, 235, 237, 239
    Max: 239   Min: 214

13. Sample answer: Users spend the most amount of time on MySpace and the least amount of time on Twitter. Answers will vary.

14. Sample answer: Motor vehicle thefts decreased between 2003 and 2008. Answers will vary.

15. Answers will vary. Sample answer: Tailgaters irk drivers the most, while too cautious drivers irk drivers the least.

16. Answers will vary. Sample answer: The most frequent incident occurring while driving and using a cell phone is swerving. Twice as many people "sped up" than "cut off a car."

17. Key: $6|7 = 67$

    ```
    6|7  8
    7|3  5  5  6  9
    8|0  0  2  3  5  5  7  7  8
    9|0  1  1  1  2  4  5  5
    ```

    It appears that most grades for the biology midterm were in the 80s or 90s. (Answers will vary.)

18. Key: $4|9 = 49$

```
4 | 8  9
5 | 0  0  0  1  2
5 | 5  5  5  6  7  7  8  9  9
6 | 0  0  0  1  2  2  2  3  3  4  4  4
6 | 7
7 | 4
```

It appears that most of the highest paid CEOs are between 55 and 65 years old. (Answers will vary.)

19. Key: $4|3 = 4.3$

```
4 | 3  9
5 | 1  8  8  8  9
6 | 4  8  9  9  9
7 | 0  0  2  2  2  5
8 | 0  1
```

It appears that most ice had a thickness of 5.8 centimeters to 7.2 centimeters. (Answers will vary.)

20. Key: $17|5 = 17.5$

```
16 | 4  8
17 | 1  1  3  4  5  5  6  7  9
18 | 1  3  4  4  6  6  6  9
19 | 0  0  2  3  3  5  6
20 | 1  8
```

It appears that most farmers charge 17 to 19 cents per pound of apples. (Answers will vary.)

21.

Systolic Blood Pressures

100 110 120 130 140 150 160 170 180 190 200
Systolic blood pressure (in mmHg)

It appears that systolic blood pressure tends to be between 120 and 150 millimeters of mercury. (Answers will vary.)

22.

Housefly Life Spans

4 5 6 7 8 9 10 11 12 13 14
Life span (in days)

It appears that the lifespan of a housefly tends to be between 8 and 11 days. (Answers will vary.)

23.

Category	Frequency, f	Relative Frequency	Angle
United States	15	0.375	135°
Italy	4	0.100	36°
Ethiopia	1	0.025	9°
South Africa	2	0.050	18°
Tanzania	1	0.025	9°
Kenya	8	0.200	72°
Mexico	4	0.100	36°
Morocco	1	0.025	9°
Great Britain	1	0.025	9°
Brazil	2	0.050	18°
New Zealand	1	0.025	9°
	$\sum f = 40$	$\sum \dfrac{f}{N} = 1$	$\sum = 360°$

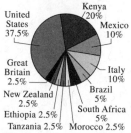

Marathon Winners' Countries of Origin

Most of the New York City Marathon winners are from the United States and Kenya. (Answers will vary.)

24.

Category	Frequency, f	Relative Frequency	Angle
Science, aeronautics, exploration	8947	0.479	172.4°
Space operations	6176	0.331	119.2°
Education	126	0.007	2.5°
Cross-agency support	3401	0.182	65.5°
Inspector general	36	0.002	0.7°
	$\sum f = 18,686$	$\sum \dfrac{f}{N} \approx 1$	$\sum \approx 360°$

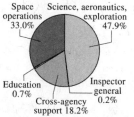

2010 NASA Budget

It appears that most of NASA's budget was spent on science, aeronautics, and exploration. (Answers will vary.)

25.

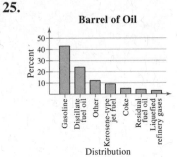

It appears that the largest portion of a 42-gallon barrel of crude oil is used for making gasoline. (Answers will vary.)

26.

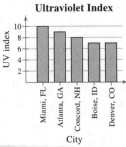

It appears that Boise, ID and Denver, CO have the same UV index. (Answers will vary.)

27.

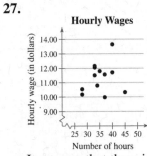

It appears that there is no relation between wages and hours worked. (Answers will vary.)

28.

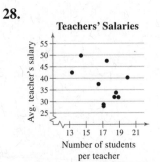

It appears that there is no relation between a teacher's average salary and the number of students per teacher. (Answers will vary.)

29.

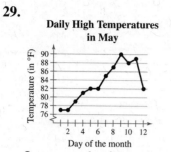

It appears that it was hottest from May 7 to May 11. (Answers will vary.)

30.

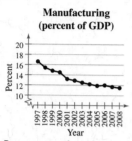

It appears that the largest decrease in manufacturing as a percent of GDP was from 2000 to 2001. (Answers will vary.)

31. Variable: Scores

Key: $5|5 = 5.5$

```
 5 | 5
 6 | 2
 6 | 8
 7 | 0  1
 7 | 5  6
 8 | 0  2  3
 8 | 5  6  7  8  8  9
 9 | 0  3  3
 9 | 5  5  8  9
10 | 0
```

It appears that most scores on the final exam in economics were in the 80's and 90's. (Answers will vary.)

32.

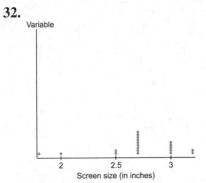

It appears that most screen sizes are between 2.5 and 3 inches. (Answers will vary.)

33a.

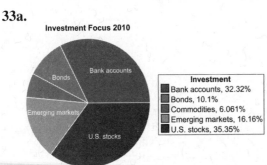

It appears that a large portion of adults said that the type of the investment that they would focus on in 2010 was U.S. stocks or bank accounts. (Answers will vary.)

b.

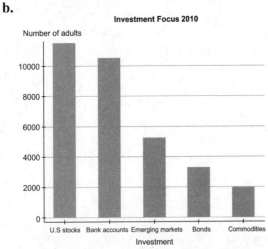

It appears that most adults said that the type of investment that they would focus on in 2010 was U.S. stocks or bank accounts. (Answers will vary.)

34a.

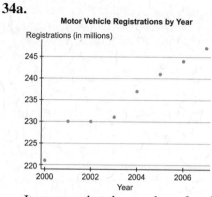

It appears that the number of registrations is increasing over time. (Answers will vary.)

b.

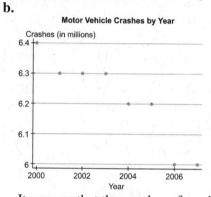

It appears that the number of crashes is decreasing over time. (Answers will vary.)

c.

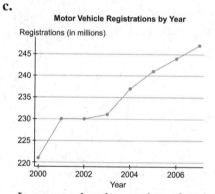

It appears that the number of registrations is increasing over time. (Answers will vary.)

d.

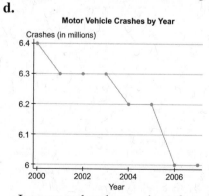

It appears that the number of crashes is decreasing over time. (Answers will vary.)

35a. The graph is misleading because the large gap from 0 to 90 makes it appear that the sales for the 3rd quarter are disproportionately larger than the other quarters. (Answers will vary.)

   b.

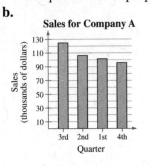

36a. The graph is misleading because the vertical axis has no break. The percent of middle schoolers that responded "yes" appears three times larger than either of the others when the difference is only 10%. (Answers will vary.)

   b.

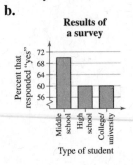

37a. The graph is misleading because the angle makes it appear as though the 3rd quarter had a larger percent of sales than the others, when the 1st and 3rd quarters have the same percent.

   b.

38a. The graph is misleading because the "OPEC countries" bar is wider than the "non-OPEC countries" bar.

   b.

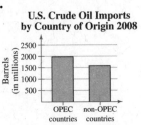

39a. At Law Firm A, the lowest salary was $90,000 and the highest salary was $203,000. At Law Firm B, the lowest salary was $90,000 and the highest salary was $190,000.

   b. There are 30 lawyers at Law Firm A and 32 lawyers at Law Firm B.

   c. At Law Firm A, the salaries tend to be clustered at the far ends of the distribution range and at Law Firm B, the salaries tend to fall in the middle of the distribution range.

40a. Key: $5|3|1 = 35$-year-old in 3:00 P.M. class and 31-year old in 8:00 P.M. class.

```
                          1|8  8  8  8  8  9  9  9  9  9
                          2|0  0  0  2  3  4  4  5  5  8  9  9
                 8  5|3|1  1  9
                    0|4|3  4  4
        9  7  5  3  1|5|6
  9  8  8  8  8  4  2  0|6|
  7  7  6  5  5  5  3  3|7|1
              5  4|8|
```

   b. In the 3:00 P.M. class, the youngest participant is 35 years old and the oldest participant is 85 years old. In the 8:00 P.M. class, the youngest participant is 18 years old and the oldest participant is 71 years old.

   c. In the 3:00 P.M. class, there are 26 participants and in the 8:00 P.M. class there are 30 participants.

   d. The participants in each class are clustered at one of the ends of their distribution range. The 3:00 P.M. class mostly has participants over 50 years old and the 8:00 P.M. class mostly has participants under 50 years old. (Answers will vary.)

2.3 MEASURES OF CENTRAL TENDENCY

2.3 Try It Yourself Solutions

1a. $\sum x = 74 + 78 + 81 + 87 + 81 + 80 + 77 + 80 + 85 + 78 + 80 + 83 + 75 + 81 + 73 = 1193$

   b. $\bar{x} = \dfrac{\sum x}{n} = \dfrac{1193}{15} \approx 79.5$

   c. The mean height of the player is about 79.5 inches.

2a. 18, 18, 19, 19, 19, 20, 21, 21, 21,21, 23, 24, 24, 26, 27, 27, 29, 30, 30, 30, 33, 33, 34, 35, 38

   b. median = 24

   c. The median age of the sample of fans at the concert is 24.

3a. 25, 60, 80, 97, 100, 130, 140, 200, 220, 250

   b. median $= \dfrac{100 + 130}{2} = 115$

   c. The median price of the sample of digital photo frames is $115.

4a. 324, 385, 450, 450, 462, 475, 540, 540, 564, 618, 624, 638, 670, 670, 670, 705, 720, 723, 750, 750, 825, 830, 912, 975, 980, 980, 1100, 1260, 1420, 1650

   b. The price that occurs with the greatest frequency is $670 per square foot.

   c. The mode of the prices for the sample of South Beach, FL condominiums is $670 per square foot.

5a. "Yes" occurs with the greatest frequency (510).

b. The mode of the responses to the survey is "Yes." In this sample, there were more people who thought public cell phone conversations were rude than people who did not or had no opinion.

6a. $\bar{x} = \dfrac{\sum x}{n} = \dfrac{410}{19} \approx 21.6$

median = 21

mode = 20

b. The mean in Example 6 ($\bar{x} \approx 23.8$) was heavily influenced by the entry 65. Neither the median nor the mode was affected as much by the entry 65.

7a, b.

Source	Score, x	Weight, w	$x \cdot w$
Test mean	86	0.50	43.0
Midterm	96	0.15	14.4
Final exam	98	0.20	19.6
Computer lab	98	0.10	9.8
Homework	100	0.05	5.0
		$\sum w = 1$	$\sum(x \cdot w) = 91.8$

c. $\bar{x} = \dfrac{\sum(x \cdot w)}{\sum w} = \dfrac{91.8}{1} = 91.8$

d. The weighted mean for the course is 91.8. So, you did get an A.

8a, b, c.

Class	Midpoint, x	Frequency, f	$x \cdot f$
35-41	38	2	76
42-48	45	5	225
49-55	52	7	364
56-62	59	7	413
63-69	66	10	660
70-76	73	5	365
77-83	80	8	640
84-90	87	6	552
		$N = 50$	$\sum(x \cdot f) = 3265$

d. $\mu = \dfrac{\sum(x \cdot f)}{N} = \dfrac{3265}{50} = 65.3$

The mean age of the 50 richest people is 65.3

2.3 EXERCISE SOLUTIONS

1. True

2. False. All quantitative data sets have a median.

3. True

4. True

5. 1, 2, 2, 2, 3 (Answers will vary.)

6. 2, 4, 5, 5, 6, 8 (Answers will vary.)

7. 2, 5, 7, 9, 35 (Answers will vary.)

8. 1, 2, 3, 3, 3, 4, 5 (Answers will vary.)

9. Skewed right because the "tail" of the distribution extends to the right.

10. Symmetric because the left and right halves of the distribution are approximately mirror images.

11. Uniform because the bars are approximately the same height.

12. Skewed left because the "tail" of the distribution extends to the left.

13. (11), because the distribution values range from 1 to 12 and has (approximately) equal frequencies.

14. (9), because the distribution has values in the thousands of dollars and is skewed right due to the few executives that make a much higher salary than the majority of the employees.

15. (12), because the distribution has a maximum value of 90 and is skewed left due to a few students scoring much lower than the majority of the students.

16. (10), because the distribution is rather symmetric due to the nature of the weights of seventh grade boys.

17. $\bar{x} = \dfrac{\sum x}{n} = \dfrac{64}{13} \approx 4.9$

2 2 3 4 4 4 ⑤ 5 6 6 7 8 8
      └─ median = 5

mode = 4 (occurs 3 times)

18. $\bar{x} = \dfrac{\sum x}{n} = \dfrac{396}{10} = 39.6$

35 37 38 38 <u>39 39</u> 39 40 40 51
       └─ median = $\dfrac{39 + 39}{2} = 39$

mode = 39 (occurs 3 times)

19. $\bar{x} = \dfrac{\sum x}{n} = \dfrac{76.8}{7} = 11.0$

9.7 10.3 10.7 ⑪.0⃝ 11.7 11.7 11.7
       └─ median = 11.0

mode = 11.7 (occurs 3 times)

20. $\bar{x} = \dfrac{\sum x}{n} = \dfrac{2004}{10} = 200.4$

154 171 173 181 184 188 203 235 240 275

median $= \dfrac{184 + 188}{2} = 186$

mode = none
The mode cannot be found because no data points are repeated.

21. $\bar{x} = \dfrac{\sum x}{n} = \dfrac{686.8}{32} = 21.46$

10.9 12.3 15.2 15.3 16.1 16.4 16.6 17.5 18.1 18.4 19.1 19.7 20.4 20.4 20.6
21.8 22.1 22.5 22.6 22.7 23.0 23.4 24.2 24.4 25.1 26.0 26.7 26.8 28.4 28.8 29.4 31.9

median $= \dfrac{21.8 + 22.1}{2} = 21.95$

mode = 20.4 (occurs 2 times)

22. $\bar{x} = \dfrac{\sum x}{n} = \dfrac{1223}{20} = 61.2$

12 18 26 28 31 33 40 44 45 49 61 63 75 80 80 89 96 103 125 125

median $= \dfrac{49 + 61}{2} = 55$

mode = 80, 125
The modes do not represent the center of the data set because they are large values compared to the rest of the data.

23. $\bar{x}$ = not possible (nominal data)
median = not possible (nominal data)
mode = "Eyeglasses"
The mean and median cannot be found because the data are at the nominal level of measurement.

24. $\bar{x}$ = not possible (nominal data)
median = not possible (nominal data)
mode = "Money needed"
The mean and median cannot be found because the data are at the nominal level of measurement.

25. $\bar{x} = \dfrac{\sum x}{n} = \dfrac{1194.4}{7} \approx 170.63$

155.7 158.1 162.2 169.3 180 181.8 187.3

median = 169.3

mode = none
The mode cannot be found because no data points are repeated.

26. $\bar{x}$ = not possible (nominal data)
median = not possible (nominal data)
mode = "Mashed"
The mean and median cannot be found because the data are at the nominal level of measurement.

27. $\bar{x} = \dfrac{\sum x}{n} = \dfrac{1687}{10} = 168.7$

125 125 132 140 $\underline{155 \quad 170}$ 175 210 225 230

median $= \dfrac{155 + 170}{2} = 162.5$

mode = 125 (occurs 2 times)

The mode does not represent the center of the data because 125 is the smallest number in the data set.

28. $\bar{x} = \dfrac{\sum x}{n} = \dfrac{83}{5} = 16.6$

1 10 (15) 25.5 31.5

median = 15

mode = none

The mode cannot be found because no data points are repeated.

29. $\bar{x} = \dfrac{\sum x}{n} = \dfrac{197.5}{14} \approx 14.11$

1.5 2.5 2.5 5 10.5 11 $\underline{13 \quad 15.5}$ 16.5 17.5 20 26.5 27 28.5

median $= \dfrac{13 + 15.5}{2} = 14.25$

mode = 2.5 (occurs 2 times)

The mode does not represent the center of the data set because 2.5 is much smaller than most of the data in the set.

30. $\bar{x} = \dfrac{\sum x}{n} = \dfrac{3605}{15} \approx 240.3$

9 28 28 32 38 52 110 (136) 142 350 354 409 537 625 755

median = 136

mode = 28 (occurs 2 times)

The mode does not represent the center of the data because it is the second smallest number in the data set.

31. $\bar{x} = \dfrac{\sum x}{n} = \dfrac{835}{28} = 29.82$

6 7 12 15 18 19 20 24 24 24 25 28 29 $\underline{32 \quad 32}$ 33 35 35 35 36 38 39 40 41 42 47 48 51

median $= \dfrac{32 + 32}{2} = 32$

mode = 24, 35 (occurs 3 times each)

32. $\bar{x} = \dfrac{\sum x}{n} = \dfrac{29.9}{12} \approx 2.49$

0.8 1.5 1.6 1.8 2.1 $\underbrace{2.3 \quad 2.4}$ 2.5 3.0 3.9 4.0 4.0

$\text{median} = \dfrac{2.3 + 2.4}{2} = 2.35$

mode = 4.0 (occurs 2 times)

The mode does not represent the center of the data set because it is the largest value in the data set.

33. $\bar{x} = \dfrac{\sum x}{n} = \dfrac{292}{15} \approx 19.47$

5 8 10 15 15 15 17 ⑳ 21 22 22 25 28 32 37

median = 20

mode = 15 (occurs 3 times)

34. $\bar{x} = \dfrac{\sum x}{n} = \dfrac{3110}{15} \approx 207.3$

170 180 190 200 200 210 210 ⑩⑩⑩ 210 210 220 220 220 220 240

median = 210

mode = 210 (occurs 5 times)

35. The data are skewed right.

A = mode, because it is the data entry that occurred most often.

B = median, because the median is to the left of the mean in a skewed right distribution.

C = mean, because the mean is to the right of the median in a skewed right distribution.

36. The data are skewed left.

A = mean, because the mean is to the left of the median in a skewed left distribution.

B = median, because the median is to the right of the mean in a skewed left distribution.

C = mode, because it is the data entry that occurred most often.

37. Mode, because the data are at the nominal level of measurement.

38. Mean, because the data are symmetric.

39. Mean, because there are no outliers.

40. Median, because there is an outlier.

41.

Source	Score, x	Weight, w	$x \cdot w$
Homework	85	0.05	4.25
Quiz	80	0.35	28
Project	100	0.20	20
Speech	90	0.15	13.5
Final exam	93	0.25	23.25
		$\sum w = 1$	$\sum (x \cdot w) = 89$

$$\bar{x} = \frac{\sum (x \cdot w)}{\sum w} = \frac{89}{1} = 89$$

42.

Source	Score, x	Weight, w	$x \cdot w$
MBAs	92,500	8	740,000
BAs	68,000	17	1,156,000
		$\sum w = 25$	$\sum (x \cdot w) = 1{,}896{,}000$

$$\bar{x} = \frac{\sum (x \cdot w)}{\sum w} = \frac{1{,}896{,}000}{25} = 75{,}840$$

43.

Balance, x	Days, w	$x \cdot w$
$523	24	12,552
$2415	2	4830
$250	4	1000
	$\sum w = 30$	$\sum (x \cdot w) = 18{,}382$

$$\bar{x} = \frac{\sum (x \cdot w)}{\sum w} = \frac{18{,}382}{30} \approx \$612.73$$

44.

Balance, x	Days, w	$x \cdot w$
$759	15	11,385
$1985	5	9925
$1410	5	7050
$348	6	2088
	$\sum w = 31$	$\sum (x \cdot w) = 30{,}448$

$$\bar{x} = \frac{\sum (x \cdot w)}{\sum w} = \frac{30{,}448}{31} \approx \$982.19$$

45.

Grade	Points, x	Credits, w	$x \cdot w$
B	3	3	9
B	3	3	9
A	4	4	16
D	1	2	2
C	2	3	6
		$\sum w = 15$	$\sum (x \cdot w) = 42$

$$\bar{x} = \frac{\sum (x \cdot w)}{\sum w} = \frac{42}{15} = 2.8$$

46.

Source	Score, x	Weight, w	$x \cdot w$
Engineering	85	9	765
Business	81	13	1053
Math	90	5	450
		$\sum w = 27$	$\sum (x \cdot w) = 2268$

$$\bar{x} = \frac{\sum (x \cdot w)}{\sum w} = \frac{2268}{27} = 84$$

47.

Source	Score, x	Weight, w	$x \cdot w$
Homework	85	0.05	4.25
Quiz	80	0.35	28
Project	100	0.20	20
Speech	90	0.15	13.5
Final exam	85	0.25	21.25
		$\sum w = 1$	$\sum (x \cdot w) = 87$

$$\bar{x} = \frac{\sum (x \cdot w)}{\sum w} = \frac{87}{1} = 87$$

48.

Grade	Points, x	Credits, w	$x \cdot w$
A	4	3	12
B	3	3	9
A	4	4	16
D	1	2	2
C	2	3	6
		$\sum w = 15$	$\sum (x \cdot w) = 45$

$$\bar{x} = \frac{\sum (x \cdot w)}{\sum w} = \frac{45}{15} = 3$$

49.

Class	Midpoint, x	Frequency, f	$x \cdot f$
29-33	31	11	341
34-38	36	12	432
39-43	41	2	82
44-48	46	5	230
		$n = 30$	$\sum (x \cdot f) = 1085$

$$\bar{x} = \frac{\sum (x \cdot f)}{n} = \frac{1085}{30} \approx 36.2 \text{ miles per gallon}$$

50.

Class	Midpoint, x	Frequency, f	$x \cdot f$
22-27	24.5	16	392
28-33	30.5	2	61
34-39	36.5	2	73
40-45	42.5	3	127.5
46-51	48.5	1	48.5
		$n = 24$	$\sum (x \cdot f) = 702$

$$\bar{x} = \frac{\sum (x \cdot f)}{n} = \frac{702}{24} \approx 29.3 \text{ miles per gallon}$$

51.

Class	Midpoint, x	Frequency, f	$x \cdot f$
0-9	4.5	55	247.5
10-19	14.5	70	1015
20-29	24.5	35	857.5
30-39	34.5	56	1932
40-49	44.5	74	3293
50-59	54.5	42	2289
60-69	64.5	38	2451
70-79	74.5	17	1266.5
80-89	84.5	10	845
		$n = 397$	$\sum (x \cdot f) = 14{,}196.5$

$$\bar{x} = \frac{\sum (x \cdot f)}{n} = \frac{14{,}196.5}{397} \approx 35.8 \text{ years old}$$

52.

Class	Midpoint, x	Frequency, f	$x \cdot f$
1-5	3	12	36
6-10	8	26	208
11-15	13	20	260
16-20	18	7	126
21-25	23	11	253
26-30	28	7	196
31-35	33	4	132
36-40	38	4	152
41-45	43	1	43
		$n = 92$	$\sum(x \cdot f) = 1406$

$$\overline{x} = \frac{\sum(x \cdot f)}{n} = \frac{1406}{92} \approx 15.3 \text{ minutes}$$

53. Class width $= \dfrac{\text{Range}}{\text{Number of classes}} = \dfrac{297 - 127}{5} = 34 \Rightarrow 35$

Class	Midpoint	Frequency, f
127-161	144	9
162-196	179	8
197-231	214	3
232-266	249	3
267-301	284	1
		$\sum f = 24$

Shape: Positively skewed

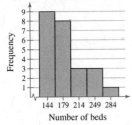

Hospital Beds

54. Class width $= \dfrac{\text{Range}}{\text{Number of classes}} = \dfrac{14 - 3}{6} \approx 1.83 \Rightarrow 2$

Class	Midpoint	Frequency, f
3-4	3.5	3
5-6	5.5	8
7-8	7.5	4
9-10	9.5	2
11-12	11.5	2
13-14	13.5	1
		$\sum f = 20$

Shape: Positively skewed

Hospitalization

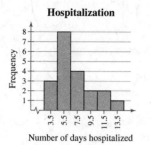

Number of days hospitalized

55. Class width = $\dfrac{\text{Range}}{\text{Number of classes}} = \dfrac{76-62}{5} = 2.8 \Rightarrow 3$

Class	Midpoint	Frequency, f
62-64	63	3
65-67	66	7
68-70	69	9
71-73	72	8
74-76	75	3
		$\sum f = 30$

Shape: Symmetric

Heights of Males

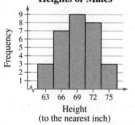

Height
(to the nearest inch)

56. Class width = $\dfrac{\text{Range}}{\text{Number of classes}} = \dfrac{6-1}{6} = 0.8333 \Rightarrow 1$

Class	Frequency, f
1	6
2	5
3	4
4	6
5	4
6	5
	$\sum f = 30$

Shape: Uniform

**Results of Rolling
Six-Sided Die**

Number rolled

57a. $\bar{x} = \dfrac{\sum x}{n} = \dfrac{36.03}{6} = 6.005$

5.59 5.99 $\underbrace{6\ \ 6.02}$ 6.03 6.40

median $= \dfrac{6 + 6.02}{2} = 6.01$

b. $\bar{x} = \dfrac{\sum x}{n} = \dfrac{35.67}{6} = 5.945$

5.59 5.99 $\underbrace{6\ \ 6.02}$ 6.03 6.04

median $= \dfrac{6 + 6.02}{2} = 6.01$

c. The mean was affected more.

58a. $\bar{x} = \dfrac{\sum x}{n} = \dfrac{966.6}{19} \approx 50.87$

9.1 12.5 12.9 15.5 22.0 22.2 24.9 27.9 28.8 $\boxed{28.9}$ 32.3 34.7
39.7 53.6 54.5 65.1 69.7 151.2 261.1

median $= 28.9$

b. $\bar{x} = \dfrac{\sum x}{n} = \dfrac{705.5}{18} \approx 39.19$

9.1 12.5 12.9 15.5 22.0 22.2 24.9 27.9 $\underbrace{28.8\ \ 28.9}$ 32.3 34.7
39.7 53.6 54.5 65.1 69.7 151.2

median $= \dfrac{28.8 + 28.9}{2} = 28.85$

The mean was affected more.

c. $\bar{x} = \dfrac{\sum x}{n} = \dfrac{984.3}{20} \approx 49.22$

9.1 12.5 12.9 15.5 17.7 22.0 22.2 24.9 27.9 $\underbrace{28.8\ \ 28.9}$ 32.3 34.7
39.7 53.6 54.5 65.1 69.7 151.2 261.1

median $= \dfrac{28.8 + 28.9}{2} = 28.85$

The mean was affected more.

59. Summary Statistics:

Column	n	Mean	Median	Min	Max
Amount (in dollars)	11	112.11364	105.25	79	151.5

60. Summary Statistics:

Column	n	Mean	Median	Min	Max
Price (in dollars)	30	47.26433	43.585	15.9	132.39

61a. $\bar{x} = \dfrac{\sum x}{n} = \dfrac{3222}{9} = 358$

147 177 336 360 $\boxed{375}$ 393 408 504 522

median $= 375$

b. $\bar{x} = \dfrac{\sum x}{n} = \dfrac{9666}{9} = 1074$

441 531 1008 1080 ⟨1125⟩ 1179 1224 1512 1566

⌐ median = 1125

c. The mean and median in part (b) are three times the mean and median in part (a).

d. If you multiply the mean and median from part (b) by 3, you will get the mean and median of the data set in inches.

62. Car A

$\bar{x} = \dfrac{\sum x}{n} = \dfrac{152}{5} = 30.4$

28 28 ⟨30⟩ 32 34

⌐ median = 30

mode = 28 (occurs 2 times)

Car B

$\bar{x} = \dfrac{\sum x}{n} = \dfrac{151}{5} = 30.2$

29 29 ⟨31⟩ 31 31

⌐ median = 31

mode = 31 (occurs 3 times)

Car C

$\bar{x} = \dfrac{\sum x}{n} = \dfrac{151}{5} = 30.2$

28 29 ⟨30⟩ 32 32

⌐ median = 30

mode = 32 (occurs 2 times)

a. Mean should be used because Car A has the highest mean of the three.
b. Median should be used because Car B has the highest median of the three.
c. Mode should be used because Car C has the highest mode of the three.

63. Car A: Midrange = $\dfrac{34 + 28}{2} = 31$

Car B: Midrange = $\dfrac{31 + 29}{2} = 30$

Car C: Midrange = $\dfrac{32 + 28}{2} = 30$

Car A because it has the highest midrange of the three.

64a. $\bar{x} = \dfrac{\sum x}{n} = \dfrac{1477}{30} \approx 49.2$

11 13 22 28 36 36 36 37 37 37 38 41 43 44 46 47 51 51 51
53 61 62 63 64 72 72 74 76 85 90   ⌐ median = $\dfrac{46 + 47}{2} = 46.5$

b. Key: $3|6 = 36$ **c.** Positively skewed

```
1 | 1  3
2 | 2  8                   median
3 | 6  6  6  7 / 7  7  8
4 | 1  3  4  6  7
5 | 1  1  1  3             mean
6 | 1  2  3  4
7 | 2  2  4  6
8 | 5
9 | 0
```

c. The distribution is approximately symmetric.

65a. Order the data values.

11 13 22 28 36 36 36 37 37 37 38 41 43 44 46
47 51 51 51 53 61 62 63 64 72 72 74 76 85 90

Delete the lowest 10%, smallest 3 observations (11, 13, 22).
Delete the highest 10%, largest 3 observations (76, 85, 90).
Find the 10% trimmed mean using the remaining 24 observations.
   10% trimmed mean ≈ 49.2

b. $\bar{x} \approx 49.2$
median = 46.5
mode = 36, 37, 51
midrange = $\dfrac{90 + 11}{2} = 50.5$

c. Using a trimmed mean eliminates potential outliers that may affect the mean of all the observations.

2.4 MEASURES OF VARIATION

2.4 Try It Yourself Solutions

1a. Min = 23, or $23,000 and Max = 58, or $58,000
b. Range = Max − Min = 58 − 23 = 35, or $35,000
c. The range of the starting salaries for Corporation B is 35, or $35,000. This is much larger than the range for Corporation A.

2a. $\mu = \dfrac{\sum x}{N} = \dfrac{415}{10} = 41.5$, or $41,500

b.

Salary, x (1000s of dollars)	Deviation, $x - \mu$ (100s of dollars)
23	–18.5
29	–12.5
32	–9.5
40	–1.5
41	–0.5
41	–0.5
49	7.5
50	8.5
52	10.5
58	16.5
$\sum x = 415$	$\sum(x - \mu) = 0$

3ab. $\mu = 41.5$, or \$41,500

Salary, x	$x - \mu$	$(x - \mu)^2$
23	–18.5	342.25
29	–12.5	156.25
32	–9.5	90.25
40	–1.5	2.25
41	–0.5	0.25
41	–0.5	0.25
49	7.5	56.25
50	8.5	72.25
52	10.5	110.25
58	16.5	272.25
$\sum x = 415$	$\sum(x - \mu) = 0$	$\sum(x - \mu)^2 = 1102.5$

c. $\sigma^2 = \dfrac{\sum(x - \mu)^2}{N} = \dfrac{1102.5}{10} \approx 110.3$

d. $\sigma = \sqrt{\sigma^2} = \sqrt{\dfrac{1102.5}{10}} = 10.5$, or \$10,500

e. The population variance is about 110.3 and the population standard deviation is 10.5, or \$10,500.

4a. From 3ab, $SS_x = \sum\left(x - \overline{x}\right)^2 = 1102.5$.

b. $s^2 = \dfrac{\sum\left(x - \overline{x}\right)^2}{n-1} = \dfrac{1102.5}{9} = 122.5$

c. $s = \sqrt{s^2} = \sqrt{122.5} \approx 11.1$, or \$11,100

d. The sample variance is 122.5 and the sample standard deviation is 11.1, or \$11,100.

5a. Enter the data in a computer or a calculator.

b. $\overline{x} = 37.89$, $s = 3.98$

6a. 7, 7, 7, 7, 7, 13, 13, 13, 13, 13

b.

Salary, x	$x - \mu$	$(x - \mu)^2$
7	−3	9
7	−3	9
7	−3	9
7	−3	9
7	−3	9
13	3	9
13	3	9
13	3	9
13	3	9
13	3	9
$\sum x = 100$	$\sum (x - \mu) = 0$	$\sum (x - \mu)^2 = 90$

$$\mu = \frac{\sum x}{N} = \frac{100}{10} = 10$$

$$\sigma = \sqrt{\frac{\sum (x - \mu)^2}{N}} = \sqrt{\frac{90}{10}} = \sqrt{9} = 3$$

7a. 66.92 − 64.3 = 2.62 = 1 standard deviation

b. 34%

c. Approximately 34% of women ages 20-29 are between 64.3 and 66.92 inches tall.

8a. 31.6 − 2(19.5) = −7.4

Because −7.4 does not make sense for an age, use 0.

b. 31.6 + 2(19.5) = 70.6

c. $1 - \dfrac{1}{k^2} = 1 - \dfrac{1}{(2)^2} = 1 - \dfrac{1}{4} = 0.75$

At least 75% of the data lie within 2 standard deviations of the mean. At least 75% of the population of Alaska is between 0 and 70.6 years old.

9a.

x	f	xf
0	10	0
1	19	19
2	7	14
3	7	21
4	5	20
5	1	5
6	1	6
	$n = 50$	$\sum xf = 85$

b. $\bar{x} = \dfrac{\sum xf}{n} = \dfrac{85}{50} = 1.7$

c.

$x - \bar{x}$	$\left(x - \bar{x}\right)^2$	$\left(x - \bar{x}\right)^2 f$
−1.7	2.89	28.90
−0.7	0.49	9.31
0.3	0.09	0.63
1.3	1.69	11.83
2.3	5.29	26.45
3.3	10.89	10.89
4.3	18.49	18.49
		$\sum \left(x - \bar{x}\right)^2 f = 106.5$

d. $s = \sqrt{\dfrac{\sum \left(x - \bar{x}\right)^2 f}{n - 1}} = \sqrt{\dfrac{106.5}{49}} \approx 1.5$

10a.

Class	x	f	xf
1-99	49.5	380	18,810
100-199	149.5	230	34,385
200-299	249.5	210	52,395
300-399	349.5	50	17,475
400-499	449.5	60	26,970
500+	650	70	45,500
		$n = 1000$	$\sum xf = 195,535$

b. $\bar{x} = \dfrac{\sum xf}{n} = \dfrac{195,535}{1000} \approx 195.5$

c.

$x - \bar{x}$	$\left(x - \bar{x}\right)^2$	$\left(x - \bar{x}\right)^2 f$
−146	21,316	8,100,080
−46	2116	486,680
54	2916	612,360
154	23,716	1,185,800
254	64,516	3,870,960
454.5	206,570.25	14,459,917.5
		$\sum \left(x - \bar{x}\right)^2 f = 28,715,797.5$

d. $s = \sqrt{\dfrac{\sum \left(x - \bar{x}\right)^2 f}{n - 1}} = \sqrt{\dfrac{28,715,797.5}{999}} \approx 169.5$

2.4 EXERCISE SOLUTIONS

1. The range is the difference between the maximum and minimum values of a data set. The advantage of the range is that it is easy to calculate. The disadvantage is that it uses only two entries from the data set.

2. A deviation $(x - \mu)$ is the difference between an entry x and the mean of the data μ. The sum of the deviations is always zero.

3. The units of variance are squared. Its units are meaningless. (Example: dollars^2)

4. The standard deviation is the positive square root of the variance. Because squared deviations can never be negative, the standard deviation and variance can never be negative.

5. $\{9, 9, 9, 9, 9, 9, 9\}$

   $n = 7$

   $$\bar{x} = \frac{\sum x}{n} = \frac{63}{7} = 9$$

x	$x - \bar{x}$	$\left(x - \bar{x}\right)^2$
9	0	0
9	0	0
9	0	0
9	0	0
9	0	0
9	0	0
9	0	0
$\sum x = 63$	$\sum\left(x - \bar{x}\right) = 0$	$\sum\left(x - \bar{x}\right)^2 = 0$

   $$s = \sqrt{\frac{\sum\left(x - \bar{x}\right)^2}{n - 1}} = \sqrt{\frac{0}{6}} = 0$$

6. $\{3, 3, 3, 7, 7, 7\}$

   $n = 6$

   $$\mu = \frac{\sum x}{n} = \frac{30}{6} = 5$$

x	$x - \mu$	$\left(x - \mu\right)^2$
3	−2	4
3	−2	4
3	−2	4
7	2	4
7	2	4
7	2	4
$\sum x = 30$	$\sum\left(x - \mu\right) = 0$	$\sum\left(x - \mu\right)^2 = 24$

   $$\sigma = \sqrt{\frac{\sum\left(x - \mu\right)^2}{N}} = \sqrt{\frac{24}{6}} = \sqrt{4} = 2$$

7. When calculating the population standard deviation, you divide the sum of the squared deviations by N, then take the square root of that value. When calculating the sample standard deviation, you divide the sum of the squared deviations by $n - 1$, then take the square root of that value.

8. When given a data set one would have to determine if it represented the population or if it was a sample taken from the population. If the data are a population, then σ is calculated. If the data are a sample, then s is calculated.

9. Similarity: Both estimate proportions of the data contained within k standard deviations of the mean.
   Difference: The Empirical Rule assumes the distribution is bell-shaped. Chebychev's Theorem makes no such assumption.

10. You must know that the distribution is bell-shaped.

11. Range = Max − Min = 12 − 5 = 7
    $$\mu = \frac{\sum x}{N} = \frac{90}{10} = 9$$

x	$x - \mu$	$(x - \mu)^2$
9	0	0
5	−4	16
9	0	0
10	1	1
11	2	4
12	3	9
7	−2	4
7	−2	4
8	−1	1
12	3	9
$\sum x = 90$	$\sum (x - \mu) = 0$	$\sum (x - \mu)^2 = 48$

$$\sigma^2 = \frac{\sum (x - \mu)^2}{N} = \frac{48}{10} = 4.8$$

$$\sigma = \sqrt{\frac{\sum (x - \mu)^2}{N}} = \sqrt{4.8} \approx 2.2$$

12. Range = Max − Min = 25 − 15 = 10

$$\mu = \frac{\sum x}{N} = \frac{266}{14} = 19$$

x	$x - \mu$	$(x - \mu)^2$
18	−1	1
20	1	1
19	0	0
21	2	4
19	0	0
17	−2	4
15	−4	16
17	−2	4
25	6	36
22	3	9
19	0	0
20	1	1
16	−3	9
18	−1	1
$\sum x = 90$	$\sum(x - \mu) = 0$	$\sum(x - \mu)^2 = 86$

$$\sigma^2 = \frac{\sum(x - \mu)^2}{N} = \frac{86}{14} \approx 6.1$$

$$\sigma = \sqrt{\frac{\sum(x - \mu)^2}{N}} = \sqrt{\frac{86}{14}} \approx 2.5$$

13. Range = Max − Min = 19 − 4 = 15

$$\bar{x} = \frac{\sum x}{n} = \frac{108}{9} = 12$$

x	$x - \bar{x}$	$(x - \bar{x})^2$
4	−8	64
15	3	9
9	−3	9
12	0	0
16	4	16
8	−4	16
11	−1	1
19	7	49
14	2	4
$\sum x = 108$	$\sum(x - \bar{x}) = 0$	$\sum(x - \bar{x})^2 = 168$

$$s^2 = \frac{\sum(x - \bar{x})^2}{n - 1} = \frac{168}{9 - 1} = 21$$

$$s = \sqrt{\frac{\sum(x - \bar{x})^2}{n - 1}} = \sqrt{21} \approx 4.6$$

14. Range = Max − Min = 28 − 7 = 21

$$\bar{x} = \frac{\sum x}{n} = \frac{238}{13} \approx 18.3$$

x	$x - \bar{x}$	$\left(x - \bar{x}\right)^2$
28	9.7	94.09
25	6.7	44.89
21	2.7	7.29
15	−3.3	10.89
7	−11.3	127.69
14	−4.3	18.49
9	−9.3	86.49
27	8.7	75.69
21	2.7	7.29
24	5.7	32.49
14	−4.3	18.49
17	−1.3	1.69
16	−2.3	5.29
$\sum x = 238$	$\sum \left(x - \bar{x}\right) \approx 0$	$\sum \left(x - \bar{x}\right)^2 = 530.77$

$$s^2 = \frac{\sum \left(x - \bar{x}\right)^2}{n-1} = \frac{530.77}{13-1} \approx 44.2$$

$$s = \sqrt{\frac{\sum \left(x - \bar{x}\right)^2}{n-1}} = \sqrt{\frac{530.77}{12}} \approx 6.7$$

15. Range = Max − Min = 96 − 23 = 73

16. Range = Max − Min = 34 − 24 = 10

17. Range = Max − Min = 98 − 74 = 24

18. Range = Max − Min = 6.7 − 0.5 = 6.2

19a. Range = Max − Min = 38.5 − 20.7 = 17.8
   b. Range = Max − Min = 60.5 − 20.7 = 39.8

20. Changing the maximum value of the data set greatly affects the range.

21. Graph (a) has a standard deviation of 24 and graph (b) has a standard deviation of 16 because graph (a) has more variability.

22. Graph (a) has a standard deviation of 2.4 and graph (b) has a standard deviation of 5 because graph (b) has more variability.

23. Company B. An offer of $33,000 is two standard deviations from the mean of Company A's starting salaries, which makes it unlikely. The same offer is within one standard deviation of the mean of Company B's starting salaries, which makes the offer likely.

24. Player B. A smaller standard deviation means that Player B's scores tend to fall within a smaller interval of values than Player A's scores.

25a. Dallas:

$$\bar{x} = \frac{\sum x}{n} = \frac{398.5}{9} \approx 44.28$$

38.7 39.9 40.5 41.6 ⟨44.7⟩ 45.8 47.8 49.5 50.0

median = 44.7

Range = Max − Min = 50.0 − 38.7 = 11.3

x	$x - \bar{x}$	$\left(x - \bar{x}\right)^2$
38.7	−5.58	31.1364
39.9	−4.38	19.1844
40.5	−3.78	14.2884
41.6	−2.68	7.1824
44.7	0.42	0.1764
45.8	1.52	2.3104
47.8	3.52	12.3904
49.5	5.22	27.2484
50.0	5.72	32.7184
		$\sum\left(x - \bar{x}\right)^2 = 146.6356$

$$s^2 = \frac{\sum\left(x - \bar{x}\right)^2}{n-1} = \frac{146.6356}{8} \approx 18.33$$

$$s = \sqrt{\frac{\sum\left(x - \bar{x}\right)^2}{n-1}} = \sqrt{\frac{146.6356}{8}} \approx 4.28$$

New York City:

$$\bar{x} = \frac{\sum x}{n} = \frac{458.2}{9} \approx 50.91$$

41.5 42.3 45.6 47.2 ⟨50.6⟩ 55.1 57.6 59.0 59.3

median = 50.6

Range = Max − Min = 59.3 − 41.5 = 17.8

x	$x - \bar{x}$	$\left(x - \bar{x}\right)^2$
41.5	−9.41	88.5481
42.3	−8.61	74.1321
45.6	−5.31	28.1961
47.2	−3.71	13.7641
50.6	−0.31	0.0961
55.1	4.19	17.5561
57.6	6.69	44.7561
59.0	8.09	65.4481
59.3	8.39	70.3921
		$\sum\left(x - \bar{x}\right)^2 = 402.8889$

$$s^2 = \frac{\sum(x-\overline{x})^2}{n-1} = \frac{402.8889}{9-1} \approx 50.36$$

$$s = \sqrt{\frac{\sum(x-\overline{x})^2}{n-1}} = \sqrt{\frac{402.8889}{8}} \approx 7.10$$

b. It appears from the data that the annual salaries in New York City are more variable than the annual salaries in Dallas. The annual salaries in Dallas have a lower mean and a lower median than the annual salaries in New York City.

26a. Boston:

$$\overline{x} = \frac{\sum x}{n} = \frac{667.4}{9} \approx 74.16$$

58.5 64.5 69.9 70.4 (71.6) 79.9 80.1 84.2 88.3

└─── median = 71.6

Range = Max − Min = 88.3 − 58.5 = 29.8

x	$x - \overline{x}$	$(x - \overline{x})^2$
58.5	−15.66	245.2356
64.5	−9.66	93.3156
69.9	−4.26	18.1476
70.4	−3.76	14.1376
71.6	−2.56	6.5536
79.9	5.74	32.9476
80.1	5.94	35.2836
84.2	10.04	100.8016
88.3	14.14	199.9396
		$\sum(x-\overline{x})^2 = 746.3624$

$$s^2 = \frac{\sum(x-\overline{x})^2}{n-1} = \frac{746.3624}{9-1} \approx 93.30$$

$$s = \sqrt{\frac{\sum(x-\overline{x})^2}{n-1}} = \sqrt{\frac{746.3624}{8}} \approx 9.66$$

Chicago:

$$\bar{x} = \frac{\sum x}{n} = \frac{599.5}{9} \approx 66.61$$

59.9 60.9 62.9 65.4 (68.5) 69.4 70.1 70.9 71.5

└── median = 68.5

Range = Max − Min = 71.5 − 59.9 = 11.6

x	$x - \bar{x}$	$\left(x - \bar{x}\right)^2$
59.9	−6.71	45.0241
60.9	−5.71	32.6041
62.9	−3.71	13.7641
65.4	−1.21	1.4641
68.5	1.89	3.5721
69.4	2.79	7.7841
70.1	3.49	12.1801
70.9	4.29	18.4041
71.5	4.89	23.9121
		$\sum\left(x - \bar{x}\right)^2 = 158.7089$

$$s^2 = \frac{\sum\left(x - \bar{x}\right)^2}{n-1} = \frac{158.7089}{9-1} \approx 19.84$$

$$s = \sqrt{\frac{\sum\left(x - \bar{x}\right)^2}{n-1}} = \sqrt{\frac{158.7089}{8}} \approx 4.45$$

b. It appears from the data that the annual salaries in Boston are more variable than the annual salaries in Chicago. The annual salaries in Boston have higher mean and median than the annual salaries in Chicago.

27a. Male:

$$\bar{x} = \frac{\sum x}{n} = \frac{13{,}144}{8} = 1643$$

1033 1380 1520 1645 1714 1750 1982 2120

└── median = $\frac{1645 + 1714}{2}$ = 1679.5

Range = Max − Min = 2120 − 1033 = 1087

x	$x - \bar{x}$	$\left(x - \bar{x}\right)^2$
1033	−610	372,100
1380	−263	69,169
1520	−123	15,129
1645	2	4
1714	71	5041
1750	107	11,449
1982	339	114,921
2120	477	227,529
		$\sum\left(x - \bar{x}\right)^2 = 815{,}342$

$$s^2 = \frac{\sum\left(x - \bar{x}\right)^2}{n-1} = \frac{815{,}342}{8-1} \approx 116{,}477.4$$

$$s = \sqrt{\frac{\sum\left(x - \bar{x}\right)^2}{n-1}} = \sqrt{\frac{815{,}342}{7}} \approx 341.3$$

Female:

$$\bar{x} = \frac{\sum x}{n} = \frac{13{,}673}{8} \approx 1709.1$$

1263 1497 1507 1588 1785 1871 1952 2210

$$\text{median} = \frac{1588 + 1785}{2} = 1686.5$$

Range = Max − Min = 2210 − 1263 = 947

x	$x - \bar{x}$	$\left(x - \bar{x}\right)^2$
1263	−446.1	199,005.21
1497	−212.1	44,986.41
1507	−202.1	40,844.41
1588	−121.1	14,665.21
1785	75.9	5760.81
1871	161.9	26,211.61
1952	242.9	59,000.41
2210	500.9	250,900.81
		$\sum\left(x - \bar{x}\right)^2 = 641{,}374.88$

$$s^2 = \frac{\sum\left(x - \bar{x}\right)^2}{n-1} = \frac{641{,}374.88}{8-1} \approx 91{,}625.0$$

$$s = \sqrt{\frac{\sum\left(x - \bar{x}\right)^2}{n-1}} = \sqrt{\frac{641{,}374.88}{7}} = 302.7$$

b. It appears from the data that the SAT scores for males are more variable than the SAT scores for females. The SAT scores for males have a lower mean and median than the SAT scores for females.

28a. Team A:

$$\bar{x} = \frac{\sum x}{n} = \frac{2.694}{9} \approx 0.2993$$

0.235 0.256 0.272 0.295 ⟨0.297⟩ 0.310 0.320 0.325 0.384

⊥━━ median = 0.297

Range = Max − Min = 0.384 − 0.235 = 0.149

x	$x - \bar{x}$	$\left(x - \bar{x}\right)^2$
0.235	−0.0643	0.00413449
0.256	−0.0433	0.00187489
0.272	−0.0273	0.00074529
0.295	−0.0043	0.00001849
0.297	−0.0023	0.00000529
0.310	0.0107	0.00011449
0.320	0.0207	0.00042849
0.325	0.0257	0.00066049
0.384	0.0847	0.00717409
		$\sum\left(x - \bar{x}\right)^2 = 0.01515601$

$$s^2 = \frac{\sum\left(x - \bar{x}\right)^2}{n-1} = \frac{0.01515601}{9-1} \approx 0.0019$$

$$s = \sqrt{\frac{\sum\left(x - \bar{x}\right)^2}{n-1}} = \sqrt{\frac{0.01515601}{8}} = 0.0435$$

Team B:

$$\bar{x} = \frac{\sum x}{n} = \frac{2.69}{9} \approx 0.2989$$

0.268 0.270 0.285 0.290 ⟨0.292⟩ 0.305 0.315 0.330 0.335

⊥━━ median = 0.292

Range = Max − Min = 0.335 − 0.268 = 0.067

x	$x - \bar{x}$	$\left(x - \bar{x}\right)^2$
0.268	−0.0309	0.00095481
0.270	−0.0289	0.00083521
0.285	−0.0139	0.00019321
0.290	−0.0089	0.00007921
0.292	−0.0069	0.00004761
0.305	0.0061	0.00003721
0.315	0.0161	0.00025921
0.330	0.0311	0.00096721
0.335	0.0361	0.00130321
		$\sum\left(x - \bar{x}\right)^2 = 0.00467689$

$$s^2 = \frac{\sum\left(x - \bar{x}\right)^2}{n-1} = \frac{0.00467689}{9-1} \approx 0.0006$$

$$s = \sqrt{\frac{\sum\left(x - \bar{x}\right)^2}{n-1}} = \sqrt{\frac{0.00467689}{8}} \approx 0.02418$$

   b. It appears form the data that the batting averages for Team A are more variable than the batting averages for Team B. The batting averages for Team A have a higher mean and a higher median than those for Team B.

29a. Greatest sample standard deviation: (ii)
Data set (ii) has more entries that are farther away from the mean.
Least sample standard deviation: (iii)
Data set (iii) has more entries that are close to the mean.
   b. The three data sets have the same mean but have different standard deviations.

30a. Greatest sample standard deviation: (i)
Data set (i) has more entries that are farther away from the mean.
Least sample standard deviation: (iii)
Data set (iii) has more entries that are close to the mean.
   b. The three data sets have the same mean, median, and mode, but have different standard deviations.

31a. Greatest sample standard deviation: (ii)
Data set (ii) has more entries that are farther away from the mean.
Least sample standard deviation: (iii)
Data set (iii) has more entries that are close to the mean.
   b. The three data sets have the same mean, median, and mode, but have different standard deviations.

32a. Greatest sample standard deviation: (iii)
Data set (iii) has more entries that are farther away from the mean.
Least sample standard deviation: (i)
Data set (i) has more entries that are close to the mean.
   b. The three data sets have the same mean and median but have different modes and standard deviations.

33. $\left(1300, 1700\right) \rightarrow \left(1500 - 1\left(200\right),\ 1500 + 1\left(200\right)\right) \rightarrow \left(\bar{x} - s,\ \bar{x} + s\right)$
68% of the farms have values between \$1300 and \$1700 per acre.

34. 95% of the data falls between $\bar{x} - 2s$ and $\bar{x} + 2s$.
$\bar{x} - 2s = 2400 - 2\left(450\right) = 1500$
$\bar{x} + 2s = 2400 + 2\left(450\right) = 3300$
95% of the farms have values between \$1500 and \$3300 per acre.

35a. $n = 75$
$68\%(75) = (0.68)(75) \approx 51$ farms have values between \$1300 and \$1700 per acre.
   b. $n = 25$
$68\%(25) = (0.68)(25) \approx 17$ farms have values between \$1300 and \$1700 per acre.

36a. $n = 40$

$95\%(40) = (0.95)(40) \approx 38$ farms have values between \$1500 and \$3300 per acre.

b. $n = 20$

$95\%(20) = (0.95)(20) \approx 19$ farms have values between \$1500 and \$3300 per acre.

37. $\overline{x} = 1500 \qquad s = 200$

{\$950, \$1000, \$2000, \$2180} are outliers. They are more than 2 standard deviations from the mean (1100, 1900). \$2180 is very unusual because it is more than 3 standard deviations from the mean.

38. $\overline{x} = 2400 \qquad s = 450$

{\$1045, \$1490, \$3325, \$3800} are outliers. They are more than 2 standard deviations from the mean (1500, 3300). \$1045 and \$3800 are very unusual because they are more than 3 standard deviations from the mean.

39. $\left(\overline{x} - 2s, \overline{x} + 2s\right) \rightarrow \left(1.14, 5.5\right)$ are 2 standard deviations from the mean.

$1 - \dfrac{1}{k^2} = 1 - \dfrac{1}{(2)^2} = 1 - \dfrac{1}{4} = 0.75 \Rightarrow$ At least 75% of the eruption times lie between 1.14 and 5.5 minutes.

If $n = 32$, at least $(0.75)(32) = 24$ eruptions will lie between 1.14 and 5.5 minutes.

40. $1 - \dfrac{1}{k^2} = 1 - \dfrac{1}{(2)^2} = 1 - \dfrac{1}{4} = 0.75$

At least 75% of the 400-meter dash times lie within 2 standard deviations of the mean.

$\left(\overline{x} - 2s, \overline{x} + 2s\right) \rightarrow \left(54.97, 59.17\right)$

At least 75% of the 400-meter dash times lie between 54.97 and 59.17 seconds.

41.

x	f	xf	$x - \overline{x}$	$\left(x - \overline{x}\right)^2$	$\left(x - \overline{x}\right)^2 f$
0	5	0	−2.1	4.41	22.05
1	11	11	−1.1	1.21	13.31
2	7	14	−0.1	0.01	0.07
3	10	30	0.9	0.81	8.10
4	7	28	1.9	3.61	25.27
	$n = 40$	$\sum xf = 83$			$\sum\left(x - \overline{x}\right)^2 f = 68.8$

$\overline{x} = \dfrac{\sum xf}{n} = \dfrac{83}{40} \approx 2.1$

$s = \sqrt{\dfrac{\sum\left(x - \overline{x}\right)^2 f}{n - 1}} = \sqrt{\dfrac{68.8}{39}} \approx 1.3$

42.

x	f	xf	$x - \bar{x}$	$(x - \bar{x})^2$	$(x - \bar{x})^2 f$
0	3	0	−1.7	2.89	8.67
1	15	15	−0.7	0.49	7.35
2	24	48	0.3	0.09	2.16
3	8	24	1.3	1.69	13.52
	$n = 50$	$\sum xf = 87$			$\sum (x - \bar{x})^2 f = 31.7$

$$\bar{x} = \frac{\sum xf}{n} = \frac{87}{50} \approx 1.7$$

$$s = \sqrt{\frac{\sum (x - \bar{x})^2 f}{n - 1}} = \sqrt{\frac{31.7}{49}} \approx 0.8$$

43. Class width = $\dfrac{\text{Max} - \text{Min}}{5} = \dfrac{14 - 1}{5} = \dfrac{13}{5} = 2.6 \Rightarrow 3$

Class	Midpoint, x	f	xf
1-3	2	3	6
4-6	5	6	30
7-9	8	13	104
10-12	11	7	77
13-15	14	3	42
		$N = 32$	$\sum xf = 259$

$$\mu = \frac{\sum xf}{N} = \frac{259}{32} \approx 8.1$$

$x - \mu$	$(x - \mu)^2$	$(x - \mu)^2 f$
−6.1	37.21	111.63
−3.1	9.61	57.66
−0.1	0.01	0.13
2.9	8.41	58.87
5.9	34.81	104.43
		$\sum (x - \mu)^2 f = 332.72$

$$\sigma = \sqrt{\frac{\sum (x - \mu)^2 f}{N}} = \sqrt{\frac{332.72}{32}} \approx 3.2$$

44. Class width = $\dfrac{\text{Max} - \text{Min}}{5} = \dfrac{244 - 145}{5} = \dfrac{99}{5} = 19.8 \Rightarrow 20$

Class	Midpoint, x	f	xf
145-164	154.5	8	1236.0
165-184	174.5	7	1221.5
185-204	194.5	3	583.5
205-224	214.5	1	214.5
225-244	234.5	1	234.5
		$N = 20$	$\sum xf = 3490.0$

$$\mu = \frac{\sum xf}{N} = \frac{3490}{20} = 174.5$$

$x - \mu$	$(x - \mu)^2$	$(x - \mu)^2 f$
−20	400	3200
0	0	0
20	400	1200
40	1600	1600
60	3600	3600
		$\sum (x - \mu)^2 f = 9600$

$$\sigma = \sqrt{\frac{\sum (x - \mu)^2 f}{N}} = \sqrt{\frac{9600}{20}} = \sqrt{480} \approx 21.9$$

45.

Midpoint, x	f	xf
70.5	1	70.5
92.5	12	1110.0
114.5	25	2862.5
136.5	10	1365.0
158.5	2	317.0
	$n = 50$	$\sum xf = 5725$

$$\bar{x} = \frac{\sum xf}{n} = \frac{5725}{50} = 114.5$$

$x - \bar{x}$	$(x - \bar{x})^2$	$(x - \bar{x})^2 f$
−44	1936	1936
−22	484	5808
0	0	0
22	484	4840
44	1936	3872
		$\sum (x - \bar{x})^2 f = 16,456$

$$s = \sqrt{\frac{\sum (x - \bar{x})^2 f}{n - 1}} = \sqrt{\frac{16,456}{49}} \approx 18.33$$

46.

x	f	xf
0	1	0
1	9	9
2	13	26
3	5	15
4	2	8
	$n = 30$	$\sum xf = 58$

$$\bar{x} = \frac{\sum xf}{n} = \frac{58}{30} \approx 1.9$$

$x - \bar{x}$	$\left(x - \bar{x}\right)^2$	$\left(x - \bar{x}\right)^2 f$
−1.9	3.61	3.61
−0.9	0.81	7.29
0.1	0.01	0.13
1.1	1.21	6.05
2.1	4.41	8.82
		$\sum\left(x - \bar{x}\right)^2 f = 25.9$

$$s = \sqrt{\frac{\sum\left(x - \bar{x}\right)^2 f}{n-1}} = \sqrt{\frac{25.9}{29}} \approx 0.9$$

47.

Class	Midpoint, x	f	xf
0-4	2.0	22.1	44.20
5-14	9.5	43.4	412.30
15-19	17.0	21.2	360.40
20-24	22.0	22.3	490.60
25-34	29.5	44.5	1312.75
35-44	39.5	41.3	1631.35
45-64	54.5	83.9	4572.55
65+	70.0	46.8	3276.00
		$n = 325.5$	$\sum xf = 12{,}100.15$

$$\bar{x} = \frac{\sum xf}{n} = \frac{12{,}100.15}{325.5} \approx 37.17$$

$x - \bar{x}$	$\left(x - \bar{x}\right)^2$	$\left(x - \bar{x}\right)^2 f$
−35.17	1236.9289	27,336.12869
−27.67	765.6289	33,228.29426
−20.17	406.8289	8624.77268
−15.17	230.1289	5131.87447
−7.67	58.8289	2617.88605
2.33	5.4289	224.21357
17.33	300.3289	25,197.59471
32.83	1077.8089	50,441.45642
		$\sum\left(x - \bar{x}\right)^2 f = 152{,}802.22085$

$$s = \sqrt{\frac{\sum\left(x - \bar{x}\right)^2 f}{n-1}} = \sqrt{\frac{152{,}802.22085}{324.5}} \approx 21.70$$

48.

Midpoint, x	f	xf
4.5	35.4	159.30
14.5	35.3	511.85
24.5	33.5	820.75
34.5	33.6	1159.20
44.5	28.8	1281.60
54.5	21.9	1193.55
64.5	13.9	896.55
74.5	7.2	536.40
84.5	2.6	219.70
94.5	0.3	28.35
	$n = 212.5$	$\sum xf = 6807.25$

$$\bar{x} = \frac{\sum xf}{n} = \frac{6807.25}{212.5} \approx 32.03$$

$x - \bar{x}$	$\left(x - \bar{x}\right)^2$	$\left(x - \bar{x}\right)^2 f$
−27.53	757.9009	26,829.69186
−17.53	307.3009	10,847.72117
−7.53	56.7009	1899.48015
2.47	6.1009	204.99024
12.47	155.5009	4478.42592
22.47	504.9009	11,057.32971
32.47	1054.3009	14,654.78251
42.47	1803.7009	12,986.64648
52.47	2753.1009	7158.06234
62.47	3902.5009	1170.75027
		$\sum\left(x - \bar{x}\right)^2 f = 91,287.88065$

$$s = \sqrt{\frac{\sum\left(x - \bar{x}\right)^2 f}{n-1}} = \sqrt{\frac{91,287.88065}{211.5}} \approx 20.78$$

49. **Summary Statistics:**

Column	n	Mean	Variance
Amount (in dollars)	15	58.8	239.74286

Std. Dev.	Median	Range	Min	Max
15.483632	60	59	30	89

50. **Summary Statistics:**

Column	n	Mean	Variance
Price (in dollars)	12	216.65666	14,442.424

Std. Dev.	Median	Range	Min	Max
120.176636	189.99	410	89.99	499.99

51. Heights:

$$\mu = \frac{\sum x}{N} = \frac{873}{12} = 72.75$$

x	$x - \mu$	$(x - \mu)^2$
68	−4.75	22.5625
69	−3.75	14.0625
69	−3.75	14.0625
70	−2.75	7.5625
72	−0.75	0.5625
72	−0.75	0.5625
73	0.25	0.0625
74	1.25	1.5625
74	1.25	1.5625
76	3.25	10.5625
77	4.25	18.0625
79	6.25	39.0625
		$\sum(x - \mu)^2 = 130.25$

$$\sigma = \sqrt{\frac{\sum(x - \mu)^2}{N}} = \sqrt{\frac{130.25}{12}} \approx 3.29$$

$$CV_{heights} = \frac{\sigma}{\mu} \cdot 100\% = \frac{3.29}{72.75} \cdot 100 \approx 4.5\%$$

Weights:

$$\mu = \frac{\sum x}{N} = \frac{2254}{12} = 187.83$$

x	$x - \mu$	$(x - \mu)^2$
162	−25.83	667.1889
168	−19.83	393.2289
171	−16.83	283.2489
174	−13.83	191.2689
180	−7.83	61.3089
185	−2.83	8.0089
189	1.17	1.3689
192	4.17	17.3889
197	9.17	84.0889
201	13.17	173.4489
210	22.17	491.5089
225	37.17	1381.6089
		$\sum(x - \mu)^2 = 3753.6668$

$$\sigma = \sqrt{\frac{\sum(x - \mu)^2}{N}} = \sqrt{\frac{3753.6668}{12}} \approx 17.69$$

$$CV_{weights} = \frac{\sigma}{\mu} \cdot 100\% = \frac{17.69}{187.83} \cdot 100 \approx 9.4\%$$

It appears that weight is more variable than height.

52a. Male:

x	x^2
1520	2,310,400
1750	3,062,500
2120	4,494,400
1380	1,904,400
1982	3,928,324
1645	2,706,025
1033	1,067,089
1714	2,937,796
$\sum x = 13,144$	$\sum x^2 = 22,410,934$

$$s = \sqrt{\frac{\sum x^2 - \frac{(\sum x)^2}{n}}{n-1}} = \sqrt{\frac{22,410,934 - \frac{(13,144)^2}{8}}{8-1}} = \sqrt{\frac{815,342}{7}} \approx 341.3$$

Female:

x	x^2
1785	3,186,225
1507	2,271,049
1497	2,241,009
1952	3,810,304
2210	4,884,100
1871	3,500,641
1263	1,595,169
1588	2,521,744
$\sum x = 13,673$	$\sum x^2 = 24,010,241$

$$s = \sqrt{\frac{\sum x^2 - \frac{(\sum x)^2}{n}}{n-1}} = \sqrt{\frac{24,010,241 - \frac{(13,673)^2}{8}}{8-1}} = \sqrt{\frac{641,374.875}{7}} \approx 302.7$$

b. The answers are the same as from Exercise 27.

53a. $\bar{x} \approx 41.5$ $s \approx 5.3$

b. $\bar{x} \approx 43.6$ $s \approx 5.6$

c. $\bar{x} \approx 3.5$ $s \approx 0.4$

d. By multiplying each entry by a constant k, the new sample mean is $k \cdot \bar{x}$ and the new sample standard deviation is $k \cdot s$.

54a. $\bar{x} \approx 41.7$ $s \approx 6.0$

b. $\bar{x} \approx 42.7$ $s \approx 6.0$

c. $\bar{x} \approx 39.7$ $s \approx 6.0$

d. By adding a constant k to, or subtracting it from, each entry, the new sample mean will be $\bar{x} + k$ with the sample standard being unaffected.

55a. Male: $\bar{x} = 1643$

x	$|x - \bar{x}|$
1520	123
1750	107
2120	477
1380	263
1982	339
1645	2
1033	610
1714	71
	$\sum|x - \bar{x}| = 1992$

$$\frac{\sum|x - \bar{x}|}{n} = \frac{1992}{8} = 249$$

$s = 341.3$

Female: $\bar{x} \approx 1709.1$

x	$|x - \bar{x}|$
1785	75.9
1507	202.1
1497	212.1
1952	242.9
2210	500.9
1871	161.9
1263	446.1
1588	121.1
	$\sum|x - \bar{x}| = 1963$

$$\frac{\sum|x - \bar{x}|}{n} = \frac{1963}{8} \approx 245.4$$

$s = 302.7$

The mean absolute deviation is less than the sample standard deviation.

b. Team A: $\overline{x} \approx 0.2993$

x	$\left|x - \overline{x}\right|$
0.295	0.0043
0.310	0.0107
0.325	0.0257
0.272	0.0273
0.256	0.0433
0.297	0.0023
0.320	0.0207
0.384	0.0847
0.235	0.0643
	$\sum\left|x - \overline{x}\right| = 0.2833$

$$\frac{\sum\left|x - \overline{x}\right|}{n} = \frac{0.2833}{9} \approx 0.0315$$

$s = 0.0435$

Team B: $\overline{x} \approx 0.2989$

x	$\left|x - \overline{x}\right|$
0.285	0.0139
0.305	0.0061
0.315	0.0161
0.270	0.0289
0.292	0.0069
0.330	0.0311
0.335	0.0361
0.268	0.0309
0.290	0.0089
	$\sum\left|x - \overline{x}\right| = 0.1789$

$$\frac{\sum\left|x - \overline{x}\right|}{n} = \frac{0.1789}{9} \approx 0.0199$$

$s = 0.0242$

The mean absolute deviation is less than the sample standard deviation.

56. $1 - \dfrac{1}{k^2} = 0.99 \Rightarrow 1 - 0.99 = \dfrac{1}{k^2} \Rightarrow k^2 = \dfrac{1}{0.01} \Rightarrow k = \sqrt{\dfrac{1}{0.01}} = 10$

At least 99% of the data in any data set lie within 10 standard deviations of the mean.

57a. $P = \dfrac{3\left(\overline{x} - \text{median}\right)}{s} = \dfrac{3(17 - 19)}{2.3} \approx -2.61;$ skewed left

b. $P = \dfrac{3\left(\overline{x} - \text{median}\right)}{s} = \dfrac{3(32 - 25)}{5.1} \approx 4.12;$ skewed right

c. $P = \dfrac{3\left(\overline{x} - \text{median}\right)}{s} = \dfrac{3(9.2 - 9.2)}{1.8} = 0;$ symmetric

d. $P = \dfrac{3(\bar{x} - \text{median})}{s} = \dfrac{3(42 - 40)}{6.0} = 1;$ skewed right

2.5 MEASURES OF POSITION

2.5 Try It Yourself Solutions

1a. 35, 36, 42, 43, 44, 46, 47, 49, 51, 51, 53, 53, 54, 54, 56, 57, 58, 59, 60, 61, 61, 63, 64, 65, 65, 66, 66, 67, 68, 69, 69, 72, 73, 73, 73, 76, 77, 78, 78, 80, 81, 82, 83, 83, 85, 86, 86, 87, 89, 89

b. $Q_2 = 65.5$

c. $Q_1 = 54$, $Q_3 = 78$

d. About one fourth of the 50 richest people are 54 years old or younger; one half are 65.5 years old or younger; and about three fourths of the 50 richest people are 78 years old or younger.

2a. (Enter the data)

b. $Q_1 = 17$, $Q_2 = 23$ $Q_3 = 28.5$

c. One quarter of the tuition costs is $17,000 or less, one half is $23,000 or less, and three quarters is $28,500 or less.

3a. $Q_1 = 54$, $Q_3 = 78$

b. IQR $= Q_3 - Q_1 = 78 - 54 = 24$

c. The ages of the 50 richest people in the middle portion of the data set vary by at most 24 years.

4a. Min = 35, $Q_1 = 54$, $Q_2 = 65.5$, $Q_3 = 78$, Max = 89

b,c.

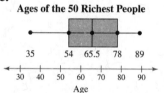

Ages of the 50 Richest People

35   54 65.5 78   89

30 40 50 60 70 80 90
Age

d. It appears that half of the ages are between 54 and 78.

5a. 50th percentile

b. 50% of the 50 richest people are younger than 66.

6a. $x = 60:$ $z = \dfrac{x - \mu}{\sigma} = \dfrac{60 - 70}{8} = -1.25$

$x = 71:$ $z = \dfrac{x - \mu}{\sigma} = \dfrac{71 - 70}{8} = 0.125$

$x = 92:$ $z = \dfrac{x - \mu}{\sigma} = \dfrac{92 - 70}{8} = 2.75$

b. From the z-scores, the utility bill of $60 is 1.25 standard deviations below the mean, the bill of $71 is 0.125 standard deviation above the mean, and the bill of $92 is 2.75 standard deviations above the mean.

7a. Best actor: $\mu = 43.7$, $\sigma = 8.7$

Best actress: $\mu = 35.9$, $\sigma = 11.4$

b. Sean Penn: $x = 48$: $z = \dfrac{x - \mu}{\sigma} = \dfrac{48 - 43.7}{8.7} \approx 0.49$

Kate Winslet: $x = 33$: $z = \dfrac{x - \mu}{\sigma} = \dfrac{33 - 35.9}{11.4} \approx -0.25$

c. Sean Penn's age is 0.49 standard deviation above the mean of the best actors. Kate Winslet's age is -0.25 standard deviation below the mean of the best actresses. Neither actor's age is unusual.

2.5 EXERCISE SOLUTIONS

1. The soccer team scored fewer points per game than 75% of the teams in the league.

2. The salesperson sold more hardware equipment than 80% of the other sales people.

3. The student scored higher than 78% of the students who took the actuarial exam.

4. The child's IQ is higher than 93% of the other children in the same age group.

5. The interquartile range of a data set can be used to identify outliers because data values that are greater than $Q_3 + 1.5(\text{IQR})$ or less than $Q_1 - 1.5(\text{IQR})$ are considered outliers.

6. Quartiles are special cases of percentiles. Q_1 is the 25th percentile, Q_2 is the 50th percentile, and Q_3 is the 75th percentile.

7. False. The median of a data set is a fractile, but the mean may or may not be fractile depending on the distribution of the data.

8. True

9. True

10. False. The five numbers you need to graph a box-and-whisper plot are the minimum, the maximum, Q_1, Q_3, and the median (Q_2).

11. False. The 50th percentile is equivalent to Q_2.

12. False. Any score equal to the mean will have a corresponding z-score of zero.

13. False. A z-score of -2.5 is considered unusual.

14. True

15a. Min = 10, $Q_1 = 13$, $Q_2 = 15$, $Q_3 = 17$, Max = 20

b. IQR = $Q_3 - Q_1 = 17 - 13 = 4$

16a. Min = 100, $Q_1 = 130$, $Q_2 = 205$, $Q_3 = 270$, Max = 320

b. $IQR = Q_3 - Q_1 = 270 - 130 = 140$

17a. $Min = 900$, $Q_1 = 1250$, $Q_2 = 1500$, $Q_3 = 1950$, $Max = 2100$

   b. $IQR = Q_3 - Q_1 = 1950 - 1250 = 700$

18a. $Min = 25$, $Q_1 = 50$, $Q_2 = 65$, $Q_3 = 70$, $Max = 85$

   b. $IQR = Q_3 - Q_1 = 70 - 50 = 20$

19a. $Min = -1.9$, $Q_1 = -0.5$, $Q_2 = 0.1$, $Q_3 = 0.7$, $Max = 2.1$

   b. $IQR = Q_3 - Q_1 = 0.7 - (-0.5) = 1.2$

20a. $Min = -1.3$, $Q_1 = -0.3$, $Q_2 = 0.2$, $Q_3 = 0.4$, $Max = 2.1$

   b. $IQR = Q_3 - Q_1 = 0.4 - (-0.3) = 0.7$

21a.

$Min = 24$, $Q_1 = 28$, $Q_2 = 35$, $Q_3 = 41$, $Max = 60$

   b.

22a.

$Min = 150$, $Q_1 = 172$, $Q_2 = 177$, $Q_3 = 180$, $Max = 182$

   b.

23a.

$Min = 1$, $Q_1 = 4.5$, $Q_2 = 6$, $Q_3 = 7.5$, $Max = 9$

b.

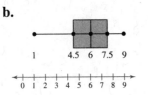

24a.

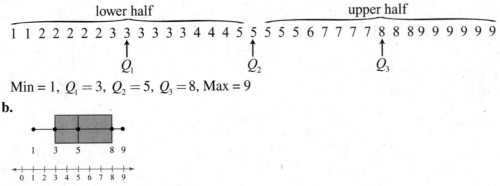

Min = 1, $Q_1 = 3$, $Q_2 = 5$, $Q_3 = 8$, Max = 9

b.

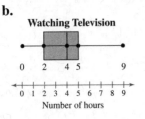

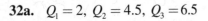

25. None. The Data are not skewed or symmetric.

26. Skewed right. Most of the data lie to the left in the box-and-whisker plot.

27. Skewed left. Most of the data lie to the right in the box-and-whisker plot.

28. Symmetric. The data are evenly spaced to the left and to the right of the median.

29. $Q_1 = B$, $Q_2 = A$, $Q_3 = C$

25% of the values are below B, 50% of the values are below A, and 75% of the values are below C.

30. $P_{10} = T$, $P_{50} = R$, $P_{80} = S$

10% of the values are below T, 50% of the values are below R, and 80% of the values are below S.

31a. $Q_1 = 2$, $Q_2 = 4$, $Q_3 = 5$

b.

Watching Television

0   2   4 5   9

0 1 2 3 4 5 6 7 8 9
Number of hours

32a. $Q_1 = 2$, $Q_2 = 4.5$, $Q_3 = 6.5$

b.

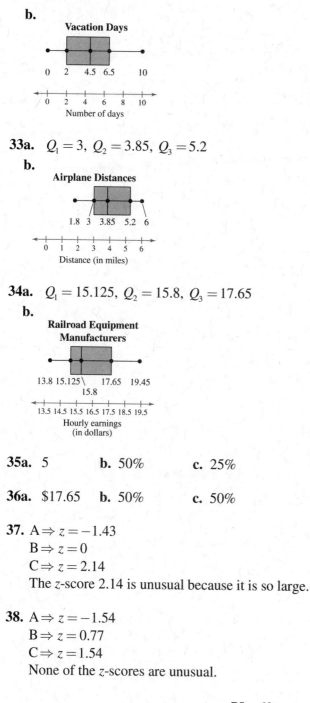

33a. $Q_1 = 3, \ Q_2 = 3.85, \ Q_3 = 5.2$

b.

34a. $Q_1 = 15.125, \ Q_2 = 15.8, \ Q_3 = 17.65$

b.

35a. 5   **b.** 50%   **c.** 25%

36a. $17.65   **b.** 50%   **c.** 50%

37. $A \Rightarrow z = -1.43$
  $B \Rightarrow z = 0$
  $C \Rightarrow z = 2.14$
  The z-score 2.14 is unusual because it is so large.

38. $A \Rightarrow z = -1.54$
  $B \Rightarrow z = 0.77$
  $C \Rightarrow z = 1.54$
  None of the z-scores are unusual.

39a. Statistics: $x = 75 \Rightarrow z = \dfrac{x - \mu}{\sigma} = \dfrac{75 - 63}{7} \approx 1.71$

  Biology: $x = 25 \Rightarrow z = \dfrac{x - \mu}{\sigma} = \dfrac{25 - 23}{3.9} \approx 0.51$

  b. The student had a better score on the statistics test.

40a. Statistics: $x = 60 \Rightarrow z = \dfrac{x - \mu}{\sigma} = \dfrac{60 - 63}{7} \approx -0.43$

Biology: $x = 22 \Rightarrow z = \dfrac{x - \mu}{\sigma} = \dfrac{22 - 23}{3.9} \approx -0.26$

b. The student had a better score on the biology test.

41a. Statistics: $x = 78 \Rightarrow z = \dfrac{x - \mu}{\sigma} = \dfrac{78 - 63}{7} \approx 2.14$

Biology: $x = 29 \Rightarrow z = \dfrac{x - \mu}{\sigma} = \dfrac{29 - 23}{3.9} \approx 1.54$

b. The student had a better score on the statistics test.

42a. Statistics: $x = 63 \Rightarrow z = \dfrac{x - \mu}{\sigma} = \dfrac{63 - 63}{7} = 0$

Biology: $x = 23 \Rightarrow z = \dfrac{x - \mu}{\sigma} = \dfrac{23 - 23}{3.9} = 0$

b. The student performed equally well on the two tests.

43a. $x = 34,000 \Rightarrow z = \dfrac{x - \mu}{\sigma} = \dfrac{34,000 - 35,000}{2,250} \approx -0.44$

$x = 37,000 \Rightarrow z = \dfrac{x - \mu}{\sigma} = \dfrac{37,000 - 35,000}{2,250} \approx 0.89$

$x = 30,000 \Rightarrow z = \dfrac{x - \mu}{\sigma} = \dfrac{30,000 - 35,000}{2,250} \approx -2.22$

The tire with a life span of 30,000 miles has an unusually short life span.

b. $x = 30,500 \Rightarrow z = \dfrac{x - \mu}{\sigma} = \dfrac{30,500 - 35,000}{2,250} = -2 \Rightarrow$ 2.5th percentile

$x = 37,250 \Rightarrow z = \dfrac{x - \mu}{\sigma} = \dfrac{37,250 - 35,000}{2,250} = 1 \Rightarrow$ 84th percentile

$x = 35,000 \Rightarrow z = \dfrac{x - \mu}{\sigma} = \dfrac{35,000 - 35,000}{2,250} = 0 \Rightarrow$ 50th percentile

44a. $x = 34 \Rightarrow z = \dfrac{x - \mu}{\sigma} = \dfrac{34 - 33}{4} = 0.25$

$x = 30 \Rightarrow z = \dfrac{x - \mu}{\sigma} = \dfrac{30 - 33}{4} = -0.75$

$x = 42 \Rightarrow z = \dfrac{x - \mu}{\sigma} = \dfrac{42 - 33}{4} = 2.25$

The fruit fly with a life span of 42 days has an unusually long life span.

b. $x = 29 \Rightarrow z = \dfrac{x - \mu}{\sigma} = \dfrac{29 - 33}{4} = -1 \Rightarrow$ 16th percentile

$x = 41 \Rightarrow z = \dfrac{x - \mu}{\sigma} = \dfrac{41 - 33}{4} = 2 \Rightarrow$ 97.5th percentile

$x = 25 \Rightarrow z = \dfrac{x - \mu}{\sigma} = \dfrac{25 - 33}{4} = -2 \Rightarrow$ 2.5th percentile

45. 72 inches

60% of the heights are below 72 inches.

46. 98th percentile

98% of the heights are below 77 inches

47. $x = 74 \Rightarrow z = \dfrac{x - \mu}{\sigma} = \dfrac{74 - 69.9}{3.0} \approx 1.37$

$x = 62 \Rightarrow z = \dfrac{x - \mu}{\sigma} = \dfrac{62 - 69.9}{3.0} \approx -2.63$

$x = 80 \Rightarrow z = \dfrac{x - \mu}{\sigma} = \dfrac{80 - 69.9}{3.0} \approx 3.37$

The height of 62 inches is unusual due to a rather small z-score. The height of 80 inches is very unusual due to a rather large z-score.

48. $x = 70 \Rightarrow z = \dfrac{x - \mu}{\sigma} = \dfrac{70 - 69.9}{3.0} \approx 0.03$

$x = 66 \Rightarrow z = \dfrac{x - \mu}{\sigma} = \dfrac{66 - 69.9}{3.0} = -1.3$

$x = 68 \Rightarrow z = \dfrac{x - \mu}{\sigma} = \dfrac{68 - 69.9}{3.0} \approx -0.63$

49. $x = 71.1 \Rightarrow z = \dfrac{x - \mu}{\sigma} = \dfrac{71.1 - 71.1}{3.0} = 0.0$

Approximately the 50th percentile.

50. $x = 66.3 \Rightarrow z = \dfrac{x - \mu}{\sigma} = \dfrac{66.3 - 69.9}{3.0} = -1.2$

Approximately the 10th percentile.

51a.

```
27  28  31  32  32  33  35  36  36  36  36  37  38  39  39  40  40  40  41  41
41  42  42  42  42  42  42  43  43  43  44  44  45  45  46  47  47  47  47  47
48  48  48  48  48 │49  49  49  49  49  49  50  50  51  51  51  51  51  51  52
52  52  53  53  54 │54  54  54  54  54 │54  54  55  56  56  56  57  57  57  59
59  59  60  60  60 │61  61  61  62  62 │63  63  63  63  64 │65  67  68  74  82
```

$\qquad\qquad\qquad Q_1 \qquad\qquad\qquad Q_2 \qquad\qquad\qquad Q_3$

Min = 27, $Q_1 = 42$, $Q_2 = 49$, $Q_3 = 56$, Max = 82

b.

Ages of Executives

27   42 49 56   82

25   35   45   55   65   75   85

Age

c. Half of the executives are between 42 and 56 years old.

d. About 49 years old because half of the executives are older and half are younger.

e. The age groups 20-29, 70-79, and 80-89 would all be considered unusual because they are more than two standard deviations from the mean.

52.

1 2 3 3 5 5 7 7 8 10

$\uparrow$ Q_1 $\uparrow$ Q_2 $\uparrow$ Q_3

$\text{Midquartile} = \dfrac{Q_1 + Q_3}{2} = \dfrac{3 + 7}{2} = 5$

53.

22 23 24 32 33 34 36 38 39 40 41 47

$\uparrow$ Q_1 $\uparrow$ Q_2 $\uparrow$ Q_3

$\text{Midquartile} = \dfrac{Q_1 + Q_3}{2} = \dfrac{28 + 39.5}{2} = 33.75$

54.

7.9 8 8.1 9.7 10.3 11.2 11.8 12.2 12.3 12.7 13.4 15.4 16.1

$\uparrow$ $Q_1 = 8.9$ $\uparrow$ Q_2 $\uparrow$ $Q_3 = 13.05$

$\text{Midquartile} = \dfrac{Q_1 + Q_3}{2} = \dfrac{8.9 + 13.05}{2} = 10.975$

55.

13.4 15.2 15.6 16.7 17.2 18.7 19.7 19.8 19.8 20.8 21.4 22.9 28.7 30.1 31.9

$\uparrow$ Q_1 $\uparrow$ Q_2 $\uparrow$ Q_3

$\text{Midquartile} = \dfrac{Q_1 + Q_3}{2} = \dfrac{16.7 + 22.9}{2} = 19.8$

56a. Concert 1: Symmetric

Concert 2: Skewed right

Concert 1 has less variation.

b. Concert 2 is more likely to have outliers because its distribution is wider.

c. Concert 1, because 68% of the data should be between ± 16.3 of the mean.

d. No, you do not know the number of songs played at either concert or the actual lengths of the songs.

57.

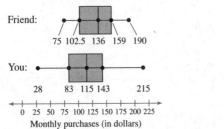

Credit Card Purchases

Friend: 75 102.5 136 159 190

You: 28 83 115 143 215

0 25 50 75 100 125 150 175 200 225

Monthly purchases (in dollars)

Your distribution is symmetric and your friend's distribution is uniform.

58. $\text{Percentile} = \dfrac{\text{Number of data values less than } x}{\text{Total number of data values}} \cdot 100$

$= \dfrac{3}{73} \cdot 100 \approx \text{4th percentile}$

59. $\text{Percentile} = \dfrac{\text{Number of data values less than } x}{\text{Total number of data values}} \cdot 100$

$= \dfrac{30}{73} \cdot 100 \approx \text{41st percentile}$

60a.

$$\overbrace{2\ \ 7\ \ 8\ \ 9\ \ 9\ \ 10\ \ 10\ \ 11}^{\text{lower half}}\ \overbrace{11\ \ 12\ \ 12\ \ 13\ \ 15\ \ 16\ \ 24}^{\text{upper half}}$$

with arrows pointing to Q_1, Q_2, Q_3

$Q_1 = 9,\ Q_2 = 11,\ Q_3 = 13$

$\text{IQR} = Q_3 - Q_1 = 13 - 9 = 4$

$1.5 \times \text{IQR} = 6$

$Q_1 - (1.5 \times \text{IQR}) = 9 - 6 = 3$

$Q_3 + (1.5 \times \text{IQR}) = 13 + 6 = 19$

Any values less than 6 or greater than 19 is an outlier. So, 2 and 24 are outliers.

b.

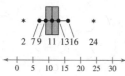

61a.

$$\overbrace{62\ \ 72\ \ 72\ \ 74\ \ 75\ \ 75}^{\text{lower half}}\ \overbrace{75\ \ 76\ \ 78\ \ 80\ \ 80\ \ 95}^{\text{upper half}}$$

with arrows pointing to Q_1, Q_2, Q_3

$Q_1 = 73,\ Q_2 = 75,\ Q_3 = 79$

$\text{IQR} = Q_3 - Q_1 = 79 - 73 = 6$

$1.5 \times \text{IQR} = 9$

$Q_1 - (1.5 \times \text{IQR}) = 73 - 9 = 64$

$Q_3 + (1.5 \times \text{IQR}) = 79 + 9 = 88$

Any values less than 64 or greater than 88 is an outlier. So, 62 and 95 are outliers.

b.

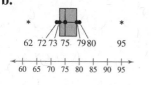

62a. Summary statistics:

Column	Min	Q_1	Median	Q_3	Max
Speed (in miles per hour)	52	65	70	72	88

b. **c.**

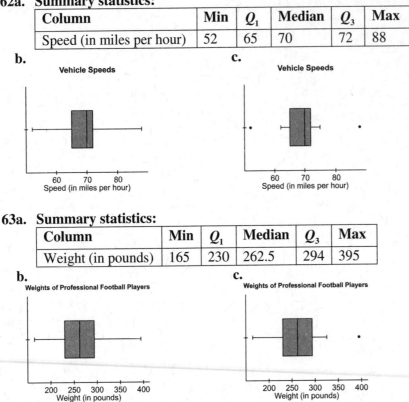

63a. Summary statistics:

Column	Min	Q_1	Median	Q_3	Max
Weight (in pounds)	165	230	262.5	294	395

b. **c.**

CHAPTER 2 REVIEW EXERCISE SOLUTIONS

1. Class width $= \dfrac{\text{Max} - \text{Min}}{\text{Number of classes}} = \dfrac{30 - 8}{5} = 4.4 \Rightarrow 5$

Class	Midpoint, x	Boundaries	Frequency, f	Relative frequency	Cumulative frequency
8-12	10	7.5-12.5	2	0.10	2
13-17	15	12.5-17.5	10	0.50	12
18-22	20	17.5-22.5	5	0.25	17
23-27	25	22.5-27.5	1	0.05	18
28-32	30	27.5-32.5	2	0.10	20
			$\sum f = 20$	$\sum \dfrac{f}{n} = 1$	

2.

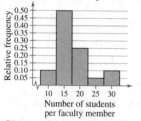

Students Per Faculty Member

Class with greatest relative frequency: 13-17
Class with least relative frequency: 23-27

3. Class width = $\dfrac{\text{Max} - \text{Min}}{\text{Number of classes}} = \dfrac{12.10 - 11.86}{7} \approx 0.03 \Rightarrow 0.04$

Class	Midpoint	Frequency, f	Relative frequency
11.86-11.89	11.875	3	0.125
11.90-11.93	11.915	5	0.208
11.94-11.97	11.955	8	0.333
11.98-12.01	11.995	7	0.292
12.02-12.05	12.035	0	0
12.06-12.09	12.075	0	0
12.10-12.13	12.115	1	0.042
		$\sum f = 24$	$\sum \dfrac{f}{n} = 1$

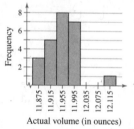

Liquid Volume 12-oz Cans

4. Class width = $\dfrac{\text{Max} - \text{Min}}{\text{Number of classes}} = \dfrac{12.10 - 11.86}{7} \approx 0.03 \Rightarrow 0.04$

Class	Midpoint	Frequency, f	Relative frequency
11.86-11.89	11.875	3	0.125
11.90-11.93	11.915	5	0.208
11.94-11.97	11.955	8	0.333
11.98-12.01	11.995	7	0.292
12.02-12.05	12.035	0	0
12.06-12.09	12.075	0	0
12.10-12.13	12.115	1	0.042
		$\sum f = 24$	$\sum \dfrac{f}{n} = 1$

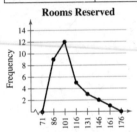

Liquid Volume 12-oz Cans

5.

Class	Midpoint	Frequency, f	Cumulative frequency
79-93	86	9	9
94-108	101	12	21
109-123	116	5	26
124-138	131	3	29
139-153	146	2	31
154-168	161	1	32
		$\sum f = 32$	

Rooms Reserved

6.

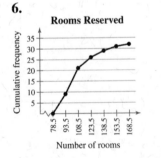

Rooms Reserved

7.

```
1 | 0   0              Key: 1|0 = 10
2 | 0   0   2   5   5
3 | 0   3   4   5   5   8
4 | 1   2   4   4   7   8
5 | 2   3   3   7   9
6 | 1   1   5
7 | 1   5
8 | 9
```

8.

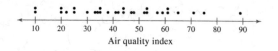

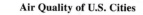

Air Quality of U.S. Cities

Air quality index

9.

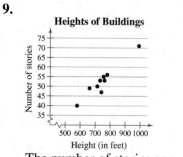

The number of stories appears to increase with height.

10.

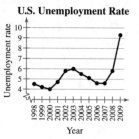

11.

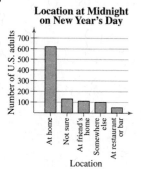

12.

Location	Frequency	Relative frequency	Degrees
At home	620	0.6139	221°
At friend's home	110	0.1089	39°
At restaurant or bar	50	0.0495	18°
Somewhere else	100	0.0990	36°
Not sure	130	0.1287	46°
		$\sum \dfrac{f}{n} = 1$	

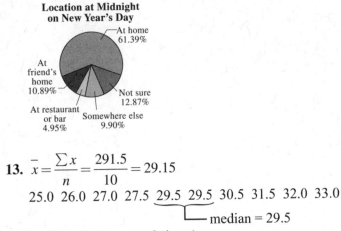

**Location at Midnight
on New Year's Day**

At home
61.39%

At
friend's
home
10.89%

Not sure
12.87%

At restaurant
or bar
4.95%

Somewhere else
9.90%

13. $\bar{x} = \dfrac{\sum x}{n} = \dfrac{291.5}{10} = 29.15$

25.0 26.0 27.0 27.5 $\underbrace{29.5 \quad 29.5}$ 30.5 31.5 32.0 33.0

median = 29.5

Mode = 29.5 (occurs 2 times)

14. $\bar{x}$ = not possible

median = not possible

mode = "Approved"

The mean and median cannot be found because the data are at the nominal level of measurement.

15.

Midpoint, x	Frequency, f	$x \cdot f$
10	2	20
15	10	15
20	5	100
25	1	25
30	2	60
	$n = 20$	$\sum (x \cdot f) = 355$

$\bar{x} = \dfrac{\sum (x \cdot f)}{n} = \dfrac{355}{20} \approx 17.8$

16.

x	f	$x \cdot f$
0	13	0
1	9	9
2	19	38
3	8	24
4	5	20
5	2	10
6	4	24
	$n = 60$	$\sum (x \cdot f) = 125$

$\bar{x} = \dfrac{\sum (x \cdot f)}{n} = \dfrac{125}{60} \approx 2.1$

17.

Source	Score, x	Weight, w	$x \cdot w$
Test 1	78	0.15	11.7
Test 2	72	0.15	10.8
Test 3	86	0.15	12.9
Test 4	91	0.15	13.65
Test 5	87	0.15	13.05
Test 6	80	0.25	20
		$\sum w = 1$	$\sum (x \cdot w) = 82.1$

$$\bar{x} = \frac{\sum (x \cdot w)}{\sum w} = \frac{82.1}{1} = 82.1$$

18.

Source	Score, x	Weight, w	$x \cdot w$
Test 1	96	0.2	19.2
Test 2	85	0.2	17
Test 3	91	0.2	18.2
Test 4	86	0.4	34.4
		$\sum w = 1$	$\sum (x \cdot w) = 88.8$

$$\bar{x} = \frac{\sum (x \cdot w)}{\sum w} = \frac{88.8}{1} = 88.8$$

19. Skewed   **20.** Skewed   **21.** Skewed left   **22.** Skewed right

23. Median, because the mean is to the left of the median in a skewed left distribution.

24. Mean, because the mean is to the right of the median in a skewed right distribution.

25. Range = Max – Min = 8.26 – 5.46 = $2.80

26. Range = Max – Min = 19.73 – 15.89 = $3.84

27. $\mu = \dfrac{\sum x}{N} = \dfrac{96}{14} \approx 6.9$

x	$x - \mu$	$(x - \mu)^2$
4	−2.9	8.41
2	−4.9	24.01
9	2.1	4.41
12	5.1	26.01
15	8.1	65.61
3	−3.9	15.21
6	−0.9	0.81
8	1.1	1.21
1	−5.9	34.81
4	−2.9	8.41
14	7.1	50.41
12	5.1	26.01
3	−3.9	15.21
3	−3.9	15.21
$\sum x = 96$	$\sum (x - \mu) \approx 0$	$\sum (x - \mu)^2 = 295.74$

$\sigma = \sqrt{\dfrac{\sum (x - \mu)^2}{N}} = \sqrt{\dfrac{295.74}{14}} \approx 4.6$

28. $\mu = \dfrac{\sum x}{N} = \dfrac{612}{9} = 68$

x	$x - \mu$	$(x - \mu)^2$
55	−13	169
89	21	441
73	5	25
73	5	25
61	−7	49
76	8	64
71	3	9
59	−9	81
55	−13	169
$\sum x = 612$	$\sum (x - \mu) = 0$	$\sum (x - \mu)^2 = 1032$

$\sigma = \sqrt{\dfrac{\sum (x - \mu)^2}{N}} = \sqrt{\dfrac{1032}{9}} \approx 10.7$

29. $\bar{x} = \dfrac{\sum x}{n} = \dfrac{36{,}801}{15} = 2453.4$

x	$x - \bar{x}$	$\left(x - \bar{x}\right)^2$
2445	–8.4	70.56
2940	486.6	236,779.56
2399	–54.4	2959.36
1960	–493.4	243,443.56
2421	–32.4	1049.76
2940	486.6	236,779.56
2657	203.6	41,452.96
2153	–300.4	90,240.16
2430	–23.4	547.56
2278	–175.4	30,765.16
1947	–506.4	256,440.96
2383	–70.4	4956.16
2710	256.6	65,843.56
2761	307.6	94,617.76
2377	–76.4	5836.96
$\sum x = 36{,}801$	$\sum\left(x - \bar{x}\right) = 0$	$\sum\left(x - \bar{x}\right)^2 = 1{,}311{,}783.6$

$s = \sqrt{\dfrac{\sum\left(x - \bar{x}\right)^2}{n-1}} = \sqrt{\dfrac{1{,}311{,}783.6}{14}} \approx 306.1$

30. $\bar{x} = \dfrac{\sum x}{n} = \dfrac{416{,}659}{8} \approx 52{,}082.4$

x	$x - \bar{x}$	$\left(x - \bar{x}\right)^2$
49,632	–2450.4	6,004,460.16
54,619	2536.6	6,434,339.56
58,298	6215.6	38,633,683.36
48,250	–3832.4	14,687,289.76
51,842	–240.4	57,792.16
50,875	–1207.4	1,457,814.76
53,219	1136.6	1,291,859.56
49,924	–2158.4	4,658,690.56
$\sum x = 416{,}659$	$\sum\left(x - \bar{x}\right) \approx 0$	$\sum\left(x - \bar{x}\right)^2 = 73{,}225{,}929.88$

$s = \sqrt{\dfrac{\sum\left(x - \bar{x}\right)^2}{n-1}} = \sqrt{\dfrac{73{,}225{,}929.88}{7}} \approx 3234.3$

31. 99.7% of the distribution lies within 3 standard deviations of the mean.

$\mu - 3\sigma = 49 - (3)(2.50) = 41.5$

$\mu + 3\sigma = 49 + (3)(2.50) = 56.5$

99.7% of the distribution lies between \$41.50 and \$56.50.

32. $\left(46.75,\ 52.25\right) \to \left(49.50 - 1(2.75),\ 49.50 + 1(2.75)\right) \to \left(\bar{x} - s,\ \bar{x} + s\right)$

68% of the cable rates lie between \$46.75 and \$52.25.

33. $\left(\bar{x} - 2s,\ \bar{x} + 2s\right) \to \left(20,\ 52\right)$ are 2 standard deviations from the mean.

$$1 - \frac{1}{k^2} = 1 - \frac{1}{(2)^2} = 1 - \frac{1}{4} = 0.75$$

At least $(40)(0.75) = 30$ customers have a mean sale between \$20 and \$52.

34. $\left(\bar{x} - 2s,\ \bar{x} + 2s\right) \to \left(3,\ 11\right)$ are 2 standard deviations from the mean.

$$1 - \frac{1}{k^2} = 1 - \frac{1}{(2)^2} = 1 - \frac{1}{4} = 0.75$$

At least $(20)(0.75) = 15$ shuttle flights lasted between 3 days and 11 days.

35.

x	f	xf	$x - \bar{x}$	$\left(x - \bar{x}\right)^2$	$\left(x - \bar{x}\right)^2 f$
0	1	0	−2.5	6.25	6.25
1	8	8	−1.5	2.25	18.00
2	13	26	−0.5	0.25	3.25
3	10	30	0.5	0.25	2.50
4	5	20	1.5	2.25	11.25
5	3	15	2.5	6.25	18.75
	$n = 40$	$\sum xf = 99$			$\sum \left(x - \bar{x}\right)^2 f = 60$

$$\bar{x} = \frac{\sum xf}{n} = \frac{99}{40} \approx 2.5$$

$$s = \sqrt{\frac{\sum \left(x - \bar{x}\right)^2 f}{n - 1}} = \sqrt{\frac{60}{39}} \approx 1.2$$

36.

x	f	xf	$x - \bar{x}$	$\left(x - \bar{x}\right)^2$	$\left(x - \bar{x}\right)^2 f$
0	4	0	−2.4	5.76	23.04
1	5	5	−1.4	1.96	9.80
2	2	4	−0.4	0.16	0.32
3	9	27	0.6	0.36	3.24
4	1	4	1.6	2.56	2.56
5	3	15	2.6	6.76	20.28
6	1	6	3.6	12.96	12.96
	$n = 25$	$\sum xf = 61$			$\sum \left(x - \bar{x}\right)^2 f = 72.2$

$$\bar{x} = \frac{\sum xf}{n} = \frac{61}{25} \approx 2.4$$

$$s = \sqrt{\frac{\sum \left(x - \bar{x}\right)^2 f}{n - 1}} = \sqrt{\frac{72.2}{24}} \approx 1.7$$

37.

$$\overbrace{\text{lower half}} \qquad\qquad \overbrace{\text{upper half}}$$

42 42 42 47 47 48 48 50 53 53 53 | 53 54 54 54 54 54 57 57 60 60

$\uparrow$ Q_1 $\qquad$ $\uparrow$ Q_2 $\qquad\qquad$ $\uparrow$ Q_3

Min = 42, $Q_1 = 47.5$, $Q_2 = 53$, $Q_3 = 54$, Max = 60

38. IQR = $Q_3 - Q_1 = 54 - 47.5 = 6.5$

39.

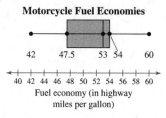

Motorcycle Fuel Economies

42   47.5   53 54   60

40 42 44 46 48 50 52 54 56 58 60

Fuel economy (in highway
miles per gallon)

40. 15

41.

$$\overbrace{\text{lower half}} \qquad \overbrace{\text{upper half}}$$

25.0 26.0 27.0 27.5 29.5 | 29.5 30.5 31.5 32.0 33.0

$\uparrow$ Q_1 $\qquad$ $\uparrow$ Q_2 $\qquad$ $\uparrow$ Q_3

IQR = $Q_3 - Q_1 = 31.5 - 27.0 = 4.5$

42.

$$\overbrace{\text{lower half}} \qquad\qquad\qquad \overbrace{\text{upper half}}$$

145 156 167 172 173 184 185 185 190 | 190 192 195 197 205 208 212 227 228 240

$\uparrow$ Q_1 $\qquad\qquad$ $\uparrow$ Q_2 $\qquad\qquad$ $\uparrow$ Q_3

Min = 145, $Q_1 = 173$, $Q_2 = 190$, $Q_3 = 208$, Max = 240

Weight of Football Players

145   173 190 208   240

140 150 160 170 180 190 200 210 220 230 240

Weight

The distribution is symmetric.

43. The 65th percentile means that 65% had a test grade of 75 or less. So, 35% scored higher than 75.

44. 14th percentile

45. $z = \dfrac{16{,}500 - 11{,}830}{2370} = 1.97$ $\qquad\qquad$ **46.** $z = \dfrac{5500 - 11{,}830}{2370} = -2.67$

47. $z = \dfrac{18,000 - 11,830}{2370} = 2.60$ **48.** $z = \dfrac{11,300 - 11,830}{2370} = -0.22$

CHAPTER 2 QUIZ SOLUTIONS

1a. Class width $= \dfrac{\text{Max} - \text{Min}}{\text{Number of classes}} = \dfrac{157 - 101}{5} = 11.2 \Rightarrow 12$

Class	Midpoint	Class boundaries	Frequency, f	Relative frequency	Cumulative frequency
101-112	106.5	100.5-112.5	3	0.12	3
113-124	118.5	112.5-124.5	11	0.44	14
125-136	130.5	124.5-136.5	7	0.28	21
137-148	142.5	136.5-148.5	2	0.08	23
149-160	154.5	148.5-160.5	2	0.08	25
			$\sum f = 25$	$\sum \dfrac{f}{n} = 1$	

b. Frequency histogram and polygon   **c.** Relative frequency histogram

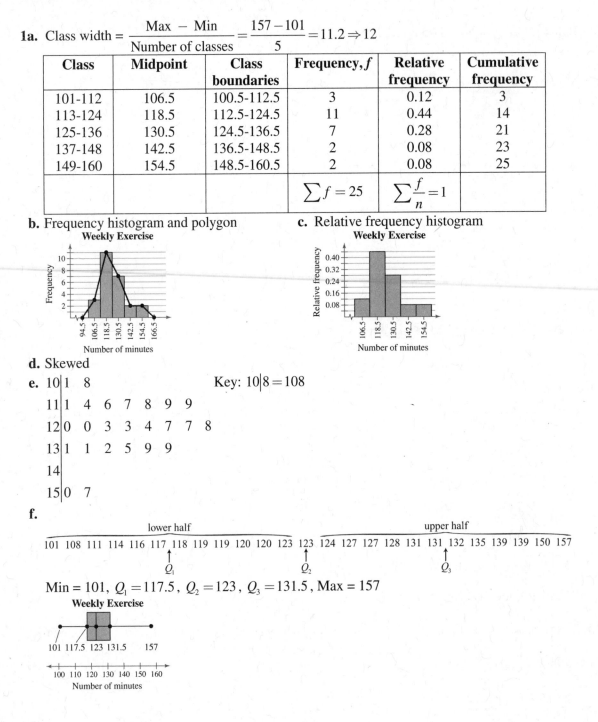

d. Skewed

e.
```
10 | 1  8                    Key: 10|8 = 108
11 | 1  4  6  7  8  9  9
12 | 0  0  3  3  4  7  7  8
13 | 1  1  2  5  9  9
14 |
15 | 0  7
```

f.

lower half   upper half

101 108 111 114 116 117 118 119 119 120 120 123 123 124 127 127 128 131 131 132 135 139 139 150 157

⟶ Q_1 ⟶ Q_2 ⟶ Q_3

Min $= 101$, $Q_1 = 117.5$, $Q_2 = 123$, $Q_3 = 131.5$, Max $= 157$

Weekly Exercise

101 117.5 123 131.5   157

100 110 120 130 140 150 160
Number of minutes

g.

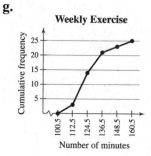

Weekly Exercise

Cumulative frequency vs. Number of minutes

2.

Midpoint, x	Frequency, f	xf	$x - \overline{x}$	$\left(x - \overline{x}\right)^2$	$\left(x - \overline{x}\right)^2 f$
106.5	3	319.5	−18.7	349.69	1049.07
118.5	11	1303.5	−6.7	44.89	493.79
130.5	7	913.5	5.3	28.09	196.63
142.5	2	285.0	17.3	299.29	598.58
154.5	2	309.0	29.3	858.49	1716.98
	$n = 25$	$\sum xf = 3130.5$			$\sum\left(x - \overline{x}\right)^2 f = 4055.05$

$$\overline{x} = \frac{\sum xf}{n} = \frac{3130.5}{25} \approx 125.2$$

$$s = \sqrt{\frac{\sum\left(x - \overline{x}\right)^2 f}{n - 1}} = \sqrt{\frac{4055.05}{24}} \approx 13.0$$

3a.

Category	Frequency	Relative frequency	Degrees
Clothing	10.6	0.1330	48°
Footwear	17.2	0.2158	78°
Equipment	24.9	0.3124	112°
Rec. Transport	27.0	0.3388	122°
	$n = 79.7$	$\sum \dfrac{f}{n} = 1$	

U.S. Sporting Goods

Recreational transport 33.88%

Clothing 13.30%

Footwear 21.58%

Equipment 31.24%

b.

4a. $\bar{x} = \dfrac{\sum x}{n} = \dfrac{6013}{8} \approx 751.6$

444 446 667 $\underbrace{774\ \ 795}$ 908 960 1019

$\quad\quad\quad\quad\quad$ median $= \dfrac{774 + 795}{2} = 784.5$

mode = none

The mean best describes a typical salary because there are no outliers.

b. Range = Max – Min = 1019 – 444 = 575

x	$x - \bar{x}$	$\left(x - \bar{x}\right)^2$
774	22.4	501.76
446	–305.6	93,391.36
1019	267.4	71,502.76
795	43.4	1883.56
908	156.4	24,460.96
667	–84.6	7157.16
444	–307.6	94,617.76
960	208.4	43,430.56
		$\sum\left(x - \bar{x}\right)^2 = 336,945.88$

$s^2 = \dfrac{\sum\left(x - \bar{x}\right)^2}{n - 1} = \dfrac{336,945.88}{7} \approx 48,135.1$

$s = \sqrt{\dfrac{\sum\left(x - \bar{x}\right)^2}{n - 1}} = \sqrt{\dfrac{336,945.88}{7}} \approx 219.4$

5. $\bar{x} - 2s = 155,000 - 2 \cdot 15,000 = \$125,000$

$\bar{x} + 2s = 155,000 + 2 \cdot 15,000 = \$185,000$

95% of the new home prices fall between \$125,000 and \$185,000.

6a. $x = 200,000 : \ z = \dfrac{x - \mu}{\sigma} = \dfrac{200,000 - 155,000}{15,000} = 3.0 \Rightarrow$ unusual price

b. $x = 55,000 : \ z = \dfrac{x - \mu}{\sigma} = \dfrac{55,000 - 155,000}{15,000} = -6.67 \Rightarrow$ very unusual price

c. $x = 175,000 : \ z = \dfrac{x - \mu}{\sigma} = \dfrac{175,000 - 155,000}{15,000} \approx 1.33 \Rightarrow$ not unusual

d. $x = 122,000$: $z = \dfrac{x - \mu}{\sigma} = \dfrac{122,000 - 155,000}{15,000} = -2.2 \Rightarrow$ unusual price

7a.

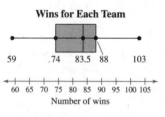

59 62 64 65 65 70 70 74 75 75 75 78 79 80 83 84 85 86 86 87 87 87 88 91 92 93 95 95 97 103

Min = 59, $Q_1 = 74$, $Q_2 = 83.5$, $Q_3 = 88$, Max = 103

b. IQR = $Q_3 - Q_1 = 88 - 74 = 14$

c.

CUMULATIVE REVIEW FOR CHAPTERS 1 AND 2

1. Systematic sampling. A bias may enter this study if the machine makes a consistent error.

2. Simple Random Sampling. A bias of this type of study is that the researchers did not include people without telephones.

3.

Reason for Baggage Delay

4. $2,996,106 is a parameter because it is describing the average salary of all Major League Baseball players.

5. 19% is a statistic because it is describing a proportion within a sample of 100 adults.

6a. $\bar{x} = 83,500$, $s = \$1500$

$(80,500 \ \ 86,500) = 83,500 \pm 2(1500) \Rightarrow 2$ standard deviations away form the mean.

Approximately 95% of the electrical engineers will have salaries between (80,500 86,500).

b. 40(0.95) = 38

c. $x = \$90,500$: $z = \dfrac{x - \mu}{\sigma} = \dfrac{90,500 - 83,500}{1500} \approx 4.67$

$x = \$79,750$: $z = \dfrac{x - \mu}{\sigma} = \dfrac{79,750 - 83,500}{1500} = -2.5$

$x = \$82,600$: $z = \dfrac{x - \mu}{\sigma} = \dfrac{82,600 - 83,500}{1500} = -0.6$

The salaries of $90,500 and $79,750 are unusual.

7. Population: Collection of the career interests of all college and university students
   Sample: Collection of the career interests of the 195 college and university students whose career counselors were surveyed

8. Population: Collection of the life spans of all people
   Sample: Collection of the life spans of the 232,606 people in the study

9. Census, because there are only 100 members in the Senate.

10. Experiment, because we want to study the effects of removing recess from schools.

11. Quantitative: The data are at the ratio level.

12. Qualitative: The data are at the nominal level.

13.

Q_1
↓

0 0 0 0 0 0 0 0 1 1 1 1 2 2 4 4 4 4 5 6 6 7 8 10
11 14 14 17 19 21 23 23 23 24 27 30 34 39 40 46 53 54 56 63 69 71 81 105 105 136
↑   ↑
Q_2 Q_3

Min $= 0$, $Q_1 = 2$, $Q_2 = 12.5$, $Q_3 = 39$, Max $= 136$

b.

Number of Tornadoes by State

0 2 12.5 39   136

0   20   40   60   80 100 120 140
Number of tornadoes

c. The distribution of the number of tornadoes is skewed right.

14.

Source	Score, x	Weight, w	$x \cdot w$
Test 1	85	0.15	12.75
Test 2	92	0.15	13.80
Test 3	84	0.15	12.60
Test 4	89	0.15	13.35
Test 5	91	0.40	36.40
		$\sum w = 1$	$\sum (x \cdot w) = 88.9$

$$\bar{x} = \frac{\sum (x \cdot w)}{\sum w} = \frac{88.9}{1} = 88.9$$

15a. $\bar{x} = \dfrac{49.4}{9} \approx 5.49$

3.4 3.9 4.2 4.6 (5.4) 6.5 6.8 7.1 7.5

median = 5.4

mode = none

Both the mean and median accurately describe a typical American alligator tail length.
(Answers will vary.)

b. Range – Max – Min – 7.5 – 3.4 = 4.1

x	$x - \bar{x}$	$(x - \bar{x})^2$
3.4	−2.09	4.3681
3.9	−1.59	2.5281
4.2	−1.29	1.6641
4.6	−0.89	0.7921
5.4	−0.09	0.0081
6.5	1.01	1.0201
6.8	1.31	1.7161
7.1	1.61	2.5921
7.5	2.01	4.0401
		$\sum (x - \bar{x})^2 = 18.7289$

$$s^2 = \frac{\sum (x - \bar{x})^2}{n-1} = \frac{18.7289}{8} \approx 2.34$$

$$s = \sqrt{\frac{\sum (x - \bar{x})^2}{n-1}} = \sqrt{\frac{18.7289}{8}} \approx 1.53$$

The maximum difference in alligator tail lengths is 4.1 feet and the standard deviation of tail lengths is about 1.53 feet.

16a. The number of deaths due to heart disease for women will continue to decrease.

  b. The study was only conducted over the past 5 years and deaths may not decrease in the next year.

17. Class width = $\dfrac{\text{Max} - \text{Min}}{\text{Number of classes}} = \dfrac{65 - 0}{8} = 8.125 \Rightarrow 9$

Class limits	Midpoint	Class boundaries	Frequency	Relative frequency	Cumulative frequency
0-8	4	–0.5-8.5	8	0.27	8
9-17	13	8.5-17.5	5	0.17	13
18-26	22	17.5-26.5	7	0.23	20
27-35	31	26.5-35.5	3	0.10	23
36-44	40	35.5-44.5	4	0.13	27
45-53	49	44.5-53.5	1	0.03	28
54-62	58	53.5-62.5	0	0.00	28
63-71	67	62.5-71.5	2	0.07	30
			$\sum f = 30$	$\sum \dfrac{f}{n} = 1$	

18. The distribution is skewed right.

19.

Montreal Canadiens Points Scored

Class with greatest frequency: 0-8
Class with least frequency: 54-62

3.1 BASIC CONCEPTS OF PROBABILITY AND COUNTING

3.1 Try It Yourself Solutions

1ab. (1)   (2)

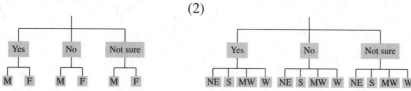

c. (1) 6 outcomes   (2) 12 outcomes

d. (1) Let Y = Yes, N = No, NS = Not sure, M = Male and F = Female.
Sample space = {*YM*, *YF*, *NM*, *NF*, *NSM*, *NSF*}

(2) Let Y = Yes, N = No, NS = Not sure, NE = Northeast, S = South, MW = Midwest, and W = West
Sample space = {*YNE*, *YS*, *YMW*, *YW*, *NNE*, *NS*, *NMW*, *NW*, *NSNE*, *NSS*, *NSMW*, *NSW*}

2a. (1) Event C has six outcomes: choosing the ages 18, 19, 20, 21, 22, and 23.
(2) Event D has one outcome: choosing the age 20.

b. (1) The event is not a simple event because it consists of more than a single outcome.
(2) The event is a simple event because it consists of a single outcome.

3a. Manufacturer: 4   **b.** (4)(2)(5) = 40 ways   **c.** Tree Diagram for Car Selections
Size: 2
Color: 5

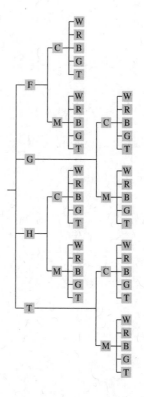

4a. (1) Each letter is an event (26 choices for each).
(2) Each letter is an event (26, 25, 24, 23, 22, and 21 choices).
(3) Each letter is an event (22, 26, 26, 26, 26, and 26 choices).

b. (1) $26 \cdot 26 \cdot 26 \cdot 26 \cdot 26 \cdot 26 = 308,915,776$
(2) $26 \cdot 25 \cdot 24 \cdot 23 \cdot 22 \cdot 21 = 165,765,600$
(3) $22 \cdot 26 \cdot 26 \cdot 26 \cdot 26 \cdot 26 = 261,390,272$

5a. (1) 52   (2) 52   (3) 52

b. (1) 1   (2) 13   (3) 52

c. (1) $P(9 \text{ of clubs}) = \dfrac{1}{52} \approx 0.019$

(2) $P(\text{heart}) = \dfrac{13}{52} = 0.25$

(3) $P(\text{diamond, heart, club, or spade}) = \dfrac{52}{52} = 1$

6a. The event is "the next claim processed is fraudulent." The frequency is 4.

b. Total Frequency = 100

c. $P(\text{fraudulent claim}) = \dfrac{4}{100} = 0.04$

7a. Frequency = 54

b. Total of the Frequencies = 1000

c. $P(\text{age 15 to 24}) = \dfrac{54}{1000} = 0.054$

8a. The event is "salmon successfully passing through a dam on the Columbia River."

b. The probability is estimated from the results of an experiment.

c. Empirical probability

9a. $P(\text{age 45 to 54}) = \dfrac{180}{1000} = 0.18$

b. $P(\text{age is not 45 to 54}) = 1 - \dfrac{180}{1000} = \dfrac{820}{1000} = 0.82$

c. $\dfrac{820}{1000}$ or 0.82

10a. There are 5 outcomes in the event: {T1, T2, T3, T4, T5}.

b. $P(\text{tail and less than 6}) = \dfrac{5}{16} \approx 0.313$

11a. $10 \cdot 10 \cdot 10 \cdot 10 \cdot 10 \cdot 10 \cdot 10 = 10{,}000{,}000$

b. $\dfrac{1}{10{,}000{,}000}$

3.1 EXERCISE SOLUTIONS

1. An outcome is the result of a single trial in a probability experiment, whereas an event is a set of one or more outcomes.

2. (a) Yes, the probability of an event occurring must be contained in the interval [0, 1] or [0%, 100%].

   (b) No, the probability of an event occurring cannot be less than 0.

   (c) Yes, the probability of an event occurring must be contained in the interval [0, 1] or [0%, 100%].

   (d) Yes, the probability of an event occurring must be contained in the interval [0, 1] or [0%, 100%].

   (e) Yes, the probability of an event occurring must be contained in the interval [0, 1] or [0%, 100%].

   (f) No, the probability of an event cannot be greater than 1.

3. It is impossible to have more than a 100% chance of rain.

4. The Fundamental Counting Principle counts the number of ways that two or more events can occur in sequence.

5. The law of large numbers states that as an experiment is repeated over and over, the probabilities found in the experiment will approach the actual probabilities of the event. Examples will vary.

6. $P(E) + P(E') = 1, \ P(E) = 1 - P(E'), \ P(E') = 1 - P(E)$

7. False. If you roll a six-sided die six times, the probability of rolling an even number at least once is approximately 0.984.

8. False. You flip a fair coin nine times and it lands tails up each time. The probability it will land heads up on the tenth flip is 0.5.

9. False. A probability of less than 0.05 indicates an unusual event.

10. True

11. b   **12.** d   **13.** c   **14.** a

15. {A, B, C, D, E, F, G, H, I, J, K, L, M, N, O, P, Q, R, S, T, U, V, W, X, Y, Z}; 26

16. {A, B, C, D, F}; 5

17. {A♥, K♥, Q♥, J♥, 10♥, 9♥, 8♥, 7♥, 6♥, 5♥, 4♥, 3♥, 2♥,
  A♦, K♦, Q♦, J♦, 10♦, 9♦, 8♦, 7♦, 6♦, 5♦, 4♦, 3♦, 2♦,
  A♠, K♠, Q♠, J♠, 10♠, 9♠, 8♠, 7♠, 6♠, 5♠, 4♠, 3♠, 2♠,
  A♣, K♣, Q♣, J♣, 10♣, 9♣, 8♣, 7♣, 6♣, 5♣, 4♣, 3♣, 2♣}; 52

18. {HHH, HHT, HTH, HTT, THH, THT, TTH, TTT}; 8

19.

{(A, +), (B, +), (AB, +), (O, +), (A, −), (B, −), (AB, −), (O, −)}, where (A, +) represents positive Rh-factor with blood type A and (A, −) represents negative Rh-factor with blood type A; 8.

20. {(1, 1), (1, 2), (1, 3), (1, 4), (1, 5), (1, 6), (2, 1), (2, 2,), (2, 3), (2, 4), (2, 5), (2, 6), (3, 1), (3, 2),
  (3, 3), (3, 4), (3, 5), (3, 6), (4, 1), (4, 2), (4, 3), (4, 4), (4, 5), (4, 6), (5, 1), (5, 2), (5, 3), (5, 4),
  (5, 5), (5, 6), (6, 1), (6, 2), (6, 3), (6, 4), (6, 5), (6, 6)}; 36

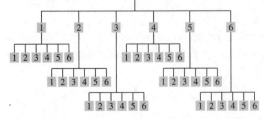

21. 1 outcome; simple event because it is an event that consists of a single outcome.

22. Number less than 500 = {1, 2, 3 . . . 499}; 499 outcomes
  Not a simple event because it is an event that consists of more than a single outcome.

23. Ace = {Ace of hearts, Ace of spades, Ace of clubs, Ace of diamonds}; 4 outcomes
  Not a simple event because it is an event that consists of more than a single outcome.

24. 1 outcome; simple event because it is an event that consists of a single outcome.

25. $(12)(17) = 204$

26. $(5)(10)(4) = 200$

27. $(9)(10)(10)(5) = 4500$

28. $(2)(2)(2)(2)(2)(2) = 64$

29. $P(A) = \dfrac{1}{12} \approx 0.083$

30. $P(B) = \dfrac{1}{12} \approx 0.083$

31. $P(C) = \dfrac{8}{12} = \dfrac{2}{3} \approx 0.667$

32. $P(D) = \dfrac{6}{12} = \dfrac{1}{2} = 0.5$

33. $P(E) = \dfrac{5}{12} \approx 0.417$

34. $P(F) = \dfrac{2}{12} = \dfrac{1}{6} \approx 0.167$

35. Empirical probability because company records were used to calculate the frequency of a washing machine breaking down.

36. Classical probability because each outcome is equally likely to occur.

37. $P(\text{less than } 1000) = \dfrac{999}{6296} \approx 0.159$

38. $P(\text{greater than } 1000) = \dfrac{5296}{6296} \approx 0.841$

39. $P(\text{number divisible by } 1000) = \dfrac{6}{6296} \approx 0.000953$

40. $P(\text{number not divisible by } 1000) = \dfrac{6290}{6296} \approx 0.999$

41-44.

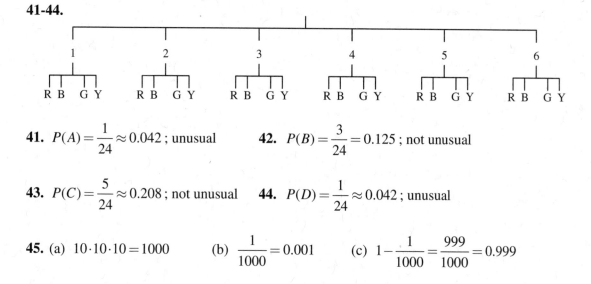

41. $P(A) = \dfrac{1}{24} \approx 0.042$; unusual

42. $P(B) = \dfrac{3}{24} = 0.125$; not unusual

43. $P(C) = \dfrac{5}{24} \approx 0.208$; not unusual

44. $P(D) = \dfrac{1}{24} \approx 0.042$; unusual

45. (a) $10 \cdot 10 \cdot 10 = 1000$ (b) $\dfrac{1}{1000} = 0.001$ (c) $1 - \dfrac{1}{1000} = \dfrac{999}{1000} = 0.999$

46. (a) $26 \cdot 9 \cdot 10 \cdot 10 \cdot 5 = 117{,}000$ (b) $\dfrac{1}{117{,}000} \approx 0.00000855$

(c) $1 - \dfrac{1}{117{,}000} = \dfrac{116{,}999}{117{,}000} \approx 0.99999$

47. {(SSS), (SSR), (SRS), (SRR), (RSS), (RSR), (RRS), (RRR)}

48. {(RRR)}

49. {(SSR), (SRS), (RSS)}

50. {(SSR), (SRS), (SRR), (RSS), (RSR), (RRS), (RRR)}

51. Let S = sunny day and R = rainy day.

(a)

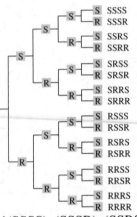

(b) {(SSSS), (SSSR), (SSRS), (SSRR), (SRSS), (SRSR), (SRRS), (SRRR), (RSSS), (RSSR), (RSRS), (RSRR), (RRSS), (RRSR), (RRRS), (RRRR)}

(c) {(SSSR), (SSRS), (SRSS), (RSSS)}

52.

53. $P(\text{voted in 2009 Gubernatorial election}) = \dfrac{1{,}982{,}432}{4{,}964{,}024} \approx 0.399$

54. $P(\text{did not vote Democratic}) = \dfrac{57{,}930{,}888}{122{,}959{,}841} \approx 0.471$

55. $P(\text{between 18 and 20}) = \dfrac{5.8}{146.2} \approx 0.040$

56. $P(\text{between 35 and 44}) = \dfrac{25.4}{146.2} \approx 0.174$

57. $P(\text{not between 21 and 24}) = 1 - \dfrac{9.3}{146.2} \approx 1 - 0.064 \approx 0.936$

58. $P(\text{not between 45 and 64}) = 1 - \dfrac{54.9}{146.2} \approx 1 - 0.396 \approx 0.624$

59. $P(\text{doctorate}) = \dfrac{3}{91} \approx 0.033$ **60.** $P(\text{associate}) = \dfrac{23}{91} \approx 0.253$

61. $P(\text{master's}) = \dfrac{25}{91} \approx 0.275$ **62.** $P(\text{high school diploma}) = \dfrac{4}{91} \approx 0.044$

63. Yes; the event in Exercise 55 can be considered unusual because its probability is 0.05 or less.

64. Yes; the events in Exercises 59 and 62 can be considered unusual because their probabilities are 0.05 or less.

65. (a) $P(\text{pink}) = \dfrac{2}{4} = 0.5$ (b) $P(\text{red}) = \dfrac{1}{4} = 0.25$ (c) $P(\text{white}) = \dfrac{1}{4} = 0.25$

66. $P(\text{same coloring as one of its parents}) = \dfrac{8}{16} = 0.5$

67. $P(\text{service industry}) = \dfrac{115,498}{145,363} \approx 0.795$

68. $P(\text{manufacturing industry}) = \dfrac{15,904}{145,363} \approx 0.109$

69. $P(\text{not in service industry}) = 1 - P(\text{service industry}) \approx 1 - 0.795 = 0.205$

70. $P(\text{not in agriculture, forestry, fishing, and hunting industry})$
$= 1 - P(\text{agriculture, forestry, fishing, and hunting industry})$
$= 1 - \dfrac{2168}{145,363} \approx 0.985$

71. (a) $P(\text{at least 51}) = \dfrac{27}{120} = 0.225$

     (b) $P(\text{between 20 and 30 inclusive}) = \dfrac{16}{120} \approx 0.133$

(c) $P(\text{more than } 69) = \dfrac{2}{120} \approx 0.017$; This event is unusual because its probability is 0.05 or less.

72. (a) $P(\text{less than } \$21) = 0.25$; $Q_1 = 21$

(b) $P(\text{between } \$21 \text{ and } \$50) = 0.5$; $Q_1 = 21$ and $Q_3 = 50$

(c) $P(\$30 \text{ or more}) = 0.5$; med $= 30$

73. The probability of randomly choosing a tea drinker who does not have a college degree

74. The probability of randomly choosing a smoker whose mother did not smoke

75. (a)

Sum	Outcomes	P(sum)	Probability
2	(1, 1)	1/36	0.028
3	(1, 2), (2, 1)	2/36	0.056
4	(1, 3), (2, 2,), (3, 1)	3/36	0.083
5	(1, 4), (2, 3), (3, 2), (4, 1)	4/36	0.111
6	(1, 5), (2, 4), (3, 3), (4, 2), (5, 1)	5/36	0.139
7	(1, 6), (2, 5), (3, 4), (4, 3), (5, 2), (6, 1)	6/36	0.167
8	(2, 6), (3, 5), (4, 4), (5, 3), (6, 2)	5/36	0.139
9	(3, 6), (4, 5), (5, 4), (6, 3)	4/36	0.111
10	(4, 6), (5, 5), (6, 4)	3/36	0.083
11	(5, 6), (6, 5)	2/36	0.056
12	(6, 6)	1/36	0.028

(b) Answers will vary.

(c) Answers will vary.

76. No, the odds of winning a prize are 1 : 6 (one winning cap and six losing caps). So, the statement should read, "one in seven game pieces win a prize."

77. The first game; the probability of winning the second game is $\dfrac{1}{11} \approx 0.091$, which is less than $\dfrac{1}{10}$.

78. (a) $P(\text{event will occur}) = \dfrac{4}{9} \approx 0.444$

(b) $P(\text{event will not occur}) = \dfrac{5}{9} \approx 0.556$

79. $13 : 39 = 1 : 3$

80. $39 : 13 = 3 : 1$

81. $p = $ number of successful outcomes

$q = $ number of unsuccessful outcomes

$P(A) = \dfrac{\text{number of successful outcomes}}{\text{total number of outcomes}} = \dfrac{p}{p + q}$

3.2 CONDITIONAL PROBABILITY AND THE MULTIPLICATION RULE

3.2 Try It Yourself Solutions

1a. (a) 30 and 102   (2) 11 and 50

b. $P(\text{does not have gene}) = \dfrac{30}{102} \approx 0.294$ (2) $P(\text{does not have gene} \mid \text{normal IQ}) = \dfrac{11}{50} = 0.22$

2a. (1) Yes   (2) No

b. (1) Dependent   (2) Independent

3a. (1) Independent   (2) Dependent

b. (1) Let $A = \{\text{first salmon swims successfully through the dam}\}$
$B = \{\text{second salmon swims successfully through the dam}\}$
$P(A \text{ and } B) = P(A) \cdot P(B) = (0.85) \cdot (0.85) \approx 0.723$

(2) Let $A = \{\text{selecting a heart}\}$
$B = \{\text{selecting a second heart}\}$
$P(A \text{ and } B) = P(A) \cdot P(B|A) = \left(\dfrac{13}{52}\right) \cdot \left(\dfrac{12}{51}\right) \approx 0.059$

4a. (1) Find probability of the event   (2) Find probability of the event
(3) Find probability of the compliment of the event

b. (1) $P(\text{3 surgeries are successful}) = (0.90) \cdot (0.90) \cdot (0.90) = 0.729$

(2) $P(\text{none are successful}) = (0.10) \cdot (0.10) \cdot (0.10) = 0.001$

(3) $P(\text{at least one rotator cuff surgery is successful}) = 1 - P(\text{none are successful})$
$= 1 - 0.001 = 0.999$

c. (1) The event cannot be considered unusual because its probability is not less than or equal to 0.05.
(2) The event can be considered unusual because its probability is less than or equal to 0.05.
(3) The event cannot be considered unusual because its probability is not less than or equal to 0.05.

5a. (1),(2) $A = \{\text{is female}\}$; $B = \{\text{works in health field}\}$

b. (1) $P(A \text{ and } B) = P(A) \cdot P(B|A) = (0.65) \cdot (0.25)$

(2) $P(A \text{ and } B') = P(A) \cdot P(B'|A) = P(A) \cdot (1 - P(B|A)) = (0.65) \cdot (0.75)$

c. (1) 0.136   (2) 0.488

3.2 EXERCISE SOLUTIONS

1. Two events are independent if the occurrence of one of the events does not affect the probability of the occurrence of the other event, whereas two events are dependent if the occurrence of one of the events does affect the probability of the occurrence of the other event.

2. Answers will vary. Sample answers are given.
   (a) Roll a die twice. The outcome of the second roll is independent of the outcome of the first roll.
   (b) Draw two cards (without replacement) from a standard 52-card deck. The outcome of the second draw is dependent on the outcome of the first draw.

3. The notation $P(B|A)$ means the probability of B, given A.

4. The compliment of "at least one" is "none." So the probability of getting at least one item is equal to $1 - P(\text{none of the items})$.

5. False. If two events are independent, $P(A|B) = P(A)$.

6. False. If events A and B are independent, then $P(A \text{ and } B) = P(A) \cdot P(B)$.

7. These events are independent because the outcome of the first card drawn does not affect the outcome of the second card drawn.

8. These events are dependent because returning a movie after its due date affects the outcome of receiving a late fee.

9. These events are dependent because the outcome of a father having hazel eyes affects the outcome of a daughter having hazel eyes.

10. These events are dependent because the outcome of not putting money in a parking meter affects the outcome of getting a parking ticket.

11. These events are dependent because the sum of the rolls depends on which numbers were rolled first and second.

12. These events are independent because the outcome of the first ball drawn does not affect the outcome of the second ball drawn.

13. Events: moderate to severe sleep apnea, high blood pressure
    These events are dependent because people with moderate to severe sleep apnea are more likely to have high blood pressure.

14. Events: stress, ulcers
    These events are independent because stress only irritates already existing ulcers.

15. Events: exposure to aluminum, Alzheimer's disease
    These events are independent because exposure to everyday sources of aluminum does not cause Alzheimer's disease.

16. Events: diabetes, obesity
These events are dependent because in societies, the number of cases of diabetes increases as the number of cases of obesity increases.

17. Let $A = \{$have mutated BRCA gene$\}$ and $B = \{$develop breast cancer$\}$.

So, $P(B) = \dfrac{1}{8}$, $P(A) = \dfrac{1}{600}$, and $P(B|A) = \dfrac{6}{10}$.

(a) $P(B|A) = \dfrac{6}{10} = 0.6$

(b) $P(A \text{ and } B) = P(A) \cdot P(B|A) = \left(\dfrac{1}{600}\right) \cdot \left(\dfrac{6}{10}\right) = 0.001$

(c) Dependent, because $P(B|A) \neq P(B)$.

18. Let $A = \{$drives pickup truck$\}$ and $B = \{$drives a Ford$\}$.

So, $P(A) = \dfrac{1}{6}$, $P(B) = \dfrac{3}{10}$, and $P(A|B) = \dfrac{2}{9}$.

(a) $P(A|B) = \dfrac{2}{9} \approx 0.222$

(b) $P(A \text{ and } B) = P(B) \cdot P(A|B) = \left(\dfrac{3}{10}\right) \cdot \left(\dfrac{2}{9}\right) \approx 0.067$

(c) Dependent, because $P(A|B) \neq P(A)$.

19. Let $A = \{$own a computer$\}$ and $B = \{$summer vacation this year$\}$.

(a) $P(B') = \dfrac{45}{146} \approx 0.308$

(b) $P(A) = \dfrac{115}{146} \approx 0.788$

(c) $P(B|A) = \dfrac{87}{115} \approx 0.757$

(d) $P(A \text{ and } B) = P(A) \cdot P(B|A) = \left(\dfrac{115}{146}\right)\left(\dfrac{87}{115}\right) = 0.596$

(e) Dependent, because $P(B|A) \neq P(B)$.

20. Let $A = \{$male$\}$ and $B = \{$nursing major$\}$.

(a) $P(B) = \dfrac{1167}{3964} \approx 0.294$ (b) $P(A) = \dfrac{1255}{3964} \approx 0.317$

(c) $P(B|A) = \dfrac{151}{1255} \approx 0.120$

(d) $P(A \text{ and } B) = P(A) \cdot P(B|A) = \left(\dfrac{1255}{3964}\right)\left(\dfrac{151}{1255}\right) \approx 0.038$

(e) Dependent, because $P(B|A) \neq P(B)$

21. Let A = {pregnant} and B = {multiple births}. So, $P(A) = 0.37$ and $P(B|A) = 0.25$.

(a) $P(A \text{ and } B) = P(A) \cdot P(B|A) = (0.37) \cdot (0.25) \approx 0.093$

(b) $P(B'|A) = 1 - P(B|A) = 1 - 0.25 = 0.75$

(c) No, this is not unusual because the probability is not less than or equal to 0.05.

22. Let A = {has the opinion that the U.S. government is broken} and B = {has the opinion that the government can be fixed}.
So, $P(A) = 0.86$ and $P(B|A) = 0.8$.

(a) $P(A \text{ and } B) = P(A) \cdot P(B|A) = (0.86) \cdot (0.8) = 0.688$

(b) $P(B'|A) = 1 - P(B|A) = 1 - 0.8 = 0.2$

(c) No, this is not unusual because the probability is not less than or equal to 0.05.

23. Let A = {household in U.S. has a computer} and B = {has Internet access}.
$P(A \text{ and } B) = P(A) \cdot P(B|A) = (0.8) \cdot (0.92) \approx 0.745$

24. Let A = {survives bypass surgery} and B = {heart damage will heal}.
$P(A \text{ and } B) = P(A) \cdot P(B|A) = (0.6) \cdot (0.5) = 0.3$

25. Let A = {first person can wiggle their ears} and B = {second person can wiggle their ears}.

(a) $P(A \text{ and } B) = P(A) \cdot P(B|A) = \left(\dfrac{130}{1000}\right) \cdot \left(\dfrac{129}{999}\right) \approx 0.017$

(b) $P(A' \text{ and } B') = P(A') \cdot P(B'|A') = \left(\dfrac{870}{1000}\right) \cdot \left(\dfrac{869}{999}\right) \approx 0.757$

(c) $P(\text{at least one can wiggle their ears}) = 1 - P(A' \text{ and } B') \approx 1 - 0.757 = 0.243$

(d) The event in part (a) is unusual because its probability is less than or equal to 0.05.

26. Let A = {first battery fails} and B = {second battery fails}.

(a) $P(A \text{ and } B) = P(A) \cdot P(B|A) = \left(\dfrac{4}{16}\right) \cdot \left(\dfrac{3}{15}\right) \approx 0.05$

(b) $P(A' \text{ and } B') = P(A') \cdot P(B'|A') = \left(\dfrac{12}{16}\right) \cdot \left(\dfrac{11}{15}\right) = 0.55$

(c) $P(\text{at least one battery failed}) = 1 - P(\text{none failed})$
$$= 1 - P(A' \text{ and } B')$$
$$= 1 - 0.55$$
$$= 0.45$$

(d) The event in part (a) is unusual because its probability is less than or equal to 0.05.

27. Let A = {have one month's income or more} and B = {male}.

(a) $P(A) = \dfrac{138}{287} \approx 0.481$

(b) $P(A'|B) = \dfrac{66}{142} \approx 0.465$

(c) $P(B'|A) = \dfrac{62}{138} \approx 0.449$

(d) Dependent, because $P(A') \approx 0.519 \neq 0.465 \approx P(A'|B)$

28. Let $A = \{\$100 \text{ or more}\}$ and $B = \{\text{purebred}\}$.

(a) $P(A) = \dfrac{50}{90} \approx 0.556$

(b) $P(B'|A') = \dfrac{21}{40} = 0.525$

(c) $P(A \text{ and } B') = P(A) \cdot P(B'|A) = \left(\dfrac{50}{90}\right) \cdot \left(\dfrac{15}{50}\right) \approx 0.167$

(d) Dependent, because $P(A) \approx 0.556 \neq 0.417 \approx P(A|B')$

29. (a) $P(\text{all five have B+}) = (0.09) \cdot (0.09) \cdot (0.09) \cdot (0.09) \cdot (0.09) \approx 0.00000590$

(b) $P(\text{none have B+}) = (0.91) \cdot (0.91) \cdot (0.91) \cdot (0.91) \cdot (0.91) \approx 0.624$

(c) $P(\text{at least one has B+}) = 1 - P(\text{none have B+}) \approx 1 - 0.624 = 0.376$

30. (a) $P(\text{all three have A+}) = (0.31) \cdot (0.31) \cdot (0.31) \approx 0.030$

(b) $P(\text{none have A+}) = (0.69) \cdot (0.69) \cdot (0.69) \approx 0.329$

(c) $P(\text{at least one has A+}) = 1 - P(\text{none have A+}) \approx 1 - 0.329 = 0.671$

31. (a) $P(\text{first question correct}) = 0.25$

(b) $P(\text{first two questions correct}) = (0.25) \cdot (0.25) \approx 0.063$

(c) $P(\text{all five questions correct}) = (0.25) \cdot (0.25) \cdot (0.25) \cdot (0.25) \cdot (0.25) \approx 0.000977$

(d) $P(\text{none correct}) = (0.75) \cdot (0.75) \cdot (0.75) \cdot (0.75) \cdot (0.75) \approx 0.237$

(e) $P(\text{at least one correct}) = 1 - P(\text{none correct}) \approx 1 - 0.237 = 0.763$

32. (a) $P(\text{none are defective}) = (0.995) \cdot (0.995) \cdot (0.995) \approx 0.985$

(b) $P(\text{at least one defective}) = 1 - P(\text{none are defective}) \approx 1 - 0.985 = 0.015$

(c) $P(\text{all are defective}) = (0.005) \cdot (0.005) \cdot (0.005) = 0.000000125$

33. (a) $P(\text{all three products came form the third factory}) = \dfrac{25}{110} \cdot \dfrac{24}{109} \cdot \dfrac{23}{108} \approx 0.011$

(b) $P(\text{none of the three products came from the third factory}) = \dfrac{85}{110} \cdot \dfrac{84}{109} \cdot \dfrac{83}{108} \approx 0.458$

34. (a) $P(\text{all share same birthday}) = \left(\dfrac{365}{365}\right) \cdot \left(\dfrac{1}{365}\right) \cdot \left(\dfrac{1}{365}\right) \approx 0.00000751$

(b) $P(\text{none share same birthday}) = \left(\dfrac{365}{365}\right) \cdot \left(\dfrac{364}{365}\right) \cdot \left(\dfrac{363}{365}\right) = 0.992$

35. $P(A|B) = \dfrac{P(A) \cdot P(B|A)}{P(A) \cdot P(B|A) + P(A') \cdot P(B|A')}$

$= \dfrac{\left(\dfrac{2}{3}\right) \cdot \left(\dfrac{1}{5}\right)}{\left(\dfrac{2}{3}\right) \cdot \left(\dfrac{1}{5}\right) + \left(\dfrac{1}{3}\right) \cdot \left(\dfrac{1}{2}\right)} = \dfrac{\dfrac{2}{15}}{\dfrac{3}{10}} = \dfrac{4}{9} \approx 0.444$

36. $P(A|B) = \dfrac{P(A) \cdot P(B|A)}{P(A) \cdot P(B|A) + P(A') \cdot P(B|A')}$

$= \dfrac{\left(\dfrac{3}{8}\right) \cdot \left(\dfrac{2}{3}\right)}{\left(\dfrac{3}{8}\right) \cdot \left(\dfrac{2}{3}\right) + \left(\dfrac{5}{8}\right) \cdot \left(\dfrac{3}{5}\right)} = \dfrac{\dfrac{1}{4}}{\dfrac{5}{8}} = \dfrac{2}{5} = 0.4$

37. $P(A|B) = \dfrac{P(A) \cdot P(B|A)}{P(A) \cdot P(B|A) + P(A') \cdot P(B|A')}$

$= \dfrac{(0.25) \cdot (0.3)}{(0.25) \cdot (0.3) + (0.75) \cdot (0.5)} = \dfrac{0.075}{0.45} \approx 0.167$

38. $P(A|B) = \dfrac{P(A) \cdot P(B|A)}{P(A) \cdot P(B|A) + P(A') \cdot P(B|A')}$

$= \dfrac{(0.62) \cdot (0.41)}{(0.62) \cdot (0.41) + (0.38) \cdot (0.17)} = \dfrac{0.2542}{0.3188} \approx 0.797$

39. $P(A) = \dfrac{1}{200} = 0.005$

$P(B|A) = 0.8$

$P(B|A') = 0.05$

(a) $P(A|B) = \dfrac{P(A) \cdot P(B|A)}{P(A) \cdot P(B|A) + P(A') \cdot P(B|A')}$

$= \dfrac{(0.005) \cdot (0.8)}{(0.005) \cdot (0.8) + (0.995) \cdot (0.05)} = \dfrac{0.004}{0.05375} \approx 0.074$

(b) $P(A'|B') = \dfrac{P(A') \cdot P(B'|A')}{P(A') \cdot P(B'|A') + P(A) \cdot P(B'|A)}$

$= \dfrac{(0.995) \cdot (0.95)}{(0.995) \cdot (0.95) + (0.005) \cdot (0.2)} = \dfrac{0.94525}{0.94625} \approx 0.999$

40. (a) $P(\text{different birthdays}) = \dfrac{365}{365} \cdot \dfrac{364}{365} \cdot \dfrac{363}{365} \cdot \dfrac{362}{365} \cdot \ldots \cdot \dfrac{343}{365} \cdot \dfrac{342}{365} \approx 0.462$

(b) $P(\text{at least two have same birthday}) = 1 - P(\text{different birthdays}) \approx 1 - 0.462 = 0.538$

(c) Yes, there were 2 birthdays on the 118th day.

(d) Answers will vary.

41. Let A = {flight departs on time} and B = {flight arrives on time}.

$$P(A|B) = \frac{P(A \text{ and } B)}{P(B)} = \frac{0.83}{0.87} \approx 0.954$$

42. Let A = {flight departs on time} and B = {flight arrives on time}.

$$P(B|A) = \frac{P(A \text{ and } B)}{P(A)} = \frac{0.83}{0.89} \approx 0.933$$

3.3 THE ADDITION RULE

3.3 Try It Yourself Solutions

1a. (1) None of the statements are true.

(2) None of the statements are true.

(3) All of the statements are true.

b. (1) A and B are not mutually exclusive.

(2) A and B are not mutually exclusive.

(3) A and B are mutually exclusive.

2a. (1) Mutually exclusive   (2) Not mutually exclusive

b. (1) Let A = {6} and B = {odd}.

$$P(A) = \frac{1}{6} \text{ and } P(B) = \frac{3}{6} = \frac{1}{2}$$

(2) Let A = {face card} and B = {heart}.

$$P(A) = \frac{12}{52}, \ P(B) = \frac{13}{52}, \text{ and } P(A \text{ and } B) = \frac{3}{52}$$

c. (1) $P(A \text{ or } B) = P(A) + P(B) = \dfrac{1}{6} + \dfrac{1}{2} \approx 0.667$

(2) $P(A \text{ or } B) = P(A) + P(B) - P(A \text{ and } B) = \dfrac{12}{52} + \dfrac{13}{52} - \dfrac{3}{52} \approx 0.423$

3a. Let A = {sales between \$0 and \$24,999}

Let B = {sales between \$25,000 and \$49,999}.

b. A and B cannot occur at the same time. So A and B are mutually exclusive.

c. $P(A) = \dfrac{3}{36}$ and $P(B) = \dfrac{5}{36}$

   d. $P(A \text{ or } B) = P(A) + P(B) = \dfrac{3}{36} + \dfrac{5}{36} \approx 0.222$

4a. (1) Let A = {type B} and B = {type AB}.
     (2) Let A = {type O} and B = {Rh-positive}.

  b. (1) A and B cannot occur at the same time. So, A and B are mutually exclusive.
     (2) A and B can occur at the same time. So, A and B are not mutually exclusive.

  c. (1) $P(A) = \dfrac{45}{409}$ and $P(B) = \dfrac{16}{409}$

     (2) $P(A) = \dfrac{184}{409}$, $P(B) = \dfrac{344}{409}$, and $P(A \text{ and } B) = \dfrac{156}{409}$

  d. (1) $P(A \text{ or } B) = P(A) + P(B) = \dfrac{45}{409} + \dfrac{16}{409} \approx 0.149$

     (2) $P(A \text{ or } B) = P(A) + P(B) - P(A \text{ and } B) = \dfrac{184}{409} + \dfrac{344}{409} - \dfrac{156}{409} \approx 0.910$

5a. Let A = {linebacker} and B = {quarterback}.

    $P(A \text{ or } B) = P(A) + P(B) = \dfrac{24}{256} + \dfrac{12}{256} \approx 0.141$

  b. $P(\text{not a linebacker or quarterback}) = 1 - P(A \text{ or } B) \approx 1 - 0.141 = 0.859$

3.3 EXERCISE SOLUTIONS

1. $P(A \text{ and } B) = 0$ because A and B cannot occur at the same time.

2. Answers will vary. Sample answers are given.
   (a) Toss coin once: A = {head} and B = {tail}
   (b) Draw one card: A = {ace} and B = {spade}

3. True

4. False. Two events being independent does not imply they are mutually exclusive. Example: Toss a coin then roll a 6-sided die. Let A = {head} and B = {6 on die}. $P(B|A) = \dfrac{1}{6} = P(B)$ implies A and B are independent events. However, $P(A \text{ and } B) = \dfrac{1}{12}$ implies A and B are not mutually exclusive.

5. False. The probability that event A or event B will occur is
   $P(A \text{ or } B) = P(A) + P(B) - P(A \text{ and } B)$

6. True

7. Not mutually exclusive because a student can be an athlete and on the Dean's list.

8. Mutually exclusive because a movie cannot have two ratings.

9. Not mutually exclusive because a public school teacher can be female and be 25 years old.

10. Not mutually exclusive because a member of Congress can be a male senator.

11. Mutually exclusive because a student cannot have a birthday in both months.

12. Not mutually exclusive because a person can be between 18 and 24 years old and drive a convertible.

13. (a) Not mutually exclusive because for five weeks the events overlapped.

(b) $P(\text{OT or temp}) = P(\text{OT}) + P(\text{temp}) - P(\text{OT and temp}) = \dfrac{18}{52} + \dfrac{9}{52} - \dfrac{5}{52} \approx 0.423$

14. (a) Not mutually exclusive because an attendee can be a female and be a college professor.

(b) $P(\text{female or professor}) = P(\text{female}) + P(\text{professor}) - P(\text{female and professor})$

$$= \dfrac{2575}{4950} + \dfrac{2110}{4950} - \dfrac{960}{4950} \approx 0.753$$

15. (a) Not mutually exclusive because a carton can have a puncture and a smashed corner.

(b) $P(\text{puncture or corner}) = P(\text{puncture}) + P(\text{corner}) - P(\text{puncture and corner})$

$$= 0.05 + 0.08 - 0.004 = 0.126$$

16. (a) Not mutually exclusive because a can may have no punctures and no smashed edges.

(b) $P(\text{does not have puncture or does not have smashed edge})$

$= P(\text{does not have puncture}) + P(\text{does not have smashed edge})$

$\qquad - \ P(\text{does not have puncture and does not have smashed edge})$

$= 0.96 + 0.93 - 0.893 = 0.997$

17. (a) $P(\text{club or 3}) = P(\text{club}) + P(3) - P(\text{club and 3})$

$$= \dfrac{13}{52} + \dfrac{4}{52} - \dfrac{1}{52} \approx 0.308$$

(b) $P(\text{red or king}) = P(\text{red}) + P(\text{king}) - P(\text{red and king})$

$$= \dfrac{26}{52} + \dfrac{4}{52} - \dfrac{2}{52} \approx 0.538$$

(c) $P(\text{9 or face card}) = P(9) + P(\text{face card}) - P(\text{9 and face card})$

$$= \dfrac{4}{52} + \dfrac{12}{52} - 0 \approx 0.308$$

18. $P(\text{5 or greater than 3}) = P(5) + P(\text{greater than 3}) - P(\text{5 and greater than 3})$

$$= \dfrac{1}{6} + \dfrac{3}{6} - \dfrac{1}{6} = 0.5$$

(b) $P(\text{less than 4 or even}) = P(\text{less than 4}) + P(\text{even}) - P(\text{less than 4 and even})$

$$= \dfrac{3}{6} + \dfrac{3}{6} - \dfrac{1}{6} \approx 0.833$$

(c) $P(2 \text{ or odd}) = P(2) + P(\text{odd}) - P(2 \text{ and odd})$

$$= \frac{1}{6} + \frac{3}{6} - 0 \approx 0.667$$

19. (a) $P(\text{under 5}) = 0.067$

(b) $P(\text{not 65+}) = 1 - P(65+) = 1 - 0.16 = 0.84$

(c) $P(\text{between 20 and 34})$
$= P(\text{between 20 and 24 or between 25 and 34})$
$= P(\text{between 20 and 24}) + P(\text{between 25 and 34}) = 0.064 + 0.135 = 0.199$

20. (a) $P(2) = 0.298$

(b) $P(2 \text{ or more}) = 1 - P(1) = 1 - 0.555 = 0.445$

(c) $P(\text{between 2 and 5}) = P(2) + P(3) + P(4) + P(5) = 0.298 + 0.076 + 0.047 + 0.014 = 0.435$

21. (a) $P(\text{not A}) = 1 - P(A) = 1 - \dfrac{52}{1026} = \dfrac{974}{1026} \approx 0.949$

(b) $P(\text{D or F}) = P(\text{D}) \text{ or } P(\text{F}) = \dfrac{272}{1026} + \dfrac{126}{1026} = \dfrac{398}{1026} \approx 0.388$

22. (a) $P(\text{not at all likely}) = \dfrac{190}{1000} = 0.19$

(b) $P(\text{not sure}) = \dfrac{10}{1000} = 0.01$

(c) $P(\text{not somewhat likely nor very likely}) = 1 - P(\text{somewhat likely or very likely})$
$$= 1 - [P(\text{somewhat likely}) + P(\text{very likely})]$$
$$= 1 - \left(\frac{320}{1000} + \frac{200}{1000} \right)$$
$$= \frac{480}{1000}$$
$$= 0.48$$

23. $A = \{\text{male}\}; B = \{\text{nursing major}\}$

(a) $P(A \text{ or } B) = P(A) + P(B) - P(A \text{ and } B)$
$$= \frac{1255}{3964} + \frac{1167}{3964} - \frac{151}{3964} = 0.573$$

(b) $P(A' \text{ or } B') = P(A') + P(B') - P(A' \text{ and } B')$
$$= \frac{2709}{3964} + \frac{2797}{3964} - \frac{1693}{3964} = 0.962$$

(c) $P(A \text{ or } B) \approx 0.573$

(d) Not mutually exclusive. A male can be a nursing major.

24. $A = \{\text{left handed}\}; B = \{\text{male}\}$

(a) $P(A \text{ or } B') = P(A) + P(B') - P(A \text{ and } B')$
$$= \frac{113}{1000} + \frac{475}{1000} - \frac{50}{1000} = 0.538$$

(b) $P(A' \text{ or } B) = P(A') + P(B) - P(A' \text{ and } B)$
$$= \frac{887}{1000} + \frac{525}{1000} - \frac{462}{1000} = 0.95$$

(c) $P(A \text{ or } B) = P(A) + P(B) - P(A \text{ and } B)$
$$= \frac{113}{1000} + \frac{525}{1000} - \frac{63}{1000} = 0.575$$

(d) $P(A' \text{ and } B') = \frac{425}{1000} = 0.425$

(e) Not mutually exclusive. A woman can be right-handed.

25. $A = \{\text{frequently}\}; B = \{\text{occasionally}\}; C = \{\text{not at all}\}; D = \{\text{male}\}$

(a) $P(A \text{ or } B) = \frac{428}{2850} + \frac{886}{2850} \approx 0.461$

(b) $P(D' \text{ or } C) = P(D') + P(C) - P(D' \text{ and } C)$
$$= \frac{1378}{2850} + \frac{1536}{2850} - \frac{741}{2850} \approx 0.762$$

(c) $P(D \text{ or } A) = P(D) + P(A) - P(D \text{ and } A)$
$$= \frac{1472}{2850} + \frac{428}{2850} - \frac{221}{2850} \approx 0.589$$

(d) $P(D' \text{ or } A') = P(D') + P(A') - P(D' \text{ and } A')$
$$= \frac{1378}{2850} + \frac{2422}{2850} - \frac{1171}{2850} \approx 0.922$$

(e) Not mutually exclusive. A female can be frequently involved in charity work.

26. $A = \{\text{only contacts}\}, B = \{\text{only glasses}\}, C = \{\text{both}\}, D = \{\text{neither}\}, E = \{\text{male}\}$

(a) $P(A \text{ or } B) = P(A) + P(B) = \frac{253}{3203} + \frac{1268}{3203} \approx 0.475$

(b) $P(E \text{ or } C) = P(E) + P(C) - P(E \text{ and } C) = \frac{1538}{3203} + \frac{545}{3203} - \frac{177}{3203} \approx 0.595$

(c) $P(E' \text{ or } D) = P(E') + P(D) - P(E' \text{ and } D) = \frac{1665}{3203} + \frac{1137}{3203} - \frac{681}{3203} \approx 0.662$

(d) $P(E \text{ or } (A \text{ or } D)) = P(E) + P(A \text{ or } D) - P(E \text{ and } A) - P(E \text{ and } D)$
$$= \frac{1538}{3203} + \frac{253 + 1137}{3203} - \frac{64}{3203} - \frac{456}{3203} \approx 0.752$$

(e) Mutually exclusive. A person who wears only contacts cannot wear both glasses and contacts.

27. Answers will vary.
Conclusion: If two events, A and B, are independent, $P(A \text{ and } B) = P(A) \cdot P(B)$. If two events are mutually exclusive, $P(A \text{ and } B) = 0$. The only scenario when two events can be independent and mutually exclusive is if $P(A) = 0$ or $P(B) = 0$.

28. $P(A \text{ or } B \text{ or } C) = P(A) + P(B) + P(C) - P(A \text{ and } B) - P(A \text{ and } C) - P(B \text{ and } C) + P(A \text{ and } B \text{ and } C)$
$$= 0.40 + 0.10 + 0.50 - 0.05 - 0.25 - 0.10 + 0.03$$
$$= 0.63$$

29. $P(A \text{ or } B \text{ or } C) = P(A) + P(B) + P(C) - P(A \text{ and } B) - P(A \text{ and } C) - P(B \text{ and } C) + P(A \text{ and } B \text{ and } C)$
$$= 0.38 + 0.26 + 0.14 - 0.12 - 0.03 - 0.09 + 0.01$$
$$= 0.55$$

30. If events A, B, and C are not mutually exclusive, $P(A$ and B and $C)$ must be added because $P(A) + P(B) + P(C)$ counts the intersection of all three events three times and $- P(A$ and $B) - P(A$ and $C) - P(B$ and $C)$ subtracts the intersection of all three events three times. So, if $P(A$ and B and $C)$ is not added at the end, it will not be counted.

3.4 ADDITIONAL TOPICS IN PROBABILITY AND COUNTING

3.4 Try It Yourself Solutions

1a. $n = 8$ teams   **b.** $8! = 40,320$

2a. $_8P_3 = \dfrac{8!}{(8-3)!} = \dfrac{8!}{5!} = \dfrac{8 \cdot 7 \cdot 6 \cdot 5 \cdot 4 \cdot 3 \cdot 2 \cdot 1}{5 \cdot 4 \cdot 3 \cdot 2 \cdot 1} = 8 \cdot 7 \cdot 6 = 336$

b. There are 336 possible ways that the subject can pick a first, second, and third activity.

3a. $n = 12$, $r = 4$

b. $_{12}P_4 = \dfrac{12!}{(12-4)!} = \dfrac{12!}{8!} = 12 \cdot 11 \cdot 10 \cdot 9 = 11,880$

4a. $n = 20$, $n_1 = 6$, $n_2 = 9$, $n_3 = 5$

b. $\dfrac{n!}{n_1! \, n_2! \, n_3!} = \dfrac{20!}{6! \, 9! \, 5!} = 77,597,520$

5a. $n = 20$, $r = 3$

b. $_{20}C_3 = \dfrac{20!}{(20-3)! \, 3!} = \dfrac{20!}{17! \, 3!} = \dfrac{20 \cdot 19 \cdot 18 \cdot 17!}{17! \, 3!} = 1140$

c. There are 1140 different possible three-person committees that can be selected from 20 employees.

6a. $_{20}P_2 = \dfrac{20!}{(20-2)!} = \dfrac{20!}{18!} = \dfrac{20 \cdot 19 \cdot 18!}{18!} = 20 \cdot 19 = 380$

b. $P(\text{selecting the two members}) = \dfrac{1}{380} \approx 0.003$

7a. One favorable outcome and $\dfrac{6!}{1! \, 2! \, 2! \, 1!} = 180$ distinguishable permutations.

b. $P(\text{letter}) = \dfrac{1}{180} \approx 0.006$

8a. $_{15}C_5 = 3003$ **b.** $_{54}C_5 = 3,162,510$ **c.** $\dfrac{3003}{3,162,510} \approx 0.0009$

9a. $_5C_3 \cdot {}_7C_0 = 10 \cdot 1 = 10$ **b.** $_{12}C_3 = 220$ **c.** $\dfrac{10}{220} \approx 0.045$

3.4 EXERCISE SOLUTIONS

1. The number of ordered arrangements of n objects taken r at a time. An example of a permutation is the number of seating arrangements of you and three friends.

2. A selection of r of the n objects without regard to order. An example of a combination is the number of selections of different playoff teams from a volleyball tournament.

3. False. A permutation is an ordered arrangement of objects.

4. True   **5.** True   **6.** True

7. $_9P_5 = \dfrac{9!}{(9-5)!} = \dfrac{9!}{4!} = 9 \cdot 8 \cdot 7 \cdot 6 \cdot 5 = 15,120$

8. $_{16}P_2 = \dfrac{16!}{(16-2)!} = \dfrac{16!}{14!} = 16 \cdot 15 = 240$

9. $_8C_3 = \dfrac{8!}{(8-3)!3!} = \dfrac{8!}{5!3!} = \dfrac{8 \cdot 7 \cdot 6 \cdot 5!}{5! \, 3!} = 56$

10. $_7P_4 = \dfrac{7!}{(7-4)!} = \dfrac{7!}{3!} = 7 \cdot 6 \cdot 5 \cdot 4 = 840$

11. $_{21}C_8 = \dfrac{21!}{(21-8)!8!} = \dfrac{21!}{13!8!} = \dfrac{21 \cdot 20 \cdot 19 \cdot 18 \cdot 17 \cdot 16 \cdot 15 \cdot 14 \cdot 13!}{13! \, 8!} = 203,490$

12. $\dfrac{_8C_4}{_{12}C_6} = \dfrac{\dfrac{8!}{(8-4)!4!}}{\dfrac{12!}{(12-6)!6!}} = \dfrac{\dfrac{8!}{4!4!}}{\dfrac{12!}{6!6!}} = \dfrac{70}{924} \approx 0.076$

13. $\dfrac{_6P_2}{_{11}P_3} = \dfrac{\dfrac{6!}{(6-2)!}}{\dfrac{11!}{(11-3)!}} = \dfrac{\dfrac{6!}{4!}}{\dfrac{11!}{8!}} = \dfrac{6 \cdot 5}{11 \cdot 10 \cdot 9} \approx 0.030$

14. $\dfrac{{}_{10}C_7}{{}_{14}C_7} = \dfrac{\dfrac{10!}{(10-7)!7!}}{\dfrac{14!}{(14-7)!7!}} = \dfrac{\dfrac{10!}{3!7!}}{\dfrac{14!}{7!7!}} = \dfrac{120}{3432} \approx 0.035$

15. Permutation, because the order of the 8 cars in line matters.

16. Combination, because the order of the committee members does not matter.

17. Combination, because the order of the captains does not matter.

18. Permutation, because the order of the letters matters.

19. $7! = 5040$ **20.** $8! = 40{,}320$

21. $6! = 720$ **22.** $10! = 3{,}628{,}800$

23. ${}_{52}C_6 = 20{,}358{,}520$ **24.** $4! = 24$

25. $\dfrac{22!}{4!\,10!\,8!} = 320{,}089{,}770$ **26.** ${}_{20}C_4 = 4845$

27. 3 S's, 3 T's, 1 A, 2 I's, 1 C

$\dfrac{10!}{3!\,3!\,1!\,2!\,1!} = 50{,}400$

28. ${}_{40}C_{12} = 5{,}586{,}853{,}480$

29. $10 \cdot 8 \cdot {}_{13}C_2 = 6240$ **30.** $12 \cdot {}_{10}C_2 \cdot 6 = 3240$

31. ${}_5C_1 \cdot {}_{75}C_5 = 86{,}296{,}950$ **32.** ${}_8C_2 \cdot {}_{42}C_8 = 3{,}304{,}845{,}180$

33. (a) $6! = 720$
  (b) sample
  (c) $\dfrac{1}{720} \approx 0.001$
  The event can be considered unusual because its probability is less than or equal to 0.05.

34. (a) 1 N, 2 E's, 1 V, 1 T
  $\dfrac{5!}{1!\,2!\,1!\,1!} = 60$
  (b) event
  (c) $\dfrac{1}{60} = 0.017$
  The event can be considered unusual because its probability is less than or equal to 0.05.

35. (a) 2 E's, 1 T, 1 R

$$\frac{4!}{2!\,1!\,1!}=12$$

(b) tree

(c) $\dfrac{1}{12}\approx 0.083$

The event cannot be considered unusual because its probability is not less than or equal to 0.05.

36. (a) 1 R, 1 N, 1 C, 1 T, 2 E's

$$\frac{6!}{1!\,1!\,1!\,1!\,2!}=360$$

(b) center

(c) $\dfrac{1}{360}\approx 0.003$

The event can be considered unusual because its probability is less than or equal to 0.05.

37. (a) 1 U, 1 N, 2 O's, 2 P's, 1 L, 1 A, 1 T, 1 I

$$\frac{10!}{1!\,1!\,2!\,2!\,1!\,1!\,1!\,1!}=907,200$$

(b) population

(c) $\dfrac{1}{907,200}\approx 0.000001$

The event can be considered unusual because its probability is less than or equal to 0.05.

38. (a) 1 S, 3 I's, 1 D, 2 T's, 1 B, 1 O, 1 U, 1 R, 1 N

$$\frac{12!}{1!\,3!\,1!\,2!\,1!\,1!\,1!\,1!\,1!}=39,916,800$$

(b) distribution

(c) $\dfrac{1}{39,916,800}\approx 0.00000003$

The event can be considered unusual because its probability is less than or equal to 0.05.

39. $\dfrac{1}{_{12}C_3}=\dfrac{1}{220}\approx 0.005$

40. $\dfrac{1}{_{9}C_3}=\dfrac{1}{84}\approx 0.012$

41. (a) $\dfrac{_{15}C_3}{_{56}C_3}=\dfrac{455}{27,720}\approx 0.0164$

(b) $\dfrac{_{41}C_3}{_{56}C_3}=\dfrac{10,660}{27,720}\approx 0.385$

42. (a) $\dfrac{_{6}C_4}{_{14}C_4}=\dfrac{15}{1001}\approx 0.015$

(b) $\dfrac{_{8}C_4}{_{14}C_4}=\dfrac{70}{1001}\approx 0.070$

43. (a) $_{8}C_4=70$

(b) $\left(_{2}C_1\right)\cdot\left(_{2}C_1\right)\cdot\left(_{2}C_1\right)\cdot\left(_{2}C_1\right)=2\cdot 2\cdot 2\cdot 2=16$

(c) $_4C_2 \left[\dfrac{\left(_2C_0\right)\cdot\left(_2C_0\right)\cdot\left(_2C_2\right)\cdot\left(_2C_2\right)}{_8C_4} \right] \approx 0.086$

44. (a) $26 \cdot 26 \cdot 10 \cdot 10 \cdot 10 \cdot 10 = 6{,}760{,}000$

(b) $24 \cdot 24 \cdot 10 \cdot 10 \cdot 10 \cdot 10 = 5{,}760{,}000$

(c) 0.5

45. (a) $(26)(26)(10)(10)(10)(10)(10) = 67{,}600{,}000$

(b) $(26)(25)(10)(9)(8)(7)(6) = 19{,}656{,}000$

(c) $\dfrac{1}{67{,}600{,}000} \approx 0.000000015$

46. (a) $(10)(10)(10) = 1000$

(b) $(8)(10)(10) = 800$

(c) $\dfrac{(8)(10)(5)}{(8)(10)(10)} = \dfrac{1}{2} = 0.5$

47. (a) $5! = 120$ (b) $2! \, 3! = 12$ (c) $3! \, 2! = 12$ (d) $\dfrac{_2C_1}{_5C_1} = \dfrac{2}{5} = 0.4$

48. (a) $\left(_8C_3\right)\cdot\left(_2C_0\right) = (56)\cdot(1) = 56$

(b) $\left(_8C_2\right)\cdot\left(_2C_1\right) = (28)\cdot(2) = 56$

(c) At least two good units
   = one or fewer defective units
   $= 56 + 56 = 112$

(d) $P(\text{at least 2 good units}) = P(\text{2 good units}) + P(\text{3 good units})$

$$= \dfrac{\left(_8C_2\right)\cdot\left(_2C_1\right)}{_{10}C_3} + \dfrac{\left(_8C_3\right)\cdot\left(_2C_0\right)}{_{10}C_3}$$

$$= \dfrac{56}{120} + \dfrac{56}{120} \approx 0.933$$

49. $(7\%)(1200) = (0.07)(1200) = 84$ of the 1200 rate financial shape as excellent.

$P(\text{all four rate excellent}) = \dfrac{_{84}C_4}{_{1200}C_4} = \dfrac{1{,}929{,}501}{85{,}968{,}659{,}700} \approx 0.000022$

50. $(24\%)(1200) = (0.24)(1200) = 288$ of 1200 rate financial shape as poor.

$P(\text{all 10 rate poor}) = \dfrac{_{288}C_{10}}{_{1200}C_{10}} \approx 0.000000562$

51. $(39\%)(500) = (0.39)(500) = 195$ of the 500 rate financial shape as fair $\Rightarrow 500 - 195 = 305$ rate financial shape as not fair.

$P(\text{none of 80 rate fair}) = \dfrac{_{305}C_{80}}{_{500}C_{80}} \approx 6.00 \times 10^{-20}$

52. $(28\%)(500) = (0.28)(500) = 140$ of 500 rate financial shape as good $\Rightarrow 500 - 140 = 360$ rate financial shape as not good.

$$P(\text{none of 55 rate good}) \frac{_{360}C_{55}}{_{500}C_{55}} \approx 0.00000000401$$

53. (a) $_{40}C_5 = 658,008$ 　　　　(b) $P(\text{win}) = \dfrac{1}{658,008} \approx 0.00000152$

54. (a) $_{200}C_{15} = 1.46 \times 10^{22}$ 　　　(b) $_{144}C_{15} = 8.53 \times 10^{19}$

   (c) $P(\text{no minorities}) = \dfrac{_{144}C_{15}}{_{200}C_{15}} \approx 0.006$

   (d) The committee selection is biased because there is a very low probability of randomly selecting 15 non-minorities.

55. (a) $\dfrac{\left(_{13}C_1\right)\left(_4C_4\right)\left(_{12}C_1\right)\left(_4C_1\right)}{_{52}C_5} = \dfrac{(13)(1)(12)(4)}{2,598,960} \approx 0.0002$

   (b) $\dfrac{\left(_{13}C_1\right)\left(_4C_3\right)\left(_{12}C_1\right)\left(_4C_2\right)}{_{52}C_5} = \dfrac{(13)(4)(12)(6)}{2,598,960} \approx 0.0014$

   (c) $\dfrac{\left(_{13}C_1\right)\left(_4C_3\right)\left(_{12}C_2\right)\left(_4C_1\right)\left(_4C_1\right)}{_{52}C_5} = \dfrac{(13)(4)(66)(4)(4)}{2,598,960} \approx 0.0211$

   (d) $\dfrac{\left(_{13}C_2\right)\left(_{13}C_1\right)\left(_{13}C_1\right)\left(_{13}C_1\right)}{_{52}C_5} = \dfrac{(78)(13)(13)(13)}{2,598,960} \approx 0.0659$

56. (a) $\dfrac{_{24}C_8}{_{41}C_8} = \dfrac{735,471}{95,548,245} \approx 0.0077$ 　　(b) $\dfrac{_{17}C_8}{_{41}C_8} = \dfrac{24,310}{95,548,245} \approx 0.0003$

   (c) $\dfrac{\left(_{24}C_6\right)\left(_{17}C_2\right)}{_{41}C_8} = \dfrac{(134,596)(136)}{95,548,245} \approx 0.1916$ 　(d) $\dfrac{\left(_{24}C_4\right)\left(_{17}C_4\right)}{_{41}C_8} = \dfrac{(10,626)(2380)}{95,548,245} \approx 0.2647$

57. $_{14}C_4 = 1001$ possible 4 digit arrangements if order is not important.

   Assign 1000 of the 4 digit arrangements to the 13 teams since 1 arrangement is excluded.

58. $_{14}P_4 = 24,024$

59. $P(\text{1st}) = \dfrac{250}{1000} = 0.250$ $P(\text{8th}) = \dfrac{28}{1000} = 0.028$

$P(\text{2nd}) = \dfrac{199}{1000} = 0.199$ $P(\text{9th}) = \dfrac{17}{1000} = 0.017$

$P(\text{3rd}) = \dfrac{156}{1000} = 0.156$ $P(\text{10th}) = \dfrac{11}{1000} = 0.011$

$P(\text{4th}) = \dfrac{119}{1000} = 0.119$ $P(\text{11th}) = \dfrac{8}{1000} = 0.008$

$P(\text{5th}) = \dfrac{88}{1000} = 0.088$ $P(\text{12th}) = \dfrac{7}{1000} = 0.007$

$P(\text{6th}) = \dfrac{63}{1000} = 0.063$ $P(\text{13th}) = \dfrac{6}{1000} = 0.006$

$P(\text{7th}) = \dfrac{43}{1000} = 0.043$ $P(\text{14th}) = \dfrac{5}{1000} = 0.005$

Events in which any of Teams 7-14 would win the first pick would be considered unusual because the probabilities are all less than or equal to 0.05.

60. Let A = {team with the worst record wins second pick} and B = {team with the best record, ranked 14th, wins first pick}.

$$P(A|B) = \frac{250}{1000 - 5} = \frac{250}{995} \approx 0.251$$

61. Let A = {team with the worst record wins third pick} and
B = {team with the best record, ranked 14th, wins first pick} and
C = {team ranked 2nd wins the second pick}.

$$P(A|B \text{ and } C) = \frac{250}{1000 - 199 - 5} = \frac{250}{796} \approx 0.314$$

62. Let A = {neither the first- nor the second-worst teams will get the first pick} and
B = {the first- or second-worst team will get the first pick}.

$$P(A) = 1 - P(B) = 1 - \left(\frac{199}{1000} + \frac{250}{1000}\right) = 1 - \frac{449}{1000} = 1 - 0.449 = 0.551$$

CHAPTER 3 REVIEW EXERCISE SOLUTIONS

1. Sample space:
    {HHHH, HHHT, HHTH, HHTT, HTHH, HTHT, HTTH, HTTT, THHH, THHT, THTH, THTT, TTHH, TTHT, TTTH, TTTT}

    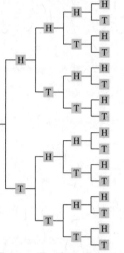

    Event: Getting three heads
    {HHHT, HHTH, HTHH, THHH}
    There are 4 outcomes.

2. Sample space:
    {(1, 1), (1, 2), (1, 3), (1, 4), (1, 5), (1, 6), (2, 1), (2, 2,), (2, 3), (2, 4), (2, 5), (2, 6), (3, 1), (3, 2), (3, 3), (3, 4), (3, 5), (3, 6), (4, 1), (4, 2), (4, 3), (4, 4), (4, 5), (4, 6), (5, 1), (5, 2), (5, 3), (5, 4), (5, 5), (5, 6), (6, 1), (6, 2), (6, 3), (6, 4), (6, 5), (6, 6)}

    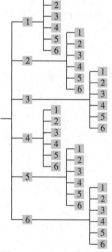

    Event: sum of 4 or 5
    {(1, 3), (1, 4), (2, 2), (2, 3), (3, 1), (3, 2), (4, 1)}
    There are 7 outcomes.

3. Sample space: {January, February, March, April, May, June, July, August, September, October, November, December}
   Event: {January, June, July}
   There are 3 outcomes.

4. Sample space: {GGG, GGB, GBG, GBB, BGG, BGB, BBG, BBB}

   Event: The family has two boys.
   {BGB, BBG, GBB}
   There are 3 outcomes.

5. $(7)(4)(3) = 84$ 6. $(26)(26)(26)(10)(10)(10)(10) = 175{,}760{,}000$

7. Empirical probability because it is based on observations obtained from probability experiments.

8. Classical probability because each outcome in the sample space is equally likely to occur.

9. Subjective probability because it is based on opinion.

10. Empirical probability because it is based on observations obtained from probability experiments.

11. Classical probability because each outcome in the sample space is equally likely to occur.

12. Empirical probability because it is based on observations obtained from probability experiments.

13. $P(\text{at least } 10) = 0.107 + 0.090 + 0.018 = 0.215$

14. $P(\text{less than } 20) = 0.609 + 0.176 + 0.107 = 0.892$

15. $\dfrac{1}{(8)(10)(10)(10)(10)(10)(10)} = 1.25 \times 10^{-7}$

16. $1 - \dfrac{1}{(8)(10)(10)(10)(10)(10)(10)} = 0.999999875$

17. $P(\text{undergrad} \,|\, +) = 0.92$

18. $P(\text{graduate} \,|\, -) = 0.07$

19. Independent. The outcomes of the first four coin tosses do not affect the outcome of the fifth coin toss.

20. Dependent. The outcome of taking a driver's education course affects the outcome of passing the driver's license exam.

21. Dependent. The outcome of getting high grades affects the outcome of being awarded an academic scholarship.

22. No. You do not know whether events A and B are independent or dependent.

23. P(correct toothpaste and correct dental rinse) = P(correct toothpaste) · P(correct dental rinse)

$$= \frac{1}{8} \cdot \frac{1}{5}$$
$$= \frac{1}{40}$$
$$= 0.025$$

The event is unusual because its probability is less than or equal to 0.05.

24. P(black and (blue or white)) = P(black) · P(blue or white | black)

$$= \frac{6}{18} \cdot \frac{12}{17}$$
$$\approx 0.235$$

The event is not unusual because its probability is not less than or equal to 0.05.

25. Mutually exclusive. A jelly bean cannot be both completely red and completely yellow.

26. Not mutually exclusive. A person who loves cats can also own a dog.

27. Mutually exclusive. A person cannot be registered legally to vote in more than one state.

28. No. You do not know whether events A and B are mutually exclusive.

29. P(home or work) = P(home) + P(work) − P(home and work) = 0.44 + 0.37 − 0.21 = 0.6
30. P(silver or SUV) = P(silver) + P(SUV) − P(silver and SUV) = 0.19 + 0.22 − 0.16 = 0.25

31. P(4-8 or club) = P(4-8) + P(club) − P(4-8 and club) = $\frac{20}{52} + \frac{13}{52} - \frac{5}{52} \approx 0.538$

32. P(red or queen) = P(red) + P(queen) − P(red and queen) = $\frac{26}{52} + \frac{4}{52} - \frac{2}{52} \approx 0.538$

33. P(odd or less than 4) = P(odd) + P(less than 4) − P(odd and less than 4) = $\frac{6}{12} + \frac{3}{12} - \frac{2}{12} \approx 0.583$

34. P(even or greater than 6) = P(even) + P(greater than 6) − P(even and greater than 6)

$$= \frac{4}{8} + \frac{2}{8} - \frac{1}{8} = \frac{5}{8} = 0.625$$

35. P(600 or more) = P(600-999) + P(1000 or more)
$$= 0.244 + 0.047 = 0.291$$

36. $P(300\text{-}999) = P(300\text{-}599) + P(600\text{-}999)$
$$= 0.474 + 0.244 = 0.718$$

37. $P(\text{action or horror}) = P(\text{action}) + P(\text{horror})$
$$= \frac{112}{874} + \frac{52}{874} = \frac{164}{874} \approx 0.188$$

38. $P(\text{drama or musical}) = P(\text{drama}) + P(\text{musical})$
$$= \frac{242}{874} + \frac{26}{874} = \frac{268}{874} \approx 0.307$$

39. $P(\text{not comedy}) = 1 - P(\text{comedy})$
$$= 1 - \frac{260}{874} = \frac{614}{874} \approx 0.703$$

40. $P(\text{not science fiction or action}) = 1 - P(\text{science fiction or action})$
$$= 1 - \left(\frac{95}{874} + \frac{112}{874} \right) = 1 - \frac{207}{874} \approx 0.763$$

41. $_{11}P_2 = \dfrac{11!}{(11-2)!} = \dfrac{11!}{9!} = 11 \cdot 10 = 110$

42. $_8P_6 = \dfrac{8!}{(8-6)!} = \dfrac{8!}{2!} = 8 \cdot 7 \cdot 6 \cdot 5 \cdot 4 \cdot 3 \cdot 2 = 40,320$

43. $_7C_4 = \dfrac{7!}{(7-4)!4!} = \dfrac{7!}{3!4!} = 35$

44. $\dfrac{_5C_3}{_{10}C_3} = \dfrac{\dfrac{5!}{(5-3)!3!}}{\dfrac{10!}{(10-3)!3!}} = \dfrac{\dfrac{5!}{2!3!}}{\dfrac{10!}{7!3!}} = \dfrac{10}{120} \approx 0.083$

45. $_{50}P_5 = 254,251,200$

46. $_{38}C_{25} = 5,414,950,296$

47. Order is important: $_{15}P_3 = 2730$

48. $5! = 120$

49. Order is not important: $_{17}C_4 = 2380$

50. Order is not important: $_{13}C_2 = 78$

CHAPTER 3 | PROBABILITY **133**

51. $P(3 \text{ kings and } 2 \text{ queens}) = \dfrac{\left(_4C_3\right) \cdot \left(_4C_2\right)}{_{52}C_5} = \dfrac{4 \cdot 6}{2,598,960} \approx 0.00000923$

The event is unusual because its probability is less than or equal to 0.05.

52. $\dfrac{1}{(23)(26)(26)(10)} = \dfrac{1}{155,480} \approx 0.00000643$

The event is unusual because its probability is less than or equal to 0.05.

53. (a) $P(\text{no defective}) = \dfrac{_{197}C_3}{_{200}C_3} = \dfrac{1,254,890}{1,313,400} \approx 0.955$

The event is not unusual because its probability is not less than or equal to 0.05.

(b) $P(\text{all defective}) = \dfrac{_3C_3}{_{200}C_3} = \dfrac{1}{1,313,400} \approx 0.000000761$

The event is unusual because its probability is less than or equal to 0.05.

(c) $P(\text{at least one defective}) = 1 - P(\text{no defective}) \approx 1 - 0.955 = 0.045$

The event is unusual because its probability is less than or equal to 0.05.

(d) $P(\text{at least one non-defective}) = 1 - P(\text{all defective}) \approx 1 - 0.000000761 \approx 0.999999239$

The event is not unusual because its probability is not less than or equal to 0.05.

54. (a) $P(\text{no winning tickets}) = \dfrac{_{346}C_4}{_{350}C_4} = \dfrac{586,862,710}{614,597,725} \approx 0.955$

The event is not unusual because its probability is not less than or equal to 0.05.

(b) $P(\text{all winning tickets}) = \dfrac{_4C_4}{_{350}C_4} = \dfrac{1}{614,597,725} \approx 0.000000002$

(c) $P(\text{at least one winner}) = 1 - P(\text{no winning tickets}) \approx 1 - 0.955 = 0.045$

The event is unusual because its probability is less than or equal to 0.05.

(d) $P(\text{at least one non-winner}) = 1 - P(\text{all winning tickets}) \approx 1 - 0.000000002 = 0.999999998$

The event is not unusual because its probability is not less than or equal to 0.05.

55. (a) $P(4 \text{ men}) = \dfrac{_6C_4}{_{10}C_4} = \dfrac{15}{210} \approx 0.071$

The event is not unusual because its probability is not less than or equal to 0.05.

(b) $P(4 \text{ women}) = \dfrac{_4C_4}{_{10}C_4} = \dfrac{1}{210} \approx 0.005$

The event is unusual because its probability is less than or equal to 0.05.

(c) $P(2 \text{ men and } 2 \text{ women}) = \dfrac{\left(_6C_2\right) \cdot \left(_4C_2\right)}{_{10}C_4} = \dfrac{15 \cdot 6}{210} \approx 0.429$

The event is not unusual because its probability is not less than or equal to 0.05.

(d) $P(1 \text{ man and } 3 \text{ women}) = \dfrac{\left(_6C_1\right) \cdot \left(_4C_3\right)}{_{10}C_4} = \dfrac{6 \cdot 4}{210} \approx 0.114$

The event is not unusual because its probability is not less than or equal to 0.05.

CHAPTER 3 QUIZ SOLUTIONS

1. (a) $P(\text{bachelor's degree}) = \dfrac{1525}{2917} \approx 0.523$

    (b) $P(\text{bachelor's degree}|\text{female}) = \dfrac{875}{1724} \approx 0.508$

    (c) $P(\text{bachelor's degree}|\text{male}) = \dfrac{650}{1193} \approx 0.545$

    (d) $P(\text{associate's degree or bachelor's degree}) = P(\text{associate's degree}) + P(\text{bachelor's degree})$
    $$= \dfrac{728}{2917} + \dfrac{1252}{2917}$$
    $$\approx 0.772$$

    (e) $P(\text{doctorate}|\text{male}) = \dfrac{30}{1193} \approx 0.025$

    (f) $P(\text{master's degree or female}) = P(\text{master's degree}) + P(\text{female})$
    $$- P(\text{master's degree and female})$$
    $$= \dfrac{604}{2917} + \dfrac{1724}{2917} - \dfrac{366}{2917}$$
    $$\approx 0.673$$

    (g) $P(\text{associate's degree and male}) = P(\text{associate's degree}) \cdot P(\text{male}|\text{associate's degree})$
    $$= \dfrac{728}{2917} \cdot \dfrac{275}{728}$$
    $$\approx 0.094$$

    (h) $P(\text{female}|\text{bachelor's degree}) = \dfrac{875}{1525} \approx 0.574$

2. The event in part (e) is unusual because its probability is less than or equal to 0.05.

3. Not mutually exclusive. A golfer can score the best round in a four-round tournament and still lose the tournament.
    Dependent. The outcome of scoring the best round in a four-round tournament affects the outcome of losing the golf tournament.

4. (a) ${}_{247}C_3 = 2,481,115$

    (b) ${}_{3}C_3 = 1$

    (c) ${}_{250}C_3 - {}_{3}C_3 = 2,573,000 - 1 = 2,572,999$

5. (a) $\dfrac{{}_{247}C_3}{{}_{250}C_3} = \dfrac{2,481,115}{2,573,000} \approx 0.96$

    (b) $\dfrac{{}_{3}C_3}{{}_{250}C_3} = \dfrac{1}{2,573,000} \approx 3.88 \times 10^{-7}$

    (c) $\dfrac{{}_{250}C_3 - {}_{3}C_3}{{}_{250}C_3} = \dfrac{2,572,999}{2,573,000} \approx 0.9999996$

6. $9 \cdot 10 \cdot 10 \cdot 10 \cdot 10 \cdot 5 = 450,000$

7. $_{30}P_4 = 657,720$

8. There are 27 ways of getting a sum of 11 and 3 ways of getting a sum of 17, out of 216 different outcomes when you roll three dice. Thus the corresponding probabilities $P(\text{sum} = 11) = \dfrac{27}{216} = 0.125$ and $P(\text{sum} = 17) = \dfrac{3}{216} = 0.014$. Since getting the sum of 17 has a probability less than or equal to 0.05, it is unusual.

Discrete Probability Distributions

4.1 Try It Yourself Solutions

1a. (1) measured   (2) counted

b. (1) The random variable is continuous because x can be any speed up to the maximum speed of a space shuttle.

(2) The random variable is discrete because the number of calves born on a farm in one year is countable.

2ab.

x	f	$P(x)$
0	16	0.16
1	19	0.19
2	15	0.15
3	21	0.21
4	9	0.09
5	10	0.10
6	8	0.08
7	2	0.02
	$n = 100$	$\sum P(x) = 1$

c.

New Employee Sales

3a. Each $P(x)$ is between 0 and 1.

b. $\sum P(x) = 1$

c. Because both conditions are met, the distribution is a probability distribution.

4a. (1) Yes, each outcome is between 0 and 1.   (2) Yes, each outcome is between 0 and 1.

b. (1) Yes, $\sum P(x) = 1$.   (2) Yes, $\sum P(x) = 1$.

c. (1) Is a probability distribution   (2) Is a probability distribution.

5ab.

x	$P(x)$	$xP(x)$
0	0.16	$(0)(0.16) = 0.00$
1	0.19	$(1)(0.19) = 0.19$
2	0.15	$(2)(0.15) = 0.30$
3	0.21	$(3)(0.21) = 0.63$
4	0.09	$(4)(0.09) = 0.36$
5	0.10	$(5)(0.10) = 0.50$
6	0.08	$(6)0.08 = 0.48$
7	0.02	$(7)(0.02) = 0.14$
	$\sum P(x) = 1$	$\sum xP(x) = 2.60$

c. $\mu = \sum xP(x) = 2.6$

On average, a new employee makes 2.6 sales per day.

6ab. From 5, $\mu - 2.6$,

x	f	$x - \mu$	$(x - \mu)^2$	$P(x)(x - \mu)^2$
0	0.16	−2.6	6.76	$(0.16)(6.76) = 1.0816$
1	0.19	−1.6	2.56	$(0.19)(2.56) = 0.4864$
2	0.15	−0.6	0.36	$(0.15)(0.36) = 0.0540$
3	0.21	0.4	0.16	$(0.21)(0.16) = 0.0336$
4	0.09	1.4	1.96	$(0.09)(1.96) = 0.1764$
5	0.10	2.4	5.76	$(0.10)(5.76) = 0.5760$
6	0.08	3.4	11.56	$(0.08)(11.56) = 0.9248$
7	0.02	4.4	19.36	$(0.02)(19.36) = 0.3872$
	$\sum P(x) = 1$			$\sum P(x)(x - \mu)^2 = 3.72$

c. $\sigma = \sqrt{\sigma^2} = \sqrt{3.72} \approx 1.9$

d. Most of the data valves differ from the mean by no more than 1.9 sales per day.

7ab.

Gain, x	$P(x)$	$xP(x)$
$1995	$\dfrac{1}{2000}$	$\dfrac{1995}{2000}$
$ 995	$\dfrac{1}{2000}$	$\dfrac{995}{2000}$
$ 495	$\dfrac{1}{2000}$	$\dfrac{495}{2000}$
$ 245	$\dfrac{1}{2000}$	$\dfrac{245}{2000}$
$ 95	$\dfrac{1}{2000}$	$\dfrac{95}{2000}$
$ −5	$\dfrac{1995}{2000}$	$-\dfrac{9975}{2000}$
	$\sum P(x) = 1$	$\sum xP(x) \approx -3.08$

c. $E(x) = \sum xP(x) = -\$3.08$

d. Because the expected value is negative, you can expect to lose an average of $3.08 for each ticket you buy.

4.1 EXERCISE SOLUTIONS

1. A random variable represents a numerical value associated with each outcome of a probability experiment. Examples: Answers will vary.

2. A discrete probability distribution lists each possible value a random variable can assume, together with its probability.
   Condition 1: $0 \leq P(x) \leq 1$
   Condition 2: $\sum P(x) = 1$

3. No; Expected value may not be a possible value of x for one trial, but it represents the average value of x over a large number of trials.

4. The mean of a probability distribution represent the "theoretical average" of a probability experiment.

5. False. In most applications, discrete random variables represent counted data, while continuous random variables represent measured data.

6. True

7. True

8. False. The expected value of a discrete random variable is equal to the mean of the random variable.

9. Discrete, because attendance is a random variable that is countable.

10. Continuous, because length of time is a random variable that has an infinite number of possible outcomes and cannot be counted.

11. Continuous, because the distance a baseball travels after being hit is a random variable that must be measured.

12. Discrete, because the number of fatalities is a random variable that is countable.

13. Discrete, because the number of books in a university library is a random variable that is countable.

14. Continuous, because the length of time it takes to get to work is a random variable that has an infinite number of possible outcomes and cannot be counted.

15. Continuous, because the volume of blood drawn for a blood test is a random variable that must be measured.

16. Discrete, because the number of tornadoes in the month of June in Oklahoma is a random variable that is countable.

17. Discrete, because the number of measures that is posted each month on a social networking site is a random variable that is countable.

18. Continuous, because the tension at which a randomly selected guitar's strings have been strung is a random variable that cannot be counted.

19. Continuous, because the amount of snow that fell in Nome, Alaska last winter is a random variable that cannot be counted.

20. Discrete, because the total number of die rolls required to roll a 5 is a random variable that is countable.

21. (a) $P(x > 2) = 0.25 + 0.10 = 0.35$
(b) $P(x < 4) = 1 - P(4) = 1 - 0.10 = 0.90$

22. (a) $P(x > 1) = 1 - P(x < 2) = 1 - (0.30 + 0.25) = 0.45$
(b) $P(x < 3) = 0.30 + 0.25 + 0.25 = 0.80$

23. $\sum P(x) = 1 \rightarrow P(3) = 0.22$ **24.** $\sum P(x) = 1 \rightarrow P(1) = 0.15$

25. Because each $P(x)$ is between 0 and 1, and $\sum P(x) = 1$, the distribution is a probability distribution.

26. No, $\sum P(x) = 0.97$.

27. (a)

x	f	$P(x)$
0	1491	0.686
1	425	0.195
2	168	0.077
3	48	0.022
4	29	0.013
5	14	0.006
	$n = 2175$	$\sum P(x) \approx 1$

(b)

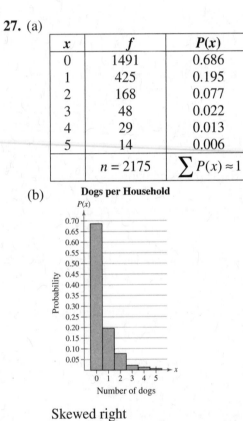

Dogs per Household

Skewed right

(c)

$xP(x)$	$(x - \mu)$	$(x - \mu)^2$	$(x - \mu)^2 P(x)$
0	−0.497	0.247	0.169
0.195	0.503	0.253	0.049
0.154	1.503	2.259	0.174
0.066	2.503	6.265	0.138
0.052	3.503	12.271	0.160
0.030	4.503	20.277	0.122
$\sum xP(x) = 0.497$			$\sum (x - \mu)^2 P(x) = 0.812$

$$\mu = \sum xP(x) = 0.497 \approx 0.5$$

$$\sigma^2 = \sum (x - \mu)^2 P(x) = 0.812 \approx 0.8$$

$$\sigma = \sqrt{\sigma^2} = \sqrt{0.812} \approx 0.9$$

(d) The mean is 0.5, so the average number of dogs per household is about 0 or 1 dog. The standard deviation is 0.9, so most of the households differ from the mean by no more than 1 dog.

28. (a)

x	f	$P(x)$
4	20	0.190
5	23	0.219
6	23	0.219
7	36	0.343
8	3	0.029
	$n = 105$	$\sum P(x) = 1$

(b)

Games per World Series

Skewed left

(c)

$xP(x)$	$(x - \mu)$	$(x - \mu)^2$	$(x - \mu)^2 P(x)$
0.760	−1.802	3.247	0.617
1.095	−0.802	0.643	0.141
1.314	0.198	0.039	0.009
2.401	1.198	1.435	0.492
0.232	2.198	4.831	0.140
$\sum xP(x) = 5.802$			$\sum (x - \mu)^2 P(x) = 1.399$

$$\mu = \sum xP(x) = 5.802 \approx 5.8$$

$$\sigma^2 = \sum (x - \mu)^2 P(x) = 1.399 \approx 1.4$$

$$\sigma = \sqrt{\sigma^2} = \sqrt{1.399} \approx 1.2$$

(d) The mean is 5.8, so the average number of games played per World Series was about 6. The standard deviation is 1.2, so most of the World Series differed from the mean by no more than about 1 game.

29. (a)

x	f	P(x)
0	26	0.01
1	442	0.17
2	728	0.28
3	1404	0.54
	$n = 2600$	$\sum P(x) = 1$

(b)

Televisions per Household

Skewed left

(c)

xP(x)	$(x - \mu)$	$(x - \mu)^2$	$(x - \mu)^2 P(x)$
0.00	−2.35	5.523	0.055
0.17	−1.35	1.823	0.310
0.56	−0.35	0.123	0.034
1.62	0.65	0.423	0.228
$\sum xP(x) = 2.35$			$\sum (x - \mu)^2 P(x) = 0.627$

$$\mu = \sum xP(x) = 2.35 \approx 2.4$$

$$\sigma^2 = \sum (x - \mu)^2 P(x) = 0.627 \approx 0.6$$

$$\sigma = \sqrt{\sigma^2} = \sqrt{0.627} \approx 0.8$$

(d) The mean is 2.4, so the average household in the town has about 2 televisions. The standard deviation is 0.8, so most of the households differ from the mean by no more than 1 television.

30. (a)

x	f	P(x)
0	95	0.250
1	113	0.297
2	87	0.229
3	64	0.168
4	13	0.034
5	8	0.021
	$n = 380$	$\sum P(x) \approx 1$

(b)

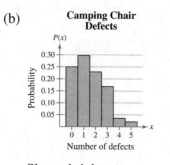

Camping Chair Defects

Skewed right

(c)

$xP(x)$	$(x - \mu)$	$(x - \mu)^2$	$(x - \mu)^2 P(x)$
0	−1.5	2.25	0.563
0.297	−0.5	0.25	0.074
0.458	0.5	0.25	0.057
0.504	1.5	2.25	0.378
0.136	2.5	6.25	0.213
0.105	3.5	12.25	0.257
$\sum xP(x) = 1.5$			$\sum (x - \mu)^2 P(x) = 1.542$

$$\mu = \sum xP(x) = 1.5$$

$$\sigma^2 = \sum (x - \mu)^2 P(x) = 1.542 \approx 1.5$$

$$\sigma = \sqrt{\sigma^2} = \sqrt{1.542} \approx 1.2$$

(d) The mean is 1.5, so the average batch of camping chairs has about 1 or 2 defects. The standard deviation is 1.2, so most of the batches differ from the mean by no more than about 1 defect.

31. (a)

x	f	$P(x)$
0	6	0.031
1	12	0.063
2	29	0.151
3	57	0.297
4	42	0.219
5	30	0.156
6	16	0.083
	$n = 192$	$\sum P(x) = 1$

(b)

Overtime

Approximately symmetric

(c)

$xP(x)$	$(x - \mu)$	$(x - \mu)^2$	$(x - \mu)^2 P(x)$
0	−3.41	11.628	0.360
0.063	−2.41	5.808	0.366
0.302	−1.41	1.988	0.300
0.891	−0.41	0.168	0.050
0.876	−0.59	0.348	0.076
0.780	1.59	2.528	0.394
0.498	2.59	6.708	0.557
$\sum xP(x) = 3.410$			$\sum (x - \mu)^2 P(x) = 2.103$

$$\mu = \sum xP(x) = 3.410 \approx 3.4$$

$$\sigma^2 = \sum (x - \mu)^2 P(x) = 2.103 \approx 2.1$$

$$\sigma = \sqrt{\sigma^2} = \sqrt{2.103} \approx 1.5$$

(d) The mean is 3.4, so the average employee worked 3.4 hours of overtime. The standard deviation is 1.5, so the overtime worked by most of the employees differed from the mean by no more than 1.5 hours.

32. (a)

x	f	$P(x)$
0	19	0.059
1	39	0.122
2	52	0.163
3	57	0.178
4	68	0.213
5	41	0.128
6	27	0.084
7	17	0.053
	$n = 320$	$\sum P(x) = 1$

(b)

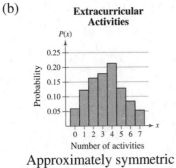

Extracurricular Activities

Approximately symmetric

(c)

$xP(x)$	$(x - \mu)$	$(x - \mu)^2$	$(x - \mu)^2 P(x)$
0	−3.349	11.216	0.662
0.122	−2.349	5.518	0.673
0.326	−1.349	1.820	0.297
0.534	−0.349	0.122	0.022
0.852	0.651	0.424	0.090
0.640	1.651	2.726	0.349
0.504	2.651	7.028	0.590
0.371	3.651	13.330	0.706
$\sum xP(x) = 3.349$			$\sum (x - \mu)^2 P(x) = 3.389$

$$\mu = \sum xP(x) = 3.349 \approx 3.3$$

$$\sigma^2 = \sum (x - \mu)^2 P(x) = 3.389 \approx 3.4$$

$$\sigma = \sqrt{\sigma^2} = \sqrt{3.389} \approx 1.8$$

(d) The mean is 3.3, so the average student is involved in about 3 extracurricular activities. The standard deviation is 1.8, so most of the students differ from the mean by no more than about 2 activities.

33. An expected value of 0 means that the money gained is equal to the spent, representing the breakeven point.

34. A "fair bet" in a game of chance has an expected value of 0, which means that the chances of losing are equal to the chances of winning.

35.

x	$P(x)$	$xP(x)$	$(x - \mu)$	$(x - \mu)^2$	$(x - \mu)^2 P(x)$
0	0.02	0.00	−5.30	28.09	0.562
1	0.02	0.02	−4.30	18.49	0.370
2	0.06	0.12	−3.30	10.89	0.653
3	0.06	0.18	−2.30	5.29	0.317
4	0.08	0.32	−1.30	1.69	0.135
5	0.22	1.10	−0.30	0.09	0.020
6	0.30	1.80	0.70	0.49	0.147
7	0.16	1.12	1.70	2.89	0.462
8	0.08	0.64	2.70	7.29	0.583
		$\sum xP(x) = 5.30$			$\sum (x - \mu)^2 P(x) = 3.249$

(a) $\mu = \sum xP(x) = 5.3$ (b) $\sigma^2 = \sum (x - \mu)^2 P(x) = 3.249 \approx 3.3$

(c) $\sigma = \sqrt{\sigma^2} = \sqrt{3.249} \approx 1.9$ (d) $E(x) = \mu = \sum xP(x) = 5.3$

(e) The expected value is 5.3, so an average student is expected to answer about 5 questions correctly. The standard deviation is 1.9, so most of the student's quiz results differ from the expected value by no more than about 2 questions.

36.

x	$P(x)$	$xP(x)$	$(x - \mu)$	$(x - \mu)^2$	$(x - \mu)^2P(x)$
0	0.01	0	−3.02	9.120	0.091
1	0.10	0.10	−2.02	4.080	0.408
2	0.26	0.52	−1.02	1.040	0.270
3	0.33	0.99	−0.02	0.0004	0.000132
4	0.18	0.72	0.98	0.960	0.173
5	0.06	0.30	1.98	3.920	0.235
6	0.03	0.18	2.98	8.880	0.266
7	0.03	0.21	3.18	15.840	0.475
		$\sum xP(x) = 3.02$			$\sum (x - \mu)^2 P(x) = 1.918$

(a) $\mu = \sum xP(x) = 3.02 \approx 3.0$ (b) $\sigma^2 = \sum (x - \mu)^2 P(x) = 1.918 \approx 1.9$

(c) $\sigma = \sqrt{\sigma^2} = \sqrt{1.918} \approx 1.4$ (d) $E(x) = \mu = 3.0$

(e) The expected value is 3.0, so in an average hour the expected number of calls is 3. The standard deviation is 1.4, so the number of calls for most of the hours should differ from the expected value by no more than about 1 or 2 calls.

37.

x	$P(x)$	$xP(x)$	$(x - \mu)$	$(x - \mu)^2$	$(x - \mu)^2P(x)$
1	0.392	0.392	−1.04	1.082	0.424
2	0.265	0.530	−0.04	0.002	0.001
3	0.269	0.807	0.96	0.922	0.248
4	0.064	0.256	1.96	3.842	0.246
5	0.011	0.055	2.96	8.762	0.096
		$\sum xP(x) = 2.04$			$\sum (x - \mu)^2 P(x) = 1.015$

(a) $\mu = \sum xP(x) = 2.04 \approx 2.0$ (b) $\sigma^2 = \sum (x - \mu)^2 P(x) = 1.015 \approx 1.0$

(c) $\sigma = \sqrt{\sigma^2} = \sqrt{1.015} \approx 1.0$ (d) $E(x) = \mu = 2.0$

(e) The expected value is 2.0, so an average hurricane that hits the U.S. mainland is expected to be a category 2 hurricane. The standard deviation is 1.0, so most of the hurricanes differ from the expected value by no more than 1 category level.

38.

x	$P(x)$	$xP(x)$	$(x - \mu)$	$(x - \mu)^2$	$(x - \mu)^2P(x)$
1	0.555	0.555	−0.697	0.486	0.270
2	0.298	0.596	0.303	0.092	0.027
3	0.076	0.228	1.303	1.698	0.129
4	0.047	0.188	2.303	5.304	0.249
5	0.014	0.070	3.303	10.910	0.153
6	0.010	0.060	4.303	18.516	0.185
		$\sum xP(x) = 1.697$			$\sum (x - \mu)^2 P(x) = 1.013$

(a) $\mu = \sum xP(x) = 1.697 \approx 1.7$ (b) $\sigma^2 = \sum (x - \mu)^2 P(x) = 1.013 \approx 1.0$

(c) $\sigma = \sqrt{\sigma^2} = \sqrt{1.013} \approx 1.0$ (d) $E(x) = \mu = 1.7$

(e) The expected value is 1.7, so an average car crossing the Tacoma Narrows Bridge is expected to have either 1 or 2 people in it. The standard deviation is 1.0, so most of the car occupancies differ from the expected value by no more than 1 occupant.

39.

x	$P(x)$	$xP(x)$	$(x - \mu)$	$(x - \mu)^2$	$(x - \mu)^2 P(x)$
1	0.275	0.275	−1.491	2.223	0.611
2	0.332	0.664	−0.491	0.241	0.080
3	0.159	0.447	0.509	0.259	0.041
4	0.136	0.544	1.509	2.277	0.310
5	0.063	0.315	2.509	6.295	0.397
6+	0.036	0.216	3.509	12.313	0.443
		$\sum xP(x) = 2.491$			$\sum (x - \mu)^2 P(x) = 1.882$

(a) $\mu = \sum xP(x) = 2.491 \approx 2.5$ (b) $\sigma^2 = \sum (x - \mu)^2 P(x) = 1.882 \approx 1.9$

(c) $\sigma = \sqrt{\sigma^2} = \sqrt{1.882} \approx 1.4$ (d) $E(x) = \mu = 2.5$

(e) The expected value is 2.5, so an average household is expected to have either 2 or 3 people. The standard deviation is 1.4, so most of the household sites differ from the expected value by no more than 1 or 2 people.

40.

x	$P(x)$	$xP(x)$	$(x - \mu)$	$(x - \mu)^2$	$(x - \mu)^2 P(x)$
0	0.29	0	−1.59	2.528	0.733
1	0.25	0.25	−0.59	0.348	0.087
2	0.17	0.34	0.41	0.168	0.029
3	0.16	0.48	1.41	1.988	0.318
4	0.13	0.52	2.41	5.808	0.755
		$\sum xP(x) = 1.59$			$\sum (x - \mu)^2 P(x) = 1.922$

(a) $\mu = \sum xP(x) = 1.59 \approx 1.6$ (b) $\sigma^2 = \sum (x - \mu)^2 P(x) = 1.922 \approx 1.9$

(c) $\sigma = \sqrt{\sigma^2} = \sqrt{1.922} \approx 1.4$ (d) $E(x) = \mu = 1.6$

(e) The expected value is 1.6, so an average household is expected to have either 1 or 2 cars. The standard deviation is 1.4, so most of the households differ from the expected value by no more than 1 or 2 cars.

41. (a) $P(x < 2) = 0.686 + 0.195 = 0.881$

(b) $P(x \geq 1) = 1 - P(x = 0) = 1 - 0.686 = 0.314$

(c) $P(1 \leq x \leq 3) = 0.195 + 0.077 + 0.022 = 0.294$

42. (a) $P(x = 4) = 0.190$

(b) $P(x \geq 5) = 1 - P(x = 4) = 1 - 0.190 = 0.810$

(c) $P(4 \leq x \leq 6) = 0.190 + 0.219 + 0.019 = 0.628$

43. A household with three dogs is unusual because the probability of this event is 0.022, which is less than or equal to 0.05.

44. A World Series in which eight games were played is unusual because the probability of this event is 0.029, which is less than 0.05.

45. $E(x) = \mu = \sum xP(x) = (-\$1) \cdot \left(\dfrac{37}{38}\right) + (\$35) \cdot \left(\dfrac{1}{38}\right) \approx -\$0.05$

46. $E(x) = \mu = \sum xP(x)$

$= (\$3445) \cdot \left(\dfrac{1}{6000}\right) + (\$745) \cdot \left(\dfrac{1}{6000}\right) + (\$20) \cdot \left(\dfrac{20}{6000}\right) + (-\$5) \cdot \left(\dfrac{5978}{6000}\right) \approx -\$4.22$

47. (a)

x	$P(x)$
0	0.432
1	0.403
2	0.137
3	0.029
	$\sum xP(x) = 1$

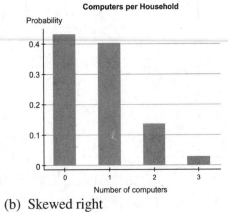

Computers per Household

(b) Skewed right

48. (a)

x	$P(x)$
1	0.128
2	0.124
3	0.124
4	0.122
5	0.123
6	0.125
7	0.127
8	0.128
	$\sum xP(x) = 1$

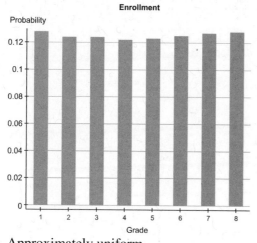

(b) Approximately uniform

49. $\mu_x = a + b\mu_x = 1000 + 1.05(36,000) = \$38,800$

50. $\sigma_y = |b|\sigma_x = (1.04)(3899) = \$4054.96$

51. $\mu_{x+y} = \mu_x + \mu_y = 1524 + 1496 = 3020$

$\mu_{x-y} = \mu_x - \mu_y = 1524 - 1496 = 28$

52. $\sigma_{x-y}^2 = \sigma_x^2 + \sigma_y^2 = (317)^2 + (307)^2 = 194,738 \Rightarrow \sigma_{x-y} = \sqrt{\sigma_{x-y}^2} = 441.29$

4.2 BINOMIAL DISTRIBUTIONS

4.2 Try It Yourself Solutions

1a. Trial answering a question
  Success: the question answered correctly
 b. Yes, the experiment satisfies the four conditions of a binomial experiment.
 c. It is a binomial experiment.
  $n = 10, p = 0.25, q = 0.75, x = 0, 1, 2, 3, 4, 5, 6, 7, 8, 9, 10$

2a. Trial: drawing a card with replacement
  Success: card drawn is a club
  Failure: card drawn is not a club
 b. $n = 5, p = 0.25, q = 0.75, x = 3$
 c. $P(3) = \dfrac{5!}{(5-3)!3!}(0.25)^3(0.75)^2 \approx 0.088$

3a. Trial: Selecting an adult and asking a question
  Success: selecting an adult who likes texting because it works where talking won't do
  Failure: selecting an adult who does not like texting because it works where talking won't do
 b. $n = 7, p = 0.75, q = 0.25, x = 0, 1, 2, 3, 4, 5, 6, 7$

c. $P(0) = {}_7C_0(0.75)^0(0.25)^7 \approx 0.00006$

$P(1) = {}_7C_1(0.75)^1(0.25)^6 \approx 0.00128$

$P(2) = {}_7C_2(0.75)^2(0.25)^5 \approx 0.01154$

$P(3) = {}_7C_3(0.75)^3(0.25)^4 \approx 0.05768$

$P(4) = {}_7C_4(0.75)^4(0.25)^3 \approx 0.17303$

$P(5) = {}_7C_5(0.75)^5(0.25)^2 \approx 0.31146$

$P(6) = {}_7C_6(0.75)^6(0.25)^1 \approx 0.31146$

$P(7) = {}_7C_7(0.75)^7(0.25)^0 \approx 0.13348$

d.

x	$P(x)$
0	0.00006
1	0.00128
2	0.01154
3	0.05768
4	0.17303
5	0.31146
6	0.31146
7	0.13348
	$\sum xP(x) = 1$

4a. $n = 250$, $p = 0.71$, $x = 178$

b. $P(178) \approx 0.056$

c. The probability that exactly 178 people from a random sample of 250 people in the United States will use more than one topping on their hot dog is about 0.056.

d. Because 0.056 is not less than or equal to 0.05, this event is not unusual.

5a. (1) $x = 2$ (2) $x = 2, 3, 4,$ or 5 (3) $x = 0$ or 1

b. (1) $P(2) = {}_5C_2(0.21)^2(0.79)^3 \approx 0.217$

(2) $P(1) = {}_5C_1(0.21)^1(0.79)^4 \approx 0.409$

$P(x \geq 2) = 1 - P(0) - P(1) \approx 1 - 0.308 - 0.409 = 0.283$

or

$P(x \geq 2) = P(2) + P(3) + P(4) + P(5)$

$\approx 0.217 + 0.058 + 0.008 + 0.0004$

≈ 0.283

(3) $P(x < 2) = P(0) + P(1) \approx 0.308 + 0.409 = 0.717$

c. (1) The probability that exactly two of the five men consider fishing their favorite leisure-time activity is about 0.217.

(2) The probability that at least two of the five men consider fishing their favorite leisure-time activity is about 0.283.

(3) The probability that fewer than two of the five men consider fishing their favorite leisure-time activity is about 0.717.

6a. Trial: Selecting a business and asking if it has a website
Success: Selecting a business with a website
Failure: Selecting a business without a website
  b. $n = 10$, $p = 0.55$, $x = 4$
  c. $P(4) \approx 0.160$
  d. The probability of randomly selecting 10 small businesses and finding exactly 4 that have a website is 0.160.
  e. Because 0.160 is not less than or equal to 0.05, this event is not unusual.

7a. $P(0) = {}_4C_0 (0.81)^0 (0.19)^4 \approx 0.001$

$P(1) = {}_4C_1 (0.81)^1 (0.19)^3 \approx 0.022$

$P(2) = {}_4C_2 (0.81)^2 (0.19)^2 \approx 0.142$

$P(3) = {}_4C_3 (0.81)^3 (0.91)^1 \approx 0.404$

$P(4) = {}_4C_4 (0.81)^4 (0.19)^0 \approx 0.430$

  b.

x	$P(x)$
0	0.001
1	0.022
2	0.142
3	0.404
4	0.430

  c.

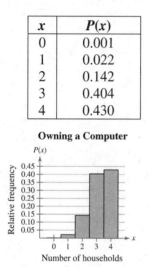

Owning a Computer

Skewed left
  d. Yes, it would be unusual if exactly zero or exactly one of the four households owned a computer, because each of these events has a probability that is less than 0.05.

8a. Success: selecting a clear day
$n = 31$, $p = 0.44$, $q = 0.56$
  b. $\mu = np = (31)(0.44) \approx 13.6$

  c. $\sigma^2 = npq = (31)(0.44)(0.56) \approx 7.6$

  d. $\sigma = \sqrt{npq} = \sqrt{(31)(0.44)(0.56)} \approx 2.8$

  e. On average, there are about 14 clear days during the month of May. The standard deviation is about 3 days.
  f. Values that are more than 2 standard deviations from the mean are considered unusual. Because $13.6 - 2(2.8) = 8$ and $13.6 + 2(2.8) = 19.2$, a May with fewer than 8 clear days, or more than 19 clear days would be unusual.

4.2 EXERCISE SOLUTIONS

1. Each trial is independent of the other trials if the outcome of one trial does not affect the outcome of any of the other trials.

2. The random variable measures the number of successes in n trials.

3. (a) $p = 0.50$ (graph is symmetric)
   (b) $p = 0.20$ (graph is skewed right $\rightarrow p < 0.5$)
   (c) $p = 0.80$ (graph is skewed left $\rightarrow p > 0.5$)

4. (a) $p = 0.75$ (graphs is skewed left $\rightarrow p > 0.5$)
   (b) $p = 0.50$ (graph is symmetric)
   (c) $p = 0.25$ (graph is skewed right $\rightarrow p < 0.5$)

5. (a) $n = 12$ ($x = 0, 1, 2, 3, 4, 5, 6, 7, 8, 9, 10, 11, 12$)
   (b) $n = 4$ ($x = 0, 1, 2, 3, 4$)
   (c) $n = 8$ ($x = 0, 1, 2, 3, 4, 5, 6, 7, 8$)
   As n increases, the distribution becomes more symmetric.

6. (a) $n = 10$ ($x = 0, 1, 2, 3, 4, 5, 6, 7, 8, 9, 10$)
   (b) $n = 15$ ($x = 0, 1, 2, 3, 4, 5, 6, 7, 8, 9, 10, 11, 12, 13, 14, 15$)
   (c) $n = 5$ ($x = 0, 1, 2, 3, 4, 5$)
   As n increases, the distribution becomes more symmetric.

7. (a) 0, 1, 2, 3, 4, 11, 12   (b) 0   (c) 0, 1, 2, 8

8. (a) 0, 1, 2, 3, 4   (b) 0, 1, 2, 3, 4, 5, 6, 7, 8, 15   (c) 0, 1

9. It is a binomial experiment.
   Success: baby recovers
   $n = 5, p = 0.80, q = 0.20, x = 0, 1, 2, 3, 4, 5$

10. It is a binomial experiment.
    Success: person does not make a purchase
    $n = 18, p = 0.74, q = 0.26, x = 0, 1, 2, 3, 4, 5, 6, 7, 8, 9, 10, 11, 12, 13, 14, 15, 16, 17, 18$

11. It is a binomial experiment.
    Success: Selecting an officer who is postponing or reducing the amount of vacation
    $n = 20, p = 0.31, q = 0.69, x = 0, 1, 2, 3, 4, 5, 6, 7, 8, 9, 10, 11, 12, 13, 14, 15, 16, 17, 18, 19, 20$

12. Not a binomial experiment because the probability of a success is not the same for each trial.

13. $\mu = np = (50)(0.4) = 20$

    $\sigma^2 = npq = (50)(0.4)(0.6) = 12$

    $\sigma = \sqrt{npq} = \sqrt{(50)(0.4)(0.6)} \approx 3.5$

14. $\mu = np = (84)(0.65) = 54.6$

    $\sigma^2 = npq = (84)(0.65)(0.35) = 19.1$

    $\sigma = \sqrt{npq} = \sqrt{(84)(0.65)(0.35)} \approx 4.4$

15. $\mu = np = (124)(0.26) = 32.2$

$\sigma^2 = npq = (124)(0.26)(0.74) = 23.9$

$\sigma = \sqrt{npq} = \sqrt{(124)(0.26)(0.74)} \approx 4.9$

16. $\mu = np = (316)(0.82) = 259.1$

$\sigma^2 = npq = (316)(0.82)(0.18) = 46.6$

$\sigma = \sqrt{npq} = \sqrt{(316)(0.82)(0.18)} \approx 6.8$

17. $n = 5, p = 0.25$
   (a) $P(3) \approx 0.088$
   (b) $P(x \geq 3) = P(3) + P(4) + P(5) \approx 0.088 + 0.015 + 0.001 = 0.104$
   (c) $P(x < 3) = 1 - P(x \geq 3) \approx 1 - 0.104 = 0.896$

18. $n = 7, p = 0.7$
   (a) $P(5) \approx 0.318$
   (b) $P(x \geq 5) = P(5) + P(6) + P(7) \approx 0.318 + 0.247 + 0.082 = 0.647$
   (c) $P(x < 5) = 1 - P(x \geq 5) \approx 1 - 0.647 = 0.353$

19. $n = 10, p = 0.59$
   (a) $P(8) \approx 0.111$
   (b) $P(x \geq 8) = P(8) + P(9) + P(10) \approx 0.111 + 0.036 + 0.005 = 0.152$
   (c) $P(x < 8) = 1 - P(x \geq 8) \approx 1 - 0.152 = 0.848$

20. $n = 12, p = 0.1$
   (a) $P(4) \approx 0.021$
   (b) $P(x \geq 4) = 1 - P(x < 4) = 1 - P(0) - P(1) - P(2) - P(3)$
       $\approx 1 - 0.282 - 0.377 - 0.230 - 0.085 = 0.026$
   (c) $P(x < 4) = 1 - P(x \geq 4) \approx 1 - 0.026 = 0.974$

21. $n = 8, p = 0.55$
   (a) $P(5) \approx 0.257$
   (b) $P(x > 5) = P(6) + P(7) + P(8) \approx 0.157 + 0.055 + 0.008 = 0.220$
   (c) $P(x \leq 5) = 1 - P(x > 5) \approx 1 - 0.220 = 0.780$

22. $n = 20, p = 0.7$
   (a) $P(1) \approx 1.627 \times 10^{-9}$
   (b) $P(x > 1) = 1 - P(x \leq 1) = 1 - P(0) - P(1)$
       $\approx 1 - 3.487 \times 10^{-11} - 1.627 \times 10^{-9} \approx 0.9999999983$
   (c) $P(x \leq 1) = P(0) + P(1) \approx 3.487 \times 10^{-11} + 1.627 \times 10^{-9} \approx 1.662 \times 10^{-9}$

23. $n = 14, p = 0.43$
   (a) $P(5) \approx 0.187$
   (b) $P(x \geq 6) = 1 - P(x \leq 5)$
       $= 1 - (P(0) + P(1) + P(2) + P(3) + P(4) + P(5))$
       $\approx 1 - (0.0004 + 0.004 + 0.020 + 0.060) + 0.124 + 0.187)$
       ≈ 0.605
   (c) $P(x \leq 3) = P(0) + P(1) + P(2) + P(3) \approx 0.0004 + 0.004 \ 0.020 + 0.060 \approx 0.084$

24. $n = 10, p = 0.14$

    (a) $P(2) \approx 0.264$

    (b) $P(x > 6) = P(7) + P(8) + P(9) + P(10)$

$$\approx 8.046 \times 10^{-5} + 4.912 \times 10^{-6} + 1.777 \times 10^{-7} + 2.893 \times 10^{-9}$$

$$\approx 8.555 \times 10^{-5}$$

    (c) $P(x \leq 5) = P(0) + P(1) + P(2) + P(3) + P(4) + P(5)$

$$\approx 0.221 + 0.360 + 0.264 + 0.115 + 0.033 + 0.006$$

$$= 0.999$$

25. $n = 10, p = 0.28$

    (a) $P(2) \approx 0.255$

    (b) $P(x > 2) = 1 - P(x \leq 2) = 1 - (P(0) + P(1) + P(2))$

$$\approx 1 - (0.037 + 0.146 + 0.255)$$

$$\approx 0.562$$

    (c) $P(x \leq 2 \leq 5) = P(2) + P(3) + P(4) + P(5)$

$$\approx 0.255 + 0.264 + 0.180 + 0.084$$

$$= 0.783$$

26. $n = 12, p = 0.25$

    (a) $P(4) \approx 0.194$

    (b) $P(x > 4) = 1 - P(x \leq 4)$

$$= 1 - (P(0) + P(1) + P(2) + P(3) + P(4))$$

$$\approx 1 - (0.032 + 0.127 + 0.232 + 0.258 + 0.194)$$

$$\approx 0.157$$

    (c) $P(4 \leq x \leq 8) = P(4) + P(5) + P(6) + P(7) + P(8)$

$$\approx 0.194 + 0.103 + 0.040 + 0.011 + 0.002$$

$$= 0.350$$

27. (a) $n = 6, p = 0.63$

x	$P(x)$
0	0.003
1	0.026
2	0.112
3	0.253
4	0.323
5	0.220
6	0.063

(b)

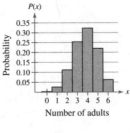

Visiting the Dentist

Skewed left

    (c) $\mu = np = (6)(0.63) \approx 3.8$

$$\sigma^2 = npq = (6)(0.63)(0.37) \approx 1.4$$

$$\sigma = \sqrt{npq} = \sqrt{(6)(0.63)(0.37)} \approx 1.2$$

    (d) On average, 3.8 out of 6 adults are visiting the dentist less because of the economy. The standard deviation is 1.2, so most samples of 6 adults would differ from the mean by no more than 1.2 people The values $x = 0$ and $x = 1$ would be unusual because their probabilities are less an 0.05.

28. (a) $n = 5, p = 0.25$

x	$P(x)$
0	0.237
1	0.396
2	0.264
3	0.088
4	0.015
5	0.001

(b)

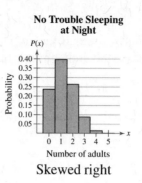

No Trouble Sleeping at Night

Skewed right

(c) $\mu = np = (5)(0.25) \approx 1.3$

$\sigma^2 = npq = (5)(0.25)(0.75) \approx 0.9$

$\sigma = \sqrt{npq} = \sqrt{(5)(0.25)(0.75)} \approx 1.0$

(d) On average, 1.3 adults out of 5 have no trouble sleeping at night. The standard deviation is 1.0 adults, so most samples of 5 adults would differ from the mean by no more than 1 person. The values $x = 4$ and $x = 5$ would be unusual because their probabilities are less than 0.05.

29. (a) $n = 4, p = 0.05$

x	$P(x)$
0	0.814506
1	0.171475
2	0.013538
3	0.000475
4	0.000006

(b)

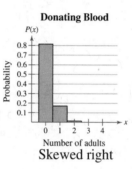

Donating Blood

Skewed right

(c) $\mu = np = (4)(0.05) \approx 0.2$

$\sigma^2 = npq = (4)(0.05)(0.95) \approx 0.2$

$\sigma = \sqrt{npq} = \sqrt{(4)(0.05)(0.95)} \approx 0.4$

(d) On average, 0.2 eligible adults out of every 4 gives blood. The standard deviation is 0.4, so most sample of 4 eligible adults would differ from the mean by at most 0.4 adult. The values $x = 2, x = 3,$ or $x = 4$ would be unusual because their probabilities are less than 0.05.

30. (a) $n = 5, p = 0.39$

x	$P(x)$
0	0.084
1	0.270
2	0.345
3	0.221
4	0.071
5	0.009

(b)

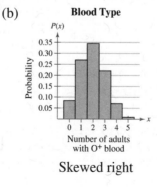

Blood Type

Skewed right

(c) $\mu = np = (5)(0.39) \approx 2.0$

$\sigma^2 = npq = (5)(0.39)(0.61) \approx 1.2$

$\sigma = \sqrt{npq} = \sqrt{(5)(0.35)(0.61)} \approx 1.1$

(d) On average, 2.0 adults out of 5 have O+ blood. The standard deviation is 1.1, so most samples of 5 adults would differ from the mean by at most 1.1 adults. The value $x = 5$ would be unusual because the probability is less than 0.05.

31. (a) $n = 6, p = 0.37$

x	$P(x)$
0	0.063
1	0.220
2	0.323
3	0.253
4	0.112
5	0.026
6	0.003

(b) $P(x = 2) \approx 0.323$

(c) $P(x \geq 5) = P(x = 5) + P(x = 6) \approx 0.026 + 0.003 = 0.029$

32. (a) $n = 5, p = 0.48$

x	$P(x)$
0	0.038
1	0.175
2	0.324
3	0.299
4	0.138
5	0.025

(b) $P(x = 2) \approx 0.324$

(c) $P(x < 4) = 1 - P(x \geq 4) = 1 - P(x = 4) - P(x = 5)$
$$\approx 1 - 0.138 - 0.025$$
$$= 0.837$$

33. $n = 6, p = 0.37, q = 0.63$

$\mu = np = (6)(0.37) \approx 2.2$

$\sigma = \sqrt{npq} = \sqrt{(6)(0.37)(0.63)} \approx 1.2$

On average, 2.2 out of 6 travelers would name "crying kids" as the most annoying. The standard deviation is 1.2, so most samples of 6 travelers would differ from the mean by at most 1.2 travelers. The values $x = 5$ and $x = 6$ would be unusual because their probabilities are less than 0.05.

34. $n = 5, p = 0.48, q = 0.52$

$\mu = np = (5)(0.48) \approx 2.4$

$\sigma = \sqrt{npq} = \sqrt{(5)(0.48)(0.52)} \approx 1.1$

On average, 2.4 out of 5 owners would name financial management as the skill they want to develop further. The standard deviation is 1.1, so most samples of 5 owners would differ from the mean by at most 1.1 owners. The values $x = 0$ and $x = 5$ would be unusual because their probabilities are less than 0.05.

35. (a) $P(x = 9) \approx 0.081$

(b) $P(x \geq 7) \approx 0.541$

(c) $P(x \leq 3) \approx 0.022$; This event is unusual because its probability is less than 0.05.

36. (a) $P(x = 4) \approx 0.270$

(b) $P(x \geq 5) \approx 0.431$

(c) $P(x < 2) \approx 0.024$; This event is unusual because its probability is less than 0.05.

37. $P(5, 2, 2, 1) = \dfrac{10!}{5!2!2!1!}\left(\dfrac{9}{16}\right)^5 \left(\dfrac{3}{16}\right)^2 \left(\dfrac{3}{16}\right)^2 \left(\dfrac{1}{16}\right)^1 = 0.033$

38. $P(5, 2, 2, 1) = \dfrac{10!}{5!2!2!1!}\left(\dfrac{5}{16}\right)^5 \left(\dfrac{4}{16}\right)^2 \left(\dfrac{1}{16}\right)^2 \left(\dfrac{6}{16}\right)^1 = 0.002$

4.3 MORE DISCRETE PROBABILITY DISTRIBUTIONS

4.3 Try It Yourself Solutions

1a. $P(1) = (0.74)(0.26)^0 \approx 0.74$

$P(2) = (0.74)(0.26)^0 \approx 0.192$

b. $P(\text{shot made before third attempt}) = P(1) + P(2) \approx 0.932$

c. The probability that LeBron makes his first free throw shot before his third attempt is 0.932.

2a. $P(0) \approx \dfrac{3^0 (2.71828)^{-3}}{0!} \approx 0.050$ $\qquad P(1) \approx \dfrac{3^1 (2.71828)^{-3}}{1!} \approx 0.149$

$P(2) \approx \dfrac{3^2 (2.71828)^{-3}}{2!} \approx 0.224$ $\qquad P(3) \approx \dfrac{3^3 (2.71828)^{-3}}{3!} \approx 0.224$

$P(4) \approx \dfrac{3^4 (2.71828)^{-3}}{4!} \approx 0.168$

b. $P(0) + P(1) + P(2) + P(3) + P(4) \approx 0.050 + 0.149 + 0.224 + 0.224 + 0.168 = 0.815$

c. $1 - 0.815 = 0185$

d. The probability that more than four accidents will occur in any given month at the intersection is 0.185.

3a. $\mu = \dfrac{2000}{20,000} = 0.10$

b. $\mu = 0.10, x = 3$

c. $P(3) = 0.0002$

d. The probability of finding three brown trout in any given cubic meter of the lake is 0.0002.

e. Because 0.0002 is less than 0.05, this can be considered an unusual event.

4.3 EXERCISE SOLUTIONS

1. $P(3) = (0.65)(0.35)^2 = 0.08$

2. $P(1) = (0.45)(0.55)^0 = 0.45$

3. $P(5) = (0.09)(0.91)^4 = 0.062$

4. $P(8) = (0.28)(0.72)^7 = 0.028$

5. $P(4) \approx \dfrac{(5)^4 (2.71828)^{-5}}{4!} = 0.175$

6. $P(3) \approx \dfrac{(6)^3 (2.71828)^{-6}}{3!} = 0.089$

7. $P(2) \approx \dfrac{(1.5)^2 (2.71828)^{-1.5}}{2!} = 0.251$

8. $P(5) \approx \dfrac{(9.8)^5 (2.71828)^{-9.8}}{5!} = 0.042$

9.   In a binomial distribution, the value of x represents the number of success in n trials, and in a geometric distribution the value of x represents the first trial that results in a success.

10. In a binomial distribution, the value of x represents the number of successes in n trials, and in a Poisson distribution the value of x represents the number of occurrences in an interval.

11. Geometric, You are interested in counting the number of trials until the first success.

12. Poisson. You are interested in counting the number of occurrences that takes place within a given unit of time.

13. Binomial. You are interested in counting the number of successes out of n trials.

14. Geometric. You are interested in counting the number of trials until the first success.

15. $p = 0.19$
   (a) $P(5) = (0.19)(0.81)^4 \approx 0.082$
   (b) P(sale on 1st, 2nd, or 3rd call) $= P(1) + P(2) + P(3)$
   $$= (0.19)(0.81)^0 + (0.19)(0.81)^1 + (0.19)(0.81)^2 \approx 0.469$$
   (c) P(no sale of first 3 calls) $= 1 - P$(sale on 1st, 2nd, or 3rd call) $\approx 1 - 0.469 = 0.531$

16. $\mu = 2$
   (a) $P(5) \approx \dfrac{(2)^5 (2.71828)^{-2}}{5!} \approx 0.036$
   This event is unusual because its probability is less than 0.05.
   (b) $P(x \geq 5) = 1 - (P(0) + P(1) + P(2) + P(3) + P(4))$
   $$\approx 1 - (0.135 + 0.271 + 0.271 + 0.180 + 0.090)$$
   $$= 0.053$$

(c) $P(x > 5) = 1 - (P(0) + P(1) + P(2) + P(3) + P(4) + P(5))$
$\approx 1 - (0.135 + 0.271 + 0.271 + 0.180 + 0.090 + 0.036)$
$= 0.017$

This event is unusual because its probability is less than 0.05.

17. $\mu = 4$

(a) $P(3) = \dfrac{(4)^3 (2.71828)^{-4}}{3!} = 0.195$

(b) $P(x \geq 3) = 1 - P(0) + P(1) + P(2) + P(3)$
$\approx 0.018 + 0.073 + 0.147 + 0.195$
$= 0.433$

(c) $P(x > 3) = 1 - (P(x \leq 3) \approx 1 - 0.433 = 0.567$

18. $p = 0.648$

(a) $P(2) = (0.648)(0.352)^1 \approx 0.228$

(b) $P(\text{completes 1st or 2nd pass}) = P(1) + P(2) = (0.648)(0.352)^0 + (0.648)(0.352)^1 \approx 0.876$

(c) $P(\text{does not complete first 2 passes}) = 1 - P(\text{completes 1st or 2nd pass})$
$\approx 1 - 0.876$
$= 0.124$

$P(0) = \dfrac{2!}{0!2!}(0.648)^0(0.352)^2 = 0.124$

19. $\mu = 0.6$

(a) $P(1) \approx \dfrac{(0.6)^1 (2.71828)^{-0.6}}{1!} = 0.329$

(b) $P(x \leq 1) = P(0) + P(1) \approx 0.549 + 0.329 = 0.878$

(c) $P(x > 1) = 1 - (P(x \leq 1) \approx 1 - 0.878 = 0.122$

20. $p = \dfrac{1}{500} = 0.002$

(a) $P(10) = (0.002)(0.998)^9 = 0.002$

This event is unusual because its probability is less than 0.05.

(b) $P(\text{1st, 2nd, or 3rd part is defective})$
$= P(1) + P(2) + P(3) = (0.002)(0.998)^0 + (0.002)(0.998)^1 + (0.002)(0.998)^2 = 0.006$

This event is unusual because its probability is less than 0.05.

(c) $P(x > 10) = 1 - P(x \leq 10) = 1 - \left[P(1) + P(2) + \cdots + P(10)\right] = 1 - 0.020 = 0.980$

21. $p = \dfrac{1}{4} = 0.25$

(a) $P(4) = (0.25)(0.75)^3 \approx 0.105$

(b) $P(\text{prize with 1st, 2nd, or 3rd purchase})$
$= P(1) + P(2) + P(3) = (0.25)(0.75)^0 + (0.25)(0.75)^1 + (0.25)(0.75)^2 = 0.578$

(c) $P(x > 4) = 1 - P(x \le 4) = 1 - \left[P(1) + P(2) + P(3) + P(4)\right] = 1 - 0.684 = 0.316$

22. $\mu = 9.5$

  (a) $P(10) \approx \dfrac{(9.5)^{10}(2.71828)^{-9.5}}{10!} = 0.124$

  (b) $P(x \le 10) \approx 0.645$

  (c) $P(x > 10) = 1 - P(x \le 10) \approx 1 - 0.645 = 0.355$

23. $\mu = 8$

  (a) $P(8) \approx 0.140$

  (b) $P(x \le 3) \approx 0.042$
    This event is unusual because its probability is less than 0.005.

  (c) $P(x > 12) \approx 0.064$

24. $\mu = 45$

  (a) $P(50) = 0.043$
    This event is unusual because its probability is less than 0.05.

  (b) $P(x \ge 65) \approx 0.003$
    This event is unusual because its probability is less than 0.05.

  (c) $P(x \le 40) \approx 0.256$

25. (a) $n = 6000, p = \dfrac{1}{2500} = 0.0004$

   $P(4) = \dfrac{6000!}{5996!\,4!}(0.0004)^4(0.9996)^{5996} \approx 0.1254235482$

  (b) $\mu = \dfrac{6000}{2500} = 2.4$ cars with defects per 6000.

   $P(4) \approx 0.1254084986$
   The results are approximately the same.

26. (a) $P(0) = \dfrac{\left(_2C_0\right)\left(_{13}C_3\right)}{_{15}C_3} = \dfrac{(1)(286)}{455} = 0.629$

  (b) $P(1) = \dfrac{\left(_2C_1\right)\left(_{13}C_2\right)}{_{15}C_3} = \dfrac{(2)(78)}{455} = 0.343$

  (c) $P(2) = \dfrac{\left(_2C_2\right)\left(_{13}C_1\right)}{_{15}C_3} = \dfrac{(1)(13)}{455} = 0.029$

27. $p = \dfrac{1}{1000} = 0.001$

(a) $\mu = \dfrac{1}{p} = \dfrac{1}{0.001} = 1000$

$\sigma^2 = \dfrac{q}{p^2} = \dfrac{0.999}{(0.001)^2} = 999,000$

$\sigma = \sqrt{\sigma^2} \approx 999.5$

On average, you would have to play 1000 times in order to win the lottery. The standard deviation is 999.5 times.

(b) 1000 times, because it is the mean.

You would expect to lose money, because, on average, you would win $500 every 1000 times you play the lottery and pay $1000 to play it. So, the net gain would be −$500.

28. $p = 0.005$

(a) $\mu = \dfrac{1}{p} = \dfrac{1}{0.005} = 200$

$\sigma^2 = \dfrac{q}{p^2} = \dfrac{0.995}{(0.005)^2} = 39,800$

$\sigma = \sqrt{\sigma^2} \approx 199.5$

On average 200 records will be examined before finding one that has been miscalculated. The standard deviation is 199.5 records.

(b) 200, because it is the mean.

29. $\mu = 3.9$

(a) $\sigma^2 = \mu = 3.9$

$\sigma = \sqrt{\sigma^2} \approx 2.0$

The standard deviation is 2.0 strokes, so most of Phil's scores per hole differ from the mean by no more than 2.0 strokes.

(b) For 18 holes, Phil's average would be $(18)(3.9) = 70.2$ strokes.
So, $\mu = 70.2$.

$P(x > 72) = 1 - P(x \le 72) \approx 1 - 0.615 = 0.385$

30. $\mu = 29.9$

(a) $\sigma^2 = \mu = 29.9$

$\sigma = \sqrt{\sigma^2} \approx 5.5$

The standard deviation to 5.5 inches, so most of the January snowfalls in Mount Shasta differ from the mean by no more than 5.5 inches.

(b) 3 feet = 36 inches

$P(x > 36) = 1 - P(x \le 36) \approx 1 - 0.884 = 0.116$

CHAPTER 4 REVIEW EXERCISE SOLUTIONS

1. Continuous, because the length of time spent sleeping is a random variable that cannot be counted.

2. Discrete, because the number of fish caught is a random variable that is countable.

3. Discrete.

4. Continuous

5. Continuous

6. Discrete

7. No, $\sum P(x) \neq 1$.

8. Yes.

9. Yes

10. No, $P(5) > 1$ and $\sum P(x) \neq 1$.

11. (a)

x	f	$P(x)$
2	3	0.005
3	12	0.018
4	72	0.111
5	115	0.177
6	169	0.260
7	120	0.185
8	83	0.128
9	48	0.074
10	22	0.034
11	6	0.009
	$n = 650$	$\sum P(x) \approx 1$

(b)

Pages per Section

Approximately symmetric

(c)

$xP(x)$	$(x - \mu)$	$(x - \mu)^2$	$(x - \mu)^2 P(x)$
0.010	−4.377	19.158	0.096
0.054	−3.377	11.404	0.205
0.444	−2.377	5.650	0.627
0.885	−1.377	1.896	0.336
1.560	−0.377	0.142	0.037
1.295	0.623	0.388	0.072
1.024	1.623	2.634	0.337
0.666	2.623	6.880	0.509
0.340	3.623	13.126	0.446
0.099	4.623	21.372	0.192
$\sum xP(x) = 6.377$			$\sum (x - \mu)^2 P(x) = 2.857$

$$\mu = \sum xP(x) = 6.377 \approx 6.4$$

$$\sigma^2 = \sum (x - \mu)^2 P(x) = 2.857 \approx 2.9$$

$$\sigma = \sqrt{\sigma^2} = \sqrt{2.857} \approx 1.7$$

(d) The mean is 6.4, so the average number of pages per section is about 6 pages. The standard deviation is 1.7, so most of the sections differ from the mean by no more than about 2 pages.

12. (a)

x	f	$P(x)$
0	29	0.207
1	62	0.443
2	33	0.236
3	12	0.086
4	3	0.021
5	1	0.007
	$n = 140$	$\sum P(x) = 1$

(b)

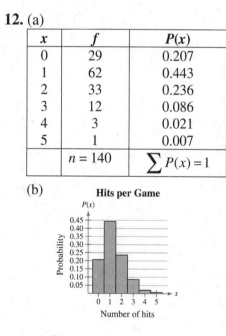

Skewed right

(c)

$xP(x)$	$(x - \mu)$	$(x - \mu)^2$	$(x - \mu)^2 P(x)$
0	−1.292	1.669	0.345
0.443	−0.292	0.085	0.038
0.472	0.708	0.501	0.118
0.258	1.708	2.917	0.251
0.084	2.708	7.333	0.154
0.035	3.708	13.749	0.096
$\sum xP(x) = 1.292$			$\sum (x - \mu)^2 P(x) = 1.002$

$$\mu = \sum xP(x) = 1.292 \approx 1.3$$
$$\sigma^2 = \sum (x - \mu)^2 P(x) = 1.002 \approx 1.0$$
$$\sigma = \sqrt{\sigma^2} = \sqrt{1.002} \approx 1.0$$

(d) The mean is 1.3, so the average number of hits per game is about 1 hit. The standard deviation is 1.0, so most of the games differ from the mean by no more than 1 hit.

13. (a)

x	f	$P(x)$
0	5	0.020
1	35	0.140
2	68	0.272
3	73	0.292
4	42	0.168
5	19	0.076
6	8	0.032
	$n = 250$	$\sum P(x) = 1$

(b)

Cellular Phones per Household

Approximately symmetric

(c)

$xP(x)$	$(x - \mu)$	$(x - \mu)^2$	$(x - \mu)^2 P(x)$
0	−2.804	7.862	0.157
0.140	−1.804	3.254	0.456
0.544	−0.804	0.646	0.176
0.876	0.196	0.038	0.011
0.672	1.196	1.430	0.240
0.380	2.196	4.822	0.366
0.192	3.196	10.214	0.327
$\sum xP(x) = 2.804$			$\sum (x - \mu)^2 P(x) = 1.733$

$$\mu = \sum xP(x) = 2.804 \approx 2.8$$

$$\sigma^2 = \sum (x - \mu)^2 P(x) = 1.733 \approx 1.7$$

$$\sigma = \sqrt{\sigma^2} = \sqrt{1.733} \approx 1.3$$

(d) The mean is 2.8, so the average number of cellular phones per household is about 3. The standard deviation is 1.3, so most of the households differ from the mean by no more than about 1 cellular phone.

14. (a)

x	f	$P(x)$
15	76	0.1342
30	445	0.7862
60	30	0.0530
90	3	0.0053
120	12	0.0212
	$n = 566$	$\sum P(x) = 1$

(b)

Advertising Sales

Skewed right

(c)

$xP(x)$	$(x - \mu)$	$(x - \mu)^2$	$(x - \mu)^2 P(x)$
2.0145	−16.8015	282.2904	37.9116
23.5860	−1.8015	3.2454	2.5515
3.1800	28.1985	795.1554	42.1432
0.4770	58.1985	3387.0654	17.9514
2.5440	88.1985	7778.9754	164.9143
$\sum xP(x) = 31.8015$			$\sum (x - \mu)^2 P(x) = 265.4720$

$$\mu = \sum xP(x) = 31.8015 \approx 31.8$$

$$\sigma^2 = \sum (x - \mu)^2 P(x) = 265.4720 \approx 265.5$$

$$\sigma = \sqrt{\sigma^2} = \sqrt{265.4720} \approx 16.3$$

(d) The mean is 31.8, so the average length of an advertising block is 31.8 seconds. The standard deviation is 16.3, so most of the commercials differ from the mean by no more than 16.3 seconds.

15. $E(x) = \mu = \sum xP(x) \approx 3.4$

16. $E(x) = \mu = \sum xP(x) \approx 2.5$

17. No; In a binomial experiment, there are only two possible outcomes: success or failure.

18. Yes; The experiment has 20 independent trials, there are two possible outcomes (C and not C), the probability of success is the same for each trial, and the random variable x represents the number of outcomes of C.
The possibility of success for each trial is 0.20.

19. It is a binomial experiment.
$n = 12$, $p = 0.24$, $q = 0.76$, $x = 0, 1, 2, 3, 4, 5, 6, 7, 8, 9, 10, 11, 12$

20. Not a binomial experiment because the experiment is not repeated for a fixed number of trials.

21. $n = 8$, $p = 0.25$
(a) $P(3) \approx 0.208$
(b) $P(x \geq 3) = 1 - P(x < 3) = 1 - \left[P(0) + P(1) + P(2) \right] = 1 - [0.100 + 0.267 + 0.311] = 0.322$
(c) $P(x > 3) = 1 - P(x \leq 3) =$
$1 - \left[P(0) + P(1) + P(2) + P(3) \right] = 1 - [0.100 + 0.267 + 0.311 + 0.208] = 0.114$

22. $n = 12$, $p = 0.25$
(a) $P(2) \approx 0.232$
(b) $P(x \geq 2) = 1 - \left[P(0) + P(1) \right] = 1 - [0.032 + 0.127] = 0.841$
(c) $P(x > 2) = 1 - P(x \leq 2) = 1 - \left[P(0) + P(1) + P(2) \right]$
$$\approx 1 - [0.032 + 0.127 + 0.232] = 0.609$$

23. $n = 9, p = 0.43$

(a) $P(5) \approx 0.196$

(b) $P(x \geq 5)$ $= P(5) + P(6) + P(7) + P(8) + P(9)$

$\approx 0.196 + 0.098 + 0.032 + 0.006 + 0.001$

$= 0.333$

(c) $P(x > 5)$ $= P(6) + P(7) + P(8) + P(9)$

$\approx 0.098 + 0.032 + 0.006 + 0.001$

$= 0.137$

24. $n = 5, p = 0.31$

(a) $P(2) \approx 0.316$

(b) $P(x \geq 2) = P(2) + P(3) + P(4) + P(5) \approx 0.316 + 0.142 + 0.032 + 0.003 = 0.493$

(c) $P(x > 2) = P(3) + P(4) + P(5) \approx 0.142 + 0.032 + 0.003 = 0.177$

25. (a) $n = 5, p = 0.34$

x	$P(x)$
0	0.125
1	0.323
2	0.332
3	0.171
4	0.044
5	0.005

(b)

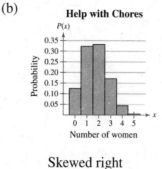

Help with Chores

Skewed right

(c) $\mu = np = (5)(0.34) = 1.7$

$\sigma^2 = npq = (5)(0.34)(0.66) \approx 1.1$

$\sigma = \sqrt{npq} = \sqrt{(5)(0.34)(0.66)} \approx 1.1$

The mean is 1.7 , so an average of 1.7 out of 5 women have spouses who never help with household chores. The standard deviation is 1.1, so most samples of 5 women differ from the mean by no more than 1.1 women.

(d) The values $x = 4$ and $x = 5$ are unusual because their probabilities are less than 0.05.

26. (a) $n = 6, p = 0.68$

x	$P(x)$
0	0.001
1	0.014
2	0.073
3	0.206
4	0.328
5	0.279
6	0.099

(b)

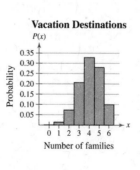

Vacation Destinations

Skewed left

(c) $\mu = np = (6)(0.68) \approx 4.1$

$\sigma^2 = npq = (5)(0.68)(0.32) \approx 1.3$

$\sigma = \sqrt{npq} = \sqrt{(6)(0.68)(0.32)} \approx 1.1$

The mean is 4.1, so an average of 4.1 out of 6 families say that their children have an influence on their vacation destinations. The standard deviation is 1.1, so most samples of 6 families differ from the mean by no more than 1.1 families.

(d) The values $x = 0$ and $x = 1$ are unusual because their probabilities are less than 0.05.

27. (a) $n = 4, p = 0.4$

x	P(x)
0	0.130
1	0.346
2	0.346
3	0.154
4	0.025

(b)

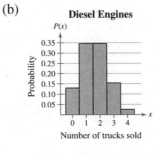

Diesel Engines

Skewed right

(c) $\mu = np = (4)(0.4) = 1.6$

$\sigma^2 = npq = (4)(0.4)(0.6) \approx 1.0$

$\sigma = \sqrt{npq} = \sqrt{(4)(0.4)(0.6)} \approx 1.0$

The mean is 1.6, so an average of 1.6 out of 4 tracks have diesel engines. The standard deviation is 1.0, so most samples of 4 trucks differ from the mean by no more than 1 truck.

(d) The value $x = 4$ is unusual because its probability is less than 0.05.

28. (a) $n = 5, p = 0.63$

x	P(x)
0	0.007
1	0.059
2	0.201
3	0.342
4	0.291
5	0.099

(b)

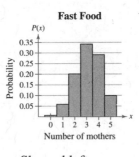

Fast Food

Skewed left

(c) $\mu = np = (5)(0.63) = 3.2$

$\sigma^2 = npq = (5)(0.63)(0.37) = 1.2$

$\sigma = \sqrt{npq} = \sqrt{(5)(0.63)(0.37)} = 1.1$

The mean is 3.2, so an average of 3.2 out of 5 mothers choose fast food one to three times a week. The standard deviation is 1.1, so most samples of 5 mothers differ from the mean by no more than 1.1 mothers.

(d) The value $x = 0$ is unusual because its probability is less than 0.05.

29. $p = 0.22$

   (a) $P(3) = (0.22)(0.78)^2 \approx 0.134$

   (b) $P(4 \text{ or } 5) = P(4) + P(5) = (0.22)(0.78)^2 + (0.22)(0.78)^4 \approx 0.186$

   (c) $P(x > 7) = 1 - P(x \le 7)$
$$= 1 - \big[P(1) + P(2) + P(3) + P(4) + P(5) + P(6) + P(7)\big]$$
$$= 1 - [0.220 + 0.172 + 0.134 + 0.104 + 0.081 + 0.064 + 0.050]$$
$$= 0.175$$

30. $p = \dfrac{33}{77} = 0.429$

   (a) $P(1) = (0.429)(0.571)^0 \approx 0.429$

   (b) $P(2) = (0.429)(0.571)^1 \approx 0.245$

   (c) $P(1 \text{ or } 2) = P(1) + P(2) \approx 0.429 + 0.245 = 0.674$

   (d) $P(\text{within first 3 games}) = P(1)\,P(2) + P(3) \approx 0.429 + 0.245 + 0.140 = 0.814$

31. $\mu = \dfrac{6755}{69} \approx 97.9$ tornado deaths/year $\rightarrow \mu = \dfrac{97.9}{365} \approx 0.268$ deaths/day

   (a) $P(0) \approx \dfrac{(0.268)^0 (2.71828)^{-0.268}}{0!} \approx 0.765$

   (b) $P(1) \approx \dfrac{(0.268)^1 (2.71828)^{-0.268}}{1!} \approx 0.205$

   (c) $P(x \le 2) = P(0) + P(1) + P(2)$
$$\approx 0.765 + 0.205 + 0.027$$
$$= 0.997$$

   (d) $P(x > 1) = 1 - P(x \le 1) = 1 - \big[P(0) + P(1)\big] = 1 - [0.765 + 0.205] = 0.030$

   This event is unusual because its probability is less than 0.05.

32. (a) $\mu = 10$
$$P(x \ge 3) = 1 - P(x < 3)$$
$$= 1 - [P(0) + P(1) + P(2) \approx 1 - [0.000 + 0.0005 + 0.0023] \approx 0.997$$

   (b) $\mu = 5$
$$P(x \ge 3) = 1 - P(x < 3)$$
$$= 1 - [P(0) + P(1) + P(2) \approx 1 - [0.00 + 0.034 + 0.084] \approx 0.875$$

   (c) $\mu = 15$
$$P(x \ge 3) = 1 - P(x < 3)$$
$$= 1 - [P(0) + P(1) + P(2) \approx 1 - [0.0000 + 0.0000 + 0.0000] \approx 1$$

33. The probability increases as the rate increases, and decreases as the rate decreases.

CHAPTER 4 QUIZ SOLUTIONS

1. (a) Discrete because the number of lightning strikes that occur in Wyoming during the month of June is a random variable that is countable.
   (b) Continuous because the fuel (in gallons) used by the Space Shuttle during takeoff is a random variable that has an infinite number of possible outcomes and cannot be counted.

2. (a)

x	f	$P(x)$
1	114	0.400
2	74	0.260
3	76	0.267
4	18	0.063
5	3	0.011
	$n = 285$	$\sum P(x) \approx 1$

(b)

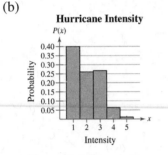

Hurricane Intensity

Skewed right

(c)

$xP(x)$	$(x - \mu)$	$(x - \mu)^2$	$(x - \mu)^2 P(x)$
0.400	−1.028	1.057	0.423
0.520	−0.028	0.001	0.000
0.801	0.972	0.945	0.252
0.252	1.972	3.889	0.245
0.055	2.972	8.833	0.097
$\sum xP(x) = 2.028$			$\sum (x - \mu)^2 P(x) = 1.017$

$\mu = \sum xP(x) = 2.028 \approx 2.0$

$\sigma^2 = \sum \le (x - \mu)^2 P(x) = 1.017 = 1.0$

$\sigma = \sqrt{\sigma^2} = \sqrt{1.017} = 1.0$

On average, the intensity of a hurricane will be 2.0. The standard deviation is 1.0, so most hurricane intensities will differ from the mean by no more than 1.0.

(d) $P(x \ge 4) = P(4) + P(5) = \dfrac{18}{285} + \dfrac{3}{285} = 0.074$

3. (a) $n = 6, p = 0.85$

x	$P(x)$
0	0.00001
1	0.00039
2	0.00549
3	0.04145
4	0.17618
5	0.39933
6	0.37715

(b)

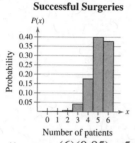

Successful Surgeries

Number of patients

(c) $\mu = np = (6)(0.85) = 5.1$

$\sigma^2 = npq = (6)(0.85)(0.15) = 0.8$

$\sigma = \sqrt{npq} = \sqrt{(16)(0.85)(0.15)} = 0.9$

The average number of successful surgeries is 5.1 out of 6. The standard deviation is 0.9, so most samples of 6 surgeries differ from the mean by no more than 0.9 surgery.

(d) $P(3) \approx 0.041$

This event is unusual because its probability is less than 0.05.

(e) $P(x < 4) = P(0) + P(1) + P(2) + P(3) \approx 0.047$

This event is unusual because its probability is less than 0.05.

4. $\mu = 5$

(a) $P(5) \approx \dfrac{(5)^5(2.71828)^{-5}}{5!} \approx 0.175$

(b) $P(x < 5) = P(0) + P(1) + P(2) + P(3) + P(4)$
$\approx 0.007 + 0.034 + 0.084 + 0.140 + 0.175$
$= 0.440$

(c) $P(0) \approx \dfrac{(5)^0(2.71828)^{-5}}{0!} \approx 0.007$

5. $p = 0.602$

$P(4) = (0.602)(0.398)^3 \approx 0.038$

This event is unusual because its probability is less than 0.05.

6. $p = 0.602$

$P(2 \text{ or } 3) = P(2) + P(3) = (0.602)(0.398)^1 + (0.602)(0.398)^2 \approx 0.335$

This event is not unusual because its probability is greater than 0.05.

5.1 INTRODUCTION TO NORMAL DISTRIBUTIONS AND THE STANDARD NORMAL DISTRIBUTION

5.1 Try It Yourself Solutions

1a. *A*: $x = 45$, *B*: $x = 60$, *C*: $x = 45$ (*B* has the greatest mean.)
 b. Curve *C* is more spread out, so curve *C* has the greatest standard deviation.

2a. Mean = 660
 b. Inflection points: 630 and 690
  Standard deviation = 30

3a. (1) 0.0143   (2) 0.9850

4a.

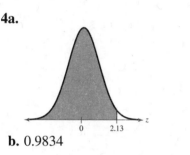

 b. 0.9834

5a.

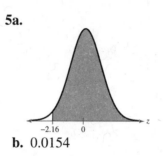

 b. 0.0154

6a. 0.0885   **b.** 0.0152
 c. Area = 0.0885 − 0.0152 = 0.0733

5.1 EXERCISE SOLUTIONS

1. Answers will vary.

2. Neither. In a normal distribution, the mean and median are equal.

3. 1

4. Points at which the curve changes from curving upward to curving downward; $\mu - \sigma$ and $\mu + \sigma$

5. Answers will vary.
    Similarities: The two curves will have the same line of symmetry.
    Differences: The curve within the larger standard deviation will be more spread out than the curve with the smaller standard deviation.

6. Answers will vary.
    Similarities: The two curves will have the same shape because they have equal standard deviations.
    Differences: The two curves will have different lines of symmetry.

7. $\mu = 0$, $\sigma = 1$

8. Transform each data value x into a z-score by subtracting the mean from x and dividing the result by the standard deviation. In symbols,

$$z = \frac{x - \mu}{\sigma}.$$

9. "The" standard normal distribution is used to describe one specific normal distribution ($\mu = 0$, $\sigma = 1$). "a" normal distribution is used to describe a normal distribution with any mean and standard deviation.

10. (c) is true because a z-score equal to 0 indicates that the corresponding x-value is equal to the mean. (a) and (b) are not true because it is possible to have a z-score equal to 0 and the mean is not 0 or the corresponding x-value is not 0.

11. No, the graph crosses the x-axis.

12. No, the graph is not symmetric.

13. Yes, the graph fulfills the properties of the normal distribution.

14. No, the graph is skewed left.

15. No, the graph is skewed to the right.

16. No, the graph is not bell-shaped.

17. The histogram represents data from a normal distribution because it is bell-shaped.

18. The histogram does not represent data from a normal distribution because it is skewed right.

19. (Area left of $z = -1.3$) = 0.0968

20. (Area left of $z = 1.7$) = 0.9554

21. (Area right of $z = 2$) = 1 − (Area left of $z = 2$)
$\qquad\qquad\qquad\quad$ = 1 − 0.9772
$\qquad\qquad\qquad\quad$ = 0.0228

22. (Area right of $z = -2.3$) = 1 − (Area left of $z = -2.3$)
$\qquad\qquad\qquad\qquad$ = 1 − 0.0107
$\qquad\qquad\qquad\qquad$ = 0.9893

23. (Area left of $z = 0$) − (Area left of $z = -2.25$) = 0.5 − 0.0122 = 0.4878

24. (Area left of $z = 1.5$) − (Area left of $z = -0.5$) = 0.9332 − 0.3085 = 0.6247

25. 0.5319 $\qquad\qquad\qquad$ **26.** 1 − 0.0008 = 0.9992 $\qquad\qquad$ **27.** 0.005

28. 0.9139 $\qquad\qquad\qquad$ **29.** 1 − 0.2578 = 0.7422 $\qquad\qquad$ **30.** 1 − 0.9994 = 0.0006

31. $1 - 0.3613 = 0.6387$

32. $1 - \dfrac{0.9463 + 0.9474}{2} \approx 0.0532$

33. $0.9979 - 0.5 = 0.4979$

34. $0.5 - 0.0630 = 0.437$

35. $0.9750 - 0.0250 = 0.950$

36. $0.9901 - 0.0099 = 0.9802$

37. $0.1003 + 0.1003 = 0.2006$

38. $0.0250 + 0.0250 = 0.05$

39. (a)

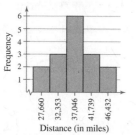

Life Spans of Tires

Distance (in miles)

It is reasonable to assume that the life spans are normally distributed because the histogram is symmetric and bell-shaped.

(b) $\bar{x} = 37{,}234.7$

$s = 6259.2$

(c) The sample mean of 37,234.7 hours is less than the claimed mean, so, on average, the tires in the sample lasted for a shorter time. The sample standard deviation of 6259.2 is greater than the claimed standard deviation, so the tires in the sample had greater variation in life span than the manufacturer's claim.

40. (a)

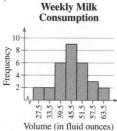

Weekly Milk Consumption

Volume (in fluid ounces)

It is reasonable to assume that the weekly milk consumptions are normally distributed because the histogram is nearly symmetric and bell-shaped.

(b) $\bar{x} = 45.9$

$s = 9.5$

(c) The mean of your sample is 2.8 fluid ounces less than that of the previous study, so the average milk consumption from the sample is less than in the previous study. The standard deviation is about 0.9 fluid ounce greater than that of the previous study, so milk consumptions are slightly more spread out than in the previous study.

41. (a) A = 105; B = 113; C = 121; D = 127

(b) $x = 105 \Rightarrow z = \dfrac{x - \mu}{\sigma} = \dfrac{105 - 115}{3.6} \approx -2.78$

$x = 113 \Rightarrow z = \dfrac{x - \mu}{\sigma} = \dfrac{113 - 115}{3.6} \approx -0.56$

$x = 121 \Rightarrow z = \dfrac{x - \mu}{\sigma} = \dfrac{121 - 115}{3.6} \approx 1.67$

$x = 127 \Rightarrow z = \dfrac{x - \mu}{\sigma} = \dfrac{127 - 115}{3.6} \approx 3.33$

(c) $x = 105$ is unusual because its corresponding z-score (-2.78) lies more than 2 standard deviations from the mean, and $x = 127$ is very unusual because its corresponding z-score (3.33) lies more than 3 standard deviations from the mean.

42. (a) A = 11.92; B = 11.99; C = 12.01; D = 12.12

(b) $x = 11.92 \Rightarrow z = \dfrac{x - \mu}{\sigma} = \dfrac{11.92 - 12}{0.05} = -1.6$

$x = 11.99 \Rightarrow z = \dfrac{x - \mu}{\sigma} = \dfrac{11.99 - 12}{0.05} = -0.2$

$x = 12.01 \Rightarrow z = \dfrac{x - \mu}{\sigma} = \dfrac{12.01 - 12}{0.05} = 0.2$

$x = 12.12 \Rightarrow z = \dfrac{x - \mu}{\sigma} = \dfrac{12.12 - 12}{0.05} = 2.4$

(c) $x = 12.12$ is unusual because its corresponding z-score (2.4) lies more than 2 standard deviations from the mean.

43. (a) A = 1241; B = 1392; C = 1924; D = 2202

(b) $x = 1241 \Rightarrow z = \dfrac{x - \mu}{\sigma} = \dfrac{1241 - 1509}{312} \approx -0.86$

$x = 1392 \Rightarrow z = \dfrac{x - \mu}{\sigma} = \dfrac{1392 - 1509}{312} = -0.375$

$x = 1924 \Rightarrow z = \dfrac{x - \mu}{\sigma} = \dfrac{1924 - 1509}{312} \approx 1.33$

$x = 2202 \Rightarrow z = \dfrac{x - \mu}{\sigma} = \dfrac{2202 - 1509}{312} \approx 2.22$

(c) $x = 2202$ is unusual because its corresponding z-score (2.22) lies more than 2 standard deviations from the mean.

44. (a) A = 9; B = 15; C = 22; D = 35

(b) $x = 9 \Rightarrow z = \dfrac{x - \mu}{\sigma} = \dfrac{9 - 21.1}{5.0} = -2.42$

$x = 15 \Rightarrow z = \dfrac{x - \mu}{\sigma} = \dfrac{15 - 21.1}{5.0} = -1.22$

$x = 22 \Rightarrow z = \dfrac{x - \mu}{\sigma} = \dfrac{22 - 21.1}{5.0} = 0.18$

$x = 35 \Rightarrow z = \dfrac{x - \mu}{\sigma} = \dfrac{35 - 21.1}{5.0} = 2.78$

(c) $x = 9$ is unusual because its corresponding z-score (-2.42) lies more than 2 standard deviations from the mean. $x = 35$ is unusual because its corresponding z-score (2.78) lies more than 2 standard deviations from the mean.

45. 0.9750

46. $\dfrac{0.1894 + 0.1922}{2} = 0.1908$

47. $1 - 0.0225 = 0.9775$

48. $1 - 0.8997 = 0.1003$

49. $0.9987 - 0.1587 = 0.8400$

50. $0.9382 - 0.5 = 0.4382$

51. $P(z < 1.45) = 0.9265$

52. $P(z < -0.18) = 0.4286$

53. $P(z > 2.175) = 1 - P(z < 2.175) = 1 - 0.9852 = 0.0148$

54. $P(z > -1.85) = 1 - P(z < -1.85) = 1 - 0.0322 = 0.9678$

55. $P(-0.89 < z < 0) = 0.5 - 0.1867 = 0.3133$

56. $P(0 < z < 0.525) = 0.7002 - 0.5 = 0.2002$

57. $P(-1.65 < z < 1.65) = 0.9505 - 0.0495 = 0.901$

58. $P(-1.54 < z < 1.54) = 0.9382 - 0.0618 = 0.8764$

59. $P(z < -2.58 \text{ or } z > 2.58) = 2(0.0049) = 0.0098$

60. $P(z < -1.54 \text{ or } z > 1.54) = 2(0.0618) = 0.1236$

61.

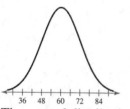

The normal distribution curve is centered at its mean (60) and has 2 points of inflection (48 and 72) representing $\mu \pm \sigma$.

62.

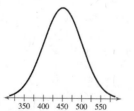

The normal distribution curve is centered at its mean (450) and has 2 points of inflection (400 and 500) representing $\mu \pm \sigma$.

63. (a) Area under curve = area of square = (base)(height) = (1)(1) = 1
(b) $P(0.25 < x \, 0.5) =$ (base)(height) = (0.25)(1) = 0.25
(c) $P(0.3 < x \, 0.7) =$ (base)(height) = (0.4)(1) = 0.4

64. (a)

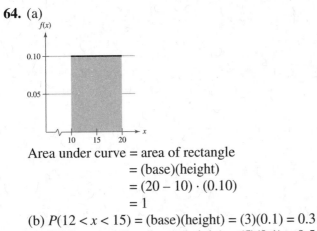

Area under curve = area of rectangle
$$= \text{(base)(height)}$$
$$= (20 - 10) \cdot (0.10)$$
$$= 1$$
(b) $P(12 < x < 15) =$ (base)(height) = (3)(0.1) = 0.3
(c) $P(13 < x < 18) =$ (base)(height) = (5)(0.1) = 0.5

5.2 NORMAL DISTRIBUTIONS: FINDING PROBABILITIES

5.2 Try It Yourself Solutions

1a.

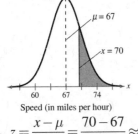

Speed (in miles per hour)

b. $z = \dfrac{x - \mu}{\sigma} = \dfrac{70 - 67}{3.5} \approx 0.86$

c. $P(z < 0.86) = 0.8051$
$P(z > 0.86) = 1 - 0.8051 = 0.1949$

d. The probability that a randomly selected vehicle is violating the 70 mile per hour speed limit is 0.1949.

2a.

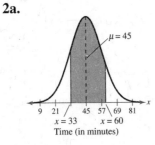

Time (in minutes)

b. $z = \dfrac{x - \mu}{\sigma} = \dfrac{33 - 45}{12} = -1$

$z = \dfrac{x - \mu}{\sigma} = \dfrac{60 - 45}{12} = 1.25$

c. $P(z < -1) = 0.1587$

$P(z > 1.25) = 0.8944$

$0.8944 - 0.1587 = 0.7357$

d. If 150 shoppers enter the store, then you would expect $150(0.7357) \approx 110$ shoppers to be in the store between 33 and 60 minutes.

3a. Read user's guide for the technology tool.

b. Enter the data.

$P(100 < x < 150) = P(-0.97 < z < 0.46) = 0.5105$

c. The probability that a randomly selected U.S. person's triglyceride level is between 100 and 150 is 0.5105.

5.2 EXERCISE SOLUTIONS

1. $P(x < 170) = P(z < -0.2) = 0.4207$

2. $P(x < 200) = P(z < 1.3) = 0.9032$

3. $P(x > 182) = P(z > 0.4) = 1 - 0.6554 = 0.3446$

4. $P(x > 155) = P(z > -0.95) = 1 - 0.1711 = 0.8289$

5. $P(160 < x < 170) = P(-0.7 < z < -0.2) = 0.4207 - 0.2420 = 0.1787$

6. $P(172 < x < 192) = P(-0.1 < z < 0.9) = 0.8159 - 0.4602 = 0.3557$

7. $P(200 < x < 450) = P(-2.64 < z < -0.39) = 0.3483 - 0.0041 = 0.3442$

8. $P(670 < x < 800) = P(1.34 < z < 2.46) = 0.9931 - 0.9099 = 0.0832$

9. $P(220 < x < 255) = P(0.29 < z < 1.22) = 0.8888 - 0.6141 = 0.2747$

10. $P(190 < x < 215) = P(-0.19 < z < 0.48) = 0.6844 - 0.4247 = 0.2597$

11. $P(145 < x < 155) = P(0.39 < z < 2.34) = 0.9904 - 0.6517 = 0.3387$

12. $P(116 < x < 125) = P(-1.94 < z < 0) = 0.5 - 0.0262 = 0.4738$

13. (a) $P(x < 66) = P(z < -1.3) = 0.0968$

(b) $P(66 < x < 72) = P(-1.3 < z < 0.7) = 0.7580 - 0.0968 = 0.6612$

(c) $P(x > 72) = P(z > 0.7) = 1 - P(z < 0.7) = 1 - 0.7580 = 0.2420$

(d) No, none of these events are unusual because their probabilities are greater than 0.05.

14. (a) $P(x < 56.5) = P(z < -3) = 0.0013$

    (b) $P(61 < x < 67) = P(-1.27 < z < 1.04) = 0.8508 - 0.1020 = 0.7488$

    (c) $P(x > 70.5) = P(z > 2.38) = 1 - P(z < 2.38) = 1 - 0.9913 = 0.0087$

    (d) Yes, the events in parts (a) and (c) are unusual because their probabilities are less than 0.05.

15. (a) $P(x < 15) = P(z < -0.89) = 0.1867$

    (b) $P(18 < x < 25) = P(-0.41 < z < 0.70) = 0.7580 - 0.3409 = 0.4171$

    (c) $P(x > 34) = P(z > 2.13) = 1 - P(z < 2.13) = 1 - 0.9834 = 0.0166$

    (d) Yes, the event in part (c) is unusual because its probability is less than 0.05.

16. (a) $P(x < 23) = P(z < -0.67) = 0.2514$

    (b) $P(24.5 < x < 25) = P(-0.17 < z < 0) = 0.5 - 0.4325 = 0.0675$

    (c) $P(x > 30) = P(z > 1.67) = 1 - P(1.67) = 1 - 0.9525 = 0.0475$

    (d) Yes, the event in part (c) is unusual because its probability is less than 0.05.

17. (a) $P(x < 5) = P(z < -2) = 0.0228$

    (b) $P(5.5 < x < 9.5) = P(-1.5 < z < 2.5) = 0.9938 - 0.0668 = 0.927$

    (c) $P(x > 10) = P(z > 3) = 1 - P(z < 3) = 1 - 0.9987 = 0.0013$

18. (a) $P(x < 70) = P(z < -2.5) = 0.0062$

    (b) $P(90 < x < 120) = P(-0.83 < z < 1.67) = 0.9525 - 0.2033 = 0.7492$

    (c) $P(x > 140) = P(z > 3.33) = 1 - P(z < 3.33) = 1 - 0.9996 = 0.0004$

19. (a) $P(x < 4) = P(z < -2.44) = 0.0073$

    (b) $P(5 < x < 7) = P(-1.33 < z < 0.89) = 0.8133 - 0.0918 = 0.7215$

    (c) $P(x > 8) = P(z > 2) = 1 - 0.9722 = 0.0228$

20. (a) $P(x < 17) = P(z < -0.6) = 0.2743$

    (b) $P(20 < x < 28) = P(0 < z < 1.6) = 0.9452 - 0.5 = 0.4452$

    (c) $P(x > 30) = P(z > 2) = 1 - 0.9772 = 0.0228$

21. (a) $P(x < 600) = P(z < 0.96) = 0.8315 \Rightarrow 83.15\%$

    (b) $P(x > 550) = P(z > 0.51) = 1 - P(z < 0.51) = 1 - 0.6950 = 0.3050$

        $(1000)(0.3050) = 305 \Rightarrow 305$ scores

22. (a) $P(x < 500) = P(z < -0.13) = 0.4483 \Rightarrow 44.83\%$

    (b) $P(x > 600) = P(z > 0.73) = 1 - P(z < 0.73) = 1 - 0.7673 = 0.2327$

        $(1500)(0.2327) = 349.05 \Rightarrow 349$ scores

23. (a) $P(x < 225) = P(z < 0.42) = 0.6628 \Rightarrow 66.28\%$

    (b) $P(x > 260) = P(z > 1.35) = 1 - P(z < 1.35) = 1 - 0.9115 = 0.0885$

        $(250)(0.0885) = 22.125 \Rightarrow 22$ men

24. (a) $P(x < 217) + P(z < 0.53) = 0.7019 \Rightarrow 70.19\%$

 (b) $P(x > 185) = P(z > -0.32) = 1 - P(z < -0.32) = 1 - 0.3745 = 0.6255$

  $(200)(0.6255) = 125.1 \Rightarrow 125$ women

25. (a) $P(x > 4) = P(z > -3) = 1 - P(z < -3) = 1 - 0.0013 = 0.9987 \Rightarrow 99.87\%$

 (b) $P(x < 5) = P(z < -2) = 0.0228$

  $(35)(0.0228) = 0.798 \Rightarrow 1$ adult

26. (a) $P(x > 125) = P(z > 2.08) = 1 - P(z < 2.08) = 1 - 0.9812 = 0.0188 \Rightarrow 1.88\%$

 (b) $P(x < 90) = P(z < -0.83) = 0.2033$

  $(300)(0.2033) = 60.99 \Rightarrow 61$ bills

27. $P(x > 2065) = P(z > 2.17) = 1 - P(z < 2.17) = 1 - 0.9850 = 0.0150 \Rightarrow 1.5\%$

It is unusual for a battery to have a life span that is more than 2065 hours because the probability is less than 0.05.

28. $P(x < 3.1) = P(z < -1.56) = 0.0594 \Rightarrow 5.94\%$

It is not unusual for a person to consume less than 3.1 pounds of peanuts because the probability is greater than 0.05.

29. (a) 0.3085

 (b) 0.1499

 (c) 0.0668

  No, because 0.0668 > 0.05, this event is not unusual.

30. (a) 0.1587

 (b) 0.1587

 (c) 0.0013

  Yes, because 0.0013 < 0.05, this event is unusual.

31. Out of control, because the 10th observation plotted beyond 3 standard deviations.

32. Out of control, because two out of three consecutive points lie more than 2 standard deviations from the mean. (8th and 10th observations)

33. Out of control, because the first nine observations lie below the mean and since two out of three consecutive points lie more than 2 standard deviations from the mean.

34. In control, because none of the three warning signals detected a change.

5.3 NORMAL DISTRIBUTIONS: FINDING VALUES

5.3 Try It Yourself Solutions

1ab. (1)   (2)

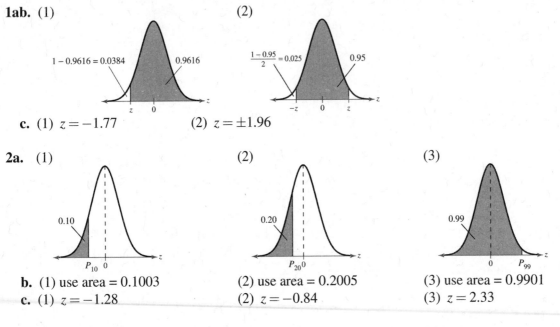

  c. (1) $z = -1.77$ (2) $z = \pm 1.96$

2a. (1)   (2)   (3)

  b. (1) use area = 0.1003   (2) use area = 0.2005   (3) use area = 0.9901
  c. (1) $z = -1.28$ (2) $z = -0.84$ (3) $z = 2.33$

3a. $\mu = 52$, $\sigma = 15$

  b. $z = -2.33 \Rightarrow x = \mu + z\sigma = 52 + (-2.33)(15) = 17.05$

  $z = 3.10 \Rightarrow x = \mu + z\sigma = 52 + (3.10)(15) = 98.50$

  $z = 0.58 \Rightarrow x = \mu + z\sigma = 52 + (0.58)(15) = 60.70$

  c. 17.05 pounds is below the mean, 60.7 pounds and 98.5 pounds are above the mean.

4a.

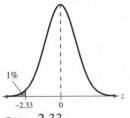

  b. $z = -2.33$

  c. $x = \mu + z\sigma = 129 + (-2.33)(5.18) \approx 116.93$

  d. So, the longest braking distance a Nissan Altima could have and still be in the bottom 1% is about 117 feet.

5a.

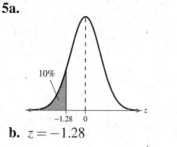

b. $z = -1.28$

c. $x = \mu + z\sigma = 11.2 + (-1.28)(2.1) \doteq 8.512$

d. So, the maximum length of time an employee could have worked and still be laid off is about 8.5 years.

5.3 EXERCISE SOLUTIONS

1. $z = -0.81$

2. $z = -0.16$

3. $z = 2.39$

4. $z = 0.84$

5. $z = -1.645$

6. $z = 1.04$

7. $z = 1.555$

8. $z = -2.605$

9. $z = -1.04$

10. $z = -0.52$

11. $z = 1.175$

12. $z = 0.44$

13. $z = -0.67$

14. $z = -0.25$

15. $z = 0.67$

16. $z = 0.84$

17. $z = -0.38$

18. $z = 0.25$

19. $z = -0.58$

20. $z = 1.99$

21. $z = \pm 1.645$

22. $z = \pm 1.96$

23. $\Rightarrow z = -1.18$

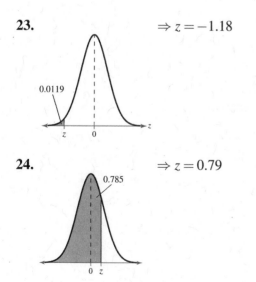

24. $\Rightarrow z = 0.79$

25. $\Rightarrow z = 1.18$

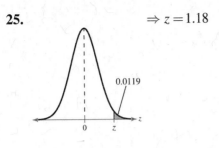

26. $\Rightarrow z = -0.79$

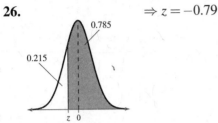

27. $\Rightarrow z = \pm 1.28$

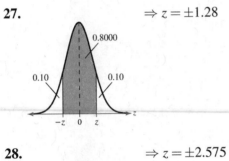

28. $\Rightarrow z = \pm 2.575$

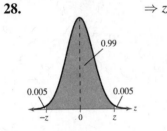

29. $\Rightarrow z = \pm 0.06$

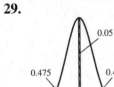

30. $\Rightarrow z = \pm 0.15$

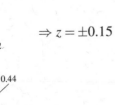

31. (a) 95th percentile $\Rightarrow$ Area = 0.95 $\Rightarrow$ $z = 1.645$

$\qquad x = \mu + z\sigma = 64.3 + (1.645)(2.6) \approx 68.58$ inches

(b) 1st quartile $\Rightarrow$ Area = 0.25 $\Rightarrow$ $z = -0.67$

$\qquad x = \mu + z\sigma = 64.3 + (-0.67)(2.6) \approx 62.56$ inches

32. (a) 90th percentile $\Rightarrow$ Area = 0.90 $\Rightarrow$ $z = 1.28$

$\qquad x = \mu + z\sigma = 69.9 + (1.28)(3.0) = 73.74$ inches

(b) 1st quartile $\Rightarrow$ Area = 0.25 $\Rightarrow$ $z = -0.67$

$\qquad x = \mu + z\sigma = 69.9 + (-0.67)(3.0) = 67.89$ inches

33. (a) 5th percentile $\Rightarrow$ Area = 0.05 $\Rightarrow$ $z = -1.645$

$\qquad x = \mu + z\sigma = 204 + (-1.645)(25.7) \approx 161.72$ days

(b) 3rd quartile $\Rightarrow$ Area = 0.75 $\Rightarrow$ $z = 0.67$

$\qquad x = \mu + z\sigma = 204 + (0.67)(25.7) \approx 221.22$ days

34. (a) 80th percentile $\Rightarrow$ Area = 0.80 $\Rightarrow$ $z = 0.84$

$\qquad x = \mu + z\sigma = 1674 + (0.84)(212.5) = 1852.5$ days

(b) 1st quartile $\Rightarrow$ Area = 0.25 $\Rightarrow$ $z = -0.67$

$\qquad x = \mu + z\sigma = 1674 + (-0.67)(212.5) \approx 1531.63$ days

35. (a) Top 5% $\Rightarrow$ Area = 0.95 $\Rightarrow$ $z = 1.645$

$\qquad x = \mu + z\sigma = 6.1 + (1.645)(1.0) \approx 7.75$ hours

(b) Middle 50% $\Rightarrow$ Area = 0.25 to 0.75 $\Rightarrow$ $z = \pm 0.675$

$\qquad x = \mu + z\sigma = 6.1 + (\pm 0.67)(1.0) = 5.43$ to 6.77 hours

36. (a) Bottom 10% $\Rightarrow$ Area = 0.10 $\Rightarrow$ $z = -1.28$

$\qquad x = \mu + z\sigma = 20.7 + (-1.28)(4.2) \approx 15.32$ pounds

(b) Middle 80% $\Rightarrow$ Area = 0.10 to 0.90 $\Rightarrow$ $z = \pm 1.28$

$\qquad x = \mu + z\sigma = 20.7 + (\pm 1.28)(4.2) \approx 15.32$ to 26.08 pounds

37. Upper 4.5% $\Rightarrow$ Area = 0.955 $\Rightarrow$ $z = 1.70$

$\quad x = \mu + z\sigma = 32 + (1.70)(0.36) \approx 32.61$ ounces

38. Top 1% $\Rightarrow$ Area = 0.99 $\Rightarrow$ $z = 2.33$

$\quad x = \mu + z\sigma \Rightarrow 8 = \mu + (2.33)(0.03) \Rightarrow \mu \approx 7.93$ ounces

39. (a) 18.89 pounds

(b) 12.05 pounds

40. (a) 13.1 pounds

(b) 5.79 pounds

41. Bottom 10% $\Rightarrow$ Area $= 0.10 \Rightarrow z = -1.28$

$x = \mu + z\sigma = 30,000 + (-1.28)(2500) = 26,800$

Tires that wear out by 26,800 miles will be replaced free of charge.

42. A: Top 10% $\Rightarrow$ Area $= 0.90 \Rightarrow z = 1.28$

$x = \mu + z\sigma = 72 + (1.28)(9) = 83.52$

B: Top 30% $\Rightarrow$ Area $= 0.70 \Rightarrow z = 0.52$

$x = \mu + z\sigma = 72 + (0.52)(9) = 76.68$

C: Top 70% $\Rightarrow$ Area $= 0.30 \Rightarrow z = -0.52$

$x = \mu + z\sigma = 72 + (-0.52)(9) = 67.32$

D: Top 90% $\Rightarrow$ Area $= 0.10 \Rightarrow z = -1.28$

$x = \mu + z\sigma = 72 + (-1.28)(9) = 60.48$

5.4 SAMPLING DISTRIBUTIONS AND THE CENTRAL LIMIT THEOREM

5.4 Try It Yourself Solutions

1a.

Sample	Mean	Sample	Mean	Sample	Mean	Sample	Mean
1, 1, 1	1	3, 1, 1	1.67	5, 1, 1	2.33	7, 1, 1	3
1, 1, 3	1.67	3, 1, 3	2.33	5, 1, 3	3	7, 1, 3	3.67
1, 1, 5	2.33	3, 1, 5	3	5, 1, 5	3.67	7, 1, 5	4.33
1, 1, 7	3	3, 1, 7	3.67	5, 1, 7	4.33	7, 1, 7	5
1, 3, 1	1.67	3, 3, 1	2.33	5, 3, 1	3	7, 3, 1	3.67
1, 3, 3	2.33	3, 3, 3	3	5, 3, 3	3.67	7, 3, 3	4.33
1, 3, 5	3	3, 3, 5	3.67	5, 3, 5	4.33	7, 3, 5	5
1, 3, 7	3.67	3, 3, 7	4.33	5, 3, 7	5	7, 3, 7	5.67
1, 5, 1	2.33	3, 5, 1	3	5, 5, 1	3.67	7, 5, 1	4.33
1, 5, 3	3	3, 5, 3	3.67	5, 5, 3	4.33	7, 5, 3	5
1, 5, 5	3.67	3, 5, 5	4.33	5, 5, 5	5	7, 5, 5	5.67
1, 5, 7	4.33	3, 5, 7	5	5, 5, 7	5.67	7, 5, 7	6.33
1, 7, 1	3	3, 7, 1	3.67	5, 7, 1	4.33	7, 7, 1	5
1, 7, 3	3.67	3, 7, 3	4.33	5, 7, 3	5	7, 7, 3	5.67
1, 7, 5	4.33	3, 7, 5	5	5, 7, 5	5.67	7, 7, 5	6.33
1, 7, 7	5	3, 7, 7	5.67	5, 7, 7	6.33	7, 7, 7	7

b.

$\overline{x}$	f	**Probability**
1	1	0.0156
1.67	3	0.0469
2.33	6	0.0938
3	10	0.1562
3.67	12	0.1875
4.33	12	0.1875
5	10	0.1563
5.67	6	0.0938
6.33	3	0.0469
7	1	0.0156

$\mu_{\overline{x}} = 4$, $\sigma_{\overline{x}}^2 \approx 1.667$, $\sigma_{\overline{x}} \approx 1.291$

c. $\mu_{\overline{x}} = \mu = 4$,

$$\sigma_{\overline{x}}^2 = \frac{\sigma^2}{n} = \frac{5}{3} \approx 1.667,$$

$$\sigma_{\overline{x}} = \frac{\sigma}{\sqrt{n}} = \frac{\sqrt{5}}{\sqrt{3}} \approx 1.291$$

2a. $\mu_{\overline{x}} = \mu = 63$, $\sigma_{\overline{x}} = \dfrac{\sigma}{\sqrt{n}} = \dfrac{11}{\sqrt{64}} \approx 1.4$

b. $n = 64$

58.8 60.2 61.6 63.0 64.4 65.8 67.2
Mean of phone bills (in dollars)

c. With a smaller sample size, the mean stays the same but the standard deviation increases.

3a. $\mu_{\overline{x}} = \mu = 3.5$, $\sigma_{\overline{x}} = \dfrac{\sigma}{\sqrt{n}} = \dfrac{0.2}{\sqrt{16}} = 0.05$

b.

3.35 3.40 3.45 3.50 3.55 3.60 3.65
Mean diameter (in feet)

4a. $\mu_{\bar{x}} = \mu = 25$, $\sigma_{\bar{x}} = \dfrac{\sigma}{\sqrt{n}} = \dfrac{1.5}{\sqrt{100}} = 0.15$

24.70   25   25.30
Mean time (in minutes)

b. $\bar{x} = 24.7$: $z = \dfrac{\bar{x} - \mu}{\dfrac{\sigma}{\sqrt{n}}} = \dfrac{24.7 - 25}{\dfrac{1.5}{\sqrt{100}}} = -\dfrac{0.3}{0.15} = -2$

$\bar{x} = 25.5$: $z = \dfrac{\bar{x} - \mu}{\dfrac{\sigma}{\sqrt{n}}} = \dfrac{25.5 - 25}{\dfrac{1.5}{\sqrt{100}}} = -\dfrac{0.5}{0.15} \approx 3.33$

c. $P(z < -2) = 0.0228$

$P(z < 3.33) = 0.9996$

$P(24.7 < \bar{x} < 25.5) = P(-2 < z < 3.33) = 0.9996 - 0.0228 = 0.9768$

d. Of the samples of 100 drivers ages 15 to 19, 97.68% will have a mean driving time that is between 24.7 and 25.5 minutes.

5a. $\mu_{\bar{x}} = \mu = 290,600$, $\sigma_{\bar{x}} = \dfrac{\sigma}{\sqrt{n}} = \dfrac{36,000}{\sqrt{12}} \approx 10,392.30$

269,816   290,600   311,385
Mean sales price (in dollars)

b. $\bar{x} = 265,000$: $z = \dfrac{\bar{x} - \mu}{\dfrac{\sigma}{\sqrt{n}}} = \dfrac{265,000 - 290,600}{\dfrac{36,000}{\sqrt{12}}} \approx \dfrac{-25,600}{10,392.30} \approx -2.46$

c. $P(\bar{x} > 265,000) = P(z > -2.46) = 1 - P(z < -2.46) = 1 - 0.0069 = 0.9931$

d. 99.31% of samples of 12 single-family houses will have a mean sales price greater than \$265,000.

6a. $x = 200$: $z = \dfrac{x - \mu}{\sigma} = \dfrac{200 - 190}{48} \approx 0.21$

$\bar{x} = 200$: $z = \dfrac{\bar{x} - \mu}{\dfrac{\sigma}{\sqrt{n}}} = \dfrac{200 - 190}{\dfrac{48}{\sqrt{10}}} \approx \dfrac{10}{15.18} \approx 0.66$

b. $P(z < 0.21) = 0.5832$

$P(z < 0.66) = 0.7454$

c. There is about a 58% chance that an LCD computer monitor will cost less than \$200. There is about a 75% chance that the mean of a sample of 10 LCD computer monitors is less than \$200.

5.4 EXERCISE SOLUTIONS

1. $\mu_{\bar{x}} = \mu = 150$

$\sigma_{\bar{x}} = \dfrac{\sigma}{\sqrt{n}} = \dfrac{25}{\sqrt{50}} \approx 3.536$

2. $\mu_{\bar{x}} = \mu = 150$

$\sigma_{\bar{x}} = \dfrac{\sigma}{\sqrt{n}} = \dfrac{25}{\sqrt{100}} = 2.5$

3. $\mu_{\bar{x}} = \mu = 150$

$\sigma_{\bar{x}} = \dfrac{\sigma}{\sqrt{n}} = \dfrac{25}{\sqrt{250}} \approx 1.581$

4. $\mu_{\bar{x}} = \mu = 150$

$\sigma_{\bar{x}} = \dfrac{\sigma}{\sqrt{n}} = \dfrac{25}{\sqrt{1000}} \approx 0.791$

5. False. As the size of a sample increases, the mean of the distribution of sample means does not change.

6. False. As the size of a sample increases, the standard deviation of the distribution of sample means decreases.

7. False. A sampling distribution is normal if either $n \geq 30$ or the population is normal.

8. True

9. (c) Because $\mu_{\bar{x}} = 16.5$, $\sigma_{\bar{x}} = \dfrac{\sigma}{\sqrt{n}} = \dfrac{11.9}{\sqrt{100}} = 1.19$, and the graph approximates a normal curve.

10. (c) Because $\mu_{\bar{x}} = 5.8$, $\sigma_{\bar{x}} = \dfrac{\sigma}{\sqrt{n}} = \dfrac{2.3}{\sqrt{100}} \approx 0.23$, and the graph approximates a normal curve.

11.

Sample	Mean	Sample	Mean	Sample	Mean
2, 2, 2	2	4, 4, 8	5.33	8, 16, 2	8.67
2, 2, 4	2.67	4, 4, 16	8	8, 16, 4	9.33
2, 2, 8	4	4, 8, 2	4.67	8, 16, 8	10.67
2, 2, 16	6.67	4, 8, 4	5.33	8, 16, 16	13.33
2, 4, 2	2.67	4, 8, 8	6.67	16, 2, 2	6.67
2, 4, 4	3.33	4, 8, 16	9.33	16, 2, 4	7.33
2, 4, 8	4.67	4, 16, 2	7.33	16, 2, 8	8.67
2, 4, 16	7.33	4, 16, 4	8	16, 2, 16	11.33
2, 8, 2	4	4, 16, 8	9.33	16, 4, 2	7.33
2, 8, 4	4.67	4, 16, 16	12	16, 4, 4	8
2, 8, 8	6	8, 2, 2	4	16, 4, 8	9.33
2, 8, 16	8.67	8, 2, 4	4.67	16, 4, 16	12
2, 16, 2	6.67	8, 2, 8	6	16, 8, 2	8.67
2, 16, 4	7.33	8, 2, 16	8.67	16, 8, 4	9.33
2, 16, 8	8.67	8, 4, 2	4.67	16, 8, 8	10.67
2, 16, 16	11.33	8, 4, 4	5.33	16, 8, 16	13.33
4, 2, 2	2.67	8, 4, 8	6.67	16, 16, 2	11.33
4, 2, 4	3.33	8, 4, 16	9.33	16, 16, 4	12
4, 2, 8	4.67	8, 8, 2	6	16, 16, 8	13.33
4, 2, 16	7.33	8, 8, 4	6.67	16, 16, 16	16
4, 4, 2	3.33	8, 8, 8	8		
4, 4, 4	4	8, 8, 16	10.67		

$\mu = 7.5,\ \sigma \approx 5.36$

$\mu_{\bar{x}} = 7.5,\ \sigma_{\bar{x}} \approx \dfrac{5.36}{\sqrt{3}} \approx 3.09$

The means are equal but the standard deviation of the sampling distribution is smaller.

12.

Sample	Mean
130, 130	130
130, 200	165
130, 230	180
130, 270	200
200, 130	165
200, 200	200
200, 230	215
200, 270	235
230, 130	180
230, 200	215
230, 230	230
230, 270	250
270, 130	200
270, 200	235
270, 230	250
270, 270	270

$\mu = 207.5, \ \sigma \approx 51.17$

$\mu_{\bar{x}} = 207.5, \ \sigma_{\bar{x}} \approx \dfrac{51.17}{\sqrt{2}} \approx 36.18$

The means are equal but the standard deviation of the sampling distribution is smaller.

13. $z = \dfrac{\bar{x} - \mu}{\dfrac{\sigma}{\sqrt{n}}} = \dfrac{24.3 - 24}{\dfrac{1.25}{\sqrt{64}}} \approx \dfrac{0.3}{0.156} \approx 1.92$

$P(\bar{x} < 24.3) = P(z < 1.92) = 0.9726$

The probability is not unusual because it is greater than 0.05.

14. $z = \dfrac{\bar{x} - \mu}{\dfrac{\sigma}{\sqrt{n}}} = \dfrac{24.3 - 24}{\dfrac{1.25}{\sqrt{100}}} = \dfrac{0.3}{0.125} = 2.40$

$P(\bar{x} > 24.3) = P(z > 2.40) = 1 - P(z < 2.40) = 1 - 0.9918 = 0.0082$

The probability is unusual because it is less than 0.05.

15. $z = \dfrac{\bar{x} - \mu}{\dfrac{\sigma}{\sqrt{n}}} = \dfrac{551 - 550}{\dfrac{3.7}{\sqrt{45}}} \approx \dfrac{1}{0.552} \approx 1.81$

$P(\bar{x} > 551) = P(z > 1.81) = 1 - P(z < 1.81) = 1 - 0.9649 = 0.0351$

The probability is unusual because it is less than 0.05.

16. $z = \dfrac{\bar{x} - \mu}{\dfrac{\sigma}{\sqrt{n}}} = \dfrac{12{,}753 - 12{,}750}{\dfrac{1.7}{\sqrt{36}}} \approx \dfrac{3}{0.283} = 10.60$

$P(\bar{x} < 12{,}750 \text{ or } \bar{x} > 12{,}753) = P(z < 0 \text{ or } z > 10.60) = 0.5 + 0.000 = 0.5$

The probability is not unusual because it is greater than 0.05.

17. $\mu_{\bar{x}} = 7.6$

$\sigma_{\bar{x}} = \dfrac{\sigma}{\sqrt{n}} = \dfrac{0.35}{\sqrt{12}} \approx 0.101$

18. $\mu_{\bar{x}} = 800$

$\sigma_{\bar{x}} = \dfrac{\sigma}{\sqrt{n}} = \dfrac{100}{\sqrt{15}} \approx 25.820$

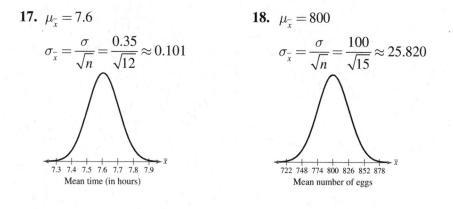

7.3 7.4 7.5 7.6 7.7 7.8 7.9
Mean time (in hours)

722 748 774 800 826 852 878
Mean number of eggs

19. $\mu_{\bar{x}} = 235$

$$\sigma_{\bar{x}} = \frac{\sigma}{\sqrt{n}} = \frac{62}{\sqrt{20}} \approx 13.864$$

207.3   235   262.7
Mean price (in dollars)

20. $\mu_{\bar{x}} = 47.2$

$$\sigma_{\bar{x}} = \frac{\sigma}{\sqrt{n}} = \frac{3.6}{\sqrt{36}} = 0.6$$

46   47.2   48.4
Mean age (in years)

21. $\mu_{\bar{x}} = 188.4$

$$\sigma_{\bar{x}} = \frac{\sigma}{\sqrt{n}} = \frac{54.5}{\sqrt{25}} = 10.9$$

166.6   188.4   210.2
Mean consumption of fresh
vegetables (in pounds)

22. $\mu_{\bar{x}} = 24.2$

$$\sigma_{\bar{x}} = \frac{\sigma}{\sqrt{n}} = \frac{8.1}{\sqrt{30}} \approx 1.479$$

21.2   24.2   27.2
Mean consumption (in gallons)

23. $n = 24$: $\mu_{\bar{x}} = 7.6$, $\sigma_{\bar{x}} = \dfrac{\sigma}{\sqrt{n}} = \dfrac{0.35}{\sqrt{24}} \approx 0.07$

$n = 36$: $\mu_{\bar{x}} = 7.6$, $\sigma_{\bar{x}} = \dfrac{\sigma}{\sqrt{n}} = \dfrac{0.35}{\sqrt{36}} \approx 0.06$

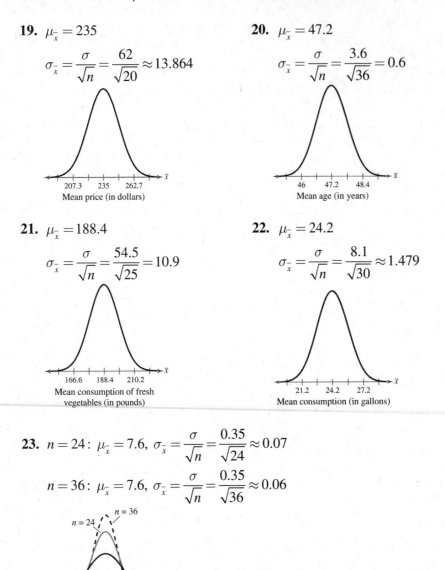

7.3 7.4 7.5 7.6 7.7 7.8 7.9
Mean time (in hours)

As the sample size increases, the standard error decreases, while the mean of the sample means remains constant.

24. $n = 30$: $\mu_{\bar{x}} = 800$, $\sigma_{\bar{x}} = \dfrac{\sigma}{\sqrt{n}} = \dfrac{100}{\sqrt{30}} \approx 18.257$

$n = 45$: $\mu_{\bar{x}} = 800$, $\sigma_{\bar{x}} = \dfrac{\sigma}{\sqrt{n}} = \dfrac{100}{\sqrt{45}} \approx 14.907$

As the sample size increases, the standard error decreases, while the mean of the sample means remains the same.

25. $z = \dfrac{\bar{x} - \mu}{\dfrac{\sigma}{\sqrt{n}}} = \dfrac{60,000 - 63,500}{\dfrac{6100}{\sqrt{35}}} \approx \dfrac{-3500}{1031.09} \approx -3.39$

$P(\bar{x} < 60,000) = P(z < -3.39) = 0.0003$

Only 0.03% of samples of 35 specialists will have a mean salary less than \$60,000. This is an extremely unusual event.

26. $z = \dfrac{\bar{x} - \mu}{\dfrac{\sigma}{\sqrt{n}}} = \dfrac{56,100 - 56,275}{\dfrac{1800}{\sqrt{48}}} \approx \dfrac{-175}{259.81} \approx -0.67$

$P(\bar{x} < 56,100) = P(z < -0.67) \approx 0.2514$

About 25% of samples of 48 flight attendants will have a mean salary less than \$56,100.

27. $z = \dfrac{\bar{x} - \mu}{\dfrac{\sigma}{\sqrt{n}}} = \dfrac{2.695 - 2.714}{\dfrac{0.045}{\sqrt{32}}} \approx \dfrac{-0.019}{0.00795} \approx -2.39$

$z = \dfrac{\bar{x} - \mu}{\dfrac{\sigma}{\sqrt{n}}} = \dfrac{2.725 - 2.714}{\dfrac{0.045}{\sqrt{32}}} \approx \dfrac{0.011}{0.00795} \approx 1.38$

$P(2.695 < \bar{x} < 2.725) = P(-2.39 < z < 1.38) \approx 0.9162 - 0.0084 = 0.9078$

About 91% of samples of 32 gas stations that week will have a mean price between \$2.695 and \$2.725.

28. $z = \dfrac{\overline{x} - \mu}{\dfrac{\sigma}{\sqrt{n}}} = \dfrac{3.010 - 2.999}{\dfrac{0.049}{\sqrt{38}}} \approx \dfrac{0.011}{0.00795} \approx 1.38$

$z = \dfrac{\overline{x} - \mu}{\dfrac{\sigma}{\sqrt{n}}} = \dfrac{3.025 - 2.999}{\dfrac{0.049}{\sqrt{38}}} \approx \dfrac{0.026}{0.00795} \approx 3.27$

$P(3.010 < \overline{x} < 3.025) = P(1.38 < z < 3.27) = 0.9995 - 0.9162 = 0.0833$

About 8% of samples of 38 gas stations that week will have a mean price between $3.010 and $3.025.

29. $z = \dfrac{\overline{x} - \mu}{\dfrac{\sigma}{\sqrt{n}}} = \dfrac{66 - 64.3}{\dfrac{2.6}{\sqrt{60}}} \approx \dfrac{1.7}{0.336} \approx 5.06$

$P(\overline{x} > 66) = P(z > 5.06) \approx 0$

There is almost no chance that a random sample of 60 women will have a mean height greater than 66 inches. This event is almost impossible.

30. $z = \dfrac{\overline{x} - \mu}{\dfrac{\sigma}{\sqrt{n}}} = \dfrac{70 - 69.9}{\dfrac{3.0}{\sqrt{60}}} \approx \dfrac{0.1}{0.387} \approx 0.26$

$P(\overline{x} > 70) = P(z > 0.26) = 1 - P(z < 0.26) = 1 - 0.6026 = 0.3974$

About 40% of samples of 60 men will have a mean height greater than 70 inches.

31. $z = \dfrac{\overline{x} - \mu}{\sigma} = \dfrac{70 - 64.3}{2.6} \approx 2.19$

$P(x < 70) = P(z < 2.19) = 0.9857$

$z = \dfrac{\overline{x} - \mu}{\dfrac{\sigma}{\sqrt{n}}} = \dfrac{70 - 64.3}{\dfrac{2.6}{\sqrt{20}}} \approx \dfrac{5.7}{0.581} \approx 9.81$

$P(\overline{x} < 70) = P(z < 9.81) \approx 1$

It is more likely to select a sample of 20 women with a mean height less than 70 inches because the sample of 20 has a higher probability.

32. $z = \dfrac{\overline{x} - \mu}{\sigma} = \dfrac{65 - 69.9}{3.0} \approx -1.63$

$P(x < 65) = P(z < -1.63) = 0.0516$

$z = \dfrac{\overline{x} - \mu}{\dfrac{\sigma}{\sqrt{n}}} = \dfrac{65 - 69.9}{\dfrac{3.0}{\sqrt{15}}} \approx \dfrac{-4.9}{0.775} \approx -6.32$

$P(\overline{x} < 65) = P(z < -6.32) \approx 0$

It is more likely to select one man with a height less than 65 inches because the probability is greater.

33. $z = \dfrac{\bar{x} - \mu}{\dfrac{\sigma}{\sqrt{n}}} = \dfrac{127.9 - 128}{\dfrac{0.20}{\sqrt{40}}} \approx \dfrac{-0.1}{0.0316} \approx -3.16$

$P(\bar{x} < 127.9) = P(z < -3.16) \approx 0.0008$

Yes, it is very unlikely that you would have randomly sampled 40 cans with a mean equal to 127.9 ounces because it is more than 2 standard deviations from the mean of the sample means.

34. $z = \dfrac{\bar{x} - \mu}{\dfrac{\sigma}{\sqrt{n}}} = \dfrac{64.05 - 64}{\dfrac{0.11}{\sqrt{40}}} \approx \dfrac{0.05}{0.0174} \approx 2.87$

$P(\bar{x} > 64.05) = P(z > 2.87) = 1 - P(z < 2.87) = 1 - 0.9979 = 0.0021$

Yes, it is very unlikely that we would have randomly sampled 40 containers with a mean equal to 64.05 ounces because it is more than 2 standard deviations from the mean of the sample means.

35. (a) $\mu = 96$

$\sigma = 0.5$

$z = \dfrac{\bar{x} - \mu}{\dfrac{\sigma}{\sqrt{n}}} = \dfrac{96.25 - 96}{\dfrac{0.5}{\sqrt{40}}} \approx \dfrac{0.25}{0.079} \approx 3.16$

$P(\bar{x} \geq 96.25) = P(z > 3.16) = 1 - P(z < 3.16) = 1 - 0.9992 = 0.0008$

(b) The seller's claim is inaccurate.

(c) Assuming the distribution is normally distributed:

$z = \dfrac{\bar{x} - \mu}{\sigma} = \dfrac{96.25 - 96}{0.5} = 0.5$

$P(x > 96.25) = P(z > 0.5) = 1 - P(z < 0.5) = 1 - 0.6915 = 0.3085$

Assuming the manufacturer's claim is true, an individual board with a length of 96.25 would not be unusual. It is within 1 standard deviation of the mean for an individual board.

36. (a) $\mu = 10$

$\sigma = 0.5$

$z = \dfrac{\bar{x} - \mu}{\dfrac{\sigma}{\sqrt{n}}} = \dfrac{10.21 - 10}{\dfrac{0.5}{\sqrt{25}}} = \dfrac{0.21}{0.1} = 2.1$

$P(\bar{x} \geq 10.21) = P(z \geq 2.1) = 1 - P(z \leq 2.1) = 1 - 0.9821 = 0.0179$

(b) The manufacturer's claim is inaccurate.

(c) Assuming the distribution is normally distributed:

$z = \dfrac{x - \mu}{\sigma} = \dfrac{10.21 - 10}{0.5} = 0.42$

$P(x \geq 10.21) = P(z \geq 0.42) = 1 - P(z \leq 0.42) = 1 - 0.6628 = 0.3372$

Assuming the manufacturer's claim is true, an individual carton with a weight of 10.21 would not be unusual because it is within 1 standard deviation of the mean for an individual ice cream carton.

37. (a) $\mu = 50,000$

$\sigma = 800$

$$z = \dfrac{\bar{x} - \mu}{\dfrac{\sigma}{\sqrt{n}}} = \dfrac{49,721 - 50,000}{\dfrac{800}{\sqrt{100}}} = \dfrac{-279}{80} \approx -3.49$$

$P(\bar{x} \leq 49,721) = P(z \leq -3.49) = 0.0002$

(b) The manufacturer's claim is inaccurate.

(c) Assuming the distribution is normally distributed:

$$z = \dfrac{x - \mu}{\sigma} = \dfrac{49,721 - 50,000}{800} \approx -0.35$$

$P(x < 49,721) = P(z < -0.35) = 0.3632$

Assuming the manufacturer's claim is true, an individual tire with a life span of 49,721 miles is not unusual. It is within 1 standard deviation of the mean for an individual tire.

38. (a) $\mu = 38,000$

$\sigma = 1000$

$$z = \dfrac{\bar{x} - \mu}{\dfrac{\sigma}{\sqrt{n}}} = \dfrac{37,650 - 38,000}{\dfrac{1000}{\sqrt{50}}} \approx \dfrac{-350}{141.42} \approx -2.47$$

$P(\bar{x} \leq 37,650) = P(z \leq -2.47) = 0.0068$

(b) The manufacturer's claim is inaccurate.

(c) Assuming the distribution is normally distributed:

$$z = \dfrac{x - \mu}{\sigma} = \dfrac{37,650 - 38,000}{1000} = -0.35$$

$P(x < 37,650) = P(z < -0.35) = 0.3632$

Assuming the manufacturer's claim is true, an individual brake pad lasting less than 37,650 miles would not be unusual because it is within 1 standard deviation of the mean for an individual brake pad.

39. $\mu = 501$

$\sigma = 112$

$$z = \dfrac{\bar{x} - \mu}{\dfrac{\sigma}{\sqrt{n}}} = \dfrac{515 - 501}{\dfrac{112}{\sqrt{50}}} \approx \dfrac{14}{15.84} \approx 0.88$$

$P(\bar{x} \geq 515) = P(z \geq 0.88) = 1 - P(z \leq 0.88) = 1 - 0.8106 = 0.1894$

The high school's claim is not justified because it is not rare to find a sample mean as large as 515.

40. $\mu = 4$

$\sigma = 0.5$

$$z = \frac{\bar{x} - \mu}{\dfrac{\sigma}{\sqrt{n}}} = \frac{4.2 - 4}{\dfrac{0.5}{\sqrt{100}}} = \frac{0.2}{0.05} = 4$$

$P(\bar{x} \geq 4.2) = P(z \geq 4) = 1 - P(z \leq 4) \approx 1 - 1 \approx 0$

It is very unlikely the machine is calibrated to produce a bolt with a mean of 4 inches.

41. Use the finite correction factor since $n = 55 > 45 = 0.05N$.

$$z = \frac{\bar{x} - \mu}{\dfrac{\sigma}{\sqrt{n}} \sqrt{\dfrac{N-n}{N-1}}} = \frac{2.698 - 2.702}{\dfrac{0.009}{\sqrt{55}} \sqrt{\dfrac{900-55}{900-1}}} \approx \frac{-0.004}{(0.00121)\sqrt{0.9399}} \approx -3.41$$

$P(\bar{x} < 2.698) = P(z < -3.41) \approx 0.0003$

42. Use the finite correction factor since $n = 30 > 25 = 0.05N$.

$$z = \frac{\bar{x} - \mu}{\dfrac{\sigma}{\sqrt{n}} \sqrt{\dfrac{N-n}{N-1}}} = \frac{2.5 - 3.32}{\dfrac{1.09}{\sqrt{30}} \sqrt{\dfrac{500-30}{500-1}}} \approx \frac{-0.82}{(0.199)\sqrt{0.9419}} \approx -4.25$$

$$z = \frac{\bar{x} - \mu}{\dfrac{\sigma}{\sqrt{n}} \sqrt{\dfrac{N-n}{N-1}}} = \frac{4 - 3.32}{\dfrac{1.09}{\sqrt{30}} \sqrt{\dfrac{500-30}{500-1}}} \approx \frac{0.68}{(0.199)\sqrt{0.9419}} \approx 3.52$$

$P(2.5 < \bar{x} < 4) = P(-4.25 < z < 3.52) \approx 1 - 0 = 1$

43.

Sample	Number of boys from 3 births	Proportion of boys from 3 births
bbb	3	1
bbg	2	$\dfrac{2}{3}$
bgb	2	$\dfrac{2}{3}$
gbb	2	$\dfrac{2}{3}$
bgg	1	$\dfrac{1}{3}$
gbg	1	$\dfrac{1}{3}$
ggb	1	$\dfrac{1}{3}$
ggg	0	0

44.

Proportion of boys from 3 births	Probability
0	$\dfrac{1}{8}$
$\dfrac{1}{3}$	$\dfrac{3}{8}$
$\dfrac{2}{3}$	$\dfrac{3}{8}$
1	$\dfrac{1}{8}$

Proportion of Boys from Three Births

The spread of the histogram for each proportion is equal to the number of occurrences of 0, 1, 2, and 3 boys, respectively, from the binomial distribution.

45.

Sample	Numerical representation	Sample mean
bbb	111	1
bbg	110	$\dfrac{2}{3}$
bgb	101	$\dfrac{2}{3}$
gbb	011	$\dfrac{2}{3}$
bgg	100	$\dfrac{1}{3}$
gbg	010	$\dfrac{1}{3}$
ggb	001	$\dfrac{1}{3}$
ggg	000	0

The sample means are equal to the proportions.

46.

Sample	Number of boys from 4 births	Proportion of boys from 4 births
bbbb	4	1
bbbg	3	$\frac{3}{4}$
bbgb	3	$\frac{3}{4}$
bbgg	2	$\frac{1}{2}$
bgbb	3	$\frac{3}{4}$
bgbg	2	$\frac{1}{2}$
bggb	2	$\frac{1}{2}$
bggg	1	$\frac{1}{4}$

Sample	Number of boys from 4 births	Proportion of boys from 4 births
gbbb	3	$\frac{3}{4}$
gbbg	2	$\frac{1}{2}$
gbgb	2	$\frac{1}{2}$
gbgg	1	$\frac{1}{4}$
ggbb	2	$\frac{1}{2}$
ggbg	1	$\frac{1}{4}$
gggb	1	$\frac{1}{4}$
gggg	0	0

Proportion of boys from 4 births	Probability
0	$\frac{1}{16}$
$\frac{1}{4}$	$\frac{1}{4}$
$\frac{1}{2}$	$\frac{3}{8}$
$\frac{1}{4}$	$\frac{1}{4}$
1	$\frac{1}{16}$

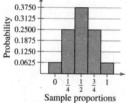

Proportion of Boys from Four Births

47. $z = \dfrac{\hat{p} - p}{\sqrt{\dfrac{pq}{n}}} = \dfrac{0.70 - 0.77}{\sqrt{\dfrac{0.77(0.23)}{105}}} = \dfrac{-0.07}{0.0411} = -1.70$

$P(p < 0.70) = P(z < -1.70) = 0.0446$

About 4.5% of samples of 105 female heart transplant patients will have a mean 3-year survival rate of less than 70%.

5.5 NORMAL APPROXIMATIONS TO BINOMIAL DISTRIBUTIONS

5.5 Try It Yourself Solutions

1a. $n = 125, p = 0.05, q = 0.95$

 b. $np = 6.25, nq = 118.75$

 c. Because $np \geq 5$ and $nq \geq 5$, the normal distribution can be used.

 d. $\mu = np = (125)(0.05) = 6.25$

  $\sigma = \sqrt{npq} = \sqrt{(125)(0.05)(0.95)} \approx 2.44$

2a. (1) $57, 58, \ldots, 83$ (2) $\ldots, 52, 53, 54$

 b. (1) $56.5 < x < 83.5$ (2) $x < 54.5$

3a. $n = 125, p = 0.05$

  $np = 6.25 \geq 5$ and $nq = 118.75 \geq 5$

  The normal distribution can be used.

 b. $\mu = np = 6.25$

  $\sigma = \sqrt{npq} \approx 2.44$

 c. $x > 9.5$

 d. $z = \dfrac{x - \mu}{\sigma} = \dfrac{9.5 - 6.25}{2.44} \approx 1.33$

 e. $P(z < 1.33) = 0.9082$

  $P(x > 9.5) = P(z > 1.33) = 1 - P(z < 1.33) = 0.0918$

  The probability that more than 9 respond yes is 0.0918.

4a. $n = 200, p = 0.58$

  $np = 116 \geq 5$ and $nq = 84 \geq 5$

  The normal distribution can be used.

 b. $\mu = np = 116$

  $\sigma = \sqrt{npq} \approx 6.98$

 c. $P(x \leq 100.5)$

d. $z = \dfrac{x-\mu}{\sigma} \approx \dfrac{100.5-116}{6.98} \approx -2.22$

e. $P(x < 100.5) = P(z < -2.22) = 0.0132$

The probability that at most 100 people will say never is approximately 0.0132.

5a. $n = 150, p = 0.24$

$np = 36 \geq 5$ and $nq = 114 \geq 5$

The normal distribution can be used.

b. $\mu = np = 36$

$\sigma = \sqrt{npq} \approx 5.23$

c. $P(26.5 < x < 27.5)$

d. $z = \dfrac{x-\mu}{\sigma} = \dfrac{26.5-36}{5.23} \approx -1.82$

$z = \dfrac{x-\mu}{\sigma} = \dfrac{27.5-36}{5.23} \approx -1.625$

e. $P(z < -1.82) = 0.0344$

$P(z < -1.625) = 0.0521$

$P(-1.82 < z < -1.63) = 0.0521 - 0.0344 = 0.0177$

The probability that exactly 27 people will respond yes is 0.0177.

5.5 EXERCISE SOLUTIONS

1. Properties of a binomial experiment:
    (1) The experiment is repeated for a fixed number of independent trials.
    (2) There are two possible outcomes: success or failure.
    (3) The probability of success is the same for each trial.
    (4) The random variable x counts the number of successful trials.

2. $np \geq 5$ and $nq \geq 5$

3. $np = (24)(0.85) = 20.4 \geq 5$

    $nq = (24)(0.15) = 3.6 < 5$

    Cannot use normal distribution.

4. $np = (15)(0.70) = 10.5 \geq 5$

    $nq = (15)(0.30) = 4.5 < 5$

    Cannot use normal distribution.

5. $np = (18)(0.90) = 16.2 \geq 5$

    $nq = (18)(0.10) = 1.8 < 5$

    Cannot use normal distribution.

6. $np = (20)(0.65) = 13 \geq 5$

    $nq = (20)(0.35) = 7 \geq 5$

    Can use normal distribution.

7. $n = 10$, $p = 0.85$, $q = 0.15$

   $np = 8.5 \geq 5$, $nq = 1.5 < 5$

   Cannot use normal distribution because $nq < 5$.

8. $n = 20$, $p = 0.63$, $q = 0.37$

   $np = 12.6 \geq 5$, $nq = 7.4 \geq 5$

   Can use normal distribution.

   $\mu = np = (20)(0.63) = 12.6$

   $\sigma = \sqrt{npq} = \sqrt{(20)(0.63)(0.37)} \approx 2.16$

9. $n = 50$, $p = 0.55$, $q = 0.45$

   $np = 27.5 \geq 5$, $nq = 22.5 \geq 5$

   Can use normal distribution.

   $\mu = np = (50)(0.55) = 27.5$

   $\sigma = \sqrt{npq} \approx 3.52$

10. $n = 30$, $p = 0.19$, $q = 0.81$

    $np = 5.7 \geq 5$, $nq = 24.3 \geq 5$

    Can use normal distribution.

    $\mu = np = (30)(0.19) = 5.7$

    $\sigma = \sqrt{npq} \approx 2.15$

11. $n = 20$, $p = 0.76$, $q = 0.24$

    $np = 15.2 \geq 5$, $nq = 4.8 < 5$

    Cannot use normal distribution because $nq < 5$.

12. $n = 15$, $p = 0.61$, $q = 0.39$

    $np = 9.15 \geq 5$, $nq = 5.85 \geq 5$

    Can use normal distribution.

    $\mu = np = (15)(0.61) = 9.15$

    $\sigma = \sqrt{npq} \approx 1.89$

13. a $\qquad$ **14.** d $\qquad$ **15.** c $\qquad$ **16.** b

17. The probability of getting fewer than 25 successes; $P(x < 24.5)$

18. The probability of getting at least 110 successes; $P(x > 109.5)$

19. The probability of getting exactly 33 successes; $P(32.5 < x < 33.5)$

20. The probability of getting more than 65 successes; $P(x > 65.5)$

21. The probability of getting at most 150 successes; $P(x < 150.5)$

22. The probability of getting between 55 and 60 successes; $P(55.5 < x < 59.5)$

23. $n = 100$, $p = 0.93$

$np = 93 \geq 5$, $nq = 7 \geq 5$

Can use normal distribution.

a. $z = \dfrac{x - \mu}{\sigma} \approx \dfrac{89.5 - 93}{2.55} \approx -1.37$

$z = \dfrac{x - \mu}{\sigma} \approx \dfrac{90.5 - 93}{2.55} \approx -0.98$

$P(x = 90) = P(89.5 < x < 90.5)$

$= P(-1.37 < z < -0.98)$

$= 0.1635 - 0.0835$

$= 0.0782$

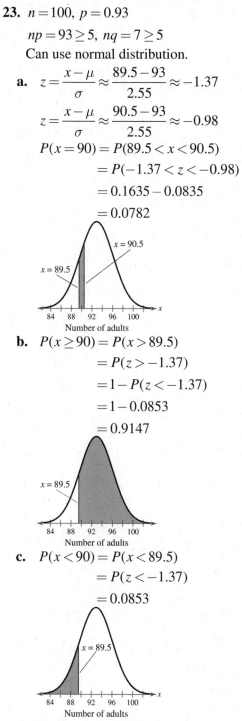

b. $P(x \geq 90) = P(x > 89.5)$

$= P(z > -1.37)$

$= 1 - P(z < -1.37)$

$= 1 - 0.0853$

$= 0.9147$

c. $P(x < 90) = P(x < 89.5)$

$= P(z < -1.37)$

$= 0.0853$

d. No, none of the probabilities are less than 0.05.

24. $n = 80$, $p = 0.70$

$np = 56 \geq 5$, $nq = 24 \geq 5$

Can use normal distribution.

a. $z = \dfrac{x - \mu}{\sigma} \approx \dfrac{69.5 - 56}{4.10} \approx 3.29$

$$\begin{aligned}
P(x \geq 70) &= P(x \geq 69.5) \\
&= P(z > 3.29) \\
&= 1 - P(z < 3.29) \\
&= 1 - 0.9995 \\
&= 0.0005
\end{aligned}$$

b. $z = \dfrac{x - \mu}{\sigma} \approx \dfrac{49.5 - 56}{4.10} \approx -1.59$

$z = \dfrac{x - \mu}{\sigma} \approx \dfrac{50.5 - 56}{4.10} \approx -1.34$

$$\begin{aligned}
P(x = 50) &= P(49.5 < x < 50.5) \\
&= P(-1.59 < z < -1.34) \\
&= 0.0901 - 0.0559 \\
&= 0.0342
\end{aligned}$$

c. $z = \dfrac{x - \mu}{\sigma} \approx \dfrac{60.5 - 56}{4.10} \approx 1.10$

$$\begin{aligned}
P(x > 60) &= P(x > 60.5) \\
&= P(z > 1.10) \\
&= 1 - P(z < 1.10) \\
&= 1 - 0.8643 \\
&= 0.1357
\end{aligned}$$

d. Yes, the events in parts (a) and (b) are unusual because their probabilities are less than 0.05.

25. $n = 150$, $p = 0.35$

$np = 52.5 \geq 5$, $nq = 97.5 \geq 5$

Can use normal distribution.

a. $z = \dfrac{x - \mu}{\sigma} \approx \dfrac{75.5 - 52.5}{5.84} \approx 3.94$

$P(x \leq 75) \approx P(x < 75.5) = P(z < 3.94) \approx 1$

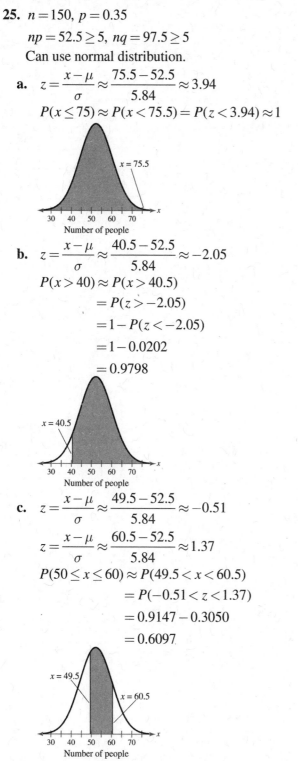

b. $z = \dfrac{x - \mu}{\sigma} \approx \dfrac{40.5 - 52.5}{5.84} \approx -2.05$

$\begin{aligned} P(x > 40) &\approx P(x > 40.5) \\ &= P(z > -2.05) \\ &= 1 - P(z < -2.05) \\ &= 1 - 0.0202 \\ &= 0.9798 \end{aligned}$

c. $z = \dfrac{x - \mu}{\sigma} \approx \dfrac{49.5 - 52.5}{5.84} \approx -0.51$

$z = \dfrac{x - \mu}{\sigma} \approx \dfrac{60.5 - 52.5}{5.84} \approx 1.37$

$\begin{aligned} P(50 \leq x \leq 60) &\approx P(49.5 < x < 60.5) \\ &= P(-0.51 < z < 1.37) \\ &= 0.9147 - 0.3050 \\ &= 0.6097 \end{aligned}$

d. No, none of the probabilities are less than 0.05.

26. $n = 50$, $p = 0.34$, $q = 0.66$

$np = 17 \geq 5$, $nq = 33 \geq 5$

Can use normal distribution.

a. $z = \dfrac{x - \mu}{\sigma} \approx \dfrac{11.5 - 17}{3.35} \approx -1.64$

$z = \dfrac{x - \mu}{\sigma} \approx \dfrac{12.5 - 17}{3.35} \approx -1.34$

$\begin{aligned} P(x = 12) &\approx P(11.5 \leq x \leq 12.5) \\ &= P(-1.64 < z < -1.34) \\ &= 0.0901 - 0.0505 \\ &= 0.0396 \end{aligned}$

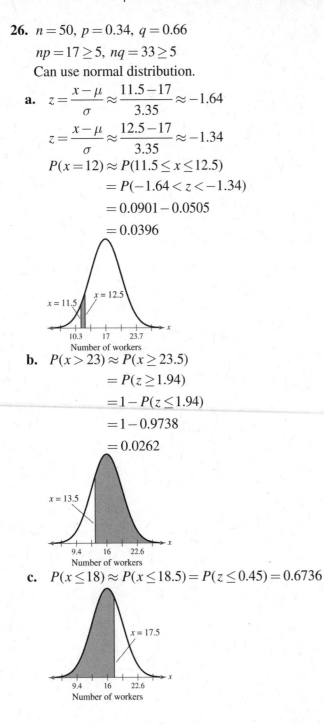

b. $\begin{aligned} P(x > 23) &\approx P(x \geq 23.5) \\ &= P(z \geq 1.94) \\ &= 1 - P(z \leq 1.94) \\ &= 1 - 0.9738 \\ &= 0.0262 \end{aligned}$

c. $P(x \leq 18) \approx P(x \leq 18.5) = P(z \leq 0.45) = 0.6736$

d. $n = 125$, $p = 0.34$, $q = 0.66$

$np = 42.5 \geq 5$, $nq = 82.5 \geq 5$

Can use normal distribution.

$$z = \frac{x - \mu}{\sigma} \approx \frac{29.5 - 42.5}{5.30} \approx -2.45$$

$$P(x < 30) \approx P(x \leq 29.5) = P(z \leq -2.45) = 0.0071$$

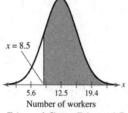

$x = 29.5$

36.6   48   59.4
Number of workers

27. $n = 250$, $p = 0.05$, $q = 0.95$

$np = 12.5 \geq 5$, $nq = 237.5 \geq 5$

Can use normal distribution.

a. $z = \dfrac{x - \mu}{\sigma} \approx \dfrac{15.5 - 12.5}{3.45} \approx 0.87$

$z = \dfrac{x - \mu}{\sigma} \approx \dfrac{16.5 - 12.5}{3.45} \approx 1.16$

$P(x = 16) \approx P(15.5 \leq x \leq 16.5) = P(0.87 \leq z \leq 1.16)$

$\qquad\qquad = 0.8770 - 0.8078 = 0.0692$

$x = 15.5$ $x = 16.5$

5.6   12.5   19.4
Number of workers

b. $P(x \geq 9) \approx P(x \geq 8.5) = P(z \geq -1.16) = 1 - P(z \leq -1.16) = 1 - 0.1230 = 0.8770$

$x = 8.5$

5.6   12.5   19.4
Number of workers

c. $P(x < 16) \approx P(x \leq 15.5) = P(z \leq 0.87) = 0.8078$

$x = 15.5$

5.6   12.5   19.4
Number of workers

d. $n = 500$, $p = 0.05$, $q = 0.95$

$np = 25 \geq 5$, $nq = 475 \geq 5$

Can use normal distribution.

$$z = \frac{x - \mu}{\sigma} \approx \frac{29.5 - 25}{4.87} \approx 0.92$$

$$P(x < 30) \approx P(x < 29.5) = P(z < 0.92) = 0.8212$$

$x = 29.5$

15.3 25 34.7
Number of workers

28. $n = 12$, $p = 0.67$

$np = 8.04 \geq 5$, $nq = 3.96 < 5$

Cannot use normal distribution because $nq < 5$.

a. $P(x < 4) = P(x = 0) + P(x = 1) + P(x = 2) + P(x = 3)$

$$= {}_{12}C_0 (0.67)^0 (0.33)^{12} + {}_{12}C_1 (0.67)^1 (0.33)^{11} + {}_{12}C_2 (0.67)^2 (0.33)^{10} + {}_{12}C_3 (0.67)^3 (0.33)^9$$

$$\approx 0.0036$$

b. $P(7 \leq x \leq 9) = P(x = 7) + P(x = 8) + P(x = 9)$

$$= {}_{12}C_7 (0.67)^7 (0.33)^5 + {}_{12}C_8 (0.67)^8 (0.33)^4 + {}_{12}C_9 (0.67)^9 (0.33)^3$$

$$\approx 0.641$$

c. $P(x \leq 10) = P(x = 0) + P(x = 1) + \ldots + P(x = 9) + P(x = 10)$

$$= {}_{12}C_0 (0.67)^0 (0.33)^{12} + {}_{12}C_1 (0.67)^1 (0.33)^{11} + {}_{12}C_2 (0.67)^2 (0.33)^{10} +$$

$$\ldots + {}_{12}C_9 (0.67)^9 (0.33)^3 + {}_{12}C_{10} (0.67)^{10} (0.33)^2$$

$$\approx 0.943$$

d. Yes, the event is part (a) is unusual because its probability is less than 0.05.

29. $n = 200$, $p = 0.34$

$np = 68 \geq 5$, $nq = 132 \geq 5$

Can use normal distribution.

a. $z = \dfrac{x - \mu}{\sigma} \approx \dfrac{84.5 - 68}{6.70} \approx 2.46$

$P(x \geq 85) \approx P(x > 84.5) = P(z > 2.46) = 1 - P(z < 2.46) = 1 - 0.9931 = 0.0069$

$x = 84.5$

50 60 70 80 90
Number of people

b. $z = \dfrac{x - \mu}{\sigma} \approx \dfrac{65.5 - 68}{6.70} \approx -0.37$

$P(x < 66) \approx P(x < 65.5) = P(z < -0.37) = 0.3557$

$x = 65.5$
50 60 70 80 90
Number of people

c. $z = \dfrac{x - \mu}{\sigma} \approx \dfrac{67.5 - 68}{6.70} \approx -0.07$

$z = \dfrac{x - \mu}{\sigma} \approx \dfrac{68.5 - 68}{6.70} \approx 0.07$

$P(x = 68) \approx P(67.5 < x < 68.5) = P(-0.07 < z < 0.07) = 0.5279 - 0.4721 = 0.0558$

$x = 68.5$
$x = 67.5$
50 60 70 80 90
Number of people

d. $n = 6$, $p = 0.34$

$np = 2.04 < 5$, $nq = 3.96 < 5$

Cannot use normal distribution because $np < 5$ and $nq < 5$.

$P(x = 6) = {}_6C_6 (0.34)^6 (0.66)^0 \approx 0.002$

30. $n = 10$, $p = 0.029$

$np = 0.29 < 5$, $nq = 9.71 \geq 5$

Cannot use normal distribution because $np < 5$.

a. $P(x \leq 3) = P(x = 0) + P(x = 1) + P(x = 2) + P(x = 3)$

$= {}_{10}C_0 (0.029)^0 (0.971)^{10} + {}_{10}C_1 (0.029)^1 (0.971)^9 + {}_{10}C_2 (0.029)^2 (0.971)^8 + {}_{10}C_3 (0.029)^3 (0.971)^7$

≈ 0.999871

b. $P(x \geq 1) = 1 - P(x < 1) = 1 - P(x + 0) \approx 0.255$

c. $P(x > 2) = 1 - P(x \leq 2)$

$\approx 1 - {}_{10}C_0 (0.029)^0 (0.971)^{10} + {}_{10}C_1 (0.029)^1 (0.971)^9 + {}_{10}C_2 (0.029)^2 (0.971)^8$

≈ 0.003

d. $n = 50$, $p = 0.029$

$np = 1.45 < 5$, $nq = 48.55 \geq 5$

Cannot use normal distribution because $np < 5$.

$P(x = 0) = {}_{50}C_0 (0.029)^0 (0.971)^{50} \approx 0.230$

31. Binomial: $P(5 \le x \le 7) = P(x = 5) + P(x = 6) + P(x = 7)$
$$= {}_{16}C_5(0.4)^5(0.6)^{11} + {}_{16}C_6(0.4)^6(0.6)^{10} + {}_{16}C_7(0.4)^7(0.6)^9$$
$$\approx 0.549$$

Normal: $\mu = np = 6.4$, $\sigma = \sqrt{npq} \approx 1.96$

$$z = \frac{x - \mu}{\sigma} \approx \frac{4.5 - 6.4}{1.96} \approx -0.97$$

$$z = \frac{x - \mu}{\sigma} \approx \frac{7.5 - 6.4}{1.96} \approx 0.56$$

$$P(5 \le x \le 7) \approx P(4.5 \le x \le 7.5) = P(-0.97 \le z \le 0.56)$$
$$= 0.7123 - 0.1660$$
$$= 0.5463$$

32. Binomial: $P(2 \le x \le 4) = P(x = 2) + P(x = 3) + P(x = 4)$
$$= {}_{12}C_2(0.5)^2(0.5)^{10} + {}_{12}C_3(0.5)^3(0.5)^9 + {}_{12}C_4(0.5)^4(0.5)^8$$
$$\approx 0.191$$

Normal: $\mu = np = 6$, $\sigma = \sqrt{npq} \approx 1.73$

$$z = \frac{x - \mu}{\sigma} \approx \frac{1.5 - 6}{1.73} \approx -2.60$$

$$z = \frac{x - \mu}{\sigma} \approx \frac{4.5 - 6}{1.73} \approx -0.87$$

$$P(2 \le x \le 4) \approx P(1.5 \le x \le 4.5) = P(-2.60 \le z \le -0.87)$$
$$= 0.1922 - 0.0047$$
$$= 0.1875$$

33. $n = 250$, $p = 0.70$

60% say no $\rightarrow$ 250(0.6) = 150 say no while 100 say yes.

$$z = \frac{x - \mu}{\sigma} \approx \frac{100.5 - 175}{7.25} \approx -10.28$$

$P(\text{less than or equal to 100 say yes}) = P(x \le 100) = P(x < 100.5) = P(z < -10.28) \approx 0$

It is highly unlikely that 60% responded no. Answers will vary.

34. $n = 200$, $p = 0.11$

9% of 200 = 18 people

$$z = \frac{x - \mu}{\sigma} \approx \frac{18.5 - 22}{4.42} \approx -0.79$$

$P(x \le 18) = P(x < 18.5) = P(z < -0.79) = 0.2148$

It is probably that 18 of the 200 people responded that they participate in hiking. Answers will vary.

35. $n = 100$, $p = 0.75$

$$z = \frac{x - \mu}{\sigma} \approx \frac{69.5 - 75}{4.33} \approx -1.27$$

$P(\text{reject claim}) = P(x < 70) = P(x < 69.5) = P(z < -1.27) = 0.1020$

36. $n = 100$, $p = 0.65$

$$z = \frac{x - \mu}{\sigma} \approx \frac{69.5 - 65}{4.77} \approx 0.94$$

$P(\text{accept claim}) = P(x \geq 70) = P(x > 69.5) = P(z > 0.94) = 1 - P(z < 0.94) = 1 - 0.8264 = 0.1736$

CHAPTER 5 REVIEW EXERCISE SOLUTIONS

1. $\mu = 15$, $\sigma = 3$ **2.** $\mu = -3$, $\sigma = 5$

3. Curve B has the greatest mean because its line of symmetry occurs the farthest to the right.

4. Curve A has the greatest standard deviation because it is the most spread out.

5. $x = 1.32$: $z = \dfrac{x - \mu}{\sigma} = \dfrac{1.32 - 1.5}{0.08} = -2.25$

$x = 1.54$: $z = \dfrac{x - \mu}{\sigma} = \dfrac{1.54 - 1.5}{0.08} = 0.5$

$x = 1.66$: $z = \dfrac{x - \mu}{\sigma} = \dfrac{1.66 - 1.5}{0.08} = 2$

$x = 1.78$: $z = \dfrac{x - \mu}{\sigma} = \dfrac{1.78 - 1.5}{0.08} = 3.5$

6. 1.32 and 1.78 are unusual.   **7.** 0.6772

8. $0.2119 - 0.0094 = 0.2025$ **9.** 0.6293

10. 0.0256   **11.** $1 - 0.2843 = 0.7157$

12. $1 - 0.9994 = 0.0006$ **13.** 0.00235

14. $1 - 0.5060 = 0.4940$ **15.** $0.5 - 0.0505 = 0.4495$

16. $0.8508 - 0.0606 = 0.7902$ **17.** $0.9564 - 0.5199 = 0.4365$

18. $0.9963 - 0.0037 = 0.9926$ **19.** $0.0668 + 0.0668 = 0.1336$

20. $0.7389 + 0.0003 = 0.7392$

21. A: 8
 B: 17
 C: 23
 D: 29

22. $x = 8 \Rightarrow z = \dfrac{x - \mu}{\sigma} = \dfrac{8 - 21.4}{6.2} \approx -2.16$

$x = 17 \Rightarrow z = \dfrac{x - \mu}{\sigma} = \dfrac{17 - 21.4}{6.2} \approx -0.71$

$x = 23 \Rightarrow z = \dfrac{x - \mu}{\sigma} = \dfrac{23 - 21.4}{6.2} \approx 0.26$

$x = 29 \Rightarrow z = \dfrac{x - \mu}{\sigma} = \dfrac{29 - 21.4}{6.2} \approx 1.23$

The test score of 8 is unusual because its corresponding z-score is more than 2 standard deviations from the mean.

23. $P(z < 1.28) = 0.8997$ **24.** $P(z > -0.74) = 0.7704$

25. $P(-2.15 < x < 1.55) = 0.9394 - 0.0158 = 0.9236$

26. $P(0.42 < z < 3.15) = 0.9992 - 0.6628 = 0.3364$

27. $P(z < -2.50 \text{ or } z > 2.50) = 2(0.0062) = 0.0124$

28. $P(z < 0 \text{ or } z > 1.68) = 0.5 + 0.0465 = 0.5465$

29. $z = \dfrac{x - \mu}{\sigma} = \dfrac{84 - 74}{8} = 1.25$

$P(x < 84) = P(z < 1.25) = 0.8944$

30. $z = \dfrac{x - \mu}{\sigma} = \dfrac{55 - 74}{8} = -2.375$

$P(x < 55) = P(z < -2.375) = 0.0088$

31. $z = \dfrac{x - \mu}{\sigma} = \dfrac{80 - 74}{8} = 0.75$

$P(x > 80) = P(z > 0.75) = 1 - P(z < 0.75) = 1 - 0.7734 = 0.2266$

32. $z = \dfrac{x - \mu}{\sigma} = \dfrac{71.6 - 74}{8} = -0.3$

$P(x > 71.6) = P(z > -0.3) = 1 - P(z < -0.3) = 1 - 0.3821 = 0.6179$

33. $z = \dfrac{x - \mu}{\sigma} = \dfrac{60 - 74}{8} = -1.75$

$z = \dfrac{x - \mu}{\sigma} = \dfrac{70 - 74}{8} = -0.5$

$P(60 < x < 70) = P(-1.75 < z < -0.5) = 0.3085 - 0.0401 = 0.2684$

34. $z = \dfrac{x - \mu}{\sigma} = \dfrac{72 - 74}{8} = -0.25$

$z = \dfrac{x - \mu}{\sigma} = \dfrac{82 - 74}{8} = 1.00$

$P(72 < x < 82) = P(-0.25 < z < 1.00) = 0.8413 - 0.4013 = 0.4400$

35. (a) $z = \dfrac{x - \mu}{\sigma} = \dfrac{1900 - 2200}{625} = -0.48$

$P(x < 1900) = P(z < -0.48) = 0.3156$

(b) $z = \dfrac{x - \mu}{\sigma} = \dfrac{2000 - 2200}{625} = -0.32$

$z = \dfrac{x - \mu}{\sigma} = \dfrac{2500 - 2200}{625} = 0.48$

$P(2000 < x < 2500) = P(-0.32 < z < 0.48) = 0.6844 - 0.3745 = 0.3099$

(c) $z = \dfrac{x - \mu}{\sigma} = \dfrac{2450 - 2200}{625} = 0.4$

$P(x > 2450) = P(z > 0.4) = 0.3446$

36. (a) $z = \dfrac{x - \mu}{\sigma} = \dfrac{1 - 1.5}{0.25} = -2$

$z = \dfrac{x - \mu}{\sigma} = \dfrac{2 - 1.5}{0.25} = 2$

$P(1 < x < 2) + P(-2 < z < 2) = 0.9722 - 0.0228 = 0.9544$

(b) $z = \dfrac{x - \mu}{\sigma} = \dfrac{1.6 - 1.5}{0.25} = 0.4$

$z = \dfrac{x - \mu}{\sigma} = \dfrac{2.2 - 1.5}{0.25} = 2.8$

$P(1.6 < x < 2.2) = P(0.4 < z < 2.8) = 0.9974 - 0.6554 = 0.3420$

(c) $z = \dfrac{x - \mu}{\sigma} = \dfrac{2.2 - 1.5}{0.25} = 2.8$

$P(x > 2.2) = P(z > 2.8) = 0.0026$

37. No, none of the events are unusual because their probabilities are greater than 0.05.

38. Yes, the event in part (c) is unusual because its probability is less than 0.05.

39. $z = -0.07$ **40.** $z = -1.28$ **41.** $z = 1.13$

42. $z = -2.05$ **43.** $z = 1.04$ **44.** $z = -0.10$

45. 0.51   **46.** 1.88

47. $x = \mu + z\sigma = 48 + (-2.5)(2.2) = 42.5$ meters

48. $x = \mu + z\sigma = 48 + (1.2)(2.2) \approx 50.6$ meters

49. 95th percentile $\Rightarrow$ Area $= 0.95 \Rightarrow z = 1.645$

$x = \mu + z\sigma = 48 + (1.645)(2.2) \approx 51.6$ meters

50. 3rd quartile $\Rightarrow$ Area $= 0.75 \Rightarrow z = 0.67$

$x = \mu + z\sigma = 48 + (0.67)(2.2) \approx 49.5$ meters

51. Top 10% $\Rightarrow$ Area $= 0.90 \Rightarrow z = 1.28$

$x = \mu + z\sigma = 48 + (1.28)(2.2) \approx 50.8$ meters

52. Bottom 5% $\Rightarrow$ Area $= 0.05 \Rightarrow z = -1.645$

$x = \mu + z\sigma = 48 + (-1.645)(2.2) \approx 44.4$ meters

53. {90 90 90, 90 90 120, 90 90 160, 90 90 210, 90 120 90, 90 120 120, 90 120 160, 90 120 210, 90 160 90, 90 160 120, 90 160 160, 90 160 210, 90 210 90, 90 210 120, 90 210 160, 90 210 210, 120 90 90, 120 90 120, 120 90 160, 120 90 210, 120 120 90, 120 120 120, 120 120 160, 120 120 210, 120 160 90, 120 160 120, 120 160 160, 120 160 210, 120 210 90, 120 210 120, 120 210 160, 120 210 210, 160 90 90, 160 90 120, 160 90 160, 160 90 210, 160 120 90, 160 120 120, 160 120 160, 160 120 210, 160 160 90, 160 160 120, 160 160 160, 160 160 210, 160 210 90, 160 210 120, 160 210 160, 160 210 210, 210 90 90, 210 90 120, 210 90 160, 210 90 210, 210 120 90, 210 120 120, 210 120 160, 210 120 210, 210 160 90, 210 160 120, 210 160 160, 210 160 210, 210 210 90, 210 210 120, 210 210 160, 210 210 210}

$\mu = 145$, $\sigma = 45$

$\mu_{\bar{x}} = 145$, $\sigma_{\bar{x}} = \dfrac{45}{\sqrt{3}} \approx 25.98$

The means are the same, but $\sigma_{\bar{x}}$ is less than σ.

54. {00, 01, 02, 03, 10, 11, 12, 13, 20, 21, 22, 23, 30, 31, 32, 33}

$\mu = 1.5$, $\sigma \approx 1.118$

$\mu_{\bar{x}} = 1.5$, $\sigma_{\bar{x}} \approx \dfrac{1.118}{\sqrt{2}} \approx 0.791$

The means are the same, but $\sigma_{\bar{x}}$ is less than σ.

55. $\mu_{\bar{x}} = 76$, $\sigma_{\bar{x}} = \dfrac{\sigma}{\sqrt{n}} = \dfrac{20.5}{\sqrt{35}} \approx 3.465$

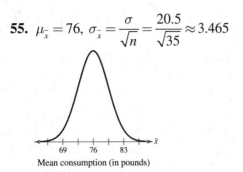

Mean consumption (in pounds)

56. $\mu_{\bar{x}} = 108.3$, $\sigma_{\bar{x}} = \dfrac{\sigma}{\sqrt{n}} = \dfrac{35.1}{\sqrt{40}} \approx 5.550$

97.3   108.3   119.3 $\bar{x}$
Mean consumption (in pounds)

57. (a) $z = \dfrac{\bar{x} - \mu}{\dfrac{\sigma}{\sqrt{n}}} = \dfrac{1900 - 2200}{\dfrac{625}{\sqrt{12}}} \approx \dfrac{-300}{180.42} \approx -1.66$

$P(\bar{x} < 1900) = P(z < -1.66) = 0.0485$

(b) $z = \dfrac{\bar{x} - \mu}{\dfrac{\sigma}{\sqrt{n}}} = \dfrac{2000 - 2200}{\dfrac{625}{\sqrt{12}}} \approx \dfrac{-200}{180.42} \approx -1.11$

$z = \dfrac{\bar{x} - \mu}{\dfrac{\sigma}{\sqrt{n}}} = \dfrac{2500 - 2200}{\dfrac{625}{\sqrt{12}}} \approx \dfrac{300}{180.42} \approx 1.66$

$P(2000 < \bar{x} < 2500) = P(-1.11 < z < 1.66) = 0.9515 - 0.1335 = 0.8180$

(c) $z = \dfrac{\bar{x} - \mu}{\dfrac{\sigma}{\sqrt{n}}} = \dfrac{2450 - 2200}{\dfrac{625}{\sqrt{12}}} \approx \dfrac{250}{180.42} \approx 1.39$

$P(\bar{x} > 2450) = P(z > 1.39) = 0.0823$

(a) and (c) are smaller, (b) is larger. This is to be expected because the standard error of the sample mean is smaller.

58. (a) $z = \dfrac{\bar{x} - \mu}{\dfrac{\sigma}{\sqrt{n}}} = \dfrac{1.0 - 1.5}{\dfrac{0.25}{\sqrt{7}}} \approx \dfrac{-0.5}{0.0945} \approx -5.29$

$z = \dfrac{\bar{x} - \mu}{\dfrac{\sigma}{\sqrt{n}}} = \dfrac{2.0 - 1.5}{\dfrac{0.25}{\sqrt{7}}} \approx \dfrac{0.5}{0.0945} \approx 5.29$

$P(1.0 < \bar{x} < 2.0) = P(-5.29 < z < 5.29) \approx 1$

(b) $z = \dfrac{\bar{x} - \mu}{\dfrac{\sigma}{\sqrt{n}}} = \dfrac{1.6 - 1.5}{\dfrac{0.25}{\sqrt{7}}} \approx \dfrac{0.1}{0.0945} \approx 1.06$

$z = \dfrac{\bar{x} - \mu}{\dfrac{\sigma}{\sqrt{n}}} = \dfrac{2.2 - 1.5}{\dfrac{0.25}{\sqrt{7}}} \approx \dfrac{0.7}{0.0945} \approx 7.41$

$P(1.6 < \bar{x} < 2.2) = P(1.06 < z < 7.41) \approx 1 - 0.8554 = 0.1446$

(c) $z = \dfrac{\overline{x} - \mu}{\dfrac{\sigma}{\sqrt{n}}} = \dfrac{2.2 - 1.5}{\dfrac{0.25}{\sqrt{7}}} \approx \dfrac{0.7}{0.0945} \approx 7.41$

$P(\overline{x} > 2.2) = P(z > 7.41) \approx 0$

(a) is larger and (b) and (c) are smaller.

59. (a) $z = \dfrac{\overline{x} - \mu}{\dfrac{\sigma}{\sqrt{n}}} = \dfrac{29,000 - 29,200}{\dfrac{1500}{\sqrt{45}}} \approx \dfrac{-200}{223.61} \approx -0.89$

$P(\overline{x} < 29,000) = P(z < -0.89) = 0.1867$

(b) $z = \dfrac{\overline{x} - \mu}{\dfrac{\sigma}{\sqrt{n}}} = \dfrac{31,000 - 29,200}{\dfrac{1500}{\sqrt{45}}} \approx \dfrac{1800}{223.61} \approx 8.05$

$P(\overline{x} > 31,000) = P(z > 8.05) \approx 0$

60. (a) $z = \dfrac{\overline{x} - \mu}{\dfrac{\sigma}{\sqrt{n}}} = \dfrac{1400 - 1300}{\dfrac{250}{\sqrt{36}}} \approx \dfrac{100}{41.67} \approx 2.4$

$P(x < 1400) = P(z < 2.4) = 0.9918$

(b) $z = \dfrac{\overline{x} - \mu}{\dfrac{\sigma}{\sqrt{n}}} = \dfrac{1150 - 1300}{\dfrac{250}{\sqrt{36}}} \approx \dfrac{-150}{41.67} \approx -3.6$

$P(x > 1150) = P(z > -3.6) \approx 1 - 0 = 1$

61. Assuming the distribution is normally distributed:

$z = \dfrac{\overline{x} - \mu}{\dfrac{\sigma}{\sqrt{n}}} = \dfrac{1.125 - 1.5}{\dfrac{0.5}{\sqrt{15}}} \approx \dfrac{-0.375}{0.1291} \approx -2.90$

$P(\overline{x} < 1.125) = P(z < -2.90) = 0.0019$

62. Assuming the distribution is normally distributed:

$z = \dfrac{\overline{x} - \mu}{\dfrac{\sigma}{\sqrt{n}}} = \dfrac{525 - 500}{\dfrac{30}{\sqrt{15}}} \approx \dfrac{25}{7.75} \approx 3.23$

$P(\overline{x} > 525) = P(z > 3.23) = 1 - P(z < 3.23) = 1 - 0.9994 = 0.0006$

63. $n = 12$, $p = 0.96$, $q = 0.04$

$np = 11.52 \geq 5$, but $nq = 0.48 < 5$

Cannot use the normal distribution because $nq < 5$.

64. $n = 30$, $p = 0.75$, $q = 0.25$

$np = 22.5 \geq 5$, and $nq = 7.5 \geq 5$

Can use the normal distribution.

$\mu = np = 22.5$, $\sigma = \sqrt{npq} = \sqrt{30(0.75)(0.25)} \approx 2.37$

65. $P(x \geq 25) = P(x > 24.5)$ **65.** $P(x \leq 36) = P(x < 36.5)$

67. $P(x = 45) = P(44.5 < x < 45.5)$ **68.** $P(x = 50) = P(49.5 < x < 50.5)$

69. $n = 45$, $p = 0.70$

$np = 31.5 \geq 5$, $nq = 13.5 \geq 5$

Can use the normal distribution.

$\mu = np = 31.5$, $\sigma = \sqrt{npq} = \sqrt{45(0.70)(0.30)} \approx 3.07$

$z = \dfrac{x - \mu}{\sigma} \approx \dfrac{20.5 - 31.5}{3.07} \approx -3.58$

$P(x \leq 20) \approx P(x < 20.5) = P(z < -3.58) \approx 0$

$x = 20.5$

25.3   31.5   37.7

Children saying yes

70. $n = 15$, $p = 0.31$

$np = 4.65 < 5$, $nq = 10.35 \geq 5$

Cannot use normal distribution because $np < 5$.

$P(x > 8) = 1 - P(x \leq 8)$

$= 1 - [P(x = 0) + P(x = 1) + \ldots + P(x = 8)]$

$= 1 - \left[{}_{15}C_0 (0.31)^0 (0.69)^{15} + {}_{15}C_1 (0.31)^1 (0.69)^{14} + \ldots + {}_{15}C_8 (0.31)^8 (0.69)^7 \right]$

≈ 0.019

CHAPTER 5 QUIZ SOLUTIONS

1. (a) $P(z > -2.54) = 0.9945$

(b) $P(z < 3.09) = 0.9990$

(c) $P(-0.88 < z < 0.88) = 0.8106 - 0.1894 = 0.6212$

(d) $P(z < -1.445 \text{ or } z > -0.715) = 0.0742 + 0.76265 = 0.83685$

2. (a) $z = \dfrac{x-\mu}{\sigma} = \dfrac{5.36-5.5}{0.08} = -1.75$

$z = \dfrac{x-\mu}{\sigma} = \dfrac{5.64-5.5}{0.08} = 1.75$

$P(5.36 < x < 5.64) = P(-1.75 < z < 1.75) = 0.9599 - 0.0401 = 0.9198$

(b) $z = \dfrac{x-\mu}{\sigma} = \dfrac{-5.00-(-8.2)}{7.84} \approx 0.41$

$z = \dfrac{x-\mu}{\sigma} = \dfrac{0-(-8.2)}{7.84} \approx 1.05$

$P(-5.00 < x < 0) = P(0.41 < z < 1.05) = 0.8531 - 0.6591 = 0.1940$

(c) $z = \dfrac{x-\mu}{\sigma} = \dfrac{0-18.5}{9.25} = -2$

$z = \dfrac{x-\mu}{\sigma} = \dfrac{37-18.5}{9.25} = 2$

$P(x < 0 \text{ or } x > 37) = P(z < -2 \text{ or } z > 2) = 2(0.0228) = 0.0456$

3. $z = \dfrac{x-\mu}{\sigma} = \dfrac{125-100}{15} \approx 1.67$

$P(x > 125) = P(z > 1.67) = 0.0475$

Yes, the event is unusual because its probability is less than 0.05.

4. $z = \dfrac{x-\mu}{\sigma} = \dfrac{95-100}{15} \approx -0.33$

$z = \dfrac{x-\mu}{\sigma} = \dfrac{105-100}{15} \approx 0.33$

$P(95 < x < 105) = P(-0.33 < z < 0.33) = 0.6293 - 0.3707 = 0.2586$

No, the event is not unusual because its probability is greater than 0.05.

5. $P(x > 112) = P(z > 0.80) = 0.2119 \rightarrow 21.19\%$

6. $z = \dfrac{x-\mu}{\sigma} = \dfrac{90-100}{15} \approx -0.67$

$P(x < 90) = P(z < -0.67) = 0.2514$

$(2000)(0.2514) = 502.8 \rightarrow 503$ students

7. Top 5% $\rightarrow z = 1.645$

$\mu + z\sigma = 100 + (1.645)(15) \approx 124.7 \rightarrow 125$

8. Bottom 10% $\rightarrow z = -1.28$

$\mu + z\sigma = 100 + (-1.28)(15) = 80.8 \rightarrow 80$

(Because you are finding the highest score that would still place you in the bottom 10%, round down, because if you rounded up you would be outside the bottom 10%.)

9. $z = \dfrac{\overline{x} - \mu}{\dfrac{\sigma}{\sqrt{n}}} = \dfrac{105 - 100}{\dfrac{15}{\sqrt{60}}} \approx \dfrac{5}{1.936} \approx 2.58$

$P(\overline{x} > 105) = P(z > 2.58) \approx 0.0049$

About 0.5% of samples of 60 students will have a mean IQ score greater than 105. This is a very unusual event.

10. $z = \dfrac{x - \mu}{\sigma} = \dfrac{105 - 100}{15} \approx 0.33$

$P(x > 105) = P(z > 0.33) = 0.3707$

$z = \dfrac{\overline{x} - \mu}{\dfrac{\sigma}{\sqrt{n}}} = \dfrac{105 - 100}{\dfrac{15}{\sqrt{15}}} \approx \dfrac{5}{3.873} \approx 1.29$

$P(\overline{x} > 105) = P(z > 1.29) \approx 0.0985$

You are more likely to select one student with a test score greater than 105 because the standard error of the mean is less than the standard deviation.

11. $n = 35$, $p = 0.81 \rightarrow np = 28.35$, $nq = 6.65$

Can use normal distribution.

$\mu = np = 28.35$, $\sigma = \sqrt{npq} \approx 2.321$

12. $z = \dfrac{x - \mu}{\sigma} \approx \dfrac{20.5 - 28.35}{2.321} \approx -3.38$

$P(x \le 20) = P(x < 20.5) = P(z < -3.38) = 0.0004$

This event is extremely unusual because its probability is much less than 0.05.

CUMULATIVE REVIEW, CHAPTERS 3-5

1. (a) $np = 50(0.15) = 7.5 \ge 5$

$nq = 50(0.85) = 42.5 \ge 5$

Can use normal distribution.

$\mu = np = 50(0.15) = 7.5$

   (b) $\sigma = \sqrt{npq} = \sqrt{50(0.15)(0.85)} \approx 2.52$

$P(x \le 14) \approx P(x \le 14.5)$

$= P\left(z \le \dfrac{14.5 - 7.5}{2.52}\right)$

$= P(z \le 2.78)$

$= 0.9973$

(c) It is unusual for 14 out of 50 voters to rate the U.S. health care system as excellent because the probability is less than 0.05.

$$P(x=14) \approx P(13.5 \leq x \leq 14.5)$$

$$= P\left(\frac{13.5-7.5}{2.52} \leq z \leq \frac{14.5-7.5}{2.52}\right)$$

$$= P(2.38 \leq z \leq 2.78)$$

$$= 0.9973 - 0.9913$$

$$= 0.0060$$

2.

x	$P(x)$	$xP(x)$	$x-\mu$	$(x-\mu)^2$	$(x-\mu)^2 P(x)$
2	0.427	0.854	−1.13	1.277	0.545
3	0.227	0.681	−0.13	0.017	0.004
4	0.200	0.800	0.87	0.757	0.151
5	0.093	0.465	1.87	3.497	0.325
6	0.034	0.204	2.87	8.237	0.280
7	0.018	0.126	3.87	14.977	0.270
		$\sum xP(x)=3.13$			$\sum(x-\mu)^2 P(x) \approx 1.575$

(a) $\mu = \sum xP(x) \approx 3.1$

(b) $\sigma^2 = \sum(x-\mu)^2 P(x) \approx 1.6$

(c) $\sigma = \sqrt{\sigma^2} \approx 1.3$

(d) $E(x) = \sum xP(x) \approx 3.1$

(e) The size of a family household on average is about 3 persons. The standard deviation is 1.3, so most households differ from the mean by no more than about 1 person.

3.

x	$P(x)$	$xP(x)$	$x-\mu$	$(x-\mu)^2$	$(x-\mu)^2 P(x)$
0	0.012	0.000	−3.596	12.931	0.155
1	0.049	0.049	−2.596	6.739	0.330
2	0.159	0.318	−1.596	2.547	0.405
3	0.256	0.768	−0.596	0.355	0.091
4	0.244	0.976	0.404	0.163	0.040
5	0.195	0.975	1.404	1.971	0.384
6	0.085	0.510	2.404	5.779	0.491
		$\sum xP(x)=3.596$			$\sum(x-\mu)^2 P(x) \approx 1.896$

(a) $\mu = \sum xP(x) \approx 3.6$

(b) $\sigma^2 = \sum(x-\mu)^2 P(x) \approx 1.9$

(c) $\sigma = \sqrt{\sigma^2} \approx 1.4$

(d) $E(x) = \mu \approx 3.6$

(e) The number of fouls for a player in a game on average is bout 4 fouls. The standard deviation is 1.4, so games differ from the mean by no more than about 1 or 2 fouls.

4. (a) $P(x < 4) = 0.012 + 0.049 + 0.159 + 0.256 = 0.476$

    (b) $P(x \geq 3) = 1 - P(x \leq 2)$

    $$= 1 - (0.012 + 0.049 + 0.159)$$

    $$= 0.78$$

    (c) $P(2 \leq x \leq 4) = 0.159 + 0.256 + 0.244 = 0.659$

5. (a) $(16)(15)(14)(13) = 43,680$

    (b) $\dfrac{(7)(6)(5)(4)}{(16)(15)(14)(13)} = \dfrac{840}{43,680} \approx 0.0192$

6. 0.7642

7. 0.0010

8. $1 - 0.2005 = 0.7995$

9. $0.9984 - 0.500 = 0.4984$

10. $0.3974 - 0.1112 = 0.2862$

11. $0.5478 + (1 - 0.9573) = 0.5905$

12. $n = 11$, $p = 0.45$

    (a) $P(8) = 0.0462$; unusual because the probability is less than 0.05.

    (b) $P(x \geq 5) = 0.6029$

    (c) $P(x < 2) = 0.0139$; unusual because the probability is less than 0.05.

13. $p = \dfrac{1}{200} = 0.005$

    (a) $P(x = 10) = (0.005)(0.995)^9 \approx 0.0048$

    (b) $P(x \leq 3) \approx 0.0149$

    (c) $P(x > 10) = 1 - P(x \leq 10) \approx 1 - 0.0489 = 0.9511$

14. (a) 0.2777

    (b) 0.8657

    (c) Dependent. P(being a public school teacher $\mid$ having 20 years or more of full-time teaching experience) $\neq P$(being a public school teacher)

    (d) $0.8799 + 0.0612 - 0.0530 = 0.8881$

    (e) $0.3438 + 0.1201 - 0.0462 = 0.4177$

15. (a) $\mu_{\bar{x}} = 70$

    $$\sigma_{\bar{x}} = \frac{\sigma}{\sqrt{n}} = \frac{1.2}{\sqrt{40}} \approx 0.1897$$

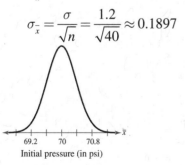

69.2   70   70.8

Initial pressure (in psi)

(b) $P(\bar{x} \leq 69) = P\left(z \leq \dfrac{69-70}{\dfrac{1.2}{\sqrt{15}}}\right) = P(z < -3.23) = 0.0006$

16. (a) $P(x < 36) = P\left(z < \dfrac{36-44}{5}\right) = P(z < -1.6) = 0.0548$

(b) $P(42 < x < 60) = P\left(\dfrac{42-44}{5} < z < \dfrac{60-44}{5}\right)$

$\qquad\qquad\qquad\quad = P(-0.4 < z < 3.2)$

$\qquad\qquad\qquad\quad = 0.9993 - 0.3446 = 0.6547$

(c) Top 5% $\Rightarrow z = 1.645$

$\qquad x = \mu + z\sigma = 44 + (1.645)(5) \approx 52.2$ months

17. (a) $_{12}C_4 = 495$

(b) $\dfrac{(1)(1)(1)(1)}{_{12}C_4} = 0.0020$

18. $n = 16,\ p = 0.50$

(a) $P(12) = 0.0278$; unusual because the probability is less than 0.05.

(b) $P(x \leq 6) = 0.2272$

(c) $P(x > 7) = 1 - P(x \leq 7) = 1 - 0.4018 = 0.5982$

Confidence Intervals

6.1 CONFIDENCE INTERVALS FOR THE MEAN (LARGE SAMPLES)

6.1 Try It Yourself Solutions

1a. $\bar{x} = \dfrac{\sum x}{n} = \dfrac{4155}{30} = 138.5$

  b. A point estimate for the population mean number of friends is 138.5.

2a. $z_c = 1.96$, $n = 30$, $s \approx 51.0$

  b. $E = z_c \dfrac{s}{\sqrt{n}} \approx 1.96 \dfrac{51.0}{\sqrt{30}} \approx 18.3$

  c. You are 95% confident that the maximum error of the estimate is about 18.3 friends.

3a. $\bar{x} = 138.5$, $E \approx 18.3$

  b. $\bar{x} = E \approx 138.5 - 18.3 = 120.2$
$\bar{x} + E \approx 138.5 + 18.3 = 156.8$

  c. With 95% confidence, you can say that the population mean number of friends is between 120.2 and 156.8. This confidence interval is wider than the one found in Example 3.

4b. 75% CI: (121.2, 140.4)
85% CI: (118.7, 142.9)
99% CI: (109.2, 152.4)

  c. As the confidence level increases, so does the width of the interval.

5a. $n = 30$, $\bar{x} = 22.9$, $\sigma = 1.5$, $z_c = 1.645$

  b. $E = z_c \dfrac{\sigma}{\sqrt{n}} = 1.645 \dfrac{1.5}{\sqrt{30}} \approx 0.5$

$\bar{x} - E \approx 22.9 - 0.5 = 22.4$
$\bar{x} + E \approx 22.9 + 0.5 = 23.4$

  c. With 90% confidence, you can way that the mean age of the students is between 22.4 and 23.4 years. Because of the larger sample size, the confidence interval is slightly narrower.

6a. $z_c = 1.96$, $E = 10$, $\sigma \approx 53.0$

  b. $n = \left(\dfrac{z_c \sigma}{E}\right)^2 \approx \left(\dfrac{1.96 \cdot 53.0}{10}\right)^2 \approx 107.91 \rightarrow 108$

  c. You should have at least 108 users in you sample. Because of the larger margin of error, the sample size needed is much smaller.

6.1 EXERCISE SOLUTIONS

1. You are more likely to be correct using an interval estimate because it is unlikely that a point estimate will equal the population mean exactly.

2. The percent of the population who fall under the "yes" category probably lies between 40% and 50%.

3. d; As the level of confidence increases, z_c increases therefore creating wider intervals.

4. No, the 95% confidence interval means that with 95% confidence you can say that the population mean is in this interval. If a large number of samples is collected and a confidence interval created for each, approximately 95% of these intervals will contain the population mean.

5. 1.28   **6.** 1.44   **7.** 1.15   **8.** 2.17

9. $\bar{x} - \mu = 3.8 - 4.27 = -0.47$ **10.** $\bar{x} - \mu = 9.5 - 8.76 = 0.74$

11. $\bar{x} - \mu = 26.43 - 24.67 = 1.76$ **12.** $\bar{x} - \mu = 46.56 - 48.12 = -1.56$

13. $E = z_c \dfrac{s}{\sqrt{n}} = 1.96 \dfrac{5.2}{\sqrt{30}} \approx 1.861$ **14.** $E = z_c \dfrac{s}{\sqrt{n}} = 1.645 \dfrac{2.9}{\sqrt{50}} \approx 0.675$

15. $E = z_c \dfrac{s}{\sqrt{n}} = 1.28 \dfrac{1.3}{\sqrt{75}} \approx 0.192$ **16.** $E = z_c \dfrac{s}{\sqrt{n}} = 2.24 \dfrac{4.6}{\sqrt{100}} \approx 1.030$

17. $c = 0.88 \Rightarrow z_c = 1.555$
    $\bar{x} = 57.2,\ s = 7.1,\ n = 50$

    $\bar{x} \pm z_c \dfrac{s}{\sqrt{n}} = 57.2 \pm 1.555 \dfrac{7.1}{\sqrt{50}} \approx 57.2 \pm 1.561 \approx (55.6,\ 58.8)$

    Answer: (c)

18. $c = 0.90 \Rightarrow z_c = 1.645$
    $\bar{x} = 57.2,\ s = 7.1,\ n = 50$

    $\bar{x} \pm z_c \dfrac{s}{\sqrt{n}} = 57.2 \pm 1.645 \dfrac{7.1}{\sqrt{50}} \approx 57.2 \pm 1.652 \approx (55.5,\ 58.9)$

    Answer: (d)

19. $c = 0.95 \Rightarrow z_c = 1.96$
    $\bar{x} = 57.2,\ s = 7.1,\ n = 50$

    $\bar{x} \pm z_c \dfrac{s}{\sqrt{n}} = 57.2 \pm 1.96 \dfrac{7.1}{\sqrt{50}} \approx 57.2 \pm 1.968 \approx (55.2,\ 59.2)$

    Answer: (b)

20. $c = 0.98 \Rightarrow z_c \approx 2.33$
$\bar{x} = 57.2,\ s = 7.1,\ n = 50$

$$\bar{x} \pm z_c \frac{s}{\sqrt{n}} \approx 57.2 \pm 2.33 \frac{7.1}{\sqrt{50}} \approx 57.2 \pm 2.340 \approx (54.9,\ 59.5)$$
Answer: (a)

21. $\bar{x} \pm z_c \dfrac{s}{\sqrt{n}} = 12.3 \pm 1.645 \dfrac{1.5}{\sqrt{50}} \approx 12.3 \pm 0.349 \approx (12.0,\ 12.6)$

22. $\bar{x} \pm z_c \dfrac{s}{\sqrt{n}} = 31.39 \pm 1.96 \dfrac{0.8}{\sqrt{82}} \approx 31.3 \pm 0.173 \approx (31.22,\ 31.56)$

23. $\bar{x} \pm z_c \dfrac{s}{\sqrt{n}} = 10.5 \pm 2.575 \dfrac{2.14}{\sqrt{45}} \approx 10.5 \pm 0.821 \approx (9.7,\ 11.3)$

24. $\bar{x} \pm z_c \dfrac{s}{\sqrt{n}} = 20.6 \pm 1.28 \dfrac{4.7}{\sqrt{100}} \approx 20.6 \pm 0.602 \approx (20.0,\ 21.2)$

25. $(12.0,\ 14.8) \Rightarrow 13.4 \pm 1.4 \Rightarrow \bar{x} = 13.4,\ E = 1.4$

26. $(21.61,\ 30.15) \Rightarrow 25.88 \pm 4.27 \Rightarrow \bar{x} = 25.88,\ E = 4.27$

27. $(1.71,\ 2.05) \Rightarrow 1.88 \pm 0.17 \Rightarrow \bar{x} = 1.88,\ E = 0.17$

28. $(3.144,\ 3.176) \Rightarrow 3.16 \pm 0.016 \Rightarrow \bar{x} = 3.16,\ E = 0.016$

29. $c = 0.90 \Rightarrow z_c = 1.645$

$$n = \left(\frac{z_c \sigma}{E} \right)^2 = \left(\frac{(1.645)(6.8)}{1} \right)^2 \approx 125.13 \Rightarrow 126$$

30. $c = 0.95 \Rightarrow z_c = 1.96$

$$n = \left(\frac{z_c \sigma}{E} \right)^2 = \left(\frac{(1.96)(2.5)}{1} \right)^2 \approx 24.01 \Rightarrow 25$$

31. $c = 0.80 \Rightarrow z_c = 1.28$

$$n = \left(\frac{z_c \sigma}{E} \right)^2 = \left(\frac{(1.28)(4.1)}{2} \right)^2 \approx 6.89 \Rightarrow 7$$

32. $c = 0.98 \Rightarrow z_c = 2.33$

$$n = \left(\frac{z_c \sigma}{E} \right)^2 = \left(\frac{(2.33)(10.1)}{2} \right)^2 \approx 138.45 \Rightarrow 139$$

33. $(26.2, 30.1) \Rightarrow 2E = 30.1 - 26.2 = 3.9 \Rightarrow E = 1.95$ and $\bar{x} = 26.2 + E$
$$= 26.2 + 1.95 = 28.15$$

34. $(44.07, 80.97) \Rightarrow 2E = 80.97 - 44.07 = 36.9 \Rightarrow E = 18.45$ and $\bar{x} = 44.07 + E$
$$= 44.07 + 18.45 = 62.52$$

35. 90% CI: $\bar{x} \pm z_c \dfrac{s}{\sqrt{n}} = 452.80 \pm 1.645 \dfrac{85.50}{\sqrt{34}} \approx 452.80 \pm 24.12 \approx (428.68,\ 476.92)$

95% CI: $\bar{x} \pm z_c \dfrac{s}{\sqrt{n}} = 452.80 \pm 1.96 \dfrac{85.50}{\sqrt{34}} \approx 452.80 \pm 28.74 \approx (424.06,\ 481.54)$

With 90% confidence, you can say that the population mean price is between \$428.68 and \$476.92 with 95% confidence, you can say that the population mean price is between \$424.06 and \$481.54.

The 95% CI is wider.

36. 90% CI: $\bar{x} \pm z_c \dfrac{s}{\sqrt{n}} = 2.34 \pm 1.645 \dfrac{0.32}{\sqrt{48}} \approx 2.34 \pm 0.076 \approx (2.26,\ 2.42)$

95% CI: $\bar{x} \pm z_c \dfrac{s}{\sqrt{n}} = 2.34 \pm 1.96 \dfrac{0.32}{\sqrt{48}} \approx 2.34 \pm 0.091 \approx (2.25,\ 2.43)$

With 90% confidence, you can say that the population mean price is between \$2.26 and \$2.42 with 95% confidence, you can say that the population mean price is between \$2.25 and \$2.43.

The 95% CI is wider.

37. 90% CI: $\bar{x} \pm z_c \dfrac{s}{\sqrt{n}} = 99.3 \pm 1.645 \dfrac{41.5}{\sqrt{31}} \approx 99.3 \pm 12.26 \approx (87.0,\ 111.6)$

95% CI: $\bar{x} \pm z_c \dfrac{s}{\sqrt{n}} = 99.3 \pm 1.96 \dfrac{41.5}{\sqrt{31}} \approx 99.3 \pm 14.61 \approx (84.7,\ 113.9)$

With 90% confidence, you can say that the population mean is between 87.0 and 111.6 with 95% confidence, you can say that the population mean is between 84.7 and 113.9 calories.

The 95% CI is wider.

38. 90% CI: $\bar{x} \pm z_c \dfrac{s}{\sqrt{n}} = 23 \pm 1.645 \dfrac{6.7}{\sqrt{36}} \approx 23 \pm 1.837 \approx (21,\ 25)$

95% CI: $\bar{x} \pm z_c \dfrac{s}{\sqrt{n}} = 23 \pm 1.96 \dfrac{6.7}{\sqrt{36}} \approx 23 \pm 2.189 \approx (21,\ 25)$

With 90% confidence and with 95% confidence, you can say that the population mean concentration is between 21 and 25 cubic centimeters per cubic meter, when rounded to the nearest whole number, both confidence intervals have the same width.

39. $\bar{x} \pm z_c \dfrac{s}{\sqrt{n}} = 2650 \pm 1.96 \dfrac{425}{\sqrt{50}} \approx 2650 \pm 117.80 \approx (2532.20,\ 2767.80)$

With 95% confidence, you can say that the population mean cost is between $2532.20 and $2767.80.

40. $\bar{x} \pm z_c \dfrac{s}{\sqrt{n}} = 150 \pm 2.575 \dfrac{15.5}{\sqrt{60}} \approx 150 \pm 5.15 \approx (144.85,\ 155.15)$

With 99% confidence, you can say that the population mean repair cost is between $144.85 and $155.15.

41. $\bar{x} \pm z_c \dfrac{s}{\sqrt{n}} = 2650 \pm 1.96 \dfrac{425}{\sqrt{80}} \approx 2650 \pm 93.13 \approx (2556.87,\ 2743.13)$

The $n = 50$ CI is wider because a smaller sample is taken, giving less information about the population.

42. $\bar{x} \pm z_c \dfrac{s}{\sqrt{n}} = 150 \pm 2.575 \dfrac{15.5}{\sqrt{40}} \approx 150 \pm 6.31 \approx (143.69,\ 156.31)$

The $n = 40$ CI is wider because a smaller sample is taken, giving less information about the population.

43. $\bar{x} \pm z_c \dfrac{s}{\sqrt{n}} = 3.12 \pm 1.96 \dfrac{0.09}{\sqrt{48}} \approx 3.12 \pm 0.03 \approx (3.09,\ 3.15)$

With 95% confidence, you can say that the population mean time is between 3.09 and 3.15 minutes.

44. $\bar{x} \pm z_c \dfrac{s}{\sqrt{n}} = 154.17 \pm 2.575 \dfrac{38.60}{\sqrt{55}} \approx 154.17 \pm 13.40 \approx (140.77,\ 167.57)$

With 99% confidence, you can say that the population mean nightly cost is between $140.77 and $167.57.

45. $\bar{x} \pm z_c \dfrac{s}{\sqrt{n}} = 3.12 \pm 1.96 \dfrac{0.06}{\sqrt{48}} \approx 3.12 \pm 0.02 \approx (3.10,\ 3.14)$

The $s = 0.09$ CI is wider because of the increased variability within the sample.

46. $\bar{x} \pm z_c \dfrac{s}{\sqrt{n}} = 154.17 \pm 2.575 \dfrac{42.50}{\sqrt{55}} \approx 154.17 \pm 14.76 \approx (139.41,\ 168.93)$

The $s = 42.50$ CI is wider because of the increased variability within the sample.

47. (a) An increase in the level of confidence will widen the confidence interval.
(b) An increase in the sample size will narrow the confidence interval.
(c) An increase in the standard deviation will widen the confidence interval.

48. Answers will vary.

49. $\bar{x} = \dfrac{\sum x}{n} = \dfrac{302}{20} \approx 15.1$

90% CI: $\bar{x} \pm z_c \dfrac{\sigma}{\sqrt{n}} = 15.1 \pm 1.645 \dfrac{1.3}{\sqrt{20}} \approx 15.1 \pm 0.478 \approx (14.6,\ 15.6)$

99% CI: $\bar{x} \pm z_c \dfrac{\sigma}{\sqrt{n}} = 15.1 \pm 2.575 \dfrac{1.3}{\sqrt{20}} \approx 15.1 \pm 0.749 \approx (14.4,\ 15.8)$

With 90% confidence, you can say that the population mean length of time is between 14.6 and 15.6 minutes. With 99% confidence, you can say that the population mean length of time is between 14.4 and 15.8 minutes.

The 99% CI is wider.

50. 90% CI: $\bar{x} \pm z_c \dfrac{\sigma}{\sqrt{n}} = 29 \pm 1.645 \dfrac{4.5}{\sqrt{27}} \approx 29 \pm 1.425 \approx (27.6,\ 30.4)$

99% CI: $\bar{x} \pm z_c \dfrac{\sigma}{\sqrt{n}} = 29 \pm 2.575 \dfrac{4.5}{\sqrt{27}} \approx 29 \pm 2.230 \approx (26.8,\ 31.2)$

With 90% confidence, you can say that the population mean length of time is between 27.6 and 30.4 minutes. With 99% confidence, you can say that the population mean length of time is between 26.8 and 31.2 minutes.

The 99% CI is wider.

51. $n = \left(\dfrac{z_c \sigma}{E}\right)^2 = \left(\dfrac{1.96 \cdot 4.8}{1}\right)^2 \approx 88.510 \rightarrow 89$

52. $n = \left(\dfrac{z_c \sigma}{E}\right)^2 = \left(\dfrac{2.575 \cdot 1.4}{2}\right)^2 \approx 3.249 \rightarrow 4$

53. (a) $n = \left(\dfrac{z_c \sigma}{E}\right)^2 = \left(\dfrac{1.96 \cdot 2.8}{0.5}\right)^2 \approx 120.473 \rightarrow 121$ servings

(b) $n = \left(\dfrac{z_c \sigma}{E}\right)^2 = \left(\dfrac{2.575 \cdot 2.8}{0.5}\right)^2 \approx 207.936 \rightarrow 208$ servings

The 99% CI requires a larger sample because more information is needed from the population to be 99% confident.

54. (a) $n = \left(\dfrac{z_c \sigma}{E}\right)^2 = \left(\dfrac{1.645 \cdot 1.2}{1}\right)^2 \approx 3.897 \rightarrow 4$ students

(b) $n = \left(\dfrac{z_c \sigma}{E}\right)^2 = \left(\dfrac{2.575 \cdot 1.2}{1}\right)^2 \approx 9.548 \rightarrow 10$ students

The 99% CI requires a larger sample because more information is needed from the population to be 99% confident.

55. (a) $n = \left(\dfrac{z_c \sigma}{E}\right)^2 = \left(\dfrac{1.645 \cdot 0.85}{0.25}\right)^2 \approx 31.282 \rightarrow 32$ cans

(b) $n = \left(\dfrac{z_c \sigma}{E}\right)^2 = \left(\dfrac{1.645 \cdot 0.85}{0.15}\right)^2 \approx 86.893 \rightarrow 87$ cans

$E = 0.15$ requires a larger sample size. As the error size decreases, a larger sample must be taken to obtain enough information from the population to ensure the desired accuracy.

56. (a) $n = \left(\dfrac{z_c \sigma}{E}\right)^2 = \left(\dfrac{1.96 \cdot 3}{1}\right)^2 \approx 34.574 \rightarrow 35$ bottles

(b) $n = \left(\dfrac{z_c \sigma}{E}\right)^2 = \left(\dfrac{1.96 \cdot 3}{2}\right)^2 \approx 8.644 \rightarrow 9$ bottles

$E = 1$ requires a larger sample size. As the error size decreases, a larger sample must be taken to obtain enough information from the population to ensure the desired accuracy.

57. (a) $n = \left(\dfrac{z_c \sigma}{E}\right)^2 = \left(\dfrac{1.96 \cdot 0.25}{0.125}\right)^2 \approx 15.3664 \rightarrow 16$ sheets

(b) $n = \left(\dfrac{z_c \sigma}{E}\right)^2 = \left(\dfrac{1.96 \cdot 0.25}{0.0625}\right)^2 \approx 61.4656 \rightarrow 62$ sheets

$E = 0.0625$ requires a larger sample size. As the error size decreases, a larger sample must be taken to obtain enough information from the population to ensure the desired accuracy.

58. (a) $n = \left(\dfrac{z_c \sigma}{E}\right)^2 = \left(\dfrac{1.645 \cdot 0.15}{0.0425}\right)^2 \approx 33.708 \rightarrow 34$ units

(b) $n = \left(\dfrac{z_c \sigma}{E}\right)^2 = \left(\dfrac{1.645 \cdot 0.15}{0.02125}\right)^2 \approx 134.833 \rightarrow 135$ units

$E = 0.02125$ requires a larger sample size. As the error size decreases, a larger sample must be taken to obtain enough information from the population to ensure the desired accuracy.

59. (a) $n = \left(\dfrac{z_c \sigma}{E} \right)^2 = \left(\dfrac{2.575 \cdot 0.25}{0.1} \right)^2 \approx 41.441 \rightarrow 42$ soccer balls

(b) $n = \left(\dfrac{z_c \sigma}{E} \right)^2 = \left(\dfrac{2.575 \cdot 0.30}{0.1} \right)^2 \approx 59.676 \rightarrow 60$ soccer balls

$\sigma = 0.3$ requires a larger sample size. Due to the increased variability in the population, a larger sample is needed to ensure the desired accuracy.

60. (a) $n = \left(\dfrac{z_c \sigma}{E} \right)^2 = \left(\dfrac{2.575 \cdot 0.20}{0.15} \right)^2 \approx 11.788 \rightarrow 12$ soccer balls

(b) $n = \left(\dfrac{z_c \sigma}{E} \right)^2 = \left(\dfrac{2.575 \cdot 0.10}{0.15} \right)^2 \approx 2.947 \rightarrow 3$ soccer balls

$\sigma = 0.2$ requires a larger sample size. Due to the increased variability in the population, a larger sample is needed to ensure the desired accuracy.

61. (a) An increase in the level of confidence will increase the minimum sample size required.
  (b) An increase (larger E) in the error tolerance will decrease the minimum sample size required.
  (c) An increase in the population standard deviation will increase the minimum sample size required.

62. *Sample answer:* A 99% CI may not be practical to use in all situations. It may produce a CI so wide that is has no practical application.

63. (212.74, 221.51)
  With 95% confidence, you can say that the population mean airfare price is between $212.74 and $221.51.

64. (19.153, 20.768)
  With 95% confidence, you can say that the population mean closing stock price is between $19.153 and $20.768.

65. 80% confidence interval results:
  μ: population mean
  standard deviation = 344.9

mean	n	Sample mean	Std. err.	L. Limit	U Limit
μ	30	1042.7	62.969837	962.0009	1123.399

90% confidence interval results:
  μ: population mean
  standard deviation = 344.9

mean	n	Sample mean	Std. err.	L. Limit	U Limit
μ	30	1042.7	62.969837	939.12384	1146.2761

95% confidence interval results:

μ: population mean

standard deviation = 344.9

mean	n	Sample mean	Std. err.	L. Limit	U Limit
μ	30	1042.7	62.969837	919.2814	1166.1187

With 80% confidence, you can say that the population mean sodium content is between 962.0 and 1123.4 milligrams. With 90% confidence, you can say it is between 929.1 and 1146.3 milligrams. With 95% confidence, you can say it is between 919.3 and 1166.1 milligrams.

66. 80% confidence interval results:

μ: mean of variable

standard deviation not specified

Variable	N	Sample mean	Std. err.	L. Limit	U Limit
Carbohydrate (grams)	30	41.966667	2.1493027	39.212223	44.721107

90% confidence interval results:

μ: mean of variable

standard deviation not specified

Variable	N	Sample mean	Std. err.	L. Limit	U Limit
Carbohydrate (grams)	30	41.966667	2.1493027	38.431377	45.501953

95% confidence interval results:

μ: mean of variable

standard deviation not specified

Variable	N	Sample mean	Std. err.	L. Limit	U Limit
Carbohydrate (grams)	30	41.966667	2.1493027	37.754112	46.179222

With 80% confidence, you can say that the population mean carbohydrate content is between 39.2 and 44.7 grams. With 90% confidence, you can say it is between 38.4 and 45.5 grams. With 95% confidence, you can say it is between 37.8 and 46.2 grams.

67. (a) $\sqrt{\dfrac{N-n}{N-1}} = \sqrt{\dfrac{1000-500}{1000-1}} \approx 0.707$ (b) $\sqrt{\dfrac{N-n}{N-1}} = \sqrt{\dfrac{1000-100}{1000-1}} \approx 0.949$

(c) $\sqrt{\dfrac{N-n}{N-1}} = \sqrt{\dfrac{1000-75}{1000-1}} \approx 0.962$ (d) $\sqrt{\dfrac{N-n}{N-1}} = \sqrt{\dfrac{1000-50}{1000-1}} \approx 0.975$

(e) The finite population correction factor approaches 1 as the sample size decreases and the population size remains the same.

68. (a) $\sqrt{\dfrac{N-n}{N-1}} = \sqrt{\dfrac{100-50}{100-1}} \approx 0.711$

        (b) $\sqrt{\dfrac{N-n}{N-1}} = \sqrt{\dfrac{400-50}{400-1}} \approx 0.937$

    (c) $\sqrt{\dfrac{N-n}{N-1}} = \sqrt{\dfrac{700-50}{700-1}} \approx 0.964$

        (d) $\sqrt{\dfrac{N-n}{N-1}} = \sqrt{\dfrac{1000-50}{1000-1}} \approx 0.975$

(e) The finite population correction factor approaches 1 as the population size increases and the sample size remains the same.

69. *Sample answer:*

$$E = \frac{z_c \sigma}{\sqrt{n}} \qquad \text{Write original equation.}$$

$$E\sqrt{n} = z_c \sigma \qquad \text{Multiply each side by } \sqrt{n}.$$

$$\sqrt{n} = \frac{z_c \sigma}{E} \qquad \text{Divide each side by } E.$$

$$n = \left(\frac{z_c \sigma}{E}\right)^2 \qquad \text{Square each side.}$$

6.2 CONFIDENCE INTERVALS FOR THE MEAN (SMALL SAMPLES)

6.2 Try It Yourself Solutions

1a. d.f. $= n - 1 = 22 - 1 = 21$

b. $c = 0.90$

c. $t_c = 1.721$

2a. 90% CI: $t_c = 1.753$

$$E = t_c \frac{s}{\sqrt{n}} = 1.753 \frac{10}{\sqrt{16}} \approx 4.4$$

99% CI: $t_c = 2.947$

$$E = t_c \frac{s}{\sqrt{n}} - 2.947 \frac{10}{\sqrt{16}} \approx 7.4$$

b. 90% CI: $\bar{x} \pm E \approx 162 \pm 4.4 = (157.6,\ 166.4)$

99% CI: $\bar{x} \pm E \approx 162 \pm 7.4 = (154.6,\ 169.4)$

c. With 90% confidence, you can say that the population mean temperature of coffee sold is between 157.6°F and 166.4°F.

With 99% confidence, you can say that the population mean temperature of coffee sold is between 154.6°F and 169.4°F.

3a. 90% CI: $t_c = 1.729$

$$E = t_c \frac{s}{\sqrt{n}} = 1.729 \frac{2.39}{\sqrt{20}} \approx 0.92$$

95% CI: $t_c = 2.093$

$$E = t_c \frac{s}{\sqrt{n}} - 2.093 \frac{2.39}{\sqrt{20}} \approx 1.12$$

  b. 90% CI: $\bar{x} \pm E \approx 9.75 \pm 0.92 = (8.83,\ 10.67)$

  95% CI: $\bar{x} \pm E \approx 9.75 \pm 1.12 = (8.63,\ 10.87)$

  c. With 90% confidence, you can say that the population mean number of days the car model sits on the lot is between 8.83 and 10.67 days.

  With 95% confidence, you can say that the population mean number of days the car model sits on the lot is between 8.63 and 10.87 days. The 90% confidence interval is slightly narrower.

4a. Is $n \geq 30$? No

  Is the population normally distributed? Yes

  Is σ known? No

  Use the t-distribution to construct the 90% CI.

6.2 EXERCISE SOLUTIONS

1. $t_c = 1.833$ **2.** $t_c = 2.201$ **3.** $t_c = 2.947$ **4.** $t_c = 2.539$

5. $E = t_c \dfrac{s}{\sqrt{n}} = 2.131 \dfrac{5}{\sqrt{16}} \approx 2.7$ **6.** $E = t_c \dfrac{s}{\sqrt{n}} = 4.032 \dfrac{3}{\sqrt{6}} \approx 4.9$

7. $E = t_c \dfrac{s}{\sqrt{n}} = 1.796 \dfrac{2.4}{\sqrt{12}} \approx 1.2$ **8.** $E = t_c \dfrac{s}{\sqrt{n}} = 2.896 \dfrac{4.7}{\sqrt{9}} \approx 4.5$

9. (a) $\bar{x} \pm t_c \dfrac{s}{\sqrt{n}} = 12.5 \pm 2.015 \dfrac{2.0}{\sqrt{6}} \approx 12.5 \pm 1.645 \approx (10.9,\ 14.1)$

  (b) $\bar{x} \pm z_c \dfrac{s}{\sqrt{n}} = 12.5 \pm 1.645 \dfrac{2.0}{\sqrt{6}} \approx 12.5 \pm 1.343 \approx (11.2,\ 13.8)$

  The t-CI is wider.

10. (a) $\bar{x} \pm t_c \dfrac{s}{\sqrt{n}} = 13.4 \pm 2.365 \dfrac{0.85}{\sqrt{8}} \approx 13.4 \pm 0.711 \approx (12.7,\ 14.1)$

  (b) $\bar{x} \pm z_c \dfrac{s}{\sqrt{n}} = 13.4 \pm 1.96 \dfrac{0.85}{\sqrt{8}} \approx 13.4 \pm 0.589 \approx (12.8,\ 14.0)$

  The t-CI is wider.

11. (a) $\bar{x} \pm t_c \dfrac{s}{\sqrt{n}} = 4.3 \pm 2.650 \dfrac{0.34}{\sqrt{14}} \approx 4.3 \pm 0.241 \approx (4.1, \ 4.5)$

(b) $\bar{x} \pm z_c \dfrac{s}{\sqrt{n}} = 4.3 \pm 2.326 \dfrac{0.34}{\sqrt{14}} \approx 4.3 \pm 0.211 \approx (4.1, \ 4.5)$

When rounded to the nearest tenth, the normal CI and the t-CI have the same width.

12. (a) $\bar{x} \pm t_c \dfrac{s}{\sqrt{n}} = 24.7 \pm 3.250 \dfrac{4.6}{\sqrt{10}} \approx 24.7 \pm 4.728 \approx (20.0, \ 29.4)$

(b) $\bar{x} \pm z_c \dfrac{s}{\sqrt{n}} = 24.7 \pm 2.575 \dfrac{4.6}{\sqrt{10}} \approx 24.7 \pm 3.746 \approx (21.0, \ 28.4)$

The t-CI is wider.

13. $(14.7, \ 22.1) \Rightarrow \bar{x} = 18.4 \Rightarrow E = 22.1 - 18.4 = 3.7$

14. $(6.17, \ 8.53) \Rightarrow \bar{x} = 7.35 \Rightarrow E = 8.53 - 7.35 = 1.18$

15. $(64.6, \ 83.6) \Rightarrow \bar{x} = 74.1 \Rightarrow E = 83.6 - 74.1 = 9.5$

16. $(16.2, \ 29.8) \Rightarrow \bar{x} = 23 \Rightarrow E = 29.8 - 23 = 6.8$

17. $E = t_c \dfrac{s}{\sqrt{n}} = 2.365 \dfrac{7.2}{\sqrt{8}} \approx 6.02$

$\bar{x} \pm E \approx 35.5 \pm 6.0 = (29.5, \ 41.5)$

With 95% confidence, you can say that the population mean commute time to work is between 29.5 and 41.5 minutes.

18. $E = t_c \dfrac{s}{\sqrt{n}} = 2.776 \dfrac{5.8}{\sqrt{5}} \approx 7.2$

$\bar{x} \pm E \approx 22.2 \pm 7.2 = (15.0, \ 29.4)$

With 95% confidence, you can say that the population mean driving distance to work is between 15.0 and 29.4 miles.

19. $E = z_c \dfrac{\sigma}{\sqrt{n}} = 1.96 \dfrac{9.3}{\sqrt{8}} \approx 6.4$

$\bar{x} \pm E \approx 35.5 \pm 6.4 = (29.1, \ 41.9)$

With 95% confidence, you can say that the population mean commute time to work is between 29.1 and 41.9 minutes. This confidence interval is slightly wider than the one found in Exercise 17.

20. $E = z_c \dfrac{\sigma}{\sqrt{n}} = 1.96 \dfrac{5.2}{\sqrt{5}} \approx 4.6$

$\bar{x} \pm E \approx 22.2 \pm 4.6 = (17.6, \ 26.8)$

With 95% confidence, you can say that the population mean driving distance to work is between 17.6 and 26.8 miles. This confidence interval is narrower than the one found in Exercise 18.

21. (a) $\bar{x} \pm t_c \dfrac{s}{\sqrt{n}} = 4.50 \pm 1.833 \dfrac{1.21}{\sqrt{10}} \approx 4.50 \pm 0.701 \approx (3.80,\ 5.20)$

(b) $\bar{x} \pm z_c \dfrac{s}{\sqrt{n}} = 4.50 \pm 1.645 \dfrac{1.21}{\sqrt{500}} \approx 4.50 \pm 0.089 \approx (4.41,\ 4.59)$

The t-CI is wider.

22. (a) $\bar{x} \pm t_c \dfrac{s}{\sqrt{n}} = 1.50 \pm 1.796 \dfrac{0.28}{\sqrt{12}} \approx 1.50 \pm 0.145 \approx (1.36,\ 1.65)$

(b) $\bar{x} \pm z_c \dfrac{s}{\sqrt{n}} = 1.50 \pm 1.645 \dfrac{0.28}{\sqrt{600}} \approx 1.50 \pm 0.019 \approx (1.48,\ 1.52)$

The t-CI is wider.

23. (a) $\bar{x} \approx 90{,}182.9$ (b) $s \approx 3724.9$

(c) $\bar{x} \pm t_c \dfrac{s}{\sqrt{n}} = 90{,}182.9 \pm 2.947 \dfrac{3724.9}{\sqrt{16}} \approx 90{,}182.9 \pm 2744.3 \approx (87{,}438.6,\ 92{,}927.2)$

24. (a) $\bar{x} \approx 68{,}555.6$ (b) $s \approx 3243.5$

(c) $\bar{x} \pm t_c \dfrac{s}{\sqrt{n}} = 68{,}555.6 \pm 3.012 \dfrac{3243.5}{\sqrt{14}} \approx 68{,}555.6 \pm 2611.0 \approx (65{,}944.6,\ 71{,}166.6)$

25. (a) $\bar{x} \approx 1767.7$
(b) $s \approx 252.2$

(c) $\bar{x} \pm t_c \dfrac{s}{\sqrt{n}} \approx 1767.7 \pm 3.106 \dfrac{252.23}{\sqrt{12}} \approx 1767.7 \pm 226.16 \approx (1541.5,\ 1993.8)$

26. (a) $\bar{x} \approx 2.35$
(b) $s \approx 1.03$

(c) $\bar{x} \pm t_c \dfrac{s}{\sqrt{n}} \approx 2.35 \pm 2.977 \dfrac{1.03}{\sqrt{15}} \approx 2.35 \pm 0.792 \approx (1.56,\ 3.14)$

27. $n \ge 30 \rightarrow$ use normal distribution

$\bar{x} \pm z_c \dfrac{s}{\sqrt{n}} = 27.7 \pm 1.96 \dfrac{6.12}{\sqrt{50}} \approx 27.7 \pm 1.70 = (26.00,\ 29.40)$

With 95% confidence, you can say that the population mean BMI is between 26.0 and 29.4.

28. $\bar{x} \approx 4.99$, $s = 0.36$, $n < 30$, σ known, and pop normally distributed $\rightarrow$ use t-distribution

$\bar{x} \pm t_c \dfrac{s}{\sqrt{n}} = 4.99 \pm 2.145 \dfrac{0.36}{\sqrt{15}} \approx 4.99 \pm 0.20 = (4.79,\ 5.19)$

With 95% confidence, you can say that the population mean interest rate is between 4.79% and 5.19%.

29. $\bar{x} \approx 21.9$, $s = 3.46$, $n < 30$, σ known, and pop normally distributed $\rightarrow$ use t-distribution

$$\bar{x} \pm t_c \frac{s}{\sqrt{n}} \approx 21.9 \pm 2.064 \frac{3.46}{\sqrt{25}} \approx 21.9 \pm 1.43 = (20.5, \ 23.3)$$

With 95% confidence, you can say that the population mean per gallon is between 20.5 and 23.3 miles per gallon.

30. $\bar{x} = 4.3$, $s = 1.14$, $n < 30$, σ known, and pop normally distributed $\rightarrow$ use normal distribution

$$\bar{x} \pm z_c \frac{\sigma}{\sqrt{n}} \approx 4.3 \pm 1.96 \frac{1.34}{\sqrt{20}} \approx 4.3 \pm 0.59 \approx (3.7, \ 4.9)$$

With 95% confidence, you can say that the population mean is between 3.7 and 4.9 yards per carry.

31. $n < 30$, σ unknown, and pop *not* normally distributed $\rightarrow$ cannot use either the normal or t-distributions.

32. $n < 30$, σ unknown, and pop normally distributed $\rightarrow$ use t-distribution

$$\bar{x} \pm t_c \frac{s}{\sqrt{n}} = 6.3 \pm 2.179 \frac{1.7}{\sqrt{13}} \approx 6.3 \pm 1.03 = (5.3, \ 7.3)$$

With 95% confidence, you can say that the population mean length of stay is between 5.3 and 7.3 days.

33. 90% confidence interval results:

μ: mean of variable

Variable	Sample mean	Std. err.	DF	L. Limit	U Limit
Time (in hours)	12.194445	0.4136141	17	11.474918	12.91397

95% confidence interval results:

μ: mean of variable

Variable	Sample mean	Std. err.	DF	L. Limit	U Limit
Time (in hours)	12.194445	0.4136141	17	11.321795	13.067094

99% confidence interval results:

μ: mean of variable

Variable	Sample mean	Std. err.	DF	L. Limit	U Limit
Time (in hours)	12.194445	0.4136141	17	10.995695	13.393193

With 90% confidence, you can say the population mean time spent on homework is between 11.5 and 12.9 hours. With 95% confidence, you can say it is between 11.3 and 13.1 hours and with 99% confidence, you can say it is between 11.0 and 13.4 hours. As the level of confidence increases, the intervals get wider.

34. **90% confidence interval results:**

μ: population mean

Mean	Sample mean	Std. err.	DF	L. Limit	U Limit
μ	7.2	0.57287157	10	6.1616926	8.238307

95% confidence interval results:

μ: population mean

Mean	Sample mean	Std. err.	DF	L. Limit	U Limit
μ	7.2	0.57287157	10	5.9235625	8.476438

99% confidence interval results:

μ: population mean

Mean	Sample mean	Std. err.	DF	L. Limit	U Limit
μ	7.2	0.57287157	10	5.3844137	9.015586

With 90% confidence, you can say the population mean weekly time spent weightlifting is between 6.2 and 8.2 hours. With 95% confidence, you can say it is between 5.9 and 8.5 hours. With 99% confidence, you can say it is between 5.4 and 9.0 hours. As the level of confidence increases, the intervals get wider.

35. $n = 25$, $\overline{x} = 56.0$, $s = 0.25$

$\pm t_{0.99} \rightarrow$ 99% t-CI

$$\overline{x} \pm t_c \frac{s}{\sqrt{n}} = 56.0 \pm 2.797 \frac{0.25}{\sqrt{25}} \approx 56.0 \pm 0.140 \approx (55.9,\ 56.1)$$

They are not making good tennis balls because desired bounce height of 55.5 inches is not contained between 55.9 and 56.1 inches.

36. $n = 16$, $\overline{x} = 1015$, $s = 25$

$\pm t_{0.99} \rightarrow$ 99% t-CI

$$\overline{x} \pm t_c \frac{s}{\sqrt{n}} = 1015 \pm 2.947 \frac{25}{\sqrt{16}} \approx 1015 \pm 18.419 \approx (997,\ 1033)$$

They are making good light bulbs because the desired bulb life of 1000 hours is between 997 and 1033 hours.

6.3 CONFIDENCE INTERVALS FOR POPULATION PROPORTIONS

6.3 Try It Yourself Solutions

1a. $x = 181$, $n = 1006$

b. $\hat{p} = \dfrac{181}{1006} \approx 0.180$

2a. $\hat{p} \approx 0.180$, $\hat{q} \approx 0.820$

  b. $n\hat{p} \approx (1006)(0.180) = 181.08 > 5$

    $n\hat{q} \approx (1006)(0.820) = 824.92 > 5$

    Distribution of $\hat{p}$ is approximately normal.

  c. $z_c = 1.645$

$$E = z_c \sqrt{\frac{\hat{p}\hat{q}}{n}} \approx 1.645 \sqrt{\frac{0.180 \cdot 0.820}{1006}} \approx 0.020$$

  d. $\hat{p} \pm E \approx 0.180 \pm 0.020 \approx (0.160,\ 0.200)$

  e. With 90% confidence, you can say that the proportion of adults who think Abraham Lincoln was the greatest president is between 16.0% and 20.0%.

3a. $n = 498$, $\hat{p} = 0.25$

    $\hat{q} = 1 = \hat{p} - 1 = 0.25 \approx 0.75$

  b. $n\hat{p} = 498 \cdot 0.25 = 124.5 > 5$

    $n\hat{q} = 498 \cdot 0.75 = 373.5 > 5$

    Distribution of $\hat{p}$ is approximately normal.

  c. $z_c = 2.575$

  d. $\hat{p} \pm E \approx 0.25 \pm 0.050 = (0.20,\ 0.30)$

  e. With 99% confidence, you can say that the proportion of adults who think that people over 65 are the more dangerous drivers is between 20% and 30%.

4a. (1) $\hat{p} = 0.5$, $\hat{q} = 0.5$

       $z_c = 1.645$, $E = 0.02$

    (2) $\hat{p} = 0.11$, $\hat{q} = 0.89$

       $z_c = 1.645$, $E = 0.02$

  b. (1) $n = \hat{p}\hat{q}\left(\dfrac{z_c}{E}\right)^2 = (0.5)(0.5)\left(\dfrac{1.645}{0.02}\right)^2 \approx 1691.266 \rightarrow 1692$

     (2) $n = \hat{p}\hat{q}\left(\dfrac{z_c}{E}\right)^2 = (0.11)(0.89)\left(\dfrac{1.645}{0.02}\right)^2 \approx 662.3 \rightarrow 663$

  c. (1) At least 1692 females should be included in the sample.

     (2) At least 663 females should be included in the sample.

6.3 EXERCISE SOLUTIONS

1. False. To estimate the value of p, the population proportion of successes, use the point estimate

$$\hat{p} = \frac{x}{n}.$$

2. True

3. $\hat{p} = \dfrac{x}{n} = \dfrac{752}{1002} \approx 0.750$

$\hat{q} = 1 - \hat{p} \approx 0.250$

4. $\hat{p} = \dfrac{x}{n} = \dfrac{2439}{2939} \approx 0.830$

$\hat{q} = 1 - \hat{p} \approx 0.170$

5. $\hat{p} = \dfrac{x}{n} = \dfrac{4912}{11,605} \approx 0.423$

$\hat{q} = 1 - \hat{p} \approx 0.577$

6. $\hat{p} = \dfrac{x}{n} = \dfrac{110}{1003} \approx 0.110$

$\hat{q} = 1 - \hat{p} \approx 0.890$

7. $(0.905, 0.933) \rightarrow \hat{p} = 0.919 \Rightarrow E = 0.933 - 0.919 = 0.014$

8. $(0.245, 0.475) \rightarrow \hat{p} = 0.360 \Rightarrow E = 0.475 - 0.360 = 0.115$

9. $(0.512, 0.596) \rightarrow \hat{p} = 0.554 \Rightarrow E = 0.596 - 0.554 = 0.042$

10. $(0.087, 0.263) \rightarrow \hat{p} = 0.175 \Rightarrow E = 0.263 - 0.175 = 0.088$

11. $\hat{p} = \dfrac{x}{n} = \dfrac{396}{674} \approx 0.588$

$\hat{q} = 1 - \hat{p} \approx 0.412$

90% CI: $\hat{p} \pm z_c \sqrt{\dfrac{\hat{p}\hat{q}}{n}} \approx 0.588 \pm 1.645 \sqrt{\dfrac{(0.588)(0.412)}{674}} \approx 0.588 \pm 0.031$

$= (0.557,\ 0.619)$

95% CI: $\hat{p} \pm z_c \sqrt{\dfrac{\hat{p}\hat{q}}{n}} \approx 0.588 \pm 1.96 \sqrt{\dfrac{(0.588)(0.412)}{674}} \approx 0.588 \pm 0.037$

$= (0.551,\ 0.625)$

With 90% confidence, you can say that the population proportion of U.S. males ages 18-64 who say they have gone to the dentist in the past year is between 55.7% and 61.9%. With 95% confidence, you can say it is between 55.1% and 62.5%. The 95% confidence interval is slightly wider.

12. $\hat{p} = \dfrac{x}{n} = \dfrac{279}{420} \approx 0.664$

$\hat{q} = 1 - \hat{p} \approx 0.336$

90% CI: $\hat{p} \pm z_c \sqrt{\dfrac{\hat{p}\hat{q}}{n}} \approx 0.664 \pm 1.645 \sqrt{\dfrac{(0.664)(0.336)}{420}} \approx 0.664 \pm 0.0379$

$= (0.626,\ 0.702)$

95% CI: $\hat{p} \pm z_c \sqrt{\dfrac{\hat{p}\hat{q}}{n}} \approx 0.664 \pm 1.96 \sqrt{\dfrac{(0.664)(0.336)}{420}} \approx 0.664 \pm 0.045$

$= (0.619,\ 0.709)$

With 90% confidence, you can say that the population proportion of U.S. females ages 18-64 who say they have gone to the dentist in the past year is between 62.6% and 70.2%. With 95% confidence, you can say it is between 61.9% and 70.9%. The 95% confidence interval is slightly wider.

13. $\hat{p} = \dfrac{x}{n} = \dfrac{1435}{3110} \approx 0.461$

$\hat{q} = 1 - \hat{p} \approx 0.539$

$\hat{p} \pm z_c \sqrt{\dfrac{\hat{p}\hat{q}}{n}} \approx 0.461 \pm 2.575 \sqrt{\dfrac{(0.461)(0.539)}{3110}} \approx 0.461 \pm 0.023$

$= (0.438,\ 0.484)$

With 99% confidence, you can say that the population proportion of U.S. adults who say they have started paying bills online in the past year is between 43.8% and 48.4%.

14. $\hat{p} = \dfrac{x}{n} = \dfrac{722}{4013} \approx 0.180$

$\hat{q} = 1 - \hat{p} \approx 0.820$

$\hat{p} \pm z_c \sqrt{\dfrac{\hat{p}\hat{q}}{n}} \approx 0.180 \pm 2.575 \sqrt{\dfrac{(0.180)(0.820)}{4013}} \approx 0.180 \pm 0.016$

$= (0.164,\ 0.196)$

With 99% confidence, you can say that the population proportion of U.S. adults who say they have seen a ghost is between 16.4% and 19.6%.

15. $\hat{p} = \dfrac{x}{n} = \dfrac{4431}{7000} \approx 0.633$

$\hat{q} = 1 - \hat{p} = 0.367$

$\hat{p} \pm z_c \sqrt{\dfrac{\hat{p}\hat{q}}{n}} \approx 0.633 \pm 1.96 \sqrt{\dfrac{(0.633)(0.367)}{7000}} \approx 0.633 \pm 0.011$

$= (0.622,\ 0.644)$

16. $\hat{p} = \dfrac{x}{n} = \dfrac{184}{891} \approx 0.207$

$\hat{q} = 1 - \hat{p} \approx 0.793$

$\hat{p} \pm z_c \sqrt{\dfrac{\hat{p}\hat{q}}{n}} \approx 0.207 \pm 1.645 \sqrt{\dfrac{(0.207)(0.793)}{891}} \approx 0.207 \pm 0.022$

$= (0.185,\ 0.229)$

17. (a) $n = \hat{p}\hat{q}\left(\dfrac{z_c}{E}\right)^2 = 0.5 \cdot 0.5\left(\dfrac{1.96}{0.04}\right)^2 \approx 600.25 \to 601$ adults

(b) $n = \hat{p}\hat{q}\left(\dfrac{z_c}{E}\right)^2 = 0.78 \cdot 0.22\left(\dfrac{1.96}{0.04}\right)^2 \approx 412.01 \to 413$ adults

(c) Having an estimate of the population proportion reduces the minimum sample size needed.

18. (a) $n = \hat{p}\hat{q}\left(\dfrac{z_c}{E}\right)^2 = 0.5 \cdot 0.5\left(\dfrac{2.575}{0.02}\right)^2 \approx 4144.14 \to 4145$ adults

(b) $n = \hat{p}\hat{q}\left(\dfrac{z_c}{E}\right)^2 = 0.47 \cdot 0.53\left(\dfrac{2.575}{0.02}\right)^2 \approx 4129.22 \to 4130$ adults

(c) Having an estimate of the population proportion reduces the minimum sample size needed.

19. (a) $n = \hat{p}\hat{q}\left(\dfrac{z_c}{E}\right)^2 = 0.5 \cdot 0.5\left(\dfrac{1.645}{0.03}\right)^2 \approx 751.67 \to 752$ adults

(b) $n = \hat{p}\hat{q}\left(\dfrac{z_c}{E}\right)^2 = 0.201 \cdot 0.799\left(\dfrac{1.645}{0.03}\right)^2 \approx 482.87 \to 483$ adults

(c) Having an estimate of the population proportion reduces the minimum sample size needed.

20. (a) $n = \hat{p}\hat{q}\left(\dfrac{z_c}{E}\right)^2 = 0.5 \cdot 0.5\left(\dfrac{1.96}{0.05}\right)^2 \approx 384.16 \to 385$ adults

(b) $n = \hat{p}\hat{q}\left(\dfrac{z_c}{E}\right)^2 = 0.27 \cdot 0.73\left(\dfrac{1.96}{0.05}\right)^2 \approx 302.87 \to 303$ adults

(c) Having an estimate of the population proportion reduces the minimum sample size needed.

21. (a) $\hat{p} = 0.27$, $\hat{q} = 0.73$, $n = 1017$

$\hat{p} \pm z_c\sqrt{\dfrac{\hat{p}\hat{q}}{n}} = 0.27 \pm 2.575\sqrt{\dfrac{(0.27)(0.73)}{1017}} \approx 0.27 \pm 0.036 = (0.234,\ 0.306)$

(b) $\hat{p} = 0.49$, $\hat{q} = 0.51$, $n = 1060$

$\hat{p} \pm z_c\sqrt{\dfrac{\hat{p}\hat{q}}{n}} = 0.49 \pm 2.575\sqrt{\dfrac{(0.49)(0.51)}{1060}} \approx 0.49 \pm 0.040 = (0.450,\ 0.530)$

(c) $\hat{p} = 0.31$, $\hat{q} = 0.69$, $n = 1126$

$$\hat{p} \pm z_c \sqrt{\frac{\hat{p}\hat{q}}{n}} = 0.31 \pm 2.575 \sqrt{\frac{(0.31)(0.69)}{1126}} \approx 0.31 \pm 0.035 = (0.275,\ 0.345)$$

22. (a) The two proportions are probably unequal because the confidence intervals (0.234, 0.306) and (0.450, 0.530) do not overlap.

(b) The two proportions are probably unequal because the confidence intervals (0.450, 0.530) and (0.275, 0.345) do not overlap.

(c) The two proportions could be equal because the confidence intervals (0.234, 0.306) and (0.275, 0.345) overlap.

23. (a) $\hat{p} = 0.32$ $\qquad\qquad \hat{q} = 1 - \hat{p} = 0.68$

$$\hat{p} \pm z_c \sqrt{\frac{\hat{p}\hat{q}}{n}} = 0.32 \pm 1.96 \sqrt{\frac{(0.32)(0.68)}{400}} \approx 0.32 \pm 0.046$$
$$= (0.274,\ 0.366)$$

(b) $\hat{p} = 0.56$ $\qquad\qquad \hat{q} = 1 - \hat{p} = 0.44$

$$\hat{p} \pm z_c \sqrt{\frac{\hat{p}\hat{q}}{n}} = 0.56 \pm 1.96 \sqrt{\frac{(0.56)(0.44)}{400}} \approx 0.56 \pm 0.049$$
$$= (0.511,\ 0.609)$$

24. (a) $\hat{p} = 0.36$ $\qquad\qquad \hat{q} = 1 - \hat{p} = 0.64$

$$\hat{p} \pm z_c \sqrt{\frac{\hat{p}\hat{q}}{n}} = 0.36 \pm 1.96 \sqrt{\frac{(0.36)(0.64)}{400}} \approx 0.36 \pm 0.047$$
$$= (0.313,\ 0.407)$$

(b) $\hat{p} = 0.26$ $\qquad\qquad \hat{q} = 1 - \hat{p} = 0.74$

$$\hat{p} \pm z_c \sqrt{\frac{\hat{p}\hat{q}}{n}} = 0.26 \pm 1.96 \sqrt{\frac{(0.26)(0.74)}{400}} \approx 0.26 \pm 0.043$$
$$= (0.217,\ 0.303)$$

25. No, it is unlikely that the two proportions are equal because the confidence intervals estimating the proportions do not overlap. The 99% confidence intervals are (0.260, 0.380) and (0.496, 0.624). Although these intervals are wider, they still do not overlap.

26. No, it is unlikely that the two proportions are equal because the confidence intervals estimating the proportions do not overlap. The 99% confidence intervals are (0.298, 0.422) and (0.204, 0.316). Using these intervals, it is possible that the two proportions are equal because the confidence intervals overlap.

27. 90% confidence interval results:
p: proportion of successes for population
method: Standard-Wald

Proportion	Count	Total	Sample Prop.	Std. err.	L. Limit	U Limit
p	802	1025	0.78243905	0.012887059	0.7612417	0.8036364

95% confidence interval results:
p: proportion of successes for population
method: Standard-Wald

Proportion	Count	Total	Sample Prop.	Std. err.	L. Limit	U Limit
p	802	1025	0.78243905	0.012887059	0.75718087	0.8076972

99% confidence interval results:
p: proportion of successes for population
method: Standard-Wald

Proportion	Count	Total	Sample Prop.	Std. err.	L. Limit	U Limit
p	802	1025	0.78243905	0.012887059	0.74924415	0.8156339

With 90% confidence, you can say the population proportion of U.S. adults who disapprove of the job Congress is doing is between 76.1% and 80.4%. With 95% confidence you can say it is between 75.7% and 80.8%. With 99% confidence you can say it is between 74.9% and 81.6%.

28. 90% confidence interval results:
p: proportion of successes for population
method: Standard-Wald

Proportion	Count	Total	Sample Prop.	Std. err.	L. Limit	U Limit
p	734	2303	0.3187147	0.009709986	0.30274323	0.33468622

95% confidence interval results:
p: proportion of successes for population
method: Standard-Wald

Proportion	Count	Total	Sample Prop.	Std. err.	L. Limit	U Limit
p	734	2303	0.3187147	0.009709986	0.2996835	0.33774593

99% confidence interval results:
p: proportion of successes for population
method: Standard-Wald

Proportion	Count	Total	Sample Prop.	Std. err.	L. Limit	U Limit
p	734	2303	0.3187147	0.009709986	0.29370347	0.34372598

With 90% confidence, you can say the population proportion of U.S. adults who believe in UFOs is between 30.3% and 33.5%. With 95% confidence you can say it is between 30.0% and 33.8%. With 99% confidence you can say it is between 29.4% and 34.4%. AS the level of confidence increases, the intervals get wider.

29. $31.4\% \pm 1\% \rightarrow (30.4\%, 32.4\%) \rightarrow (0.304, 0.324)$

$$E = z_c \sqrt{\frac{\hat{p}\hat{q}}{n}} \rightarrow z_c = E\sqrt{\frac{n}{\hat{p}\hat{q}}} = 0.01\sqrt{\frac{8451}{0.314-0.686}} \approx 1.981 \rightarrow z_c = 1.98 \rightarrow c = 0.9761$$

(30.4%, 32.4%) is approximately a 95.23% CI.

30. $19\% \pm 3\% \rightarrow (16\%, 22\%) \rightarrow (0.16, 0.22)$

$$E = z_c \sqrt{\frac{\hat{p}\hat{q}}{n}} \rightarrow z_c = E\sqrt{\frac{n}{\hat{p}\hat{q}}} = 0.03\sqrt{\frac{1000}{0.19\cdot 0.81}} \approx 2.418 \rightarrow z_c = 2.41 \rightarrow c = 0.9920$$

(16%, 22%) is approximately a 98.40% CI.

31. If $n\hat{p} < 5$ or $n\hat{q} < 5$, the sampling distribution of $\hat{p}$ may not be normally distributed, therefore preventing the use of z_c when calculating the confidence interval.

32. *Sample answer:*

$E = z_c \sqrt{\dfrac{\hat{p}\hat{q}}{n}}$ Write original equation.

$E\sqrt{n} = z_c \sqrt{\hat{p}\hat{q}}$ Multiply each side by n.

$\sqrt{n} = \sqrt{\hat{p}\hat{q}}\dfrac{z_c}{E}$ Divide each side by E.

$n = \hat{p}\hat{q}\left(\dfrac{z_c}{E}\right)^2$ Square each side.

33.

$\hat{p}$	$\hat{q} = 1 - \hat{p}$	$\hat{p}\hat{q}$		$\hat{p}$	$\hat{q} = 1 - \hat{p}$	$\hat{p}\hat{q}$
0.0	1.0	0.00		0.45	0.55	0.2475
0.1	0.9	0.09		0.46	0.54	0.2484
0.2	0.8	0.16		0.47	0.53	0.2491
0.3	0.7	0.21		0.48	0.52	0.2496
0.4	0.6	0.24		0.49	0.51	0.2499
0.5	0.5	0.25		0.50	0.50	0.2500
0.6	0.4	0.24		0.51	0.49	0.2499
0.7	0.3	0.21		0.52	0.48	0.2496
0.8	0.2	0.16		0.53	0.47	0.2491
0.9	0.1	0.09		0.54	0.46	0.2484
1.0	0.0	0.00		0.55	0.45	0.2475

$\hat{p} = 0.5$ gives the maximum value of $\hat{p}\hat{q}$.

6.4 CONFIDENCE INTERVALS FOR VARIANCE AND STANDARD DEVIATION

6.3 Try It Yourself Solutions

1a. d.f. $= n - 1 = 29$

level of confidence $= 0.90$

b. Area to the right of χ_R^2 is 0.05.

Area to the right of χ_L^2 is 0.95.

c. $\chi_R^2 = 42.557$, $\chi_L^2 = 17.708$

d. So, 90% of the area under the curve lies between 17.708 and 42.557.

2a. 90% CI: $\chi_R^2 = 42.557$, $\chi_L^2 = 17.708$

95% CI: $\chi_R^2 = 42.722$, $\chi_L^2 = 16.047$

b. 90% CI for σ^2 : $\left(\dfrac{(n-1)s^2}{\chi_R^2}, \dfrac{(n-1)s^2}{\chi_L^2} \right) = \left(\dfrac{29 \cdot (1.2)^2}{42.557} \cdot \dfrac{29 \cdot (1.2)^2}{17.708} \right) \approx (0.98,\ 2.36)$

95% CI for σ^2 : $\left(\dfrac{(n-1)s^2}{\chi_R^2}, \dfrac{(n-1)s^2}{\chi_L^2} \right) = \left(\dfrac{29 \cdot (1.2)^2}{42.722} \cdot \dfrac{29 \cdot (1.2)^2}{16.047} \right) \approx (0.91,\ 2.60)$

c. 90% CI for σ : $\left(\sqrt{0.981},\ \sqrt{2.358} \right) = (0.99, 1.54)$

95% CI for σ : $\left(\sqrt{0.913},\ \sqrt{2.602} \right) = (0.96, 1.61)$

d. With 90% confidence, you can say that the population variance is between 0.98 and 2.36 and that the populations standard deviation is between 0.99 and 1.54. With 95% confidence, you can say that the population variance is between 0.91 and 2.60, and that the population standard deviation is between 0.96 and 1.61.

6.4 EXERCISE SOLUTIONS

1. Yes.

2. It approaches the shape of the normal curve.

3. $\chi_R^2 = 14.067$, $\chi_L^2 = 2.167$ 4. $\chi_R^2 = 31.319$, $\chi_L^2 = 4.075$ 5. $\chi_R^2 = 32.852$, $\chi_L^2 = 8.907$

6. $\chi_R^2 = 44.314$, $\chi_L^2 = 11.524$ 7. $\chi_R^2 = 52.336$, $\chi_L^2 = 13.121$ 8. $\chi_R^2 = 63.167$, $\chi_L^2 = 37.689$

9. (a) $s \approx 0.00843$

$$\left(\frac{(n-1)s^2}{\chi_R^2} \cdot \frac{(n-1)s^2}{\chi_L^2} \right) \approx \left(\frac{13 \cdot (0.00843)^2}{22.362} \cdot \frac{13 \cdot (0.00843)^2}{5.892} \right) \approx (0.0000413,\ 0.000157)$$

(b) $\left(\sqrt{0.0000413},\ \sqrt{0.000157} \right) \approx (0.00643,\ 0.0125)$

With 90% confidence, you can say that the population variance is between 0.0000413 and 0.000157, and the population standard deviation is between 0.00643 and 0.0125 milligrams.

10. (a) $s \approx 0.0321$

$$\left(\frac{(n-1)s^2}{\chi_R^2} \cdot \frac{(n-1)s^2}{\chi_L^2} \right) \approx \left(\frac{14 \cdot (0.0321)^2}{23.685} \cdot \frac{14 \cdot (0.0321)^2}{6.571} \right) \approx (0.000610,\ 0.00220)$$

(b) $\left(\sqrt{0.000609},\ \sqrt{0.00220} \right) \approx (0.0247,\ 0.0469)$

With 90% confidence, you can say that the population variance is between 0.000610 and 0.00220, and the population standard deviation is between 0.0247 and 0.0469 fluid ounce.

11. (a) $s \approx 0.253$

$$\left(\frac{(n-1)s^2}{\chi_R^2} \cdot \frac{(n-1)s^2}{\chi_L^2} \right) \approx \left(\frac{17 \cdot (0.253)^2}{35.718} \cdot \frac{17 \cdot (0.253)^2}{5.697} \right) \approx (0.0305,\ 0.191)$$

(b) $\left(\sqrt{0.0305},\ \sqrt{0.191} \right) \approx (0.175,\ 0.437)$

With 99% confidence, you can say that the population variance is between 0.0305 and 0.191, and the population standard deviation is between 0.175 and 0.437 hour.

12. (a) $s \approx 0.0918$

$$\left(\frac{(n-1)s^2}{\chi_R^2} \cdot \frac{(n-1)s^2}{\chi_L^2} \right) \approx \left(\frac{16 \cdot (0.0918)^2}{28.845} \cdot \frac{16 \cdot (0.0918)^2}{6.908} \right) \approx (0.00467,\ 0.0195)$$

(b) $\left(\sqrt{0.00467}, \sqrt{0.0195}\right) \approx (0.0683, \ 0.140)$

With 95% confidence, you can say that the population variance is between 0.00467 and 0.0195, and the population standard deviation is between 0.0683 and 0.0140 inch.

13. (a) $\left(\dfrac{(n-1)s^2}{\chi_R^2} \cdot \dfrac{(n-1)s^2}{\chi_L^2}\right) \approx \left(\dfrac{13 \cdot (3.90)^2}{29.819} \cdot \dfrac{13 \cdot (390)^2}{3.565}\right) \approx (6.63, \ 55.46)$

(b) $\left(\sqrt{6.631}, \sqrt{55.464}\right) \approx (2.58, \ 7.45)$

With 99% confidence, you can say that the population variance is between 6.63 and 55.46, and the population standard deviation is between 2.58 and 7.55 dollars per year.

14. (a) $\left(\dfrac{(n-1)s^2}{\chi_R^2} \cdot \dfrac{(n-1)s^2}{\chi_L^2}\right) \approx \left(\dfrac{10 \cdot (109)^2}{15.987} \cdot \dfrac{10 \cdot (109)^2}{4.865}\right) \approx (7432, \ 24{,}421)$

(b) $\left(\sqrt{7432}, \sqrt{24{,}421}\right) \approx (86, \ 156)$

With 80% confidence, you can say that the population variance is between 7432 and 24.421, and the population standard deviation is between \$86 and \$156.

15. (a) $\left(\dfrac{(n-1)s^2}{\chi_R^2} \cdot \dfrac{(n-1)s^2}{\chi_L^2}\right) \approx \left(\dfrac{9 \cdot (30.244)^2}{21.666} \cdot \dfrac{9 \cdot (30.244)^2}{2.088}\right) \approx (380.0, \ 3942.6)$

(b) $\left(\sqrt{380}, \sqrt{3942.6}\right) \approx (19.5, \ 62.8)$

With 98% confidence, you can say that the population variance is between 380.0 and 3942.6, and the population standard deviation is between \$19.5 and \$62.8.

16. (a) $\left(\dfrac{(n-1)s^2}{\chi_R^2} \cdot \dfrac{(n-1)s^2}{\chi_L^2}\right) \approx \left(\dfrac{13 \cdot (0.875)^2}{29.819} \cdot \dfrac{13 \cdot (0.875)^2}{3.565}\right) \approx (0.33, \ 2.79)$

(b) $\left(\sqrt{0.334}, \sqrt{2.793}\right) \approx (0.58, \ 1.67)$

With 99% confidence, you can say that the population variance is between 0.33 and 2.79, and the population standard deviation is between 0.58 and 1.67 pounds.

17. (a) $\left(\dfrac{(n-1)s^2}{\chi_R^2} \cdot \dfrac{(n-1)s^2}{\chi_L^2}\right) \approx \left(\dfrac{15 \cdot (6.42)^2}{27.488} \cdot \dfrac{15 \cdot (6.42)^2}{6.262}\right) \approx (22.5, \ 98.7)$

(b) $\left(\sqrt{22.5}, \sqrt{98.7}\right) \approx (4.7, \ 9.9)$

With 95% confidence, you can say that the population variance is between 22.5 and 98.7, and the population standard deviation is between 4.7 and 9.9 beats per minute.

18. (a) $\left(\dfrac{(n-1)s^2}{\chi_R^2} \cdot \dfrac{(n-1)s^2}{\chi_L^2} \right) \approx \left(\dfrac{26 \cdot (138.33)^2}{45.642} \cdot \dfrac{26 \cdot (138.33)^2}{12.198} \right) \approx (10{,}901.37,\ 40{,}789.60)$

   (b) $\left(\sqrt{10{,}901.37},\ \sqrt{40{,}789.60} \right) \approx (104,\ 202)$

   With 98% confidence, you can say that the population variance is between 10,901.06 and 40,789.17, and the population standard deviation is between \$104 and \$202.

19. (a) $\left(\dfrac{(n-1)s^2}{\chi_R^2} \cdot \dfrac{(n-1)s^2}{\chi_L^2} \right) \approx \left(\dfrac{18 \cdot (15)^2}{31.526} \cdot \dfrac{18 \cdot (15)^2}{8.231} \right) \approx (128,\ 492)$

   (b) $\left(\sqrt{128.465},\ \sqrt{492.042} \right) \approx (11,\ 22)$

   With 95% confidence, you can say that the population variance is between 128 and 492, and the population standard deviation is between 11 and 22 grains per gallon.

20. (a) $\left(\dfrac{(n-1)s^2}{\chi_R^2} \cdot \dfrac{(n-1)s^2}{\chi_L^2} \right) \approx \left(\dfrac{29(3600)^2}{42.557} \cdot \dfrac{29(3600)^2}{17.708} \right) \approx (8{,}831{,}450,\ 21{,}224{,}305)$

   (b) $\left(\sqrt{8{,}831{,}450},\ \sqrt{21{,}224{,}305} \right) \approx (2972,\ 4607)$

   With 90% confidence, you can say that the population variance is between 8,831,450 and 21,224,305, and the population standard deviation is between \$2972 and \$4607.

21. (a) $\left(\dfrac{(n-1)s^2}{\chi_R^2} \cdot \dfrac{(n-1)s^2}{\chi_L^2} \right) \approx \left(\dfrac{13 \cdot (3725)^2}{19.812} \cdot \dfrac{13 \cdot (3725)^2}{7.042} \right) \approx (9{,}104{,}741,\ 25{,}615{,}326)$

   (b) $\left(\sqrt{9{,}104{,}741},\ \sqrt{25{,}615{,}326} \right) \approx (3017,\ 5061)$

   With 80% confidence, you can say that the population variance is between 9,104,741 and 25,615,326, and the population standard deviation is between \$3017 and \$5061.

22. (a) $\left(\dfrac{(n-1)s^2}{\chi_R^2} \cdot \dfrac{(n-1)s^2}{\chi_L^2} \right) \approx \left(\dfrac{29 \cdot (8.18)^2}{49.588} \cdot \dfrac{29 \cdot (8.18)^2}{14.256} \right) \approx (39.13,\ 136.11)$

   (b) $\left(\sqrt{39.13},\ \sqrt{136.11} \right) \approx (6.26,\ 11.67)$

   With 98% confidence, you can say that the population variance is between 39.13 and 136.11, and the population standard deviation is between 6.26 and 11.67.

23. (a) $\left(\dfrac{(n-1)s^2}{\chi_R^2} \cdot \dfrac{(n-1)s^2}{\chi_L^2} \right) \approx \left(\dfrac{(21)(3.6)^2}{38.932} \cdot \dfrac{(21)(3.6)^2}{8.897} \right) \approx (7.0,\ 30.6)$

(b) $\left(\sqrt{6.99},\ \sqrt{30.59} \right) \approx (2.6,\ 5.5)$

With 98% confidence, you can say that the population variance is between 7.0 and 30.6, and the population standard deviation is between 2.6 and 5.5 minutes.

24. (a) $\left(\dfrac{(n-1)s^2}{\chi_R^2} \cdot \dfrac{(n-1)s^2}{\chi_L^2} \right) \approx \left(\dfrac{19(3900)^2}{30.144} \cdot \dfrac{19(3900)^2}{10.117} \right) \approx (9,586,982,\ 28,564,792)$

(b) $\left(\sqrt{9,586,982},\ \sqrt{28,564,792} \right) \approx (3096,\ 5345)$

With 90% confidence, you can say that the population variance is between 9,586,982 and 28,564,792, and the population standard deviation is between \$3096 and \$5345.

25. 95% confidence interval results:

σ^2 : variance of variable

Variance	Sample Var.	DF	L. Limit	U Limit
σ^2	11.56	29	7.332092	20.891039

(2.71, 4.57)

26. 99% confidence interval results:

σ^2 : variance of variable

Variance	Sample Var.	DF	L. Limit	U Limit
σ^2	0.64	6	0.20703505	5.6827703

(0.46, 2.38)

27. 90% confidence interval results:

σ^2 : variance of variable

Variance	Sample Var.	DF	L. Limit	U Limit
σ^2	1225	17	754.8815	2401.4731

(27, 49)

28. 99% confidence interval results:

σ^2 : variance of variable

Variance	Sample Var.	DF	L. Limit	U Limit
σ^2	77339.6	44	50970.645	130062.46

(225.8, 360.6)

29. 90% CI for σ: (0.00643, 0.0125)

Yes, because all of the values in the confidence interval are less than 0.015.

30. 90% CI for σ: (0.0247, 0.0469)

No, because 0.025 is contained in the confidence interval.

31. Answers will vary. **Sample answer:** Unlike a confidence interval for a population mean or proportion, a confidence interval for a population variance does not have a margin of error. The left and right endpoints must be calculated separately.

CHAPTER 6 REVIEW EXERCISE SOLUTIONS

1. (a) $\bar{x} \approx 103.5$

(b) $s \approx 34.663$

$$E = z_c \frac{s}{\sqrt{n}} \approx 1.645 \frac{34.663}{\sqrt{40}} \approx 9.0$$

2. (a) $\bar{x} \approx 9.5$

(b) $s \approx 7.1$

$$E = z_c \frac{s}{\sqrt{n}} \approx 1.645 \frac{7.1}{\sqrt{32}} \approx 2.1$$

3. $\bar{x} \pm z_c \frac{s}{\sqrt{n}} = 15.8 \pm 2.575 \frac{0.85}{\sqrt{80}} \approx 15.3 \pm 0.245 \approx (15.6, \ 16.0)$

4. $\bar{x} \pm z_c \frac{s}{\sqrt{n}} = 7.675 \pm 1.96 \frac{0.105}{\sqrt{55}} \approx 7.675 \pm 0.028 \approx (7.647, \ 7.703)$

5. $(20.75, 24.10) \rightarrow \bar{x} = 22.425 \rightarrow E = 24.10 - 22.425 = 1.675$

6. $(7.428, 7.562) \rightarrow \bar{x} = 7.495 \rightarrow E = 7.562 - 7.495 = 0.067$

7. $s \approx 34.663$

$$n = \left(\frac{z_c \sigma}{E} \right)^2 \approx \left(\frac{1.96 \cdot 34.663}{10} \right)^2 \approx 46.158 \Rightarrow 47 \text{ people}$$

8. $n = \left(\frac{z_c \sigma}{E} \right)^2 \approx \left(\frac{2.575 \cdot 34.663}{2} \right)^2 \approx 1991.713 \Rightarrow 1992 \text{ people}$

9. $n = \left(\frac{z_c \sigma}{E} \right)^2 \approx \left(\frac{(1.96)(7.098)}{2} \right)^2 \approx 48.39 \Rightarrow 49 \text{ people}$

10. $n = \left(\frac{z_c \sigma}{E} \right)^2 \approx \left(\frac{(2.33)(7.098)}{0.5} \right)^2 \approx 1094.06 \Rightarrow 1095 \text{ people}$

11. $t_c = 1.383$ **12.** $t_c = 2.069$ **13.** $t_c = 2.624$ **14.** $t_c = 2.756$

15. $n = 20 \rightarrow t_c = 1,729$
$n = 30 \rightarrow t_c = 1.699$
$n = 20$ produces a larger critical value t_c.

16. $n = 20 \rightarrow t_c = 1,729$
$n = 30 \rightarrow t_c = 1.699$
$n = 20$ produces a wider confidence interval because $1.729 > 1.699$.

17. $E = t_c \dfrac{s}{\sqrt{n}} = 1.753 \dfrac{25.6}{\sqrt{16}} \approx 11.2$

18. $E = t_c \dfrac{s}{\sqrt{n}} = 2.064 \dfrac{1.1}{\sqrt{25}} \approx 0.5$

19. $E = t_c \dfrac{s}{\sqrt{n}} = 2.718 \left(\dfrac{0.9}{\sqrt{12}} \right) \approx 0.7$

20. $E = t_c \dfrac{s}{\sqrt{n}} = 2.861 \left(\dfrac{16.5}{\sqrt{20}} \right) \approx 10.6$

21. $\bar{x} \pm z_c \dfrac{s}{\sqrt{n}} = 72.1 \pm 1.753 \dfrac{25.6}{\sqrt{16}} \approx 72.1 \pm 11.219 \approx (60.9,\ 83.3)$

22. $\bar{x} \pm t_c \dfrac{s}{\sqrt{n}} = 3.5 \pm 2.064 \dfrac{1.1}{\sqrt{25}} \approx 3.5 \pm 0.454 \approx (3,\ 4)$

23. $\bar{x} \pm t_c \dfrac{s}{\sqrt{n}} = 6.8 \pm 2.718 \left(\dfrac{0.9}{\sqrt{12}} \right) \approx 6.8 \pm 0.706 \approx (6.1,\ 7.5)$

24. $\bar{x} \pm t_c \dfrac{s}{\sqrt{n}} = 25.2 \pm 2.861 \left(\dfrac{6.5}{\sqrt{20}} \right) \approx 25.2 \pm 10.556 \approx (14.6,\ 35.8)$

25. $\bar{x} \pm t_c \dfrac{s}{\sqrt{n}} = 2218 \pm 1.703 \dfrac{523}{\sqrt{28}} \approx 2218 \pm 168.3 \approx (2050,\ 2386)$

26. $\bar{x} \pm t_c \dfrac{s}{\sqrt{n}} = 2218 \pm 2.771 \dfrac{523}{\sqrt{28}} \approx 2218 \pm 273.9 \approx (1944,\ 2492)$

27. $\hat{p} = \dfrac{x}{n} = \dfrac{1215}{1500} = 0.81,\ \hat{q} = 0.19$

28. $\hat{p} = \dfrac{x}{n} = \dfrac{425}{500} = 0.85,\ \hat{q} = 0.15$

29. $\hat{p} = \dfrac{x}{n} = \dfrac{552}{1023} \approx 0.540,\ \hat{q} \approx 0.460$

30. $\hat{p} = \dfrac{x}{n} = \dfrac{90}{800} \approx 0.113,\ \hat{q} \approx 0.887$

31. $\hat{p} = \dfrac{x}{n} = \dfrac{141}{1008} \approx 0.140,\ \hat{q} \approx 0.860$

32. $\hat{p} = \dfrac{x}{n} = \dfrac{235}{938} \approx 0.251,\ \hat{q} \approx 0.749$

33. $\hat{p} = \dfrac{x}{n} = \dfrac{346}{706} \approx 0.490, \; \hat{q} \approx 0.510$

34. $\hat{p} = \dfrac{x}{n} = \dfrac{1230}{2365} \approx 0.520, \; \hat{q} \approx 0.480$

35. $\hat{p} \pm z_c \sqrt{\dfrac{\hat{p}\hat{q}}{n}} = 0.81 \pm 1.96 \sqrt{\dfrac{0.81 \cdot 0.19}{1500}} \approx 0.81 \pm 0.020 = (0.790, \; 0.830)$

With 95% confidence, you can say that the population proportion of U.S. adults who say they will participate in the 2010 Census is between 79.0% and 83.0%.

36. $\hat{p} \pm z_c \sqrt{\dfrac{\hat{p}\hat{q}}{n}} = 0.85 \pm 2.575 \sqrt{\dfrac{0.85 \cdot 0.15}{500}} \approx 0.85 \pm 0.041 = (0.809, \; 0.891)$

With 99% confidence, you can say that the population proportion of U.S. adults who say they would trust doctors to tell the truth is between 80.9% and 89.1%.

37. $\hat{p} \pm z_c \sqrt{\dfrac{\hat{p}\hat{q}}{n}} \approx 0.540 \pm 1.645 \sqrt{\dfrac{0.540 \cdot 0.460}{1023}} \approx 0.540 \pm 0.026 = (0.514, \; 0.566)$

With 90% confidence, you can say that the population proportion of U.S. adults who say they have worked the night shift at some point in their lives is between 51.4% and 56.6%.

38. $\hat{p} \pm z_c \sqrt{\dfrac{\hat{p}\hat{q}}{n}} \approx 0.113 \pm 2.326 \sqrt{\dfrac{0.113 \cdot 0.887}{800}} \approx 0.113 \pm 0.026 = (0.087, \; 0.139)$

With 98% confidence, you can say that the population proportion of U.S. adults who say they are making the minimum payment(s) on their credit card(s) is between 8.7% and 13.9%.

39. $\hat{p} \pm z_c \sqrt{\dfrac{\hat{p}\hat{q}}{n}} \approx 0.140 \pm 2.575 \sqrt{\dfrac{0.140 \cdot 0.860}{10008}} \approx 0.140 \pm 0.028 = (0.112, \; 0.168)$

With 99% confidence, you can say that the population proportion of U.S. adults who say that the cost of healthcare is the most important financial problem facing their family today is between 11.2% and 16.8%.

40. $\hat{p} \pm z_c \sqrt{\dfrac{\hat{p}\hat{q}}{n}} \approx 0.251 \pm 1.645 \sqrt{\dfrac{0.251 \cdot 0.749}{938}} \approx 0.251 \pm 0.023 = (0.228, \; 0.274)$

With 90% confidence, you can say that the population proportion of U.S. adults who say the phrase "you know" is the most annoying conversational phrase is between 22.8% and 27.4%.

41. $\hat{p} \pm z_c \sqrt{\dfrac{\hat{p}\hat{q}}{n}} \approx 0.490 \pm 1.28 \sqrt{\dfrac{(0.490)(0.510)}{706}} \approx 0.49 \pm 0.024 = (0.466, \; 0.514)$

With 80% confidence, you can say that the population proportion of parents with kids 4 to 8 years old who say they know their state booster seat law is between 46.6% and 51.4%.

42. $\hat{p} \pm z_c \sqrt{\dfrac{\hat{p}\hat{q}}{n}} \approx 0.520 \pm 2.326\sqrt{\dfrac{(0.52)(0.48)}{2365}} \approx 0.520 \pm 0.024 = (0.496,\ 0.544)$

With 98% confidence, you can say that the population proportion of U.S. adults who say they worry most about missing deductions when filing their taxes is between 49.6% and 54.4%.

43. (a) $n = \hat{p}\hat{q}\left(\dfrac{z_c}{E}\right)^2 = 0.50 \cdot 0.50 \left(\dfrac{1.96}{0.05}\right)^2 \approx 384.16 \rightarrow 385$ adults

(b) $n = \hat{p}\hat{q}\left(\dfrac{z_c}{E}\right)^2 = 0.63 \cdot 0.37 \left(\dfrac{1.96}{0.05}\right)^2 \approx 358.19 \rightarrow 359$ adults

(c) The minimum sample size needed is smaller when a preliminary estimate is available.

44. $n = \hat{p}\hat{q}\left(\dfrac{z_c}{E}\right)^2 = 0.63 \cdot 0.37 \left(\dfrac{2.575}{0.025}\right)^2 \approx 2472.96 \rightarrow 2473$ adults

The sample size is larger.

45. $\chi_R^2 = 23.337,\ \chi_L^2 = 4.404$ **46.** $\chi_R^2 = 42.980,\ \chi_L^2 = 10.856$

47. $\chi_R^2 = 14.067,\ \chi_L^2 = 2.167$ **48.** $\chi_R^2 = 23.589,\ \chi_L^2 = 1.735$

49. $s \approx 7.002$

95% CI for σ^2 : $\left(\dfrac{(n-1)s^2}{\chi_R^2},\ \dfrac{(n-1)s^2}{\chi_L^2}\right) \approx \left(\dfrac{16 \cdot (7.002)^2}{28.845},\ \dfrac{16 \cdot (7.002)^2}{6.908}\right) \approx (27.2,\ 113.5)$

95% CI for σ : $\left(\sqrt{27.2},\ \sqrt{113.5}\right) \approx (5.2,\ 10.7)$

50. 99% CI for σ^2 : $\left(\dfrac{(n-1)s^2}{\chi_R^2},\ \dfrac{(n-1)s^2}{\chi_L^2}\right) \approx \left(\dfrac{16 \cdot (7.002)^2}{34.267},\ \dfrac{16 \cdot (7.002)^2}{5.142}\right) \approx (22.9,\ 152.6)$

95% CI for σ : $\left(\sqrt{22.9},\ \sqrt{152.6}\right) \approx (4.8,\ 12.3)$

With 99% confidence, you can say that the population variance is between 22.9 and 152.5, and the population standard deviation is between 4.8 and 12.3 ounces. The confidence intervals in Exercise 50 are wider than those in Exercise 49.

51. $s \approx 1.190$

98% CI for σ^2 : $\left(\dfrac{(n-1)s^2}{\chi_R^2},\ \dfrac{(n-1)s^2}{\chi_L^2}\right) \approx \left(\dfrac{(25)(1.190)^2}{44.314},\ \dfrac{(25)(1.190)}{11.524}\right) \approx (0.80,\ 3.07)$

98% CI for σ : $\left(\sqrt{0.80},\ \sqrt{3.07}\right) \approx (0.89,\ 1.75)$

52. $s \approx 1.190$

$$98\% \text{ CI for } \sigma^2 : \left(\frac{(n-1)s^2}{\chi_R^2}, \frac{(n-1)s^2}{\chi_L^2} \right) \approx \left(\frac{(25)(1.190)^2}{37.652}, \frac{(25)(1.190)}{14.611} \right) \approx (0.94, \ 2.42)$$

$$98\% \text{ CI for } \sigma : \left(\sqrt{0.94}, \ \sqrt{2.42} \right) \approx (0.97, \ 1.56)$$

With 90% confidence, you can say that the population variance is between 0.94 and 2.42, and the population standard deviation is between 0.97 and 1.56 seconds. The confidence intervals in Exercise 52 are wider than those in Exercise 51.

CHAPTER 6 QUIZ SOLUTIONS

1. (a) $\bar{x} \approx 6.85$

    (b) $s \approx 1.821$

$$E = t_c \frac{s}{\sqrt{n}} \approx 1.960 \frac{1.821}{\sqrt{30}} \approx 0.65$$

You are 95% confident that the margin of error for the population mean is about 0.65 minute.

    (c) $\bar{x} \pm t_c \frac{s}{\sqrt{n}} \approx 6.848 \pm 1.960 \frac{1.821}{\sqrt{30}} = 6.848 \pm 0.652 \approx (6.196, \ 7.500)$

With 95% confidence, you can say that the population mean amount of time is between 6.20 and 7.50 minutes.

2. $n = \left(\frac{z_c \sigma}{E} \right)^2 = \left(\frac{2.575 \cdot 2.4}{1} \right)^2 \approx 38.18 \rightarrow 39$ students

3. (a) $\bar{x} \approx 33.1$

       $s \approx 2.38$

    (b) $\bar{x} \pm t_c \frac{s}{\sqrt{n}} \approx 33.11 \pm 1.833 \frac{2.38}{\sqrt{10}} \approx 33.11 \pm 1.38 = (31.73, \ 34.49)$

With 90% confidence you can say that the population mean time played in the season is between 31.73 and 34.49 minutes.

    (c) $\bar{x} \pm z_c \frac{\sigma}{\sqrt{n}} \approx 33.11 \pm 1.645 \frac{5.25}{\sqrt{10}} \approx 33.11 \pm 2.73 = (30.38, \ 35.84)$

With 90% confidence you can say that the population mean time played in the season is between 30.38 and 35.84 minutes. This confidence interval is wider than the one found in part (b).

4. $\bar{x} \pm t_c \frac{s}{\sqrt{n}} = 6824 \pm 2.447 \frac{340}{\sqrt{7}} \approx 6824 \pm 314.46 \approx (6510, \ 7138)$

5. (a) $\hat{p} = \dfrac{x}{n} = \dfrac{1079}{1383} \approx 0.780$

    (b) $\hat{p} \pm z_c \sqrt{\dfrac{\hat{p}\hat{q}}{n}} \approx 0.780 \pm 1.645 \sqrt{\dfrac{0.780 \cdot 0.220}{1383}} \approx 0.780 \pm 0.018 = (0.762,\ 0.798)$

    (c) $n = \hat{p}\hat{q} \left(\dfrac{z_c}{E}\right)^2 \approx 0.780 \cdot 0.220 \left(\dfrac{2.575}{0.04}\right)^2 \approx 711.13 \rightarrow 712$ adults

6. (a) $\left(\dfrac{(n-1)s^2}{\chi_R^2},\ \dfrac{(n-1)s^2}{\chi_L^2}\right) = \left(\dfrac{29 \cdot (1.821)^2}{45.722},\ \dfrac{29 \cdot (1.821)^2}{16.047}\right) \approx (2.10,\ 5.99)$

    (b) $\left(\sqrt{2.10},\ \sqrt{5.99}\right) \approx (1.45,\ 2.45)$

Hypothesis Testing with One Sample

7.1 INTRODUCTION TO HYPOTHESIS TESTING

7.1 Try It Yourself Solutions

1a. (1) The mean is not 74 months.
$\mu \neq 74$

(2) The variance is less than or equal to 2.7.
$\sigma^2 \leq 2.7$

(3) The proportion is more than 24%
$p > 0.24$

b. (1) $\mu = 74$ (2) $\sigma^2 > 2.7$ (3) $p \leq 0.24$

c. (1) $H_0 : \mu = 74$; $H_a : \mu \neq 74$ (claim)

(2) $H_0 : \sigma^2 \leq 2.7$ (claim); $H_a : \sigma^2 > 2.7$

(3) $p \leq 0.24$; $H_a : p > 0.24$ (claim)

2a. $H_0 : p \leq 0.01$; $H_a : p > 0.01$

b. A type I error will occur if the actual proportion is less than or equal to 0.01, but you reject H_0.

A type II error will occur if the actual proportion is greater than 0.01, but you fail to reject H_0.

c. A type II error is more serious because you would be misleading the consumer, possibly causing serious injury or death.

3a. (1) H_0 : The mean life of a certain type of automobile battery is 74 months.

H_a : The mean life of a certain type of automobile battery is not 74 months.

$H_0 : \mu = 74$; $H_a : \mu \neq 74$

(2) H_0 : The variance of the life of the home theater system is less than or equal to 2.7.

H_a : The variance of the life of the home theater system is greater than 2.7.

$H_0 : \sigma^2 \leq 2.7$; $H_a : \sigma^2 > 2.7$

(3) H_0 : The proportion of homeowners who feel their house is too small for their family is less than or equal to 24%.

H_a : The proportion of homeowners who feel their house is too small for their family is greater than 24%.

$H_0 : p \leq 0.24$; $H_a : p > 0.24$

b. (1) Two-tailed   (2) Right-tailed   (3) Right-tailed

c. (1)   (2)   (3)

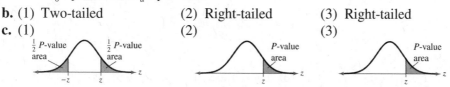

4a. There us enough evidence to support the realtor's claim that the proportion of homeowners who feel their house is too small for their family is more than 24%.

b. There is not enough evidence to support the realtor's claim that the proportion of homeowners who feel their house is too small for their family is more than 24%.

5a. (1) Support claim.   (2) Reject claim.
  b. (1) $H_0: \mu \geq 650$; $H_a: \mu < 650$ (claim)
      (2) $H_0: \mu = 98.6$ (claim); $H_a: \mu \neq 98.6$

7.1 EXERCISE SOLUTIONS

1. The two types of hypotheses used in a hypothesis test are the null hypothesis and the alternative hypothesis.
   The alternative hypothesis is the complement of the null hypothesis.

2. Type I Error: The null hypothesis is rejected when it is true.
   Type II Error: The null hypothesis is not rejected when it is false.

3. You can reject the null hypothesis, or you can fail to reject the null hypothesis.

4. No; Failing to reject the null hypothesis means that there is not enough evidence to reject it.

5. False. In a hypothesis test, you assume the null hypothesis is true.

6. False. A statistical hypothesis is a statement about a population.

7. True

8. True

9. False. A small P-value in a test will favor a rejection of the null hypothesis.

10. False. If you want to support a claim, write it as your alternative hypothesis.

11. $H_0: \mu \leq 645$ (claim); $H_a: \mu > 645$ 12. $H_0: \mu \geq 128$; $H_a: \mu < 128$ (claim)

13. $H_0: \sigma = 5$; $H_a: \sigma \neq 5$ (claim)   14. $H_0: \sigma^2 \geq 1.2$ (claim); $H_a: \sigma^2 < 1.2$

15. $H_0: p \geq 0.45$; $H_a: p < 0.45$ (claim)   16. $H_0: p = 0.21$ (claim); $H_a: p \neq 0.21$

17. c; $H_0: \mu \leq 3$ 18. d; $H_a: \mu \geq 3$

19. b; $H_0: \mu = 3$ 20. a; $H_a: \mu \leq 2$

21. Right-tailed   22. Left tailed   23. Two-tailed   24. Two-tailed

25. $\mu > 750$ 26. $\sigma < 3$
    $H_0: \mu \leq 750$; $H_a: \mu > 750$ (claim) $H_0: \sigma \geq 3$; $H_a: \sigma < 3$ (claim)

27. $\sigma \leq 320$

$H_0: \sigma \leq 320$ (claim); $H_a: \sigma > 320$

28. $\mu \geq 85$

$H_0: \mu \geq 85$ (claim); $H_a: \mu < 85$

29. $\mu < 45$

$H_0: \mu \geq 45$; $H_a: \mu < 45$ (claim)

30. $p = 0.74$

$H_0: p = 0.74$ (claim); $H_a: p \neq 0.74$

31. A type I error will occur if the actual proportion of new customers who return to buy their next piece of furniture is at least 0.60, but you reject $H_0: p \geq 0.60$.

A type II error will occur if the actual proportion of new customers who return to buy their next piece of furniture is less than 0.60, but you fail to reject $H_0: p \geq 0.60$.

32. A type I error will occur if the actual mean flow rate of the hose is 16 gallons per minute, but you reject $H_0: \mu = 16$.

A type II error will occur if the actual mean flow rate of the hose is not 16 gallons per minute, but you fail to reject $H_0: \mu = 16$.

33. A type I error will occur if the actual standard deviation of the length of time to play a game is less than or equal to 12 minutes, but you reject $H_0: \sigma \leq 12$.

A type II error will occur of the actual standard deviation of the length of time to play a game is greater than 12 minutes, but you fail to reject $H_0: \sigma \leq 12$.

34. A type I error will occur if the actual proportion of U.S. adults who own a video game system is 0.26, but you reject $H_0: p \leq 0.26$.

A type II error will occur if the actual proportion of U.S. adults who own a video game system is not 0.26, but you fail to reject $H_0: p \leq 0.26$.

35. A type I error will occur if the actual proportion of applicants who become police officers is at most 0.20, but you reject $H_0: p \leq 0.20$.

A type II error will occur if the actual proportion of applicants who become police officers is greater than 0.20, but you fail to reject $H_0: p \leq 0.20$.

36. A type I error will occur if the actual mean cost of removing a virus infection is greater than or equal to $100, but you reject $H_0: \mu \geq 100$.

A type II error will occur if the actual mean cost of removing a virus infection is less than $100, but you fail to reject $H_0: \mu \geq 100$.

37. H_0: The proportion of homeowners who have a home security alarm is greater than or equal to 14%.

H_a: The proportion of homeowners who have a home security alarm is less than 14%.

$H_0: p \geq 0.14$; $H_a: p < 0.14$

Left-tailed because the alternative hypothesis contains <.

38. H_0 : The mean time that the manufacturer's clocks lose is less than or equal to 0.02 second per day.

H_a : The mean time that the manufacturer's clocks lose is greater than 0.02 second per day.

H_0 : $\mu \leq 0.02$; H_a : $\mu > 0.02$

Right-tailed because the alternative hypothesis contains >.

39. H_0 : The standard deviation of the 18-hole scores for a golfer is greater than or equal to 2.1 strokes.

H_a : The standard deviation of the 18-hole scores for a golfer is less than 2.1 strokes.

H_0 : $\sigma \geq 2.1$; H_a : $\sigma < 2.1$

Left-tailed because the alternative hypothesis contains <.

40. H_0 : The proportion of lung cancer cases that are due to smoking is 87%.

H_a : The proportion of lung cancer cases that are due to smoking is not 87%.

H_0 : $p = 0.87$; H_a : $p \neq 0.87$

Two-tailed because the alternative hypothesis contains $\neq$.

41. H_0 : The mean length of the baseball team's games is greater than or equal to 2.5 hours.

H_a : The mean length of the baseball team's games is less than 2.5 hours.

H_0 : $\mu \geq 2.5$; H_a : $\mu < 2.5$

Left-tailed because the alternative hypothesis contains <.

42. H_0 : The mean tuition of the state's universities is less than or equal to $25,000 per year.

H_a : The mean tuition of the state's universities is greater than $25,000 per year.

H_0 : $\mu \leq 25,000$; H_a : $\mu > 25,000$

Right-tailed because the alternative hypothesis contains >.

43a. There is enough evidence to support the scientist's claim that the mean incubation period for swan eggs is less than 40 days.

b. There is not enough evidence to support the scientist's claim that the mean incubation period for swan eggs is less than 40 days.

44. (a) There is enough evidence to reject the claim that the standard deviation of the life of the lawn mower is at most 2.8 years.

(b) There is not enough evidence to reject the claim that the standard deviation of the life of the lawnmower is at most 2.8 years.

45. (a) There is enough evidence to support U.S. Department of Labor's claim that the proportion of full-time workers earning over $450 per week is greater than 75%.

(b) There is not enough evidence to support U.S. Department of Labor's claim that the proportion of full-time workers earning over $450 per week is greater than 75%.

46. (a) There is enough evidence to reject the automotive manufacturer's claim that the standard deviation for the gas mileage of its models is 3.9 miles per gallon.

(b) There is not enough evidence to reject the automotive manufacturer's claim that the standard deviation for the gas mileage of its models is 3.9 miles per gallon.

47. (a) There is enough evidence to support the researcher's claim that the proportion of people who have no health care visits in the past year is less than 17%.

(b) There is not enough evidence to support the researcher's claim that the proportion of people who have no health care visits in the past year is less than 17%.

48. (a) There is enough evidence to reject the sports drink maker's claim that the mean calorie content of its beverages is 72 calories per serving.

(b) There is not enough evidence to reject the sports drink maker's claim that the mean calorie content of its beverages is 72 calories per serving.

49. $H_0: \mu \geq 60;\ H_a: \mu < 60$ **50.** $H_0: \mu = 21;\ H_a: \mu \neq 21$

51. (a) $H_0: \mu \geq 15;\ H_a: \mu < 15$ **52.** (a) $H_0: \mu \leq 28;\ H_a: \mu > 28$

(b) $H_0: \mu \leq 15;\ H_a: \mu > 15$ (b) $H_0: \mu \geq 28;\ H_a: \mu < 28$

53. If you decrease α, you are decreasing the probability that you reject H_0. Therefore, you are increasing the probability of failing to reject H_0. This could increase β, the probability of failing to reject H_0 when H_0 is false.

54. If $\alpha = 0$, the null hypothesis cannot be rejected and the hypothesis test is useless.

55. Yes; If the P-value is less than $\alpha = 0.05$, it is also less than $\alpha = 0.10$.

56. Not necessarily; A P-value less than $\alpha = 0.10$ may or may not also be less than $\alpha = 0.05$.

57. (a) Fail to reject H_0 because the CI includes values greater than 70.

(b) Reject H_0 because the CI is located below 70.

(c) Fail to reject H_0 because the CI includes values greater than 70.

58. (a) Fail to reject H_0 because the CI includes values less than 54.

(b) Fail to reject H_0 because the CI includes values less than 54.

(c) Reject H_0 because the CI is located to the right of 54.

59. (a) Reject H_0 because the CI is located to the right of 0.20.

(b) Fail to reject H_0 because the CI includes values less than 0.20.

(c) Fail to reject H_0 because the CI includes values less than 0.20.

60. (a) Fail to reject H_0 because the CI includes values greater than 0.73.

(b) Reject H_0 because the CI is located to the left of 0.73.

(c) Fail to reject H_0 because the CI includes values greater than 0.73.

7.2 HYPOTHESIS TESTING FOR THE MEAN (LARGE SAMPLES)

7.2 Try It Yourself Solutions

1a. (1) $P = 0.0347 > 0.01 = \alpha$

    (2) $P = 0.0347 < 0.05 = \alpha$

 b. (1) Fail to reject H_0 because $0.0347 > 0.01$.

    (2) Reject H_0 because $0.0347 < 0.05$.

2a.

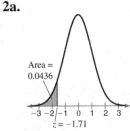

Area = 0.0436

$z = -1.71$

 b. $P = 0.0436$

 c. Reject H_0 because $P = 0.0436 < 0.05$.

3a. Area to the right of $z = 1.64$ is 0.0505.

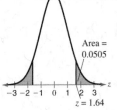

Area = 0.0505

$z = 1.64$

 b. $p = 2(\text{area}) = 2(0.0505) = 0.1010$

 c. Fail to reject H_0 because $P = 0.1010 > 0.10$.

4a. The claim is "the mean speed is greater than 35 miles per hour."

    $H_0 : \mu \le 35$; $H_\alpha : \mu > 35$ (claim)

 b. $\alpha = 0.05$

 c. $z = \dfrac{\overline{x} - \mu}{\dfrac{s}{\sqrt{n}}} = \dfrac{36 - 35}{\dfrac{4}{\sqrt{100}}} = 2.5$

 d. P-value = {Area right of $z = 2.50$} = 0.0062

 e. Reject H_0 because P-value = $0.0062 < 0.05$.

 f. There is enough evidence at the 5% level of significance to support the claim that the average speed is greater than 35 miles per hour.

5a. The claim is "one of your distributors reports an average of 150 sales per day."

    $H_0 : \mu = 150$ (claim); $H_\alpha : \mu \ne 150$

 b. $\alpha = 0.01$

c. $z = \dfrac{\bar{x} - \mu}{\dfrac{s}{\sqrt{n}}} = \dfrac{143 - 150}{\dfrac{15}{\sqrt{35}}} \approx -2.76$

d. P-value $= 2\{$Area to the left of $z = -2.76\} = 2(0.0029) = 0.0059$

e. Reject H_0 because P-value $= 0.0058 < 0.01$.

f. There is enough evidence at the 1% level of significance to reject the claim that the distributorship averages 150 sales per day.

6a. $P = 0.0440 > 0.01 = \alpha$ **b.** Fail to reject H_0.

7a.

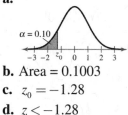

b. Area $= 0.1003$

c. $z_0 = -1.28$

d. $z < -1.28$

8a.

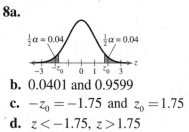

b. 0.0401 and 0.9599

c. $-z_0 = -1.75$ and $z_0 = 1.75$

d. $z < -1.75,\ z > 1.75$

9a. The claim is "the mean work day of the company's mechanical engineers is less than 8.5 hours."
$H_0:\ \mu \geq 8.5;\ H_a:\ \mu < 8.5$ (claim)

b. $\alpha = 0.01$

c. $z_0 = -2.33$; Rejection region: $z < -2.33$

d. $z = \dfrac{\bar{x} - \mu}{\dfrac{s}{\sqrt{n}}} = \dfrac{8.2 - 8.5}{\dfrac{0.5}{\sqrt{35}}} \approx -3.55$

e.   Because $-3.55 < -2.33$, reject H_0.

f. There is enough evidence at the 1% level of significance to support the claim that the mean work day is less than 8.5 hours.

10a. $\alpha = 0.01$

b. $\pm z_0 = \pm 2.575$; Rejection regions: $z < -2.575,\ z > 2.575$

c.

Fail to reject H_0.

d. There is not enough evidence at the 1% level of significance to reject the claim that the mean cost of raising a child from birth to age 2 by husband-wife families in the United States is $13,120.

7.2 EXERCISE SOLUTIONS

1. In the z-test using rejection region(s), the test statistic is compared with critical values. The z-test using a P-value compares the P-value with the level of significance α.

2. No; Both involve comparing the test statistic's probability with the level of significance. The P-value method converts the standardized test statistic to a probability (P-value) and compares this with the level of significance, whereas the critical value method converts the level of significance to a z-score and compares this with the standardized test statistic.

3.

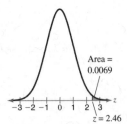

$P = 0.0934$; Reject H_0 because $P = 0.0934 < 0.10$.

4.

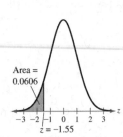

$P = 0.0606$; Fail to reject H_0 because $P = 0.0606 > 0.05$.

5.

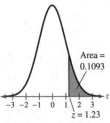

$P = 0.0069$; Reject H_0 because $P = 0.0069 < 0.01$.

6.

$P = 0.1093$; Fail to reject H_0 because $P = 0.1093 > 0.10$.

7.

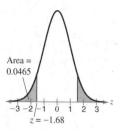

$P = 2(\text{Area}) = 2(0.0465) = 0.0930$; Fail to reject H_0 because $P = 0.0930 > 0.05$.

8.

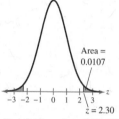

$P = 2(\text{Area}) = 2(0.0107) = 0.0214$; Fail to reject H_0 because $P = 0.0214 > 0.01$.

9. b   **10.** d   **11.** c   **12.** a

13. (a) Fail to reject H_0 $(P = 0.0461 > 0.01)$.
   (b) Reject H_0 $(P = 0.0461 < 0.05)$.

14. (a) Fail to reject H_0 $(P = 0.0691 > 0.01)$.
   (b) Fail to reject H_0 $(P = 0.0691 > 0.05)$.

15. Fail to reject H_0 $(P = 0.0628 > 0.05)$.

16. Reject H_0 $(P = 0.0065 < 0.01)$.

17. 1.645   **18.** 1.41   **19.** -1.88

20. -1.34 **21.** ± 2.33 **22.** ± 1.645

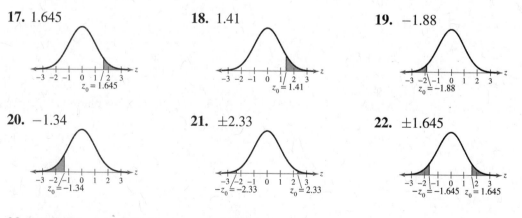

23. (a) Fail to reject H_0 because $z < 1.285$.
   (b) Fail to reject H_0 because $z < 1.285$.
   (c) Fail to reject H_0 because $z < 1.285$.
   (d) Reject H_0 because $z > 1.285$.

24. (a) Reject H_0 because $z > 1.96$.

    (b) Fail to reject H_0 because $-1.96 < z < 1.96$.

    (c) Fail to reject H_0 because $-1.96 < z < 1.96$.

    (d) Reject H_0 because $z < -1.96$.

25. $H_0 : \mu = 40$ (claim); $H_a : \mu \neq 40$

$$\alpha = 0.05 \rightarrow z_0 = \pm 1.96$$

$$z = \frac{\bar{x} - \mu}{\frac{s}{\sqrt{n}}} = \frac{39.2 - 40}{\frac{3.23}{\sqrt{75}}} \approx -2.145$$

Reject H_0. There is enough evidence at the 5% level of significance to reject the claim.

26. $H_0 : \mu \leq 1745$; $H_a : \mu > 1745$ (claim)

$$\alpha = 0.10 \rightarrow z_0 = 1.28$$

$$z = \frac{\bar{x} - \mu}{\frac{s}{\sqrt{n}}} = \frac{1752 - 1745}{\frac{38}{\sqrt{44}}} \approx 1.222$$

Fail to reject H_0. There is not enough evidence at the 10% level of significance to support the claim.

27. $H_0 : \mu = 8550$; $H_a : \mu \neq 8550$ (claim)

$$\alpha = 0.02 \rightarrow z_0 = \pm 2.33$$

$$z = \frac{\bar{x} - \mu}{\frac{s}{\sqrt{n}}} = \frac{8420 - 8550}{\frac{314}{\sqrt{38}}} \approx -2.552$$

Reject H_0. There is enough evidence at the 2% level of significance to support the claim.

28. $H_0 : \mu \leq 22{,}500$ (claim); $H_a : \mu > 22{,}500$

$$\alpha = 0.01 \rightarrow z_0 = 2.33$$

$$z = \frac{\bar{x} - \mu}{\frac{s}{\sqrt{n}}} = \frac{23{,}250 - 22{,}500}{\frac{1200}{\sqrt{45}}} \approx 4.193$$

Reject H_0. There is enough evidence at the 1% level of significance to reject the claim.

29. (a) $H_0 : \mu \leq 30$; $H_a : \mu > 30$ (claim)

    (b) $z = \dfrac{\bar{x} - \mu}{\frac{s}{\sqrt{n}}} = \dfrac{31 - 30}{\frac{2.5}{\sqrt{50}}} \approx 2.83$

    Area $= 0.9977$

    (c) *P*-value $= \{$Area to right of $z = 2.83\} = 0.0023$

    (d) Reject H_0.

(e) There is enough evidence at the 1% level of significance to support the claim that the mean raw score for the school's applicants is more than 30.

30. (a) $H_0: \mu \geq 135$ (claim); $H_a: \mu < 135$

   (b) $z = \dfrac{\bar{x} - \mu}{\frac{s}{\sqrt{n}}} = \dfrac{133 - 135}{\frac{3.3}{\sqrt{32}}} \approx -3.43$

     Area = 0.0003

   (c) *P*-value = {Area to left of $z = -3.43$ } = 0.0003

   (d) Reject H_0.

   (e) There is enough evidence at the 10% level of significance to reject the claim that the average activating temperature is at least $135°\,\text{F}$.

31. (a) $H_0: \mu = 28.5$ (claim); $H_a: \mu \neq 28.5$

   (b) $z = \dfrac{\bar{x} - \mu}{\frac{s}{\sqrt{n}}} = \dfrac{27.8 - 28.5}{\frac{4.1}{\sqrt{100}}} \approx -1.71$

     Area = 0.0436

   (c) *P*-value = 2{Area to the left of $z = -1.71$} 2(0.0436) = 0.0872

   (d) Fail to reject H_0.

   (e) There is not enough evidence at the 8% level of significance to reject the claim that the mean consumption of bottled water by a person in the United States is 28.5 gallons per year.

32. (a) $H_0: \mu = 24.2$ (claim); $H_a: \mu \neq 24.2$

   (b) $z = \dfrac{\bar{x} - \mu}{\frac{s}{\sqrt{n}}} = \dfrac{23.5 - 24.2}{\frac{3.2}{\sqrt{120}}} \approx -2.40$

     Area = 0.0082

   (c) *P*-value = 2{Area to left of $z = -2.40$ } = 2(0.0082) = 0.0164

   (d) Reject H_0.

   (e) There is enough evidence at the 5% level of significance to reject the claim that the mean consumption of coffee by a person in the United States is 24.2 gallons per year.

33. (a) $H_0: \mu = 15$ (claim); $H_a: \mu \neq 15$

   (b) $\bar{x} \approx 14.834 \qquad s \approx 4.288$

     $z = \dfrac{\bar{x} - \mu}{\frac{s}{\sqrt{n}}} = \dfrac{14.384 - 15}{\frac{4.288}{\sqrt{32}}} \approx -0.22$

     Area = 0.4129

   (c) *P*-value = 2{Area to left of $z = -0.22$ } = 2(0.4129) = 0.8258

   (d) Fail to reject H_0.

   (e) There is not enough evidence at the 5% level of significance to reject the claim that the mean time it takes smokers to quit smoking permanently is 15 years.

34. (a) $H_0 : \mu \le 66,200; H_a : \mu > 66,200$ (claim)

  (b) $\bar{x} \approx 66,592.4$ $s \approx 2384.376$

  $$z = \frac{\bar{x} - \mu}{\frac{s}{\sqrt{n}}} = \frac{66,592.4 - 66,200}{\frac{2384.376}{\sqrt{35}}} \approx 0.97$$

  Area = 0.8340

  (c) P-value = {Area to right of $z = 0.97$} ≈ 0.1660

  (d) Fail to reject H_0.

  (e) There is not enough evidence at the 9% level of significance to support the claim that the mean annual salary for advertising account executives in Denver, Colorado is more than the national mean $66,200.

35. (a) $H_0 : \mu = 40$ (claim); $H_a : \mu \ne 40$

  (b) $-z_0 = -2.575, z_0 = 2.575$;

  Rejection regions: $z < -2.575, z > 2.575$

  (c) $z = \frac{\bar{x} - \mu}{\frac{s}{\sqrt{n}}} = \frac{39.2 - 40}{\frac{7.5}{\sqrt{30}}} \approx -0.584$

  (d) Fail to reject H_0.

  (e) There is not enough evidence at the 1% level of significance to reject the claim that the mean caffeine content per 12-ounce bottle of cola is 40 milligrams.

36. (a) $H_0 : \mu = 874$ (claim); $H_a : \mu \ne 874$

  (b) $-z_0 = -1.96, z_0 = 1.96$;

  Rejection regions: $z < -1.96, z > 1.96$

  (c) $z = \frac{\bar{x} - \mu}{\frac{s}{\sqrt{n}}} = \frac{905 - 874}{\frac{125}{\sqrt{64}}} \approx 1.98$

  (d) Reject H_0.

  (e) There is enough evidence at the 5% level of significance to reject the claim that the mean monthly residential electricity consumption in your town is 874 kilowatt-hours.

37. (a) $H_0 : \mu \ge 750$ (claim); $H_a : \mu < 750$

  (b) $z_0 = -2.05$; Rejection region: $z < -2.05$

  (c) $z = \frac{\bar{x} - \mu}{\frac{s}{\sqrt{n}}} = \frac{745 - 750}{\frac{60}{\sqrt{36}}} = -0.5$

  (d) Fail to reject H_0.

  (e) There is not enough evidence at the 2% level of significance to reject the claim that the mean life of the bulb is at least 750 hours.

38. (a) $H_0 : \mu \le 920$ (claim); $H_\alpha : \mu > 920$

  (b) $z_0 = 1.28$; Rejection region: $z > 1.28$

(c) $z = \dfrac{\bar{x} - \mu}{\dfrac{s}{\sqrt{n}}} = \dfrac{925 - 920}{\dfrac{18}{\sqrt{44}}} \approx 1.84$

(d) Reject H_0.

(e) There is enough evidence at the 10% level of significance to reject the claim that the mean sodium content in one of their breakfast sandwiches is no more than 920 milligrams.

39. (a) $H_0 : \mu \le 32; H_a : \mu > 32$ (claim)

(b) $z_0 = 1.555;$ Rejection region: $z > 1.555$

(c) $\bar{x} \approx 29.676$ $s \approx 9.164$

$z = \dfrac{\bar{x} - \mu}{\dfrac{s}{\sqrt{n}}} \approx \dfrac{29.676 - 32}{\dfrac{9.164}{\sqrt{34}}} \approx -1.478$

(d) Fail to reject H_0.

(e) There is not enough evidence at the 6% level of significance to support the claim that the mean nitrogen dioxide level in Calgary is greater than 32 parts per billion.

40. (a) $H_0 : \mu \ge 10{,}000$ (claim); $H_a : \mu < 10{,}000$

(b) $z_0 = -1.34;$ Rejection region: $z < -1.34$

(c) $\bar{x} \approx 9580.9$ $s \approx 1772.4$

$z = \dfrac{\bar{x} - \mu}{\dfrac{s}{\sqrt{n}}} \approx \dfrac{9580.9 - 10{,}000}{\dfrac{1722.4}{\sqrt{32}}} \approx -1.38$

(d) Reject H_0.

(e) There is enough evidence at the 9% level of significance to reject the claim that the mean life of fluorescent lamps is at least 10,000 hours.

41. (a) $H_0 : \mu \ge 10$ (claim); $H_a : \mu < 10$

(b) $z_0 = -1.88;$ Rejection region: $z < -1.88$

(c) $\bar{x} \approx 9.780$ $s \approx 2.362$

$z = \dfrac{\bar{x} - \mu}{\dfrac{s}{\sqrt{n}}} \approx \dfrac{9.780 - 10}{\dfrac{2.362}{\sqrt{30}}} \approx -0.51$

(d) Fail to reject H_0.

(e) There is not enough evidence at the 3% level of significance to reject the claim that the mean weight loss after 1 month is at least 10 pounds.

42. (a) $H_0 : \mu \ge 60; H_a : \mu < 60$ (claim)

(b) $z_0 = -2.33;$ Rejection region: $z < -2.33$

(c) $\bar{x} = 49$ $s \approx 21.51$

$z = \dfrac{\bar{x} - \mu}{\dfrac{s}{\sqrt{n}}} \approx \dfrac{49 - 60}{\dfrac{21.51}{\sqrt{50}}} \approx -3.62$

(d) Reject H_0.

(e) There is enough evidence at the 1% level of significance to support the claim that the mean time it takes an employee to evacuate a building during a fire drill is less than 60 seconds.

43. Hypothesis test results:

μ: population mean

$H_0 : \mu = 58$

$H_a : \mu \neq 58$

Standard deviation = 2.35

Mean	n	Sample Mean	Std. Err	z-Stat	P-value
μ	80	57.6	0.262738	-1.5224292	0.1279

Fail to reject H_0. There is not enough evidence at the 10% level of significance to reject the claim.

44. Hypothesis test results:

μ: population mean

$H_0 : \mu = 495$

$H_a : \mu > 495$

Standard deviation = 17.8

Mean	n	Sample Mean	Std. Err	z-Stat	P-value
μ	65	498.4	2.2078183	1.5399818	0.0618

Fail to reject H_0. There is not enough evidence at the 5% level of significance to support the claim.

45. Hypothesis test results:

μ: population mean

$H_0 : \mu = 1210$

$H_a : \mu > 1210$

Standard deviation = 205.87

Mean	n	Sample Mean	Std. Err	z-Stat	P-value
μ	250	1234.21	13.020362	1.8593953	0.0315

Reject H_0. There is enough evidence at the 8% level of significance to reject the claim.

46. Hypothesis test results:

μ: population mean

$H_0 : \mu = 28750$

$H_a : \mu \neq 28750$

Standard deviation = 3200

Mean	n	Sample Mean	Std. Err	z-Stat	P-value
μ	600	29130	130.63945	2.9087691	0.0036

Reject H_0. There is enough evidence at the 1% level of significance to support the claim.

47. $z_0 = -2.33$; Rejection region: $z < -2.33$

$$z = \frac{\overline{x} - \mu}{\frac{s}{\sqrt{n}}} = \frac{125,270 - 127,400}{\frac{6275}{\sqrt{30}}} \approx -1.86$$

Fail to reject H_0 because the standardized test statistic $z = -1.86$ is not in the rejection region $(z < -2.33)$.

48. $z_0 = 1.645$; Rejection region: $z > 1.645$

$$z = \frac{\overline{x} - \mu}{\frac{s}{\sqrt{n}}} = \frac{22,200 - 22,000}{\frac{775}{\sqrt{36}}} \approx 1.548$$

Fail to reject H_0 because the standardized test statistic $z = 1.548$ is not in the rejection region $(z > 1.645)$.

49. (a) $\alpha = 0.02 \rightarrow z_0 = -2.05$; Rejection region: $z < -2.05$

Stays as fail to reject H_0 because the standardized test statistic $z = -1.86$ is not in the rejection region $(z < -2.05)$.

(b) $\alpha = 0.05 \rightarrow z_0 = -1.645$; Rejection region: $z < -1.645$

Changes to reject H_0 because the standardized test statistic $z = -1.86$ is in the rejection region $(z < -1.645)$.

(c) Same rejection region as Exercise 47: $z < -2.33$

$$z = \frac{\overline{x} - \mu}{\frac{s}{\sqrt{n}}} = \frac{125,270 - 127,400}{\frac{6275}{\sqrt{40}}} \approx -2.15$$

Stays as fail to reject H_0 because the standardized test statistic $z = -2.15$ is not in the rejection region $(z < -2.33)$.

(d) Same rejection region as Exercise 47: $z < -2.33$

$$z = \frac{\overline{x} - \mu}{\frac{s}{\sqrt{n}}} = \frac{125,270 - 127,400}{\frac{6275}{\sqrt{50}}} \approx -2.40$$

Changes to reject H_0 because the standardized test statistic $z = -2.40$ is in the rejection region $(z < -2.33)$.

50. (a) $\alpha = 0.06 \rightarrow z_0 = 1.555$; Rejection region: $z > 1.555$

Stays as fail to reject H_0 because the standardized test statistic $z = 1.548$ is not in the rejection region $(z > 1.555)$.

(b) $\alpha = 0.07 \rightarrow z_0 = 1.476$; Rejection region: $z > 1.476$

Changes to reject H_0 because the standardized test statistic $z = 1.548$ is in the rejection region $(z > 1.476)$.

(c) Same rejection region as Exercise 48: $z > 1.645$

$$z = \frac{\bar{x} - \mu}{\frac{s}{\sqrt{n}}} = \frac{22,200 - 22,000}{\frac{775}{\sqrt{40}}} \approx 1.63$$

Stays as fail to reject H_0 because the standardized test statistic $z = 1.63$ is not in the rejection region $(z > 1.645)$.

(d) Same rejection region as Exercise 48: $z > 1.645$

$$z = \frac{\bar{x} - \mu}{\frac{s}{\sqrt{n}}} = \frac{22,200 - 22,000}{\frac{775}{\sqrt{80}}} \approx 2.31$$

Changes to reject H_0 because the standardized test statistic $z = 2.31$ is in the rejection region $(z > 1.645)$.

7.3 HYPOTHESIS TESTING FOR THE MEAN (SMALL SAMPLES)

7.3 Try It Yourself Solutions

1a. 13   **b.** $t_0 = -2.650$

2a. 8   **b.** $t_0 = 1.397$

3a. 15   **b.** $-t_0 = -2.131,\ t_0 = 2.131$

4a. The claim is "the mean cost of insuring a 2008 Honda CR-V is less than \$1200."
    $H_0 : \mu \geq \$1200;\ H_a : \mu < \$1200$ (claim)
  b. $\alpha = 0.10$ and d.f. $= n - 1 = 6$
  c. $t_0 = -1.440;$ Rejection region: $t < -1.440$
  d. $z = \dfrac{\bar{x} - \mu}{\frac{s}{\sqrt{n}}} = \dfrac{1125 - 1200}{\frac{55}{\sqrt{7}}} \approx -3.61$

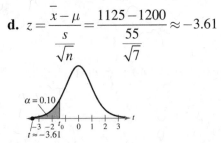

  e. Reject H_0.
  f. There is enough evidence at the 10% level of significance to support the claim that the mean cost of insuring a 2008 Honda CR-V is less than \$1200.

5a. The claim is "the mean conductivity of the river is 1890 milligrams per liter."
    $H_0 : \mu = 1890$ (claim); $H_a : \mu \neq 1890$
  b. $\alpha = 0.01$ and d.f. $= n - 1 = 18$
  c. $-t_0 = -2.878,\ t_0 = 2.878;$ Rejection regions: $t < -2.878,\ t > 2.878$

d. $z = \dfrac{\bar{x} - \mu}{\dfrac{s}{\sqrt{n}}} = \dfrac{2500 - 1890}{\dfrac{700}{\sqrt{19}}} \approx 3.798$

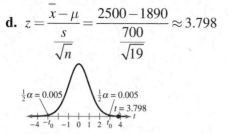

$\frac{1}{2}\alpha = 0.005$ $\frac{1}{2}\alpha = 0.005$
$t = 3.798$

e. Reject H_0.

f. There is enough evidence at the 1% level of significance to reject the claim that the mean conductivity of the river is 1890 milligrams per liter.

6a. The claim is "the mean wait time is at most 18 minutes."
  $H_0 : \mu \le 18$ minutes (claim); $H_a : \mu > 18$ minutes

b. P-value $= 0.9997$

c. P-value $= 0.9997 > 0.05 = \alpha$
  Fail to reject H_0.

d. There is not enough evidence at the 5% level of significance to reject the claim that the mean wait time is at most 18 minutes.

7.3 EXERCISE SOLUTIONS

1. Identify the level of significance α and the degrees of freedom, d.f. $= n - 1$. Find the critical value(s) using the t-distribution table in the row with $n - 1$ d.f. If the hypothesis test is:
   (1) left-tailed, use the "One Tail, α" column with a negative sign.
   (2) right-tailed, use the "One Tail, α" column with a positive sign.
   (3) two-tailed, use the "Two Tail, α," column with a negative and a positive sign.

2. Identify the claim. State H_0 and H_a. Specify the level of significance. Identify the degrees of freedom and sketch the sampling distribution. Determine the critical value(s) and rejection region(s). Find the standardized test statistic. Make a decision and interpret it in the context of the original claim. The population must be normal or nearly normal.

3. $t_0 = 1.717$ 4. $t_0 = 2.764$ 5. $t_0 = -1.328$ 6. $t_0 = -2.473$

7. $t_0 = \pm 2.056$ 8. $t_0 = \pm 1.721$

9. (a) Fail to reject H_0 because $t > -2.086$.
   (b) Fail to reject H_0 because $t > -2.086$.
   (c) Fail to reject H_0 because $t > -2.086$.
   (d) Reject H_0 because $t < -2.086$.

10. (a) Fail to reject H_0 because $-1.372 < t < 1.372$.
    (b) Reject H_0 because $t < -1.372$.
    (c) Reject H_0 because $t > 1.372$.
    (d) Fail to reject H_0 because $-1.372 < t < 1.372$.

11. (a) Fail to reject H_0 because $-2.602 < t < 2.602$.

    (b) Fail to reject H_0 because $-2.602 < t < 2.602$.

    (c) Reject H_0 because $t > 2.602$.

    (d) Reject H_0 because $t < -2.602$.

12. (a) Fail to reject H_0 because $-1.725 < t < 1.725$.

    (b) Reject H_0 because $t < -1.725$

    (c) Fail to reject H_0 because $-1.725 < t < 1.725$.

    (d) Reject H_0 because $t > 1.725$.

13. $H_0: \mu = 15$ (claim); $H_a: \mu \neq 15$

    $\alpha = 0.01$ and d.f. $= n - 1 = 5$

    $t_0 = \pm 4.032$

    $$t = \frac{\bar{x} - \mu}{\frac{s}{\sqrt{n}}} = \frac{13.9 - 15}{\frac{3.23}{\sqrt{6}}} \approx -0.834$$

    Fail to reject H_0. There is not enough evidence at the 1% level of significance to reject the claim.

14. $H_0: \mu \leq 25$; $H_a: \mu > 25$ (claim)

    $\alpha = 0.05$ and d.f. $= n - 1 = 16$

    $t_0 = 1.746$

    $$t = \frac{\bar{x} - \mu}{\frac{s}{\sqrt{n}}} = \frac{26.2 - 25}{\frac{2.32}{\sqrt{17}}} \approx 2.133$$

    Reject H_0. There is enough evidence at the 5% level of significance to support the claim.

15. $H_0: \mu \geq 8000$ (claim); $H_a: \mu < 8000$

    $\alpha = 0.01$ and d.f. $= n - 1 = 24$

    $t_0 = -2.492$

    $$t = \frac{\bar{x} - \mu}{\frac{s}{\sqrt{n}}} = \frac{7700 - 8000}{\frac{450}{\sqrt{25}}} \approx -3.333$$

    Reject H_0. There is enough evidence at the 1% level of significance to reject the claim.

16. $H_0: \mu = 52,200$; $H_a: \mu \neq 52,200$ (claim)

    $\alpha = 0.10$ and d.f. $= n - 1 = 17$

    $t_0 = \pm 1.740$

    $$t = \frac{\bar{x} - \mu}{\frac{s}{\sqrt{n}}} = \frac{53,220 - 52,200}{\frac{2700}{\sqrt{18}}} \approx 1.60$$

    Fail to reject H_0. There is not enough evidence at the 10% level of significance to support the claim.

17. (a) $H_0 : \mu = 18,000$ (claim); $H_a : \mu \neq 18,000$

(b) $-t_0 = -2.145$, $t_0 = 2.145$; Rejection region: $t < -2.145$, $t > 2.145$

(c) $t = \dfrac{\overline{x} - \mu}{\dfrac{s}{\sqrt{n}}} = \dfrac{18,550 - 18,000}{\dfrac{1767}{\sqrt{15}}} \approx 1.21$

(d) Fail to reject H_0.

(e) There is not enough evidence at the 5% level of significance to reject the claim that the mean price of a 2008 Subaru Forester is $18,000.

18. (a) $H_0 : \mu \leq 7$ (claim); $H_a : \mu > 7$

(b) $t_0 = 1.372$; Rejection region: $t > 1.372$

(c) $t = \dfrac{\overline{x} - \mu}{\dfrac{s}{\sqrt{n}}} = \dfrac{8.7 - 7}{\dfrac{2.7}{\sqrt{11}}} \approx 2.09$

(d) Reject H_0.

(e) There is enough evidence at the 10% level of significance to reject the claim that the mean wait time for callers during a recent tax filing season was at most 7 minutes.

19. (a) $H_0 : \mu \leq 60$; $H_a : \mu > 60$ (claim)

(b) $t_0 = 1.943$; Rejection region: $t > 1.943$

(c) $t = \dfrac{\overline{x} - \mu}{\dfrac{s}{\sqrt{n}}} = \dfrac{70 - 60}{\dfrac{12.5}{\sqrt{7}}} \approx 2.12$

(d) Reject H_0.

(e) There is enough evidence at the 5% level of significance to support the claim that the mean number of hours worked per week by surgical faculty who teach at an academic institution is more than 60 hours.

20. (a) $H_0 : \mu \geq 30$ (claim); $H_a : \mu < 30$

(b) $t_0 = -2.567$; Rejection region: $t < -2.567$

(c) $t = \dfrac{\overline{x} - \mu}{\dfrac{s}{\sqrt{n}}} = \dfrac{28.5 - 30}{\dfrac{1.7}{\sqrt{18}}} \approx -3.74$

(d) Reject H_0.

(e) There is enough evidence at the 1% level of significance to reject the claim that the mean battery life of their MP3 player is at least 30 hours.

21. (a) $H_0 : \mu \leq 1$; $H_a : \mu > 1$ (claim)

(b) $t_0 = 1.356$; Rejection region: $t > 1.356$

(c) $t = \dfrac{\overline{x} - \mu}{\dfrac{s}{\sqrt{n}}} = \dfrac{1.50 - 1}{\dfrac{0.28}{\sqrt{13}}} \approx 6.44$

(d) Reject H_0.

(e) There is enough evidence at the 10% level of significance to support the claim that the mean amount of waste recycled by adults in the United States is more than 1 pound per person per day.

22. (a) $H_0: \mu \leq 4$; $H_a: \mu > 4$ (claim)

 (b) $t_0 = 2.518$; Rejection region: $t > 2.518$

 (c) $t = \dfrac{\bar{x} - \mu}{\frac{s}{\sqrt{n}}} = \dfrac{4.50 - 4}{\frac{1.21}{\sqrt{22}}} \approx 1.94$

 (d) Fail to reject H_0.

 (e) There is not enough evidence at the 1% level of significance to support the claim that the mean amount of waste generated by adults in the United States is more than 4 pounds per day.

23. (a) $H_0: \mu = \$26{,}000$ (claim); $H_a: \mu \neq \$26{,}000$

 (b) $-t_0 = -2.262$, $t_0 = 2.262$; Rejection region: $t < -2.262$, $t > 2.262$

 (c) $\bar{x} \approx 25{,}852.2$, $\quad\quad\quad s \approx \$3197.1$

 $t = \dfrac{\bar{x} - \mu}{\frac{s}{\sqrt{n}}} \approx \dfrac{25{,}852.2 - 26{,}000}{\frac{3197.1}{\sqrt{10}}} \approx -0.15$

 (d) Fail to reject H_0.

 (e) There is not enough evidence at the 5% level of significance to reject the claim that the mean salary for full-time male workers over age 25 without a high school diploma is $26,000.

24. (a) $H_0: \mu \leq 18{,}500$; $H_a: \mu > 18{,}500$ (claim)

 (b) $t_0 = 1.363$; Rejection region: $t > 1.363$

 (c) $\bar{x} \approx \$19{,}086.5$, $\quad\quad\quad s \approx \$1417.7$

 $t = \dfrac{\bar{x} - \mu}{\frac{s}{\sqrt{n}}} \approx \dfrac{19{,}086.5 - 18{,}500}{\frac{1417.7}{\sqrt{12}}} \approx 1.43$

 (d) Reject H_0.

 (e) There is enough evidence at the 10% level of significance to support the claim that the mean annual salary for full-time female workers over age 25 without a high school diploma is more than $18,500.

25. (a) $H_0: \mu \leq 45$; $H_a: \mu > 45$ (claim)

 (b) $t = \dfrac{\bar{x} - \mu}{\frac{s}{\sqrt{n}}} = \dfrac{48 - 45}{\frac{5.4}{\sqrt{25}}} \approx 2.78$

 P-value = {Area to right of $t = 2.78$ } $= 0.0052$

 (c) Reject H_0.

 (d) There is enough evidence at the 10% level of significance to support the claim that the mean speed of the vehicles is greater than 45 miles per hour.

26. (a) $H_0: \mu \leq 3500$; $H_a: \mu > 3500$ (claim)

(b) $t = \dfrac{\overline{x} - \mu}{\dfrac{s}{\sqrt{n}}} = \dfrac{3375 - 3500}{\dfrac{225}{\sqrt{8}}} \approx -1.57$

P-value = {Area to right of $t = -1.57$ } = 0.9200

(c) Fail to reject H_0.

(d) There is not enough evidence at the 5% level of significance to support the claim that people travel more than 3500 miles between oil changes.

27. (a) $H_0: \mu = \$105$ (claim); $H_a: \mu \neq \$105$

(b) $t = \dfrac{\overline{x} - \mu}{\dfrac{s}{\sqrt{n}}} = \dfrac{110 - 105}{\dfrac{8.50}{\sqrt{20}}} \approx 2.63$

P-value = 2{Area to right of $t = 2.63$} = 2(0.00825) = 0.0165

(c) Fail to reject H_0.

(d) There is not enough evidence at the 1% level of significance to reject the claim that the mean daily meal cost for two adults traveling together on vacation in San Francisco is $105.

28. (a) $H_0: \mu \geq \$240$ (claim); $H_a: \mu < \$240$

(b) $t = \dfrac{\overline{x} - \mu}{\dfrac{s}{\sqrt{n}}} = \dfrac{233 - 240}{\dfrac{12.50}{\sqrt{24}}} \approx -2.74$

P-value = {Area to left of $t = -2.74$ } = 0.0058

(c) Reject H_0.

(d) There is enough evidence at the 10% level of significance to reject the claim that the mean daily lodging costs for two adults traveling together on vacation in San Francisco is at least $240.

29. (a) $H_0: \mu \geq 32$; $H_a: \mu < 32$ (claim)

(b) $\overline{x} \approx 30.167$ $\qquad\qquad s \approx 4.004$

$t = \dfrac{\overline{x} - \mu}{\dfrac{s}{\sqrt{n}}} = \dfrac{30.167 - 32}{\dfrac{4.004}{\sqrt{18}}} \approx -1.942$

P-value = {Area to left of $t = -1.942$ } = 0.0344

(c) Reject H_0.

(d) There is enough evidence at the 5% level of significance to support the claim that the mean class size for full-time faculty is fewer than 32 students.

30. (a) $H_0: \mu = 11.0$ (claim); $H_a: \mu \neq 11.0$

(b) $\overline{x} = 10.05$ $\qquad\qquad s \approx 2.485$

$t = \dfrac{\overline{x} - \mu}{\dfrac{s}{\sqrt{n}}} \approx \dfrac{10.05 - 11.0}{\dfrac{2.485}{\sqrt{8}}} \approx -1.081$

P-value = 2{Area to left of $t = -1.942$ } = 2(0.15775) = 0.3155

(c) Fail to reject H_0.

(d) There is not enough evidence at the 1% level of significance to reject the claim that the mean number of classroom hours per week for full-time faculty is 11.0.

31. Hypothesis test results:

μ: population mean

$H_0 : \mu = 75$

$H_A : \mu > 75$

Mean	Sample Mean	Std. Err	DF	T-Stat	P-value
μ	73.6	0.62757164	25	−2.2308211	0.9825

Fail to reject H_0.

There is not enough evidence at the 5% level of significance to reject the claim.

32. Hypothesis test results:

μ: population mean

$H_0 : \mu = 27$

$H_A : \mu \neq 27$

Mean	Sample Mean	Std. Err	DF	T-Stat	P-value
μ	31.5	1.3567731	11	3.316693	0.0069

Reject H_0.

There is enough evidence at the 1% level of significance to support the claim.

33. Hypothesis test results:

μ: population mean

$H_0 : \mu = 188$

$H_A : \mu < 188$

Mean	Sample Mean	Std. Err	DF	T-Stat	P-value
μ	186	4	8	−0.5	0.3153

Fail to reject H_0.

There is not enough evidence at the 5% level of significance to support the claim.

34. Hypothesis test results:

μ: population mean

$H_0 : \mu = 2118$

$H_A : \mu < 2118$

Mean	Sample Mean	Std. Err	DF	T-Stat	P-value
μ	1787	93.13368	16	−3.5540311	0.0013

Reject H_0.

There is enough evidence at the 10% level of significance to reject the claim.

35. $H_0 : \mu \leq 5000$; $H_a : \mu > 5000$ (claim)

$$t = \frac{\bar{x} - \mu}{\frac{s}{\sqrt{n}}} \approx \frac{5434 - 5000}{\frac{625}{\sqrt{6}}} \approx 1.70$$

P-value = {Area right of $t = 1.70$} ≈ 0.0748

Because $0.0748 > 0.05$, fail to reject H_0.

36. (a) Because $0.0748 > 0.01$, fail to reject H_0.

(b) Because $0.0748 < 0.10$, reject H_0.

(c) $t = \dfrac{\bar{x} - \mu}{\frac{s}{\sqrt{n}}} \approx \dfrac{5434 - 5000}{\frac{625}{\sqrt{8}}} \approx 1.96$

P-value = {Area right of $t = 1.96$} $= 0.0451$

Because $0.0451 < 0.05$, reject H_0.

(d) $t = \dfrac{\bar{x} - \mu}{\frac{s}{\sqrt{n}}} \approx \dfrac{5434 - 5000}{\frac{625}{\sqrt{24}}} \approx 3.40$

P-value = {Area right of $t = 3.40$} $= 0.0012$

Because $0.0012 < 0.05$, reject H_0.

37. Because σ is unknown, $n < 30$, and the gas mileage is normally distributed, use the t-distribution.

$H_0 : \mu \geq 23$ (claim); $H_a : \mu < 23$

$$t = \frac{\bar{x} - \mu}{\frac{s}{\sqrt{n}}} \approx \frac{22 - 23}{\frac{4}{\sqrt{5}}} \approx -0.559$$

P-value = {Area left of $t = -0.559$} $= 0.303$

Fail to reject H_0. There is not enough evidence at the 5% level of significance to reject the claim that the mean gas mileage for the luxury sedan is at least 23 miles per gallon.

38. Because σ is unknown, $n \geq 30$, use the z-distribution.

$H_0 : \mu \leq 35,000$; $H_a : \mu > 35,000$ (claim)

$$z = \frac{\bar{x} - \mu}{\frac{s}{\sqrt{n}}} \approx \frac{34,967 - 35,000}{\frac{5933}{\sqrt{50}}} \approx -0.04$$

P-value = {Area right of $z = -0.04$} $= 0.5160$

Fail to reject H_0. There is not enough evidence at the 1% level of significance to support the claim that the average in-state tuition for one year of law school at a private institution is more than \$35,000.

39. More likely; For degrees of freedom less than 30, the tails of the t-distribution curve are thicker than those of a standard normal distribution curve. So, if you incorrectly used a standard normal sampling distribution instead of a t-sampling distribution, the area under the curve at the tails will be smaller than what it would be for the t-test, meaning the critical value(s) will lie closer to the mean. This makes it more likely for the test statistic to be in the rejection region(s). This result is the same regardless of whether the test is left-tailed, right-tailed, or two-tailed; in each case, the tail thickness affects the location of the critical value(s).

7.4 HYPOTHESIS TESTING FOR PROPORTIONS

7.4 Try It Yourself Solutions

1a. $np = (125)(0.25) = 31.25 > 5$, $nq = (125)(0.75) = 93.75 > 5$

  b. The claim is "more than 25% of U.S. adults have used a cellular phone to access the internet."
  $H_0: p \leq 0.25$; $H_a: p > 0.25$ (claim)

  c. $\alpha = 0.05$

  d. $z_0 = 1.645$; Rejection region: $z > 1.645$

  e. $z = \dfrac{\hat{p} - p}{\sqrt{\dfrac{pq}{n}}} = \dfrac{0.32 - 0.25}{\sqrt{\dfrac{(0.25)(0.75)}{125}}} \approx 1.81$

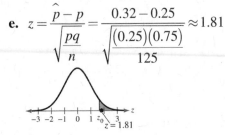

  f. Reject H_0.

  g. There is enough evidence at the 5% level of significance to support the claim that more than 25% of U.S. adults have used a cellular phone to access the Internet.

2a. $np = (250)(0.30) = 75 > 5$, $nq = (250)(0.70) = 175 > 5$

  b. The claim is "30% of U.S. adults have not purchased a certain brand because they found the advertisements distasteful."
  $H_0: p = 0.30$ (claim); $H_a: p \neq 0.30$

  c. $\alpha = 0.10$

  d. $-z_0 = -1.645$, $z_0 = 1.645$; Rejection region: $z < -1.645$, $z > 1.645$

  e. $z = \dfrac{\hat{p} - p}{\sqrt{\dfrac{pq}{n}}} = \dfrac{0.36 - 0.30}{\sqrt{\dfrac{(0.30)(0.70)}{250}}} \approx 2.07$

  f. Reject H_0.

  g. There is enough evidence at the 10% level of significance to reject the claim that 30% of U.S. adults have not purchased a certain brand because they found the advertisements distasteful.

7.4 EXERCISE SOLUTIONS

1. If $np \geq 5$ and $nq \geq 5$, the normal distribution can be used.

2. Verify that $np \geq 5$ and $nq \geq 5$. State H_0 and H_a. Specify the level of significance α. Determine the critical value(s) and rejection region(s). Find the standardized test statistic. Make a decision and interpret in the context of the original claim.

3. $np = (40)(0.12) = 4.8 < 5$

   $nq = (40)(0.88) = 35.2 > 5$

   Cannot use normal distribution because $np < 5$.

4. $np = (90)(0.48) = 43.2 > 5$

   $nq = (90)(0.52) = 46.8 > 5 \rightarrow$ use normal distribution

   $H_0: p \geq 0.48$ (claim); $H_a: p < 0.48$

   $z_0 = -1.405$; Rejection region: $z < -1.405$

   $$z = \frac{\hat{p} - p}{\sqrt{\dfrac{pq}{n}}} = \frac{0.40 - 0.48}{\sqrt{\dfrac{(0.48)(0.52)}{90}}} \approx -1.52$$

   Reject H_0. There is enough evidence at the 8% level of significance to reject the claim.

5. $np = (500)(0.15) = 75 > 5$

   $nq = (500)(0.85) = 425 > 5 \rightarrow$ use normal distribution

   $H_0: p = 0.15$; $H_a: p \neq 0.15$ (claim)

   $-z_0 = -1.96$, $z_0 = 1.96$; Rejection region: $z < -1.96$, $z > 1.96$

   $$z = \frac{\hat{p} - p}{\sqrt{\dfrac{pq}{n}}} = \frac{0.12 - 0.15}{\sqrt{\dfrac{(0.15)(0.85)}{500}}} \approx -1.88$$

   Fail to reject H_0. There is not enough evidence at the 5% level of significance to support the claim.

6. $np = (225)(0.70) = 157.5 > 5$

   $nq = (225)(0.30) = 67.5 > 5 \rightarrow$ use normal distribution

   $H_0: p \leq 0.70$; $H_a: p > 0.70$ (claim)

   $z_0 = 1.75$; Rejection region: $z > 1.75$

   $$z = \frac{\hat{p} - p}{\sqrt{\dfrac{pq}{n}}} = \frac{0.64 - 0.70}{\sqrt{\dfrac{(0.70)(0.30)}{225}}} \approx -1.96$$

   Fail to reject H_0. There is not enough evidence at the 4% level of significance to support the claim.

7. $np = (100)(0.45) = 45 > 5$

    $nq = (100)(0.55) = 55 > 5 \rightarrow$ use normal distribution

    $H_0 : p \leq 0.45$ (claim); $H_a : p > 0.45$

    $z_0 = 1.645$; Rejection region: $z > 1.645$

    $$z = \frac{\hat{p} - p}{\sqrt{\dfrac{pq}{n}}} = \frac{0.52 - 0.45}{\sqrt{\dfrac{(0.45)(0.55)}{100}}} \approx 1.41$$

    Fail to reject H_0. There is not enough evidence at the 5% level of significance to reject the claim.

8. $np = (50)(0.95) = 47.5 > 5$

    $nq = (50)(0.05) = 2.5 < 5$

    Cannot use normal distribution because $nq < 5$.

9. (a) $H_0 : p \geq 0.25$; $H_a : p < 0.25$ (claim)

    (b) $z_0 = -1.645$; Rejection region: $z < -1.645$

    (c) $z = \dfrac{\hat{p} - p}{\sqrt{\dfrac{pq}{n}}} = \dfrac{0.185 - 0.25}{\sqrt{\dfrac{(0.25)(0.75)}{200}}} \approx -2.12$

    (d) Reject H_0.

    (e) There is enough evidence at the 5% level of significance to support the claim that less than 25% of U.S. adults are smokers.

10. (a) $H_0 : p \geq 0.40$ (claim); $H_a : p < 0.40$

    (b) $z_0 = -2.05$; Rejection region: $z < -2.05$

    (c) $z = \dfrac{\hat{p} - p}{\sqrt{\dfrac{pq}{n}}} = \dfrac{0.35 - 0.40}{\sqrt{\dfrac{(0.40)(0.60)}{600}}} \approx -2.5$

    (d) Reject H_0.

    (e) There is enough evidence at the 2% level of significance to reject the claim that at least 40% of U.S. adults think the Census count is accurate.

11. (a) $H_0 : p \leq 0.50$ (claim); $H_a : p > 0.50$

    (b) $z_0 = 2.33$; Rejection region: $z > 2.33$

    (c) $z = \dfrac{\hat{p} - p}{\sqrt{\dfrac{pq}{n}}} = \dfrac{0.58 - 0.50}{\sqrt{\dfrac{(0.50)(0.50)}{150}}} \approx 1.96$

    (d) Fail to reject H_0.

    (e) There is not enough evidence at the 1% level of significance to reject the claim that at most 50% of people believe that drivers should be allowed to use cellular phone with hands-free devices while driving.

12. (a) $H_0 : p = 0.05$ (claim); $H_a : p \neq 0.05$

(b) $-z_0 = -1.75$, $z_0 = 1.75$; Rejection region: $z < -1.75$, $z > 1.75$

(c) $z = \dfrac{\hat{p} - p}{\sqrt{\dfrac{pq}{n}}} = \dfrac{0.096 - 0.05}{\sqrt{\dfrac{(0.05)(0.95)}{250}}} \approx 3.34$

(d) Reject H_0.

(e) There is enough evidence at the 8% level of significance to reject the claim that 5% of children under 18 years of age have asthma.

13. (a) $H_0 : p \leq 0.75$; $H_a : p > 0.75$ (claim)

(b) $z_0 = 1.28$; Rejection region: $z > 1.28$

(c) $z = \dfrac{\hat{p} - p}{\sqrt{\dfrac{pq}{n}}} = \dfrac{0.82 - 0.75}{\sqrt{\dfrac{(0.75)(0.25)}{150}}} \approx 1.98$

(d) Reject H_0.

(e) There is enough evidence at the 10% level of significance to support the claim that more than 75% of females ages 20-29 are taller than 62 inches.

14. (a) $H_0 : p = 0.16$ (claim); $H_a : p \neq 0.16$

(b) $-z_0 = -1.96$, $z_0 = 1.96$; Rejection region: $z < -1.96$, $z > 1.96$

(c) $z = \dfrac{\hat{p} - p}{\sqrt{\dfrac{pq}{n}}} = \dfrac{0.20 - 0.16}{\sqrt{\dfrac{(0.16)(0.84)}{300}}} \approx 1.89$

(d) Fail to reject H_0.

(e) There is not enough evidence at the 5% level of significance to reject the claim that 16% of U.S. adults say that curling is the Winter Olympic sport they would like to try the most.

15. (a) $H_0 : p \geq 0.35$; $H_a : p < 0.35$ (claim)

(b) $z_0 = -1.28$; Rejection region: $z < -1.28$

(c) $z = \dfrac{\hat{p} - p}{\sqrt{\dfrac{pq}{n}}} = \dfrac{0.39 - 0.35}{\sqrt{\dfrac{(0.35)(0.65)}{400}}} \approx 1.68$

(d) Fail to reject H_0.

(e) There is not enough evidence at the 10% level of significance to support the claim that less than 35% of U.S. households own a dog.

16. (a) $H_0 : p = 0.30$ (claim); $H_a : p \neq 0.30$

(b) $-z_0 = -1.96$, $z_0 = 1.96$; Rejection region: $z < -1.96$, $z > 1.96$

(c) $z = \dfrac{\hat{p} - p}{\sqrt{\dfrac{pq}{n}}} = \dfrac{0.36 - 0.30}{\sqrt{\dfrac{(0.30)(0.70)}{200}}} \approx 1.85$

(d) Fail to reject H_0.

(e) There is not enough evidence at the 5% level of significance to reject the claim that 30% of U.S. households own a cat.

17. H_0: $p \geq 0.52$ (claim); H_a: $p < 0.52$

$z_0 = -1.645$: Rejection region: $z < -1.645$

$$z = \frac{\hat{p} - p}{\sqrt{\dfrac{pq}{n}}} = \frac{0.48 - 0.52}{\sqrt{\dfrac{(0.52)(0.48)}{50}}} \approx -0.566$$

Fail to reject H_0. There is not enough evidence at the 5% level of significance to reject the claim that at least 52% of adults are more likely to buy a product when there are free samples.

18. Answers will vary. Sample answer: The company should continue the use of giveaways because there is not enough evidence to say that less than 52% of adults are more likely to buy a product when there are free samples.

19. H_0: $p \geq 0.35$; H_a: $p < 0.35$ (claim)

$z_0 = -1.28$: Rejection region: $z < -1.28$

$$z = \frac{x - np}{\sqrt{npq}} = \frac{156 - (400)(0.35)}{\sqrt{(400)(0.35)(0.65)}} \approx 1.68$$

Reject H_0. The results are the same.

20. $$z = \frac{\hat{p} - p}{\sqrt{\dfrac{pq}{n}}} \Rightarrow \frac{\left(\dfrac{x}{n}\right) - p}{\sqrt{\dfrac{pq}{n}}} \Rightarrow \frac{\left(\dfrac{x}{n}\right) - p}{\dfrac{\sqrt{pq}}{\sqrt{n}}} \Rightarrow \frac{\left[\left(\dfrac{x}{n}\right) - p\right]\sqrt{n}}{\sqrt{pq}} \cdot \frac{\sqrt{n}}{\sqrt{n}} \Rightarrow \frac{\left[\left(\dfrac{x}{n}\right) - p\right]n}{\sqrt{npq}} \Rightarrow \frac{x - np}{\sqrt{npq}}$$

7.5 HYPOTHESIS TESTING FOR VARIANCE AND STANDARD DEVIATION

7.5 Try It Yourself Solutions

1a. $df = 17$, $\alpha = 0.01$

b. $\chi_0^2 = 33.409$

2a. $df = 29$, $\alpha = 0.05$

b. $\chi_0^2 = 17.708$

3a. $df = 50$, $\alpha = 0.01$

b. $\chi_R^2 = 79.490$

c. $\chi_L^2 = 27.991$

4a. The claim is "the variance of the amount of sports drink in a 12-ounce bottle is no more than 0.40."

$H_0: \sigma^2 \leq 0.40$ (claim); $H_a: \sigma^2 > 0.40$

b. $\alpha = 0.01$ and d.f. $= n - 1 = 30$

c. $\chi_0^2 = 50.892$; Rejection region: $\chi^2 > 50.892$

d. $\chi^2 = \dfrac{(n-1)s^2}{\sigma^2} = \dfrac{(30)(0.75)}{0.40} = 56.250$

e. Reject H_0.

f. There is enough evidence at the 1% level of significance to reject the claim that the variance of the amount of sports drink in a 12-ounce bottle is no more than 0.40.

5a. The claim is "the standard deviation of the lengths of response times is less than 3.7 minutes."

$H_0: \sigma \geq 3.7$; $H_a: \sigma < 3.7$ (claim)

b. $\alpha = 0.05$ and d.f. $= n - 1 = 8$

c. $\chi_0^2 = 2.733$; Rejection region: $\chi^2 < 2.733$

d. $\chi^2 = \dfrac{(n-1)s^2}{\sigma^2} = \dfrac{(8)(3.0)}{(3.7)^2} \approx 5.259$

e. Fail to reject H_0.

f. There is not enough evidence at the 5% level of significance to support the claim that the standard deviation of the lengths of response times is less than 3.7 minutes.

6a. The claim is "the variance of the weight losses is 25.5."

$H_0: \sigma^2 = 25.5$ (claim); $H_a: \sigma^2 \neq 25.5$

b. $\alpha = 0.10$ and d.f. $= n - 1 = 12$

c. $\chi_L^2 = 5.226$ and $\chi_R^2 = 21.026$; Rejection region: $\chi^2 > 21.026$, $\chi^2 < 5.226$

d. $\chi^2 = \dfrac{(n-1)s^2}{\sigma^2} = \dfrac{(12)(10.8)}{25.5} \approx 5.082$

e. Reject H_0.

f. There is enough evidence at the 10% level of significance to reject the claim that the variance of the weight losses of users is 25.5.

7.5 EXERCISE SOLUTIONS

1. Specify the level of significance α. Determine the degrees of freedom. Determine the critical values using the χ^2-distribution. For a right-tailed test, use the value that corresponds to d.f. and α. For a left-tailed test, use the value that corresponds to d.f. and $1 - \alpha$. For a two-tailed test, use the value that corresponds to d.f. and $\dfrac{1}{2}\alpha$, and d.f. and $1 - \dfrac{1}{2}\alpha$.

2. No; In a χ^2-distribution, all χ^2-values are greater than or equal to 0.

3. The requirement of a normal distribution is more important when testing a standard deviation than when testing a mean. If the population is not normal, the results of the χ^2-test can be misleading because the χ^2-test is not as robust as the tests for the population mean.

4. State H_0 and H_a and identify the claim. Specify the level of significance. Determine the degrees of freedom. Determine the critical value(s) and rejection region(s) Find the standardized test statistic. Make a decision and interpret it in the context of the original claim.

5. $\chi_0^2 = 38.885$ 6. $\chi_0^2 = 14.684$ 7. $\chi_0^2 = 0.872$ 8. $\chi_0^2 = 13.091$

9. $\chi_L^2 = 60.391,\ \chi_R^2 = 101.879$ 10. $\chi_L^2 = 35.534,\ \chi_R^2 = 91.952$

11. (a) Fail to reject H_0 because $\chi^2 < 6.251$.
    (b) Fail to reject H_0 because $\chi^2 < 6.251$.
    (c) Fail to reject H_0 because $\chi^2 < 6.251$.
    (d) Reject H_0 because $\chi^2 > 6.251$.

12. (a) Fail to reject H_0 because $0.711 < \chi^2 < 9.488$.
    (b) Fail to reject H_0 because $0.711 < \chi^2 < 9.488$.
    (c) Reject H_0 because $\chi^2 < 0.711$.
    (d) Reject H_0 because $\chi^2 > 9.488$.

13. (a) Fail to reject H_0 because $8.547 < \chi^2 < 22.307$.
    (b) Reject H_0 because $\chi^2 > 22.307$.
    (c) Reject H_0 because $\chi^2 < 8.547$.
    (d) Fail to reject H_0 because $8.547 < \chi^2 < 22.307$.

14. (a) Fail to reject H_0 because $\chi^2 < 10.645$.
    (b) Fail to reject H_0 because $\chi^2 < 10.645$.
    (c) Fail to reject H_0 because $\chi^2 < 10.645$.
    (d) Reject H_0 because $\chi^2 > 10.645$.

15. $H_0 : \sigma^2 = 0.52$ (claim); $H_a : \sigma^2 \neq 0.52$

    $\chi_L^2 = 7.564,\ \chi_R^2 = 30.191$; Rejection regions: $\chi^2 < 7.564,\ \chi^2 > 30.191$

    $$\chi^2 = \frac{(n-1)s^2}{\sigma^2} = \frac{(17)(0.508)^2}{(0.52)} \approx 16.608$$

    Fail to reject H_0. There is not enough evidence at the 5% level of significance to reject the claim.

16. $H_0 : \sigma^2 \geq 8.5$ (claim); $H_a : \sigma^2 < 8.5$

$\chi_0^2 = 12.338$; Rejection region: $\chi^2 < 12.338$

$\chi^2 = \dfrac{(n-1)s^2}{\sigma^2} = \dfrac{(22)(7.45)}{8.5} \approx 19.28$

Fail to reject H_0. There is not enough evidence at the 5% level of significance to reject the claim.

17. $H_0 : \sigma = 24.9$ (claim); $H_a : \sigma \neq 24.9$

$\chi_L^2 = 34.764$, $\chi_R^2 = 67.505$; Rejection regions: $\chi^2 < 34.764$, $\chi^2 > 67.505$

$\chi^2 = \dfrac{(n-1)s^2}{\sigma^2} = \dfrac{(50)(29.1)^2}{(24.9)^2} \approx 68.29$

Reject H_0. There is enough evidence at the 10% level of significance to reject the claim.

18. $H_0 : \sigma \geq 40$; $H_a : \sigma < 40$ (claim)

$\chi_0^2 = 3.053$; Rejection region: $\chi^2 < 3.053$

$\chi^2 = \dfrac{(n-1)s^2}{\sigma^2} = \dfrac{(11)(40.8)^2}{(40)^2} \approx 11.444$

Fail to reject H_0. There is not enough evidence at the 1% level of significance to support the claim.

19. (a) $H_0 : \sigma^2 = 1.25$ (claim); $H_a : \sigma^2 \neq 1.25$

(b) $\chi_L^2 = 10.283$, $\chi_R^2 = 35.479$; Rejection regions: $\chi^2 < 10.283$, $\chi^2 > 35.479$

(c) $\chi^2 = \dfrac{(n-1)s^2}{\sigma^2} = \dfrac{(21)(1.35)}{1.25} = 22.68$

(d) Fail to reject H_0.

(e) There is not enough evidence at the 5% level of significance to reject the claim that the variance of the number of grams of carbohydrates in servings of its tortilla chips is 1.25.

20. (a) $H_0 : \sigma^2 = 1.0$ (claim); $H_a : \sigma^2 \neq 1.0$

(b) $\chi_L^2 = 12.401$, $\chi_R^2 = 39.364$; Rejection regions: $\chi^2 < 12.401$, $\chi^2 > 39.364$

(c) $\chi^2 = \dfrac{(n-1)s^2}{\sigma^2} = \dfrac{(24)(1.65)}{1.0} = 39.6$

(d) Reject H_0.

(e) There is enough evidence at the 5% level of significance to reject the claim that the variance of the gas mileages of its hybrid vehicles is 1.0.

21. (a) $H_0 : \sigma \geq 36$; $H_a : \sigma < 36$ (claim)

(b) $\chi_0^2 = 13.240$; Rejection region: $\chi^2 < 13.240$

(c) $\chi^2 = \dfrac{(n-1)s^2}{\sigma^2} = \dfrac{(21)(33.4)^2}{(36)^2} \approx 18.076$

(d) Fail to reject H_0.

(e) There is not enough evidence at the 10% level of significance to support the claim that the standard deviation for eighth graders on the examination is less than 36 points.

22. (a) $H_0 : \sigma \geq 30$; $H_a : \sigma < 30$ (claim)

   (b) $\chi_0^2 = 6.408$; Rejection region: $\chi^2 < 6.408$

   (c) $\chi^2 = \dfrac{(n-1)s^2}{\sigma^2} = \dfrac{(17)(33.6)^2}{(30)^2} \approx 21.325$

   (d) Fail to reject H_0.

   (e) There is not enough evidence at the 1% level of significance to support the claim that the standard deviation of test scores for eighth grade students who took a U.S. history assessment test is less than 30 points.

23. (a) $H_0 : \sigma \leq 25$ (claim); $H_a : \sigma > 25$

   (b) $\chi_0^2 = 36.741$; Rejection region: $\chi^2 > 36.741$

   (c) $\chi^2 = \dfrac{(n-1)s^2}{\sigma^2} = \dfrac{(27)(31)^2}{(25)^2} \approx 41.515$

   (d) Reject H_0.

   (e) There is enough evidence at the 10% level of significance to reject the claim that the standard deviation of the number of fatalities per year from tornadoes is no more than 25.

24. (a) $H_0 : \sigma = 6.14$ (claim); $H_a : \sigma \neq 6.14$

   (b) $\chi_L^2 = 8.907$, $\chi_R^2 = 32.852$; Rejection regions: $\chi^2 < 8.907$, $\chi^2 > 32.852$

   (c) $\chi^2 = \dfrac{(n-1)s^2}{\sigma^2} = \dfrac{(19)(6.5)^2}{(6.14)^2} \approx 21.293$

   (d) Fail to reject H_0.

   (e) There is not enough evidence at the 5% level of significance to reject the claim that the standard deviation of the lengths of stay for patients involved in a crash in which the vehicle struck a tree is 6.14 days.

25. (a) $H_0 : \sigma \geq \$3500$; $H_a : \sigma < \$3500$ (claim)

   (b) $\chi_0^2 = 18.114$; Rejection region: $\chi^2 < 18.114$

   (c) $\chi^2 = \dfrac{(n-1)s^2}{\sigma^2} = \dfrac{(27)(4100)^2}{(3500)^2} \approx 37.051$

   (d) Fail to reject H_0.

   (e) There is not enough evidence at the 10% level of significance to support the claim that the standard deviation of the total charges for patients involved in a crash in which the vehicle struck a construction baracade is less than $3500.

26. (a) $H_0 : \sigma \leq \$30$ (claim); $H_a : \sigma > 30$

   (b) $\chi_0^2 = 37.566$; Rejection region: $\chi^2 < 37.566$

   (c) $\chi^2 = \dfrac{(n-1)s^2}{\sigma^2} = \dfrac{(20)(35.25)^2}{(30)^2} \approx 27.613$

(d) Fail to reject H_0.

(e) There is not enough evidence at the 1% level of significance to reject the claim that the standard deviation of the room rates of hotels in the city is no more than $30.

27. (a) $H_0: \sigma \le \$6100$; $H_a: \sigma > \$6100$ (claim)

(b) $\chi_0^2 = 27.587$; Rejection region: $\chi^2 > 27.587$

(c) $s \approx 7814.23$

$$\chi^2 = \frac{(n-1)s^2}{\sigma^2} = \frac{(17)(7814.23)^2}{(6100)^2} \approx 27.897$$

(d) Reject H_0.

(e) There is enough evidence at the 5% level of significance to support the claim that the standard deviation of the annual salaries for environmental engineers is greater than $6100.

28. (a) $H_0: \sigma \ge \$10,600$ (claim); $H_a: \sigma < \$10,600$

(b) $\chi_0^2 = 11.651$; Rejection region: $\chi^2 < 11.651$

(c) $s \approx 8284.89$

$$\chi^2 = \frac{(n-1)s^2}{\sigma^2} = \frac{(19)(8284.89)^2}{(10,600)^2} \approx 11.607$$

(d) Reject H_0.

(e) There is enough evidence at the 10% level of significance to reject the claim that the standard deviation of the annual salaries of commodity buyers is at least $10,600.

29. Hypothesis test results:

σ^2: variance of variable

$H_0: \sigma^2 = 9$

$H_A: \sigma^2 < 9$

Variance	Sample Var.	DF	Chi-Squared Stat	P-value
σ^2	2.03	9	2.03	0.009

Reject H_0. There is enough evidence at the 1% level of significance to reject the claim.

30. Hypothesis test results:

σ^2: variance of variable

$H_0: \sigma^2 = 14.85$

$H_A: \sigma^2 \ne 14.85$

Variance	Sample Var.	DF	Chi-Squared Stat	P-value
σ^2	28.75	16	30.97643	0.0271

Reject H_0. There is enough evidence at the 5% level of significance to reject the claim.

31. $\sigma^2 = (4.5)^2 = 20.25$

$s^2 = (5.8)^2 = 33.64$

Hypothesis test results:

σ^2 : variance of variable

$H_0 : \sigma^2 = 20.25$

$H_A : \sigma^2 > 20.25$

Variance	Sample Var.	DF	Chi-Squared Stat	P-value
σ^2	33.64	14	23.257284	0.0562

Fail to reject H_0. There is not enough evidence at the 5% level of significance to support the claim.

32. $\sigma^2 = (418)^2 = 174,724$

$s^2 = (305)^2 = 93,025$

Hypothesis test results:

σ^2 : variance of variable

$H_0 : \sigma^2 = 174,724$

$H_A : \sigma^2 \neq 174,724$

Variance	Sample Var.	DF	Chi-Squared Stat	P-value
σ^2	93025	23	12.245456	0.067

Reject H_0. There is enough evidence at the 10% level of significance to support the claim.

33. $\chi^2 = 37.051$

P-value = {Area left of $\chi^2 = 37.051$ } = 0.9059

Fail to reject H_0 because P-value = 0.9059 > 0.10.

34. $\chi^2 = 27.613$

P-value = {Area right of $\chi^2 = 27.613$ } = 0.1189

Fail to reject H_0 because P-value = 0.1189 > 0.01.

35. $\chi^2 = 27.897$

P-value = {Area right of $\chi^2 = 27.897$ } = 0.0462

Reject H_0 because P-value = 0.0462 < 0.05.

36. $\chi^2 = 11.607$

P-value = {Area left of $\chi^2 = 11.607$ } = 0.0983

Reject H_0 because P-value = 0.0983 < 0.10.

CHAPTER 7 REVIEW EXERCISE SOLUTIONS

1. $H_0: \mu \leq 375$ (claim); $H_a: \mu > 375$ **2.** $H_0: \mu = 82$ (claim); $H_a: \mu \neq 82$

3. $H_0: p \geq 0.205$; $H_a: p < 0.205$ (claim)   **4.** $H_0: \mu = 150{,}020$; $H_a: \mu \neq 150{,}020$ (claim)

5. $H_0: \sigma \leq 1.9$; $H_a: \sigma > 1.9$ (claim)   **6.** $H_0: p \geq 0.64$ (claim); $H_a: p < 0.64$

7a. $H_0: p = 0.71$ (claim); $H_a: p \neq 0.71$

  b. A type I error will occur if the actual proportion of Americans who support plans to order deep cuts in executive compensation at companies that have received federal bailout funds is 71%, but you reject $H_0: p = 0.71$.

     A type II error will occur if the actual proportion is not 71%, but you fail to reject $H_0: p = 0.71$.

  c. Two-tailed because the alternative hypothesis contains $\neq$.

  d. There is enough evidence to reject the news outlet's claim that the proportion of Americans who support plans to order deep cuts in executive compensation at companies that have received federal bailout funds is 71%.

  e. There is not enough evidence to reject the news outlet's claim that the proportion of Americans who support plans to order deep cuts in executive compensation at companies that have received federal bailout funds is 71%.

8a. $H_0: \mu \geq 400$ (claim); $H_a: \mu < 400$

  b. A type I error will occur if the actual mean shelf life of the dried fruit is at least 400 days, but you reject $H_0: \mu \geq 400$.

     A type II error will occur if the actual mean shelf life of the dried fruit is less than 400 days, but you fail to reject $H_0: \mu \geq 400$.

  c. Left-tailed because the alternative hypothesis contains $<$.

  d. There is enough evidence to reject the agricultural cooperative's claim that the mean shelf life of the dried fruit is at least 400 days.

  e. There is not enough evidence to reject the agricultural cooperative's claim that the mean shelf life of the dried fruit is at least 400 days.

9a. $H_0: \sigma \leq 50$ (claim); $H_a: \sigma > 50$

  b. A type I error will occur if the actual standard deviation of the sodium content in one serving of a certain soup is no more than 50 milligrams, but you reject $H_0: \sigma \leq 50$.

     A type II error will occur if the actual standard deviation of the sodium content in one serving of a certain soup is more than 50 milligrams, but you fail to reject $H_0: \sigma \leq 50$.

  c. Right-tailed because the alternative hypothesis contains $>$.

  d. There is enough evidence to reject the soup maker's claim that the standard deviation of the sodium content in one serving of a certain soup is no more than 50 milligrams.

  e. There is not enough evidence to reject the soup maker's claim that the standard deviation of the sodium content in one serving of a certain soup is no more than 50 milligrams.

10a. $H_0 : \mu \geq 25$; $H_a : \mu < 25$ (claim)

    b.   A type I error will occur if the actual mean number of grams of carbohydrates in one bar is at least 25, but you reject $H_0 : \mu \geq 25$.

        A type II error will occur if the actual mean number of grams of carbohydrates in one bar is less than 25, but you fail to reject $H_0 : \mu \geq 25$.

    c.   Left-tailed because the alternative hypothesis contains <.

    d.   There is enough evidence to support the energy bar maker's claim that the mean number of grams of carbohydrates in one bar is less than 25.

    e.   There is not enough evidence to support the energy bar maker's claim that the mean number of grams of carbohydrates in one bar is less than 25.

11. P-value = {Area to left of $z = -0.94$ } = 0.1736

    Fail to reject H_0.

12. P-value = 2{Area to right of $z = 2.57$} = 2(0.0051) = 0.0102

    Reject H_0.

13. $H_0 : \mu \leq 0.05$ (claim); $H_a : \mu > 0.05$

$$z = \frac{\bar{x} - \mu}{\frac{s}{\sqrt{n}}} = \frac{0.057 - 0.05}{\frac{0.018}{\sqrt{32}}} \approx 2.20$$

    P-value = {Area to right of $z = 2.20$} = 0.0139

    $\alpha = 0.10 \Rightarrow$ Reject H_0.

    $\alpha = 0.05 \Rightarrow$ Reject H_0.

    $\alpha = 0.01 \Rightarrow$ Fail to reject H_0.

14. $H_0 : \mu = 230$; $H_a : \mu \neq 230$ (claim)

$$z = \frac{\bar{x} - \mu}{\frac{s}{\sqrt{n}}} = \frac{216.5 - 230}{\frac{17.3}{\sqrt{48}}} \approx -5.41$$

    P-value = 2{Area to left of $z \doteq -5.41$ } $\approx 2(0) = 0$

    $\alpha = 0.10 \Rightarrow$ Reject H_0.

    $\alpha = 0.05 \Rightarrow$ Reject H_0.

    $\alpha = 0.01 \Rightarrow$ Reject H_0.

15. $z_0 \approx -2.05$

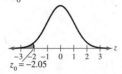

16. $-z_0 = -2.81$, $z_0 = 2.81$

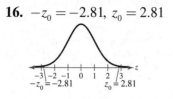

17. $z_0 = 1.96$

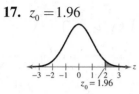

18. $-z_0 = -1.75$, $z_0 = 1.75$

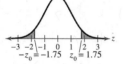

19. Fail to reject H_0 because $-1.645 < z < 1.645$.

20. Reject H_0 because $z > 1.645$.

21. Fail to reject H_0 because $-1.645 < z < 1.645$.

22. Reject H_0 because $z < -1.645$.

23. H_0: $\mu \leq 45$ (claim); H_a: $\mu > 45$

$z_0 = 1.645$; Rejection region: $z > 1.645$

$$z = \frac{\overline{x} - \mu}{\frac{s}{\sqrt{n}}} = \frac{47.2 - 45}{\frac{6.7}{\sqrt{42}}} \approx 2.128$$

Reject H_0. There is enough evidence at the 5% level of significance to reject the claim.

24. H_0: $\mu = 8.45$; H_a: $\mu \neq 8.45$ (claim)

$-z_0 = -2.17$, $z_0 = 2.17$; Rejection regions: $z < -2.17$, $z > 2.17$

$$z = \frac{\overline{x} - \mu}{\frac{s}{\sqrt{n}}} = \frac{7.88 - 8.45}{\frac{1.75}{\sqrt{60}}} \approx -2.52$$

Reject H_0. There is enough evidence at the 3% level of significance to support the claim.

25. $H_0 : \mu \geq 5.500$; $H_a : \mu < 5.500$ (claim)

$z_0 = -2.33$; Rejection region: $z < -2.33$

$$z = \frac{\bar{x} - \mu}{\frac{s}{\sqrt{n}}} = \frac{5.497 - 5.500}{\frac{0.011}{\sqrt{36}}} \approx -1.636$$

Fail to reject H_0. There is not enough evidence at the 1% level of significance to support the claim.

26. $H_0 : \mu = 7450$ (claim); $H_a : \mu \neq 7450$

$-z_0 = -1.645$, $z_0 = 1.645$; Rejection regions: $z < -1.645$, $z > 1.645$

$$z = \frac{\bar{x} - \mu}{\frac{s}{\sqrt{n}}} = \frac{7495 - 7450}{\frac{243}{\sqrt{57}}} \approx 1.398$$

Fail to reject H_0. There is not enough evidence at the 10% level of significance to reject the claim.

27. $H_0 : \mu = \$10,380$ (claim); $H_a : \mu \neq \$10,380$

$$z = \frac{\bar{x} - \mu}{\frac{s}{\sqrt{n}}} = \frac{10,240 - 10,380}{\frac{1561}{\sqrt{800}}} \approx -2.54$$

P-value $= 2\{$Area left of $z = -2.54\} = 2(0.0055) = 0.0110$

Fail to reject H_0. There is not enough evidence at the 1% level of significance to reject the claim that the mean cost of raising a child from birth to age 2 by husband-wife families in rural areas is $10,380.

28. $H_0 : \mu \leq \$650$ (claim); $H_a : \mu > \$650$

$$z = \frac{\bar{x} - \mu}{\frac{s}{\sqrt{n}}} = \frac{657 - 650}{\frac{40}{\sqrt{45}}} \approx 1.17$$

P-value $= \{$Area right of $z = 1.17\} = 0.1210$

Fail to reject H_0. There is not enough evidence at the 5% level of significance to reject the claim that the mean cost of meals and lodging for a family of 4 traveling in Hawaii is at most $650.

29. $-t_0 = -2.093$, $t_0 = 2.093$ **30.** $t_0 = 2.998$ **31.** $t_0 = -2.977$

32. $-t_0 = -2.718$, $t_0 = 2.718$

33. $H_0 : \mu = 95; H_a : \mu \neq 95$ (claim)

$-t_0 = -2.201$, $t_0 = 2.201$; Rejection regions: $t < -2.201$, $t > 2.201$

$$t = \frac{\bar{x} - \mu}{\frac{s}{\sqrt{n}}} = \frac{94.1 - 95}{\frac{1.53}{\sqrt{12}}} \approx -2.038$$

Fail to reject H_0. There is not enough evidence at the 5% level of significance to support the claim.

34. $H_0 : \mu \leq 12,700; H_a : \mu > 12,700$ (claim)

$t_0 = 2.845$; Rejection region: $t > 2.845$

$$t = \frac{\bar{x} - \mu}{\frac{s}{\sqrt{n}}} = \frac{12,855 - 12,700}{\frac{248}{\sqrt{21}}} \approx 2.864$$

Reject H_0. There is enough evidence at the 0.5% level of significance to support the claim.

35. $H_0 : \mu \geq 0$ (claim); $H_a : \mu < 0$

$t_0 = -1.341$; Rejection region: $t < -1.341$

$$t = \frac{\bar{x} - \mu}{\frac{s}{\sqrt{n}}} = \frac{-0.45 - 0}{\frac{1.38}{\sqrt{16}}} \approx -1.304$$

Fail to reject H_0. There is not enough evidence at the 10% level of significance to reject the claim.

36. $H_0 : \mu = 4.20$ (claim); $H_a : \mu \neq 4.20$

$-t_0 = -2.896$, $t_0 = 2.896$; Rejection regions: $t < -2.896$, $t > 2.896$

$$t = \frac{\bar{x} - \mu}{\frac{s}{\sqrt{n}}} = \frac{4.61 - 4.20}{\frac{0.33}{\sqrt{9}}} \approx 3.727$$

Reject H_0. There is enough evidence at the 2% level of significance to reject the claim.

37. $H_0 : \mu \leq 48$ (claim); $H_a : \mu > 48$

$t_0 = 3.143$; Rejection region: $t > 3.143$

$$t = \frac{\bar{x} - \mu}{\frac{s}{\sqrt{n}}} = \frac{52 - 48}{\frac{2.5}{\sqrt{7}}} \approx 4.233$$

Reject H_0. There is enough evidence at the 1% level of significance to reject the claim.

38. $H_0: \mu \geq 850$; $H_a: \mu < 850$ (claim)

$t_0 = -2.160$; Rejection region: $t < -2.160$

$$t = \frac{\bar{x} - \mu}{\frac{s}{\sqrt{n}}} = \frac{875 - 850}{\frac{25}{\sqrt{14}}} \approx 3.742$$

Fail to reject H_0. There is not enough evidence at the 2.5% level of significance to support the claim.

39. $H_0: \mu = \$25$ (claim); $H_a: \mu \neq \$25$

$-t_0 = -1.740$, $t_0 = 1.740$; Rejection regions: $t < -1.740$, $t > 1.740$

$$t = \frac{\bar{x} - \mu}{\frac{s}{\sqrt{n}}} = \frac{26.25 - 25}{\frac{3.23}{\sqrt{18}}} \approx 1.642$$

Fail to reject H_0. There is not enough evidence at the 10% level of significance to reject the claim that the mean monthly cost of joining a health club is $25.

40. $H_0: \mu \leq \$14$ (claim); $H_a: \mu > \$14$

$t_0 = 2.048$; Rejection region: $t > 2.048$

$$t = \frac{\bar{x} - \mu}{\frac{s}{\sqrt{n}}} = \frac{15.59 - 14}{\frac{2.60}{\sqrt{29}}} \approx 3.293$$

Reject H_0. There is enough evidence at the 2.5% level of significance to reject the claim that the mean cost of a yoga session is no more than $14.

41. $H_0: \mu \geq \$10,200$ (claim); $H_a: \mu < \$10,200$

$\bar{x} \approx 9895.8$ $s \approx 490.88$

$$t = \frac{\bar{x} - \mu}{\frac{s}{\sqrt{n}}} = \frac{9895.8 - 10,200}{\frac{490.88}{\sqrt{16}}} \approx -2.48$$

P-value = { Area to left of $t = -2.48$ } ≈ 0.0128

Fail to reject H_0. There is not enough evidence at the 1% level of significance to reject the claim that the mean expenditure per student in public elementary and secondary schools is at least $10,200.

42. $H_0: \mu = \$2698$ (claim); $H_a: \mu \neq \$2698$

$$t = \frac{\bar{x} - \mu}{\frac{s}{\sqrt{n}}} = \frac{2764 - 2698}{\frac{322}{\sqrt{28}}} \approx 1.085$$

P-value = 2{Area to right of $t = 1.085$ } ≈ 0.2877

Fail to reject H_0. There is not enough evidence at the 5% level of significance to reject the claim that the typical household spends a mean amount of $2698 per year on food away from home.

43. $np = (40)(0.15) = 6 > 5$

$nq = (40)(0.85) = 34 > 5 \rightarrow$ can use normal distribution

$H_0 : p = 0.15$ (claim); $H_a : p \neq 0.15$

$-z_0 = -1.96,\ z_0 = 1.96;$ Rejection regions: $z < -1.96,\ z > 1.96$

$$z = \frac{\hat{p} - p}{\sqrt{\dfrac{pq}{n}}} = \frac{0.09 - 0.15}{\sqrt{\dfrac{(0.15)(0.85)}{40}}} \approx -1.063$$

Fail to reject H_0. There is not enough evidence at the 5% level of significance to reject the claim.

44. $np = (68)(0.70) = 47.6 > 5$

$nq = (68)(0.30) = 20.4 > 5 \rightarrow$ can use normal distribution

$H_0 : p \geq 0.70;\ H_a : p < 0.70$ (claim)

$z_0 = -2.33;$ Rejection region: $z < -2.33$

$$z = \frac{\hat{p} - p}{\sqrt{\dfrac{pq}{n}}} = \frac{0.50 - 0.70}{\sqrt{\dfrac{(0.70)(0.30)}{68}}} \approx -3.599$$

Reject H_0. There is enough evidence at the 1% level of significance to support the claim.

45. $np = (75)(0.09) = 6.75 > 5$

$nq = (75)(0.91) = 68.25 > 5 \rightarrow$ can use normal distribution

$H_0 : p \geq 0.09;\ H_a : p < 0.09$ (claim)

$z_0 = -1.405;$ Rejection region: $z < -1.405$

$$z = \frac{\hat{p} - p}{\sqrt{\dfrac{pq}{n}}} = \frac{0.07 - 0.09}{\sqrt{\dfrac{(0.09)(0.91)}{75}}} \approx -0.605$$

Fail to reject H_0. There is not enough evidence at the 8% level of significance to support the claim.

46. $np = (116)(0.65) = 75.4 > 5$

$nq = (116)(0.35) = 40.6 > 5 \rightarrow$ can use normal distribution

$H_0 : p = 0.65$ (claim); $H_a : p \neq 0.65$

$-z_0 = -2.17,\ z_0 = 2.17;$ Rejection regions: $z < -2.17,\ z > 2.17$

$$z = \frac{\hat{p} - p}{\sqrt{\dfrac{pq}{n}}} = \frac{0.76 - 0.65}{\sqrt{\dfrac{(0.65)(0.35)}{116}}} \approx 2.48$$

Reject H_0. There is not enough evidence at the 3% level of significance to support the claim.

47. Because $np = 1.2 < 5$, the normal distribution cannot be used to approximate the binomial distribution.

48. $np = (60)(0.34) = 20.4 > 5$

$nq = (60)(0.66) = 39.6 > 5 \rightarrow$ can use normal distribution

$H_0 : p = 0.34; \ H_a : p \neq 0.34$ (claim)

$-z_0 = -2.575, \ z_0 = 2.575;$ Rejection regions: $z < -2.575, \ z > 2.575$

$$z = \frac{\hat{p} - p}{\sqrt{\dfrac{pq}{n}}} = \frac{0.29 - 0.34}{\sqrt{\dfrac{(0.34)(0.66)}{60}}} \approx -0.820$$

Fail to reject H_0. There is not enough evidence at the 1% level of significance to support the claim.

49. $np = (50)(0.24) = 12 > 5$

$nq = (50)(0.76) = 38 > 5 \rightarrow$ can use normal distribution

$H_0 : p = 0.24; \ H_a : p \neq 0.24$ (claim)

$-z_0 = -2.33, \ z_0 = 2.33;$ Rejection regions: $z < -2.33, \ z > 2.33$

$$z = \frac{\hat{p} - p}{\sqrt{\dfrac{pq}{n}}} = \frac{0.32 - 0.24}{\sqrt{\dfrac{(0.24)(0.76)}{50}}} \approx 1.32$$

Fail to reject H_0. There is not enough evidence at the 2% level of significance to support the claim.

50. $np = (43)(0.80) = 34.4 > 5$

$nq = (43)(0.20) = 8.6 > 5 \rightarrow$ can use normal distribution

$H_0 : p \leq 0.80$ (claim); $H_a : p > 0.80$

$z_0 = 1.28;$ Rejection region: $z > 1.28$

$$z = \frac{\hat{p} - p}{\sqrt{\dfrac{pq}{n}}} = \frac{0.85 - 0.80}{\sqrt{\dfrac{(0.80)(0.20)}{43}}} \approx 0.820$$

Fail to reject H_0. There is not enough evidence at the 10% level of significance to reject the claim.

51. $H_0 : p \leq 0.16; \ H_a : p > 0.16$ (claim)

$z_0 = 2.055;$ Rejection region: $z > 2.055$

$$\hat{p} = \frac{x}{n} = \frac{256}{1420} \approx 0.180$$

$$z = \frac{\hat{p} - p}{\sqrt{\dfrac{pq}{n}}} \approx \frac{0.180 - 0.16}{\sqrt{\dfrac{(0.16)(0.84)}{1420}}} \approx 2.056$$

Reject H_0. There is enough evidence at the 2% level of significance to support the claim that over 16% of U.S. adults are without health care coverage.

52. $H_0: p = 0.02$ (claim); $H_a: p \neq 0.02$

$-z_0 = -1.96$, $z_0 = 1.96$; Rejection regions: $z < -1.96$, $z > 1.96$

$$\hat{p} = \frac{x}{n} = \frac{3}{300} = 0.01$$

$$z = \frac{\hat{p} - p}{\sqrt{\dfrac{pq}{n}}} = \frac{0.01 - 0.02}{\sqrt{\dfrac{(0.02)(0.98)}{300}}} \approx -1.24$$

Fail to reject H_0. There is not enough evidence at the 5% level of significance to reject the claim that the rate of false positives for a Western blot assay is 2%.

53. $\chi_0^2 = 30.144$ **54.** $\chi_L^2 = 3.565$, $\chi_R^2 = 29.819$ **55.** $\chi_0^2 = 63.167$

56. $\chi_0^2 = 1.145$

57. $H_0: \sigma^2 \leq 2$; $H_a: \sigma^2 > 2$ (claim)

$\chi_0^2 = 24.769$; Rejection region: $\chi^2 > 24.769$

$$\chi^2 = \frac{(n-1)s^2}{\sigma^2} = \frac{(17)(2.95)}{(2)} = 25.075$$

Reject H_0. There is enough evidence at the 10% level of significance to support the claim.

58. $H_0: \sigma^2 \leq 60$ (claim); $H_a: \sigma^2 > 60$

$\chi_0^2 = 26.119$; Rejection region: $\chi^2 > 26.119$

$$\chi^2 = \frac{(n-1)s^2}{\sigma^2} = \frac{(14)(72.7)}{(60)} \approx 16.963$$

Fail to reject H_0. There is not enough evidence at the 2.5% level of significance to reject the claim.

59. $H_0: \sigma = 1.25$ (claim); $H_a: \sigma \neq 1.25$

$\chi_L^2 = 0.831$, $\chi_R^2 = 12.833$; Rejection regions: $\chi^2 < 0.831$, $\chi^2 > 12.833$

$$\chi^2 = \frac{(n-1)s^2}{\sigma^2} = \frac{(5)(1.03)^2}{(1.25)^2} \approx 3.395$$

Fail to reject H_0. There is not enough evidence at the 5% level of significance to reject the claim.

60. $H_0: \sigma = 0.035$; $H_a: \sigma \neq 0.035$ (claim)

$\chi_L^2 = 4.601$, $\chi_R^2 = 32.801$; Rejection regions: $\chi^2 < 4.601$, $\chi^2 > 32.801$

$$\chi^2 = \frac{(n-1)s^2}{\sigma^2} = \frac{(15)(0.026)^2}{(0.035)^2} \approx 8.278$$

Fail to reject H_0. There is not enough evidence at the 1% level of significance to support the claim.

61. $H_0 : \sigma^2 \leq 0.01$ (claim); $H_a : \sigma^2 > 0.01$

$\chi_0^2 = 49.645$; Rejection region: $\chi^2 > 49.645$

$\chi^2 = \dfrac{(n-1)s^2}{\sigma^2} = \dfrac{(27)(0.064)}{(0.01)} = 172.8$

Reject H_0. There is enough evidence at the 0.5% level of significance to reject the claim that the variance is at most 0.01.

62. $H_0 : \sigma = 3$ (claim); $H_a : \sigma \neq 3$

$\chi_L^2 = 11.116$, $\chi_R^2 = 48.290$; Rejection regions: $\chi^2 < 11.116$, $\chi^2 > 48.290$

$\chi^2 = \dfrac{(n-1)s^2}{\sigma^2} = \dfrac{(26)(3.9)^2}{(3)^2} = 43.94$

Fail to reject H_0. There is not enough evidence at the 1% level of significance to reject the claim that the standard deviation of the lengths of serving times is 3 minutes.

63. $\chi_L^2 = 13.844$, $\chi_R^2 = 41.923$; Rejection regions: $\chi^2 < 13.844$, $\chi^2 > 41.923$

From Exercise 62, $\chi^2 = 43.94$.

You can reject H_0 at the 5% level of significance because $\chi^2 = 43.94 > 41.923$.

CHAPTER 7 QUIZ SOLUTIONS

1. (a) $H_0 : \mu \geq 170$ (claim); $H_a : \mu < 170$

(b) One-tailed because the alternative hypothesis contains $<$; z-test because $n > 30$.

(c) $z_0 = -1.88$; Rejection region: $z < -1.88$

(d) $z = \dfrac{\bar{x} - \mu}{\frac{s}{\sqrt{n}}} = \dfrac{168.5 - 170}{\frac{11}{\sqrt{360}}} \approx -2.59$

(e) Reject H_0.

(f) There is enough evidence at the 3% level of significance to reject the claim that the mean consumption of vegetables and melons by people in the United States is at least 170 pounds per person.

2. (a) $H_0 : \mu \geq 7.25$ (claim); $H_a : \mu < 7.25$

(b) One-tailed because the alternative hypothesis contains $<$; t-test because $n < 30$, σ is unknown, and the population is normally distributed.

(c) $t_0 = -1.796$; Rejection region: $t < -1.796$

(d) $t = \dfrac{\bar{x} - \mu}{\frac{s}{\sqrt{n}}} = \dfrac{7.15 - 7.25}{\frac{0.27}{\sqrt{12}}} \approx -1.283$

(e) Fail to reject H_0.

(f) There is not enough evidence at the 5% level of significance to reject the claim that the mean hat size for a male is at least 7.25 inches.

3. (a) $H_0: p \leq 0.10$ (claim); $H_a: p > 0.10$

    (b) One-tailed because the alternative hypothesis contains $>$; z-test because $np > 5$ and $nq > 5$.

    (c) $z_0 = 1.75$; Rejection region: $z > 1.75$

    (d) $z = \dfrac{\hat{p} - p}{\sqrt{\dfrac{pq}{n}}} = \dfrac{0.13 - 0.10}{\sqrt{\dfrac{(0.10)(0.90)}{57}}} \approx 0.75$

    (e) Fail to reject H_0.

    (f) There is not enough evidence at the 4% level of significance to reject the claim that no more than 10% of microwaves need repair during the first 5 years of use.

4. (a) $H_0: \sigma = 112$ (claim); $H_a: \sigma \neq 112$

    (b) Two-tailed because the alternative hypothesis contains $\neq$; χ^2-test because the test is for a standard deviation and the population is normally distributed.

    (c) $\chi^2_L = 9.390$, $\chi^2_R = 28.869$; Rejection regions: $\chi^2 < 9.390$, $\chi^2 > 28.869$

    (d) $\chi^2 = \dfrac{(n-1)s^2}{\sigma^2} = \dfrac{(18)(143)^2}{(112)^2} \approx 29.343$

    (e) Reject H_0.

    (f) There is enough evidence at the 10% level of significance to reject the claim that the standard deviation of SAT critical reading test scores is 112.

5. (a) $H_0: \mu = \$62,569$ (claim); $H_a: \mu \neq \$62,569$

    (b) Two-tailed because the alternative hypothesis contains $\neq$; t-test because $n < 30$, σ is unknown, and the population is normally distributed.

    (c) Not necessary

    (d) $t = \dfrac{\bar{x} - \mu}{\dfrac{s}{\sqrt{n}}} = \dfrac{59,231 - 62,569}{\dfrac{5945}{\sqrt{15}}} \approx -2.175$

    P-value = 2{Area to left of $t = -2.175$} = 2(0.02365) = 0.0473

    (e) Reject H_0.

    (f) There is enough evidence at the 5% level of significance to reject the claim that the mean income for full-time workers ages 25 to 34 with a master's degree is $62,569.

6. (a) $H_0: \mu = \$201$ (claim); $H_a: \mu \neq \$201$

    (b) Two-tailed because the alternative hypothesis contains $\neq$; z-test because $n \geq 30$.

    (c) Not necessary

    (d) $z = \dfrac{\bar{x} - \mu}{\dfrac{s}{\sqrt{n}}} = \dfrac{216 - 201}{\dfrac{30}{\sqrt{35}}} \approx 2.958$

    P-value = 2{Area right of $z = 2.958$} = 2(0.0015) = 0.0030

    (e) Reject H_0.

    (f) There is enough evidence at the 5% level of significance to reject the claim that the mean daily cost of meals and lodging for a family of 4 traveling in Kansas is $201.

Hypothesis Testing with Two Samples

8.1 TESTING THE DIFFERENCE BETWEEN MEANS (LARGE INDEPENDENT SAMPLES)

8.1 Try It Yourself Solutions

Note: Answers may differ due to rounding.

1a. (1) Independent
   (2) Dependent
   b. (1) Because each sample represents blood pressures of different individuals, and it is not possible to form a pairing between the members of the samples.
   (2) Because the samples represent exam scores of the same students, the samples can be paired with respect to each student.

2. The claim is "there is a difference in the mean annual wages for forensic science technicians working for local and state governments."
   a. $H_0 : \mu_1 = \mu_2$; $H_a : \mu_1 \neq \mu_2$ (claim)
   b, $\alpha = 0.10$
   c. $z_0 = 1.645$; Rejection regions: $z > 1.645$, $z < -1.645$
   d. $z = \dfrac{(\bar{x}_1 - \bar{x}_2) - (\mu_1 - \mu_2)}{\sqrt{\dfrac{s_1^2}{n_1} + \dfrac{s_2^2}{n_2}}} = \dfrac{(53{,}000 - 51{,}910) - (0)}{\sqrt{\dfrac{(6200)^2}{100} + \dfrac{(5575)^2}{100}}} \approx 1.667$

   e. Reject H_0.
   f. There is enough evidence at the 10% level of significance to support the claim that there is a difference in the mean annual wages for forensic science technicians working for local and state governments.

3a. $z = \dfrac{(\bar{x}_1 - \bar{x}_2) - (\mu_1 - \mu_2)}{\sqrt{\dfrac{s_1^2}{n_1} + \dfrac{s_2^2}{n_2}}} = \dfrac{(274 - 271) - (0)}{\sqrt{\dfrac{(22)^2}{150} + \dfrac{(18)^2}{200}}} \approx 1.36$

   $\rightarrow$ *P*-value = {area right of $z = 1.36$} = 0.0865
   b. Fail to reject H_0.
   c. There is not enough evidence at the 5% level of significance to support the travel agency's claim that the average daily cost of meals and lodging for vacationing in Alaska is greater than the same average cost for vacationing in Colorado.

8.1 EXERCISE SOLUTIONS

1. Two samples are dependent if each member of one sample corresponds to a member of the other sample. Example: The weights of 22 people before starting an exercise program and the weights of the same 22 people 6 weeks after starting the exercise program.

    Two samples are independent if the sample selected from one population is not related to the sample from the other population. Example: The weights of 25 cats and the weights of 20 dogs.

2. State the hypotheses and identify the claim. Specify the level of significance. Find the critical values(s) and identify the rejection region(s). Find the standardized test statistic. Make a decision and interpret it in the context of the claim.

3. Use P-values.

4. (1) The samples must be randomly selected.

    (2) The samples must be independent.

    (3) $n_1 \geq 30$ and $n_2 \geq 30$, or each population must have a normal distribution with a known standard deviation.

5. Independent because different students were samples.

6. Dependent because the same students were sampled.

7. Dependent because the same football players were sampled.

8. Independent because different individuals were sampled.

9. Independent because different boats were sampled.

10. Dependent because the same workers were sampled,

11. Dependent because the same tire sets were sampled.

12. Dependent because the same people were sampled.

13. $H_0 : \mu_1 = \mu_2$ (claim); $H_a : \mu_1 \neq \mu_2$
    Rejection region: $z_0 < 2.575$, $z_0 > 2.575$
    (a) $\bar{x}_1 - \bar{x}_2 = 16 - 14 = 2$

    (b) $z = \dfrac{(\bar{x}_1 - \bar{x}_2) - (\mu_1 - \mu_2)}{\sqrt{\dfrac{s_1^2}{n_1} + \dfrac{s_2^2}{n_2}}} = \dfrac{(16 - 14) - (0)}{\sqrt{\dfrac{(3.4)^2}{30} + \dfrac{(1.5)^2}{30}}} \approx 2.95$

    (c) z is in the rejection region because $2.95 > 2.575$.
    (d) Reject H_0. There is enough evidence at the 1% level of significance to reject the claim.

14. $H_0 : \mu_1 \le \mu_2$; $H_a : \mu_1 > \mu_2$ (claim)

Rejection region: $z_0 > 1.28$

(a) $\bar{x}_1 - \bar{x}_2 = 500 - 495 = 5$

(b) $z = \dfrac{(\bar{x}_1 - \bar{x}_2) - (\mu_1 - \mu_2)}{\sqrt{\dfrac{s_1^2}{n_1} + \dfrac{s_2^2}{n_2}}} = \dfrac{(500 - 495) - (0)}{\sqrt{\dfrac{(40)^2}{100} + \dfrac{(15)^2}{75}}} \approx 1.15$

(c) z is not in the rejection region because $1.15 < 1.28$.

(d) Fail to reject H_0. There is not enough evidence at the 10% level of significance to support the claim.

15. $H_0 : \mu_1 \ge \mu_2$; $H_a : \mu_1 < \mu_2$ (claim)

Rejection region: $z_0 < -1.645$

(a) $\bar{x}_1 - \bar{x}_2 = 2435 - 2432 = 3$

(b) $z = \dfrac{(\bar{x}_1 - \bar{x}_2) - (\mu_1 - \mu_2)}{\sqrt{\dfrac{s_1^2}{n_1} + \dfrac{s_2^2}{n_2}}} = \dfrac{(2435 - 2432) - (0)}{\sqrt{\dfrac{(75)^2}{35} + \dfrac{(105)^2}{90}}} \approx 0.18$

(c) z is not in the rejection region because $0.18 > -1.645$.

(d) Fail to reject H_0. There is not enough evidence at the 5% level of significance to support the claim.

16. $H_0 : \mu_1 \le \mu_2$ (claim); $H_a : \mu_1 > \mu_2$

Rejection region: $z_0 > 1.88$

(a) $\bar{x}_1 - \bar{x}_2 = 5004 - 4895 = 109$

(b) $z = \dfrac{(\bar{x}_1 - \bar{x}_2) - (\mu_1 - \mu_2)}{\sqrt{\dfrac{s_1^2}{n_1} + \dfrac{s_2^2}{n_2}}} = \dfrac{(5004 - 4895) - (0)}{\sqrt{\dfrac{(136)^2}{144} + \dfrac{(215)^2}{156}}} \approx 5.29$

(c) z is in the rejection region because $5.29 > 1.88$.

(d) Reject H_0. There is enough evidence at the 3% level of significance to reject the claim.

17. $H_0 : \mu_1 \le \mu_2$; $H_a : \mu_1 > \mu_2$ (claim)

$z_0 = 2.33$; Rejection region: $z > 2.33$

$z = \dfrac{(\bar{x}_1 - \bar{x}_2) - (\mu_1 - \mu_2)}{\sqrt{\dfrac{s_1^2}{n_1} + \dfrac{s_2^2}{n_2}}} = \dfrac{(5.2 - 5.5) - (0)}{\sqrt{\dfrac{(0.2)^2}{45} + \dfrac{(0.3)^2}{37}}} \approx -5.207$

Fail to reject H_0. There is not enough evidence at the 1% level of significance to support the claim.

18. $H_0: \mu_1 = \mu_2$; $H_a: \mu_1 \neq \mu_2$ (claim)

$z_0 = \pm 1.96$; Rejection regions: $z < -1.96$, $z > 1.96$

$$z = \frac{(\bar{x}_1 - \bar{x}_2) - (\mu_1 - \mu_2)}{\sqrt{\dfrac{s_1^2}{n_1} + \dfrac{s_2^2}{n_2}}} = \frac{(52 - 45) - (0)}{\sqrt{\dfrac{(2.5)^2}{70} + \dfrac{(5.5)^2}{60}}} \approx 9.087$$

Reject H_0. There is enough evidence at the 5% level of significance to support the claim.

19. Because $z \approx 2.96 > 1.96$ and $P \approx 0.0031 < 0.05$, reject H_0.

20. Because $z \approx 1.94 < 2.33$ and $P \approx 0.0261 > 0.01$, reject H_0.

21. The claim is "the mean braking distances are different for the two types of tires."
  (a) $H_0: \mu_1 = \mu_2$; $H_a: \mu_1 \neq \mu_2$ (claim)
  (b) $z_0 = \pm 1.645$; Rejection regions: $z < -1.645$, $z > 1.645$

  (c) $z = \dfrac{(\bar{x}_1 - \bar{x}_2) - (\mu_1 - \mu_2)}{\sqrt{\dfrac{s_1^2}{n_1} + \dfrac{s_2^2}{n_2}}} = \dfrac{(42 - 45) - (0)}{\sqrt{\dfrac{(4.7)^2}{35} + \dfrac{(4.3)^2}{35}}} \approx -2.786$

  (d) Reject H_0.
  (e) There is enough evidence at the 10% level of significance to support the claim that the mean braking distances for the two types of tires.

22. The claim is "the mean braking distance for Type C is greater than the mean braking distance for Type D."
  (a) $H_0: \mu_1 \leq \mu_2$; $H_a: \mu_1 > \mu_2$ (claim)
  (b) $z_0 = 1.28$; Rejection region: $z > 1.28$

  (c) $z = \dfrac{(\bar{x}_1 - \bar{x}_2) - (\mu_1 - \mu_2)}{\sqrt{\dfrac{s_1^2}{n_1} + \dfrac{s_2^2}{n_2}}} = \dfrac{(55 - 51) - (0)}{\sqrt{\dfrac{(5.3)^2}{50} + \dfrac{(4.9)^2}{50}}} \approx 3.92$

  (d) Reject H_0.
  (e) There is enough evidence at the 10% level of significance to support the claim that the mean braking distance for Type C is greater than the mean braking distance for Type D.

23. The claim is "Region A's average wind speed is greater than Region B's."
  (a) $H_0: \mu_1 \leq \mu_2$; $H_a: \mu_1 > \mu_2$ (claim)
  (b) $z_0 > 1.645$; Rejection region: $z > 1.645$

  (c) $z = \dfrac{(\bar{x}_1 - \bar{x}_2) - (\mu_1 - \mu_2)}{\sqrt{\dfrac{s_1^2}{n_1} + \dfrac{s_2^2}{n_2}}} = \dfrac{(13.2 - 12.5) - (0)}{\sqrt{\dfrac{(2.3)^2}{60} + \dfrac{(2.7)^2}{60}}} \approx 1.53$

(d) Fail to reject H_0.

(e) There is not enough evidence at the 5% level of significance to conclude that Region A's average wind speed is greater than Region B's.

24. The claim is "the winds speeds for Region C and Region D are equal."

(a) $H_0 : \mu_1 = \mu_2$ (claim); $H_a : \mu_1 \neq \mu_2$

(b) $z_0 = \pm 2.17$; Rejection regions: $z < -2.17$, $z > 2.17$

(c) $z = \dfrac{(\bar{x}_1 - \bar{x}_2) - (\mu_1 - \mu_2)}{\sqrt{\dfrac{s_1^2}{n_1} + \dfrac{s_2^2}{n_2}}} = \dfrac{(14.0 - 15.1) - (0)}{\sqrt{\dfrac{(2.9)^2}{75} + \dfrac{(3.3)^2}{80}}} \approx -2.21$

(d) Reject H_0.

(e) There is enough evidence at the 3% level of significance to reject the claim that the wind speeds for Region C and Region D are equal.

25. The claim is "male and female high school students have equal ACT scores."

(a) $H_0 : \mu_1 = \mu_2$ (claim); $H_a : \mu_1 \neq \mu_2$

(b) $z_0 = \pm 2.575$; Rejection regions: $z < -2.575$, $z > 2.575$

(c) $z = \dfrac{(\bar{x}_1 - \bar{x}_2) - (\mu_1 - \mu_2)}{\sqrt{\dfrac{s_1^2}{n_1} + \dfrac{s_2^2}{n_2}}} = \dfrac{(21.0 - 20.8) - (0)}{\sqrt{\dfrac{(5.0)^2}{43} + \dfrac{(4.7)^2}{56}}} \approx 0.202$

(d) Fail to reject H_0.

(e) There is not enough evidence at the 1% level of significance to reject the claim that the male and female high school students have equal ACT scores.

26. The claim is "high school students in a college preparation program have higher ACT scores than those in a general program."

(a) $H_0 : \mu_1 \leq \mu_2$; $H_a : \mu_1 > \mu_2$ (claim)

(b) $z_0 = 1.28$; Rejection region: $z > 1.28$

(c) $z = \dfrac{(\bar{x}_1 - \bar{x}_2) - (\mu_1 - \mu_2)}{\sqrt{\dfrac{s_1^2}{n_1} + \dfrac{s_2^2}{n_2}}} = \dfrac{(22.2 - 20.0) - (0)}{\sqrt{\dfrac{(4.8)^2}{49} + \dfrac{(5.4)^2}{4}}} \approx 2.07$

(d) Reject H_0.

(e) There is enough evidence at the 10% level of significance to support the claim that the ACT scores are higher for high school students in a college preparation program.

27. The claim is "the average home sales price in Dallas, Texas is the same as in Austin, Texas."

(a) $H_0 : \mu_1 = \mu_2$ (claim); $H_a : \mu_1 \neq \mu_2$

(b) $z_0 = \pm 1.645$; Rejection regions: $z < -1.645$, $z > 1.645$

(c) $z = \dfrac{(\bar{x}_1 - \bar{x}_2) - (\mu_1 - \mu_2)}{\sqrt{\dfrac{s_1^2}{n_1} + \dfrac{s_2^2}{n_2}}} = \dfrac{(240{,}993 - 249{,}237) - (0)}{\sqrt{\dfrac{(25{,}875)^2}{35} + \dfrac{(27{,}110)^2}{35}}} \approx -1.30$

(d) Fail to reject H_0.

(e) There is not enough evidence at the 10% level of significance to reject the claim that the average home sales price in Dallas, Texas is the same as in Austin, Texas.

28. The claim is "households in the United States headed by people under the age of 25 spend less on food away from home than do households headed by people ages 65–74."

    (a) $H_0 : \mu_1 \geq \mu_2; H_a : \mu_1 < \mu_2$ (claim)

    (b) $z_0 = -1.645$; Rejection region: $z < -1.645$

    (c) $z = \dfrac{(\bar{x}_1 - \bar{x}_2) - (\mu_1 - \mu_2)}{\sqrt{\dfrac{s_1^2}{n_1} + \dfrac{s_2^2}{n_2}}} = \dfrac{(1876 - 1878) - (0)}{\sqrt{\dfrac{(113)^2}{30} + \dfrac{(85)^2}{30}}} \approx -0.08$

    (d) Fail to reject H_0.

    (e) There is not enough evidence at the 5% level of significance to support the claim that households in the United States headed by people under the age of 25 spend less on food away from home than households headed by people ages 65–74.

29. The claim is "the average home sales price in Dallas, Texas is the same as in Austin, Texas."

    (a) $H_0 : \mu_1 = \mu_2$ (claim); $H_a : \mu_1 \neq \mu_2$

    (b) $z_0 = \pm 1.645$; Rejection regions: $z < -1.645$, $z > 1.645$

    (c) $z = \dfrac{(\bar{x}_1 - \bar{x}_2) - (\mu_1 - \mu_2)}{\sqrt{\dfrac{s_1^2}{n_1} + \dfrac{s_2^2}{n_2}}} = \dfrac{(247{,}245 - 239{,}150) - (0)}{\sqrt{\dfrac{(23{,}740)^2}{50} + \dfrac{(20{,}690)^2}{50}}} \approx 1.86$

    (d) Reject H_0.

    (e) There is enough evidence at the 10% level of significance to reject the claim that the average home sales price in Dallas, Texas is the same as in Austin, Texas. The new samples do lead to a different conclusion.

30. The claim is "households in the United States headed by people under the age of 25 spend less on food away from home than do households headed by people ages 65–74."

    (a) $H_0 : \mu_1 \geq \mu_2; H_a : \mu_1 < \mu_2$ (claim)

    (b) $z_0 = -1.645$; Rejection region: $z < -1.645$

    (c) $z = \dfrac{(\bar{x}_1 - \bar{x}_2) - (\mu_1 - \mu_2)}{\sqrt{\dfrac{s_1^2}{n_1} + \dfrac{s_2^2}{n_2}}} = \dfrac{(2015 - 2090) - (0)}{\sqrt{\dfrac{(124)^2}{40} + \dfrac{(111)^2}{40}}} \approx -3.19$

(d) Reject H_0.

(e) There is enough evidence at the 5% level of significance to support the claim that households in the United States headed by people under the age of 25 spend less on food away from home than households headed by people ages 55–64.
The new samples do lead to a different conclusion.

31. The claim is "children ages 6–17 spent more time watching television in 1981 than children ages 6–17 do today."

(a) $H_0 : \mu_1 \le \mu_2$; $H_a : \mu_1 > \mu_2$ (claim)

(b) $z_0 = 1.96$; Rejection region: $z > 1.96$

(c) $\bar{x}_1 \approx 2.130$, $s_1 \approx 0.490$, $n_1 = 30$

$\bar{x}_2 \approx 1.757$, $s_2 \approx 0.470$, $n_2 = 30$

$$z = \frac{(\bar{x}_1 - \bar{x}_2) - (\mu_1 - \mu_2)}{\sqrt{\dfrac{s_1^2}{n_1} + \dfrac{s_2^2}{n_2}}} = \frac{(2.130 - 1.757) - (0)}{\sqrt{\dfrac{(0.490)^2}{30} + \dfrac{(0.470)^2}{30}}} \approx 3.01$$

(d) Reject H_0.

(e) There is enough evidence at the 2.5% level of significance to support the claim that children ages 6–17 spent more time watching television in 1981 than children ages 6–17 do today.

32. The claim is "middle school boys spent less time studying in 1981 than middle school boys do today."

(a) $H_0 : \mu_1 \ge \mu_2$; $H_a : \mu_1 < \mu_2$ (claim)

(b) $z_0 = -1.88$; Rejection region: $z < -1.88$

(c) $\bar{x}_1 \approx 32.523$, $s_1 \approx 4.477$, $n_1 = 35$

$\bar{x}_2 \approx 47.989$, $s_2 \approx 4.651$, $n_2 = 35$

$$z = \frac{(\bar{x}_1 - \bar{x}_2) - (\mu_1 - \mu_2)}{\sqrt{\dfrac{s_1^2}{n_1} + \dfrac{s_2^2}{n_2}}} = \frac{(32.523 - 47.989) - (0)}{\sqrt{\dfrac{(4.477)^2}{35} + \dfrac{(4.651)^2}{35}}} \approx -14.17$$

(d) Reject H_0.

(e) There is enough evidence at the 3% level of significance to support the claim that middle school boys spent less time studying In 1981 than middle school boys do today.

33. The claim is "there is no difference in the mean washer diameter manufactured by two different methods."

(a) $H_0 : \mu_1 = \mu_2$; (claim) $H_a : \mu_1 \ne \mu_2$

(b) $z_0 = \pm 2.575$; Rejection region: $z < -2.575, z > 2.575$

(c) $\bar{x}_1 \approx 0.875$, $s_1 \approx 0.011$, $n_1 = 35$

$\bar{x}_2 \approx 0.701$, $s_2 \approx 0.011$, $n_2 = 35$

$$z = \frac{(\bar{x}_1 - \bar{x}_2) - (\mu_1 - \mu_2)}{\sqrt{\dfrac{s_1^2}{n_1} + \dfrac{s_2^2}{n_2}}} = \frac{(0.875 - 0.701) - (0)}{\sqrt{\dfrac{(0.011)^2}{35} + \dfrac{(0.011)^2}{35}}} \approx 66.172$$

(d) Reject H_0.

(e) There is enough evidence at the 1% level of significance to reject the claim that there is no difference in the mean washer diameter manufactured by two different methods.

34. The claim is "there is no difference in the mean nut diameter manufactured by two different methods."
   (a) $H_0 : \mu_1 = \mu_2$; (claim) $H_a : \mu_1 \neq \mu_2$
   (b) $z_0 \approx \pm 2.05$; Rejection region: $z < -2.05, z > 2.05$
   (c) $\bar{x}_1 = 3.337$, $s_1 \approx 0.011$, $n_1 = 40$
   $\bar{x}_2 \approx 3.500$, $s_2 \approx 0.010$, $n_2 = 40$

   $$z = \frac{(\bar{x}_1 - \bar{x}_2) - (\mu_1 - \mu_2)}{\sqrt{\dfrac{s_1^2}{n_1} + \dfrac{s_2^2}{n_2}}} = \frac{(3.337 - 3.500) - (0)}{\sqrt{\dfrac{(0.011)^2}{40} + \dfrac{(0.010)^2}{40}}} \approx -69.346$$

   (d) Reject H_0.
   (e) There is enough evidence at the 4% level of significance to reject the claim that there is no difference in the mean nut diameter manufactured by two different methods.

35. They are equivalent through algebraic manipulation of the equation.
   $\mu_1 = \mu_2 \rightarrow \mu_1 - \mu_2 = 0$

36. They are equivalent through algebraic manipulation of the inequality.
   $\mu_1 \geq \mu_2 \rightarrow \mu_1 - \mu_2 \geq 0$

37. **Hypothesis test results:**
   μ_1 : mean of population 1 (Std. Dev. = 5.4)
   μ_2 : mean of population 2 (Std. Dev. = 7.5)
   $\mu_1 - \mu_2$: mean difference
   $H_0 : \mu_1 - \mu_2 = 0$
   $H_a : \mu_1 - \mu_2 \neq 0$

Difference	n_1	n_2	Sample Mean
$\mu_1 - \mu_2$	50	45	4

Std. Err.	z-stat.	P-value
1.3539572	2.9543033	0.0031

   $P = 0.0031 < 0.01$, so reject H_0.
   There is enough evidence at the 1% level of significance to support the claim.

38. **Hypothesis test results:**
   μ_1 : mean of population 1 (Std. Dev. = 20.8)
   μ_2 : mean of population 2 (Std. Dev. = 24.6)
   $\mu_1 - \mu_2$: mean difference
   $H_0 : \mu_1 - \mu_2 = 0$
   $H_a : \mu_1 - \mu_2 > 0$

Difference	n_1	n_2	Sample Mean
$\mu_1 - \mu_2$	80	80	3.6

Std. Err.	z-stat.	P-value
3.6017356	0.9995181	0.1588

P-value $= 0.1588 > 0.10$, so fail to reject H_0.

There is not enough evidence at the 10% level of significance to support the claim.

39. Hypothesis test results:

μ_1 : mean of population 1 (Std. Dev. = 0.92)

μ_2 : mean of population 2 (Std. Dev. = 0.73)

$\mu_1 - \mu_2$: mean difference

$H_0 : \mu_1 - \mu_2 = 0$

$H_a : \mu_1 - \mu_2 < 0$

Difference	n_1	n_2	Sample Mean
$\mu_1 - \mu_2$	35	40	-0.32

Std. Err.	z-stat.	P-value
0.193663	-1.6523548	0.0492

P-value $= 0.0492 < 0.05$, so reject H_0.

There is enough evidence at the 5% level of significance to reject the claim.

40. Hypothesis test results:

μ_1 : mean of population 1 (Std. Dev. =193.8)

μ_2 : mean of population 2 (Std. Dev. = 129.25)

$\mu_1 - \mu_2$: mean difference

$H_0 : \mu_1 - \mu_2 = 0$

$H_a : \mu_1 - \mu_2 > 0$

Difference	n_1	n_2	Sample Mean
$\mu_1 - \mu_2$	100	100	44.58

Std. Err.	z-stat.	P-value
23.294636	1.9137454	0.0278

P-value $= 0.0278 < 0.03$, so reject H_0.

There is enough evidence at the 3% level of significance to reject the claim.

41. $H_0 : \mu_1 - \mu_2 = -9 \,(\text{claim}); H_a : \mu_1 - \mu_2 \neq -9$

$z_0 = \pm 2.575;$ Rejection region: $z < -2.575, z > 2.575$

$$z = \frac{(\bar{x}_1 - \bar{x}_2) - (\mu_1 - \mu_2)}{\sqrt{\dfrac{s_1^2}{n_1} + \dfrac{s_2^2}{n_2}}} = \frac{(11.5 - 20) - (-9)}{\sqrt{\dfrac{(3.8)^2}{70} + \dfrac{(6.7)^2}{65}}} \approx 0.528$$

Fail to reject H_0. There is not enough evidence at the 1% level of significance to reject the claim that children spend 9 hours a week more in day care or preschool today than in 1981.

42. $H_0 : \mu_1 - \mu_2 = -2 \,(\text{claim}); H_a : \mu_1 - \mu_2 \neq -2$

$z_0 = \pm 1.96;$ Rejection regions: $z < -1.96, z > 1.96$

$$z = \frac{(\bar{x}_1 - \bar{x}_2) - (\mu_1 - \mu_2)}{\sqrt{\dfrac{s_1^2}{n_1} + \dfrac{s_2^2}{n_2}}} = \frac{(12.95 - 15.02) - (-2)}{\sqrt{\dfrac{(4.31)^2}{48} + \dfrac{(4.99)^2}{56}}} \approx -0.077$$

Fail to reject H_0. There is not enough evidence at the 5% level of significance to reject the claim that the mean time per week children watch television is 2 hours less than children ages 9–11.

43. $H_0 : \mu_1 - \mu_2 \leq 10,000; H_a : \mu_1 - \mu_2 > 10,000 \,(\text{claim})$

$z_0 = 1.645;$ Rejection region: $z > 1.645$

$$z = \frac{(\bar{x}_1 - \bar{x}_2) - (\mu_1 - \mu_2)}{\sqrt{\dfrac{s_1^2}{n_1} + \dfrac{s_2^2}{n_2}}} = \frac{(94,980 - 80,830) - (10,000)}{\sqrt{\dfrac{(8795)^2}{42} + \dfrac{(9250)^2}{38}}} \approx 2.05$$

Reject H_0. There is enough evidence at the 5% level of significance to support the claim that the mean annual salaries of microbiologists in California and Maryland is more than $10,000.

44. $H_0 : \mu_1 - \mu_2 \leq 15,000; H_a : \mu_1 - \mu_2 > 15,000 \,(\text{claim})$

$z_0 = 1.28;$ Rejection region: $z > 1.28$

$$z = \frac{(\bar{x}_1 - \bar{x}_2) - (\mu_1 - \mu_2)}{\sqrt{\dfrac{s_1^2}{n_1} + \dfrac{s_2^2}{n_2}}} = \frac{(88,540 - 72,870) - (15,000)}{\sqrt{\dfrac{(8225)^2}{30} + \dfrac{(7640)^2}{32}}} \approx 0.33$$

Fail to reject H_0. There is not enough evidence at the 10% level of significance to support the claim that the difference in mean annual salaries is greater than $15,000.

45.
$$(\bar{x}_1 - \bar{x}_2) - z_c \sqrt{\frac{s_1^2}{n_1} + \frac{s_2^2}{n_2}} < \mu_1 - \mu_2 < (\bar{x}_1 - \bar{x}_2) + z_c \sqrt{\frac{s_1^2}{n_1} + \frac{s_2^2}{n_2}}$$

$$(123.1 - 125) - 1.96 \sqrt{\frac{(9.9)^2}{269} + \frac{(10.1)^2}{268}} < \mu_1 - \mu_2 < (123.1 - 125) + 1.96 \sqrt{\frac{(9.9)^2}{269} + \frac{(10.1)^2}{268}}$$

$$-1.9 - 1.96\sqrt{0.745} < \mu_1 - \mu_2 < -1.9 + 1.96\sqrt{0.745}$$

$$-3.6 < \mu_1 - \mu_2 < -0.2$$

46.
$$(\bar{x}_1 - \bar{x}_2) - z_c \sqrt{\frac{s_1^2}{n_1} + \frac{s_2^2}{n_2}} < \mu_1 - \mu_2 < (\bar{x}_1 - \bar{x}_2) + z_c \sqrt{\frac{s_1^2}{n_1} + \frac{s_2^2}{n_2}}$$

$$(10.3 - 8.5) - 1.96\sqrt{\frac{(1.2)^2}{140} + \frac{(1.5)^2}{127}} < \mu_1 - \mu_2 < (10.3 - 8.5) + 1.96\sqrt{\frac{(1.2)^2}{140} + \frac{(1.5)^2}{127}}$$

$$-1.8 - 1.96\sqrt{0.028} < \mu_1 - \mu_2 < 1.8 + 1.96\sqrt{0.028}$$

$$1.5 < \mu_1 - \mu_2 < 2.1$$

47. $H_0 : \mu_1 - \mu_2 \geq 0;\ H_a : \mu_1 - \mu_2 < 0$ (claim)

$z_0 = -1.645;$ Rejection region: $z < -1.645$

$$z = \frac{(\bar{x}_1 - \bar{x}_2) - (\mu_1 - \mu_2)}{\sqrt{\frac{s_1^2}{n_1} + \frac{s_2^2}{n_2}}} = \frac{(123.1 - 125) - (0)}{\sqrt{\frac{(9.9)^2}{269} + \frac{(10.1)^2}{268}}} \approx -2.20$$

Reject H_0. There is enough evidence at the 5% level of significance to support the claim. You should recommend using the DASH diet and exercise program over the traditional diet and exercise program, because the mean systolic blood pressure was significantly lower in the DASH program.

48. $H_0 : \mu_1 - \mu_2 \leq 0;\ H_a : \mu_1 - \mu_2 > 0$ (claim)

$z_0 = 1.645;$ Rejection region: $z < 1.645$

$$z = \frac{(\bar{x}_1 - \bar{x}_2) - (\mu_1 - \mu_2)}{\sqrt{\frac{s_1^2}{n_1} + \frac{s_2^2}{n_2}}} = \frac{(10.3 - 8.5) - (0)}{\sqrt{\frac{(1.2)^2}{140} + \frac{(1.5)^2}{127}}} \approx 10.76$$

Reject H_0. There is enough evidence at the 5% level of significance to support the claim. You should recommend using Irinotecan because the average number of months with no reported cancer related pain was significantly higher with fluorouracil.

49. $H_0 : \mu_1 - \mu_2 \geq 0;\ H_a : \mu_1 - \mu_2 < 0$ (claim)

The 95% CI for $\mu_1 - \mu_2$ in Exercise 45 contained only values less than zero and, as found in Exercise 47, there was enough evidence at the 5% level of significance to support the claim. If the CI for $\mu_1 - \mu_2$ contains only negative numbers you reject H_0 because the null hypothesis states that $\mu_1 - \mu_2$ is greater than or equal to zero.

50. $H_0 : \mu_1 - \mu_2 \leq 0;\ H_a : \mu_1 - \mu_2 > 0$ (claim)

The 95% CI for $\mu_1 - \mu_2$ in Exercise 46 contained only values greater than zero and, as found in Exercise 48, there was enough evidence at the 5% level of significance to support the claim. If the CI for $\mu_1 - \mu_2$ contains only positive numbers you reject H_0 because the null hypothesis states that $\mu_1 - \mu_2$ is less than or equal to zero.

8.2 TESTING THE DIFFERENCE BETWEEN MEANS (SMALL INDEPENDENT SAMPLES)

8.2 Try It Yourself Solutions

1a. The claim is "there is a difference in the mean annual earnings based on level of education."

$H_0 : \mu_1 = \mu_2; H_a : \mu_1 \neq \mu_2$ (claim)

b. $\alpha = 0.01$; d.f. $= \min\{n_1 - 1, n_2 - 1\} = \min\{15 - 1, 12 - 1\} = 11$

c. $t_0 = \pm 3.106$; Rejection regions: $t < -3.106, t > 3.106$

d. $t = \dfrac{(\bar{x}_1 - \bar{x}_2) - (\mu_1 - \mu_2)}{\sqrt{\dfrac{s_1^2}{n_1} + \dfrac{s_2^2}{n_2}}} = \dfrac{(27{,}136 - 34{,}329) - (0)}{\sqrt{\dfrac{(2318)^2}{15} + \dfrac{(4962)^2}{12}}} \approx -4.63$

e. Reject H_0.

f. There is evidence that "there is a difference in the mean annual earnings based on level of education."

2a. The claim is "the watts usage of a manufacturer's 17-inch flat panel monitors is less than that of its leading competitor."

$H_0 : \mu_1 \geq \mu_2; H_a : \mu_1 < \mu_2$ (claim)

b. $\alpha = 0.10$; d.f. $= n_1 + n_2 - 2 = 12 + 15 - 2 = 25$

c. $t_0 = -1.316$; Rejection regions: $t < -1.316$

d. $t = \dfrac{(\bar{x}_1 - \bar{x}_2) - (\mu_1 - \mu_2)}{\sqrt{\dfrac{(n-1)s_1^2 + (n_2 - 1)s_2^2}{n_1 + n_2 - 2}}\sqrt{\dfrac{1}{n_1} + \dfrac{1}{n_2}}} = \dfrac{(32 - 35) - (0)}{\sqrt{\dfrac{(12-1)(2.1)^2 + (15-1)(1.8)^2}{12 + 15 - 2}}\sqrt{\dfrac{1}{12} + \dfrac{1}{15}}} \approx -3.997$

e. Reject H_0.

f. There is enough evidence to support the claim.

8.2 EXERCISE SOLUTIONS

1. (1) The samples must be randomly selected.
   (2) The samples must be independent
   (3) Each population must have a normal distribution.

2. State hypotheses and identify the claim. Specify the level of significance. Determine the degrees of freedom. Find the critical value(s) and identify the rejection region(s). Find the standardized test statistic. Make a decision and interpret it in the context of the original claim.

3. (a) d.f. $= n_1 + n_2 - 2 = 23$
   $t_0 = \pm 1.714$
   (b) d.f. $= \min\{n_1 - 1, \ n_2 - 1\} = 10$
   $t_0 = \pm 1.812$

4. (a) d.f. $= n_1 + n_2 - 2 = 25$
   $t_0 = 2.485$
   (b) d.f. $= \min\{n_1 - 1, \ n_2 - 1\} = 11$
   $t_0 = 2.718$

5. (a) d.f. $= n_1 + n_2 - 2 = 16$
   $t_0 = -1.746$
   (b) d.f. $= \min\{n_1 - 1, \ n_2 - 1\} = 6$
   $t_0 = -1.943$

6. (a) d.f. $= n_1 + n_2 - 2 = 39$
   $t_0 = 2.575$
   (b) d.f. $= \min\{n_1 - 1, \ n_2 - 1\} = 18$
   $t_0 = \pm 2.878$

7. (a) d.f. $= n_1 + n_2 - 2 = 19$
   $t_0 = 1.729$
   (b) d.f. $= \min\{n_1 - 1, \ n_2 - 1\} = 7$
   $t_0 = 1.895$

8. (a) d.f. $= n_1 + n_2 - 2 = 11$
   $t_0 = -1.363$
   (b) d.f. $= \min\{n_1 - 1, \ n_2 - 1\} = 3$
   $t_0 = -1.638$

9. $H_0 : \mu_1 = \mu_2$ (claim); $H_a : \mu_1 \neq \mu_2$
   d.f. $= n_1 + n_2 - 2 = 27$
   Rejection regions: $t < -2.771$, $t > 2.771$
   (a) $\bar{x}_1 - \bar{x}_2 = 33.7 - 33.5 = -1.8$

   (b) $t = \dfrac{(\bar{x}_1 - \bar{x}_2) - (\mu_1 - \mu_2)}{\sqrt{\dfrac{(n-1)s_1^2 + (n_2-1)s_2^2}{n_1 + n_2 - 2}}\sqrt{\dfrac{1}{n_1} + \dfrac{1}{n_2}}} = \dfrac{(33.7 - 35.5) - (0)}{\sqrt{\dfrac{(12-1)(3.5)^2 + (17-1)(2.2)^2}{12 + 17 - 2}}\sqrt{\dfrac{1}{12} + \dfrac{1}{17}}} \approx -1.70$

   (c) t is not in the rejection region.
   (d) Fail to reject H_0.

10. $H_0 : \mu_1 \geq \mu_2$; $H_a : \mu_1 < \mu_2$ (claim)
    d.f. $= n_1 + n_2 - 2 = 18$
    Rejection region: $t < -1.33$
    (a) $\bar{x}_1 - \bar{x}_2 = 0.345 - 0.515 = -0.17$

    (b) $t = \dfrac{(\bar{x}_1 - \bar{x}_2) - (\mu_1 - \mu_2)}{\sqrt{\dfrac{(n-1)s_1^2 + (n_2-1)s_2^2}{n_1 + n_2 - 2}}\sqrt{\dfrac{1}{n_1} + \dfrac{1}{n_2}}} = \dfrac{(0.345 - 0.515) - (0)}{\sqrt{\dfrac{(11-1)(0.305)^2 + (9-1)(0.215)^2}{11 + 9 - 2}}\sqrt{\dfrac{1}{11} + \dfrac{1}{9}}} \approx -1.41$

    (c) t is in the rejection region.
    (d) Reject H_0.

11. $H_0 : \mu_1 \leq \mu_2$ (claim); $H_a : \mu_1 > \mu_2$

d.f. $= \min\{n_1 - 1, n_2 - 1\} = 9$

Rejection region: $t > 1.833$

(a) $\bar{x}_1 - \bar{x}_2 = 2410 - 2305 = 105$

(b) $t = \dfrac{(\bar{x}_1 - \bar{x}_2) - (\mu_1 - \mu_2)}{\sqrt{\dfrac{s_1^2}{n_1} + \dfrac{s_2^2}{n_2}}} = \dfrac{(2410 - 2305) - (0)}{\sqrt{\dfrac{(175)^2}{13} + \dfrac{(52)^2}{10}}} \approx 2.05$

(c) t is in the rejection region.

(d) Reject H_0.

12. $H_0 : \mu_1 \leq \mu_2$; $H_a : \mu_1 > \mu_2$ (claim)

d.f. $= \min\{n_1 - 1, n_2 - 1\} = 14$

Rejection region: $t > 2.624$

(a) $\bar{x}_1 - \bar{x}_2 = 52 - 50 = 2$

(b) $t = \dfrac{(\bar{x}_1 - \bar{x}_2) - (\mu_1 - \mu_2)}{\sqrt{\dfrac{s_1^2}{n_1} + \dfrac{s_2^2}{n_2}}} = \dfrac{(52 - 50) - (0)}{\sqrt{\dfrac{(4.8)^2}{16} + \dfrac{(1.2)^2}{14}}} \approx 1.61$

(c) t is not in the rejection region.

(d) Fail to reject H_0.

13. (a) The claim is "the mean annual costs of routine veterinarian visits for dogs and cats are the same."

$H_0 : \mu_1 = \mu_2$ (claim); $H_a : \mu_1 \neq \mu_2$

(b) d.f. $= \min\{n_1 - 1, n_2 - 1\} = 6$

$t_0 = \pm 1.943$; Rejection regions: $t < -1.943$, $t > 1.943$

(c) $t = \dfrac{(\bar{x}_1 - \bar{x}_2) - (\mu_1 - \mu_2)}{\sqrt{\dfrac{s_1^2}{n_1} + \dfrac{s_2^2}{n_2}}} = \dfrac{(225 - 203) - (0)}{\sqrt{\dfrac{(28)^2}{7} + \dfrac{(15)^2}{10}}} \approx 1.90$

(d) Fail to reject H_0.

(e) There is not enough evidence at the 10% level of significance to reject the claim that the mean annual costs of routine veterinarians visits for dogs and cats are the same.

14. (a) The claim is "athletes have a greater mean maximal oxygen consumption than non-athletes."

$H_0 : \mu_1 \leq \mu_2$; $H_a : \mu_1 > \mu_2$ (claim)

(b) d.f. $= n_1 + n_2 - 2 = 42$

$t_0 = 1.645$; Rejection region: $t > 1.645$

(c) $t = \dfrac{(\bar{x}_1 - \bar{x}_2) - (\mu_1 - \mu_2)}{\sqrt{\dfrac{(n-1)s_1^2 + (n_2-1)s_2^2}{n_1 + n_2 - 2}}\sqrt{\dfrac{1}{n_1} + \dfrac{1}{n_2}}} = \dfrac{(56 - 47) - (0)}{\sqrt{\dfrac{(23-1)(4.9)^2 + (21-1)(3.1)^2}{23 + 21 - 2}}\sqrt{\dfrac{1}{23} + \dfrac{1}{21}}} \approx 7.20$

(d) Reject H_0.

(e) There is enough evidence at the 5% level of significance to support the claim that athletes have a greater mean maximal oxygen consumption than non-athletes

15. (a) The claim is "the mean bumper repair cost is less for mini cars than for midsize cars."

  $H_0 : \mu_1 \geq \mu_2; H_a : \mu_1 < \mu_2$ (claim)

  (b) d.f. $= n_1 + n_2 - 2 = 20$

  $t_0 = -1.325$; Rejection region: $t < -1.325$

  (c) $t = \dfrac{(\bar{x}_1 - \bar{x}_2) - (\mu_1 - \mu_2)}{\sqrt{\dfrac{(n-1)s_1^2 + (n_2-1)s_2^2}{n_1 + n_2 - 2}}\sqrt{\dfrac{1}{n_1} + \dfrac{1}{n_2}}} = \dfrac{(1621 - 1895) - (0)}{\sqrt{\dfrac{(6-1)(493)^2 + (16-1)(648)^2}{6 + 16 - 2}}\sqrt{\dfrac{1}{6} + \dfrac{1}{16}}} \approx -0.9338$

  (d) Fail to reject H_0.

  (e) There is not enough evidence at the 10% level of significance to support the claim that the mean bumper repair cost is less for mini cars than for midsize cars.

16. (a) The claim is "the mean footwell instrusions for small pickups and small SUVs are equal."

  $H_0 : \mu_1 = \mu_2$ (claim); $H_a : \mu_1 \neq \mu_2$

  (b) d.f. $= n_1 + n_2 - 2 = 18$

  $t_0 = \pm 2.878$; Rejection regions: $t < -2.878, \ t > 2.878$

  (c) $t = \dfrac{(\bar{x}_1 - \bar{x}_2) - (\mu_1 - \mu_2)}{\sqrt{\dfrac{(n-1)s_1^2 + (n_2-1)s_2^2}{n_1 + n_2 - 2}}\sqrt{\dfrac{1}{n_1} + \dfrac{1}{n_2}}} = \dfrac{(11.18 - 9.52) - (0)}{\sqrt{\dfrac{(7-1)(4.53)^2 + (13-1)(3.84)^2}{7 + 13 - 2}}\sqrt{\dfrac{1}{7} + \dfrac{1}{13}}} \approx 0.87$

  (d) Fail to reject H_0.

  (e) The evidence supports the claim at the 1% level of significance that the mean footwell intrusions for small pickups and small SUVs are equal.

17. (a) The claim is "the mean household income is greater in Allegheny County than it is in Erie County."

  $H_0 : \mu_1 \leq \mu_2; H_a : \mu_1 > \mu_2$ (claim)

  (b) d.f. $= \min\{n_1 - 1, \ n_2 - 1\} = 14$

  $t_0 = 1.761$; Rejection region: $t > 1.761$

  (c) $t = \dfrac{(\bar{x}_1 - \bar{x}_2) - (0)}{\sqrt{\dfrac{s_1^2}{n_1} + \dfrac{s_2^2}{n_2}}} = \dfrac{(48,800 - 44,400) - (0)}{\sqrt{\dfrac{(8800)^2}{19} + \dfrac{(5100)^2}{15}}} \approx 1.99$

(d) Reject H_0.

(e) There is enough evidence at the 5% level of significance to support the claim that the mean household income is greater in Allegheny County than it is in Erie County.

18. (a) The claim is "the mean household income is greater in Hillsborough County than it is in Polk County."

$H_0 : \mu_1 \le \mu_2; H_a : \mu_1 > \mu_2$ (claim)

(b) d.f. $= \min\{n_1 - 1, n_2 - 1\} = 16$

$t_0 = 2.583$; Rejection region: $t > 2.583$

(c) $t = \dfrac{(\bar{x}_1 - \bar{x}_2) - (0)}{\sqrt{\dfrac{s_1^2}{n_1} + \dfrac{s_2^2}{n_2}}} = \dfrac{(49,800 - 44,400) - (0)}{\sqrt{\dfrac{(4200)^2}{17} + \dfrac{(8600)^2}{18}}} \approx 2.38$

(d) Fail to reject H_0.

(e) There is not enough evidence at the 1% level of significance to support the claim that the mean household income is greater in Hillsborough County than it is in Polk County.

19. (a) The claim is "the new treatment makes a difference in the tensile strength of steel bars."

$H_0 : \mu_1 = \mu_2; H_a : \mu_1 \ne \mu_2$ (claim)

(b) d.f. $= n_1 + n_2 - 2 = 21$

$t_0 = \pm 2.831$; Rejection regions: $t < -2.831, t > 2.831$

(c) $\bar{x}_1 = 368.3, s_1 \approx 22.301, n_1 = 10$

$\bar{x}_2 \approx 389.538, s_2 \approx 14.512, n_2 = 13$

$t = \dfrac{(\bar{x}_1 - \bar{x}_2) - (\mu_1 - \mu_2)}{\sqrt{\dfrac{(n-1)s_1^2 + (n_2 - 1)s_2^2}{n_1 + n_2 - 2}}\sqrt{\dfrac{1}{n_1} + \dfrac{1}{n_2}}} \approx \dfrac{(368.3 - 389.538) - (0)}{\sqrt{\dfrac{(10-1)(22.301)^2 + (13-1)(14.512)^2}{10+13-2}}\sqrt{\dfrac{1}{10} + \dfrac{1}{13}}} \approx -2.76$

(d) Fail to reject H_0.

(e) There is not enough evidence at the 1% level of significance to support the claim that the new treatment makes a difference in the tensile strength of steel bars.

20. (a) The claim is "the experimental method produces steel with greater mean tensile strength."

$H_0 : \mu_1 \le \mu_2; H_a : \mu_1 > \mu_2$ (claim)

(b) d.f. $= \min\{n_1 - 1, n_2 - 1\} = 13$

$t_0 = 1.350$; Rejection region: $t > 1.350$

(c) $\bar{x}_1 \approx 402,765, s_1 \approx 11.344, n_1 = 17$

$\bar{x}_2 \approx 384, s_2 \approx 17.698, n_2 = 14$

$t = \dfrac{(\bar{x}_1 - \bar{x}_2) - (\mu_1 - \mu_2)}{\sqrt{\dfrac{s_1^2}{n_1} + \dfrac{s_2^2}{n_2}}} \approx \dfrac{(402.765 - 384) - (0)}{\sqrt{\dfrac{(11.344)^2}{17} + \dfrac{(17.698)^2}{14}}} \approx 3.429$

(d) Reject H_0.

(e) There is enough evidence at the 10% level of significance to support the claim that the experimental method produces steel with greater mean tensile strength and to recommend using the experimental method.

21. (a) The claim is "the new method of teaching reading produces higher reading test scores than the old method"

$H_0 : \mu_1 \geq \mu_2 ; H_a : \mu_1 < \mu_2$ (claim)

(b) d.f. $= n_1 + n_2 - 2 = 42$

$t_0 = -1.282$; Rejection region: $t < -1.282$

(c) $\bar{x}_1 \approx 56.684$, $s_1 \approx 6.961$, $n_1 = 19$

$\bar{x}_2 \approx 67.4$, $s_2 \approx 9.014$, $n_2 = 25$

$$ t = \frac{(\bar{x}_1 - \bar{x}_2) - (\mu_1 - \mu_2)}{\sqrt{\dfrac{(n-1)s_1^2 + (n_2 - 1)s_2^2}{n_1 + n_2 - 2}} \sqrt{\dfrac{1}{n_1} + \dfrac{1}{n_2}}} \approx \frac{(56.684 - 67.4) - (0)}{\sqrt{\dfrac{(19-1)(6.961)^2 + (25-1)(9.014)^2}{19 + 25 - 2}} \sqrt{\dfrac{1}{19} + \dfrac{1}{25}}} \approx -4.295 $$

(d) Reject H_0.

(e) There is enough evidence at the 10% level of significance to support the claim that the new method of teaching reading produces higher reading test scores than the old method.

22. (a) The claim is "the mean science test score is lower for students taught using the traditional lab method than it is for students taught using the interactive simulation software."

$H_0 : \mu_1 \geq \mu_2 ; H_a : \mu_1 < \mu_2$ (claim)

(b) d.f. $= n_1 + n_2 - 2 = 39$

$t_0 = -1.645$; Rejection region: $t < -1.645$

(c) $\bar{x}_1 \approx 79.091$, $s_1 \approx 6.900$, $n_1 = 22$

$\bar{x}_2 \approx 83$, $s_2 \approx 7.645$, $n_2 = 19$

$$ t = \frac{(\bar{x}_1 - \bar{x}_2) - (\mu_1 - \mu_2)}{\sqrt{\dfrac{(n-1)s_1^2 + (n_2 - 1)s_2^2}{n_1 + n_2 - 2}} \sqrt{\dfrac{1}{n_1} + \dfrac{1}{n_2}}} \approx \frac{(79.091 - 83) - (0)}{\sqrt{\dfrac{(22-1)(6.900)^2 + (19-1)(7.645)^2}{22 + 19 - 2}} \sqrt{\dfrac{1}{22} + \dfrac{1}{19}}} \approx -1.721 $$

(d) Reject H_0.

(e) There is enough evidence at the 5% level of significance to support the claim that the mean science test score is lower for students taught using the traditional lab method than it is for students taught using the interactive simulation software.

23. Hypothesis test results:

μ_1 : mean of population 1

μ_2 : mean of population 2

$\mu_1 - \mu_2$: mean difference

$H_0 : \mu_1 - \mu_2 = 0$

$H_a : \mu_1 - \mu_2 > 0$

Difference	Sample Mean	Std. Err.
$\mu_1 - \mu_2$	−8	16.985794

DF	T-stat.	P-value
22	−0.47098184	0.6789

$P = 0.6789 > 0.10$, so fail to reject H_0.

There is not enough evidence at the 10% level of significance to support the claim.

24. Hypothesis test results:

μ_1 : mean of population 1

μ_2 : mean of population 2

$\mu_1 - \mu_2$: mean difference

$H_0 : \mu_1 - \mu_2 = 0$

$H_a : \mu_1 - \mu_2 \neq 0$

(with pooled variances)

Difference	Sample Mean	Std. Err.
$\mu_1 - \mu_2$	−11	2.889967

DF	T-stat.	P-value
11	−3.8062718	0.0029

$P = 0.0029 < 0.01$, so reject H_0.

There is enough evidence at the 1% level of significance to support the claim.

25. Hypothesis test results:

μ_1 : mean of population 1

μ_2 : mean of population 2

$\mu_1 - \mu_2$: mean difference

$H_0 : \mu_1 - \mu_2 = 0$

$H_a : \mu_1 - \mu_2 < 0$

(without pooled variances)

Difference	Sample Mean	Std. Err.
$\mu_1 - \mu_2$	–43	28.12301

DF	T-stat.	P-value
18.990595	–1.5289971	0.0714

$P = 0.0714 > 0.05$, so fail to reject H_0.

There is enough evidence at the 5% level of significance to support the claim.

26. Hypothesis test results:

μ_1 : mean of population 1

μ_2 : mean of population 2

$\mu_1 - \mu_2$: mean difference

$H_0 : \mu_1 - \mu_2 = 0$

$H_a : \mu_1 - \mu_2 \neq 0$

(without pooled variances)

Difference	Sample Mean	Std. Err.
$\mu_1 - \mu_2$	22.4	8.114349

DF	T-stat.	P-value
6.2159977	2.7605417	0.0317

$P = 0.0317 < 0.10$, so reject H_0.

There is not enough evidence at the 10% level of significance to reject the claim.

27. $\sigma = \sqrt{\dfrac{(n-1)s_1^2 + (n_2-1)s_2^2}{n_1 + n_2 - 2}} = \sqrt{\dfrac{(21-1)(166)^2 + (11-1)(204)^2}{21+11-2}} \approx 179.56$

$(\bar{x}_1 - \bar{x}_2) \pm t_c \hat{\sigma}\sqrt{\dfrac{1}{n_1} + \dfrac{1}{n_2}} \rightarrow (1805 - 1629) \pm 1.96 \cdot 179.56\sqrt{\dfrac{1}{21} + \dfrac{1}{11}}$

$\rightarrow 176 \pm 130.99 \rightarrow 45.01 < \mu_1 - \mu_2 < 306.99 \rightarrow 45 < \mu_1 - \mu_2 < 307$

28. $\sigma = \sqrt{\dfrac{(n-1)s_1^2 + (n_2-1)s_2^2}{n_1 + n_2 - 2}} = \sqrt{\dfrac{(26-1)(8.5)^2 + (24-1)(11.5)^2}{26 + 24 - 2}} \approx 10.050$

$(\bar{x}_1 - \bar{x}_2) \pm t_c \hat{\sigma} \sqrt{\dfrac{1}{n_1} + \dfrac{1}{n_2}} \rightarrow (171-169) \pm 2.576 \cdot 10.050 \sqrt{\dfrac{1}{26} + \dfrac{1}{24}}$

$\rightarrow 2 \pm 7.328 \rightarrow -5.328 < \mu_1 - \mu_2 < 9.338 \rightarrow -5 < \mu_1 - \mu_2 < 9$

29. $(\bar{x}_1 - \bar{x}_2) \pm t_c \sqrt{\dfrac{s_1^2}{n_1} + \dfrac{s_2^2}{n_2}} \rightarrow (267-244) \pm 2.132 \sqrt{\dfrac{(6)^2}{9} + \dfrac{(12)^2}{5}}$

$\rightarrow 23 \pm 12.21 \rightarrow 10.78 < \mu_1 - \mu_2 < 35.21 \rightarrow 11 < \mu_1 - \mu_2 < 35$

30. $(\bar{x}_1 - \bar{x}_2) \pm t_c \sqrt{\dfrac{s_1^2}{n_1} + \dfrac{s_2^2}{n_2}} \rightarrow (56.0 - 16.9) \pm 2.201 \sqrt{\dfrac{(8.6)^2}{20} + \dfrac{(3.8)^2}{12}}$

$\rightarrow 39.1 \pm 4.873 \rightarrow 34.227 < \mu_1 - \mu_2 < 43.973 \rightarrow 34 < \mu_1 - \mu_2 < 44$

8.3 TESTING THE DIFFERENCE BETWEEN MEANS (DEPENDENT SAMPLES)

8.3 Try It Yourself Solutions

1a. The claim is "athletes can decrease their times in the 40-yard dash."

$H_0 : \mu_d \leq 0; H_a : \mu_d > 0$ (claim)

b. $\alpha = 0.05$ d.f. $= n - 1 = 11$

c. $t_0 = 1.796$; Rejection region: $t > 1.796$

d.

Before	After	d	d^2
4.85	4.78	0.07	0.0049
4.90	4.90	0.00	0.0000
5.08	5.05	0.03	0.0009
4.72	4.65	0.07	0.0049
4.62	4.64	−0.02	0.0004
4.54	4.50	0.04	0.0016
5.25	5.24	0.01	0.0001
5.18	5.27	−0.09	0.0081
4.81	4.75	0.06	0.0036
4.57	4.43	0.14	0.0196
4.63	4.61	0.02	0.0004
4.77	4.82	−0.05	0.0025
		$\sum d = 0.28$	$\sum d^2 = 0.047$

$\bar{d} = \dfrac{\sum d}{n} = \dfrac{0.28}{12} \approx 0.0233$

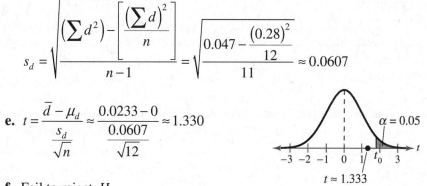

$$s_d = \sqrt{\frac{\left(\sum d^2\right) - \left[\frac{\left(\sum d\right)^2}{n}\right]}{n-1}} = \sqrt{\frac{0.047 - \frac{(0.28)^2}{12}}{11}} \approx 0.0607$$

e. $t = \dfrac{\bar{d} - \mu_d}{\frac{s_d}{\sqrt{n}}} \approx \dfrac{0.0233 - 0}{\frac{0.0607}{\sqrt{12}}} \approx 1.330$

$t \approx 1.333$

f. Fail to reject H_0.

g. There is not enough evidence at the 5% level of significance to support the claim that athletes can decrease their times in the 40-yard dash using new strength shoes.

2a. The claim is "the drug changes the body's temperature."

   $H_0 : \mu_d = 0; \; H_a : \mu_d \neq 0$ (claim)

b. $\alpha = 0.05$ d.f. $= n - 1 = 6$

c. $t_0 = \pm 2.447$; Rejection region: $t < -2.447$, $t > 2.447$

d.

Before	After	d	d^2
101.8	99.2	2.6	6.76
98.5	98.4	0.1	0.01
98.1	98.2	−0.1	0.01
99.4	99	0.4	0.16
98.9	98.6	0.3	0.09
100.2	99.7	0.5	0.25
97.9	97.8	0.1	0.01
		$\sum d = 3.9$	$\sum d^2 = 7.29$

$$\bar{d} = \frac{\sum d}{n} = \frac{3.9}{7} \approx 0.5771$$

$$s_d = \sqrt{\frac{\sum d^2 - \left[\frac{\left(\sum d\right)^2}{n}\right]}{n-1}} = \sqrt{\frac{7.29 - \frac{(3.9)^2}{7}}{6}} \approx 0.9235$$

e. $t = \dfrac{\bar{d} - \mu_d}{\frac{s_d}{\sqrt{n}}} \approx \dfrac{0.5571 - 0}{\frac{0.9235}{\sqrt{7}}} \approx 1.596$

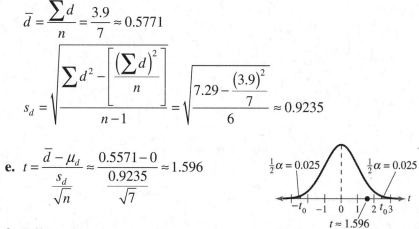

$\frac{1}{2}\alpha = 0.025$ $\frac{1}{2}\alpha = 0.025$

$t \approx 1.596$

f. Fail to reject H_0.

g. There is not enough evidence at the 5% level of significance to conclude that the drug changes the body's temperature.

8.3 EXERCISE SOLUTIONS

1. (1) Each sample must be randomly selected.
    (2) Each member of the first sample must be paired with a member of the second sample.
    (3) Each population should be normally distributed.

2. The symbol $\bar{d}$ represents the mean of the differences between the paired data entries in dependent samples. The symbol s_d represents the standard deviation of the differences between the paired data entries in the dependent samples.

3. $H_0 : \mu_d \geq 0; H_a : \mu_d < 0$ (claim)

    $\alpha = 0.05$ and d.f. $= n - 1 = 13$

    $t_0 = -1.771$ (left-tailed); Rejection region: $t < -1.771$

    $$t = \frac{\bar{d} - \mu_d}{\frac{s_d}{\sqrt{n}}} = \frac{1.5 - 0}{\frac{3.2}{\sqrt{14}}} \approx 1.754$$

    Fail to reject H_0.

4. $H_0 : \mu_d = 0$ (claim); $H_a : \mu_d \neq 0$

    $\alpha = 0.01$ and d.f. $= n - 1 = 7$

    $t_0 = \pm 3.499$ (Two-tailed); Rejection regions: $t < -3.499, t > 3.499$

    $$t = \frac{\bar{d} - \mu_d}{\frac{s_d}{\sqrt{n}}} = \frac{3.2 - 0}{\frac{8.45}{\sqrt{8}}} \approx 1.071$$

    Fail to reject H_0.

5. $H_0 : \mu_d \leq 0$ (claim); $H_a : \mu_d > 0$

    $\alpha = 0.10$ and d.f. $= n - 1 = 15$

    $t_0 = 1.341$ (Right-tailed); Rejection region: $t > 1.341$

    $$t = \frac{\bar{d} - \mu_d}{\frac{s_d}{\sqrt{n}}} = \frac{6.5 - 0}{\frac{9.54}{\sqrt{16}}} \approx 2.725$$

    Reject H_0.

6. $H_0 : \mu_d \leq 0; H_a : \mu_d > 0$ (claim)

$\alpha = 0.05$ and d.f. $= n - 1 = 27$

$t_0 = 1.703$ (Right-tailed); Rejection region: $t > 1.703$

$$t = \frac{\overline{d} - \mu_d}{\frac{s_d}{\sqrt{n}}} = \frac{0.55 - 0}{\frac{0.99}{\sqrt{28}}} \approx 2.940$$

Reject H_0.

7. $H_0 : \mu_d \geq 0$ (claim); $H_a : \mu_d < 0$

$\alpha = 0.01$ and d.f. $= n - 1 = 14$

$t_0 = -2.624$ (Left-tailed); Rejection region: $t < -2.624$

$$t = \frac{\overline{d} - \mu_d}{\frac{s_d}{\sqrt{n}}} = \frac{-2.3 - 0}{\frac{1.2}{\sqrt{15}}} \approx -7.423$$

Reject H_0.

8. $H_0 : \mu_d = 0; H_a : \mu_d \neq 0$ (claim)

$\alpha = 0.10$ and d.f. $= n - 1 = 19$

$t_0 = \pm 1.729$ (Two-tailed); Rejection region: $t < -1.729, t > 1.729$

$$t = \frac{\overline{d} - \mu_d}{\frac{s_d}{\sqrt{n}}} = \frac{-1 - 0}{\frac{2.75}{\sqrt{20}}} \approx -1.626$$

Fail to reject H_0.

9. (a) The claim is a "grammar seminar will help students reduce the number of grammatical errors."

   $H_0 : \mu_d \leq 0; H_a : \mu_d > 0$ (claim)

   (b) $t_0 = 3.143$; Rejection region: $t > 3.143$

   (c) $\overline{d} = 3.143$ and $s_d \approx 2.035$

   (d) $t = \frac{\overline{d} - \mu_d}{\frac{s_d}{\sqrt{n}}} = \frac{3.143 - 0}{\frac{2.035}{\sqrt{7}}} \approx 4.086$

   (e) Reject H_0.

   (f) There is enough evidence at the 1% level of significance to support the claim that grammar seminar will help students reduce the number of grammatical errors."

10. (a) The claim is "an SAT preparation course improves the test scores of students."

   $H_0 : \mu_d \geq 0; H_a : \mu_d < 0$ (claim)

   (b) $t_0 = -2.821$; Rejection region: $t < -2.821$

   (c) $\overline{d} = -59.9$ and $s_d \approx 26.831$

(d) $t = \dfrac{\bar{d} - \mu_d}{\dfrac{s_d}{\sqrt{n}}} = \dfrac{-59.9 - 0}{\dfrac{26.831}{\sqrt{10}}} \approx -7.060$

(e) Reject H_0.

(f) There is enough evidence at the 1% level of significance to support the claim that the SAT preparation course improves the test scores of students.

11. (a) The claim is "a particular exercise program will help participants lose weight after one month."

$H_0 : \mu_d \leq 0;\ H_a : \mu_d > 0$ (claim)

(b) $t_0 = 1.363$; Rejection region: $t > 1.363$

(c) $\bar{d} = 3.75$ and $s_d \approx 7.841$

(d) $t = \dfrac{\bar{d} - \mu_d}{\dfrac{s_d}{\sqrt{n}}} = \dfrac{3.75 - 0}{\dfrac{7.841}{\sqrt{12}}} \approx 1.657$

(e) Reject H_0.

(f) There is enough evidence at the 10% level of significance to support the claim that the exercise program helps participants lose weight after one month.

12. (a) The claim is "a baseball clinic will help players raise their batting average."

$H_0 : \mu_d \geq 0;\ H_a : \mu_d < 0$ (claim)

(b) $t_0 = -1.771$; Rejection region: $t < -1.771$

(c) $\bar{d} = -0.002$ and $s_d \approx 0.015$

(d) $t = \dfrac{\bar{d} - \mu_d}{\dfrac{s_d}{\sqrt{n}}} = \dfrac{-0.002 - 0}{\dfrac{0.015}{\sqrt{14}}} \approx -0.499$

(e) Fail to reject H_0.

(f) There is enough evidence at the 5% level of significance to support the claim that the baseball clinic will help players raise their batting averages.

13. (a) The claim is "soft tissue therapy and spinal manipulation help to reduce the length of time patients suffer from headaches."

$H_0 : \mu_d \leq 0;\ H_a : \mu_d > 0$ (claim)

(b) $t_0 = 2.764$; Rejection region; $t > 2.764$

(c) $\bar{d} = 1.225$ and $s_d \approx 0.441$

(d) $t = \dfrac{\bar{d} - \mu_d}{\dfrac{s_d}{\sqrt{n}}} = \dfrac{1.225 - 0}{\dfrac{0.441}{\sqrt{11}}} \approx 9.438$

(e) Reject H_0.

(f) There is enough evidence at the 1% level of significance to support the claim that soft tissue therapy and spinal manipulation help reduce the length of time patients suffer from headaches.

14. (a) The claim is "one 600-mg dose of Vitamin C will increase muscular endurance."

$H_0 : \mu_d \geq 0; H_a : \mu_d < 0$ (claim)

(b) $t_0 = -1.761$; Rejection region: $t < -1.761$

(c) $\overline{d} = 48.467$ and $s_d \approx 239.005$

(d) $t = \dfrac{\overline{d} - \mu_d}{\dfrac{s_d}{\sqrt{n}}} = \dfrac{48.467 - 0}{\dfrac{239.005}{\sqrt{15}}} \approx 0.785$

(e) Fail to eject H_0.

(f) There is not enough evidence at the 5% level of significance to support the claim that one 600-mg does of Vitamin C will increase muscular endurance.

15. (a) The claim is "the new drug reduces systolic blood pressure."

$H_0 : \mu_d \leq 0; H_a : \mu_d > 0$ (claim)

(b) $t_0 = 1.895$; Rejection region: $t > 1.895$

(c) $\overline{d} = 14.75$ and $s_d \approx 6.861$

(d) $t = \dfrac{\overline{d} - \mu_d}{\dfrac{s_d}{\sqrt{n}}} = \dfrac{14.75 - 0}{\dfrac{6.861}{\sqrt{8}}} \approx 6.081$

(e) Reject H_0.

(f) There is enough evidence at the 5% level of significance to support the claim that the new drug reduces systolic blood pressure

16. (a) The claim is "garlic can reduce the thickness of plaque buildup in arteries."

$H_0 : \mu_d \leq 0; H_a : \mu_d > 0$ (claim)

(b) $t_0 = 1.860$; Rejection region: $t > 1.860$

(c) $\overline{d} = 0.02$ and $s_d \approx 0.031$

(d) $t = \dfrac{\overline{d} - \mu_d}{\dfrac{s_d}{\sqrt{n}}} = \dfrac{0.02 - 0}{\dfrac{0.031}{\sqrt{9}}} \approx 1.935$

(e) Reject H_0.

(f) There is enough evidence at the 5% level of significance to support the claim that garlic can reduce the thickness of plaque buildup in arteries.

17. (a) The claim is "the product ratings have changed from last year to this year."

$H_0 : \mu_d = 0; H_a : \mu_d \neq 0$ (claim)

(b) $t_0 = \pm 2.365$; Rejection regions: $t < -2.365, t > 2.365$

(c) $\overline{d} = -1$ and $s_d \approx 1.309$

(d) $t = \dfrac{\overline{d} - \mu_d}{\dfrac{s_d}{\sqrt{n}}} = \dfrac{-1 - 0}{\dfrac{1.309}{\sqrt{8}}} \approx -2.161$

(e) Fail to reject H_0.

(f) There is not enough evidence at the 5% level of significance to support the claim that the product ratings have changed from last year to this year.

18. (a) The claim is "the scoring averages have changed.:
$$H_0: \mu_d = 0; H_a: \mu_d \neq 0 \text{ (claim)}$$

(b) $t_0 = \pm 1.833$; Rejection regions: $t < -1.833$, $t > 1.833$

(c) $\bar{d} = -1.28$ and $s_d \approx 3.051$

(d) $t = \dfrac{\bar{x} - \mu_d}{\dfrac{s_d}{\sqrt{n}}} = \dfrac{-1.28 - 0}{\dfrac{3.051}{\sqrt{10}}} \approx -1.327$

(e) Fail to reject H_0.

(f) There is not enough evidence at the 10% level of significance to support the claim that the scoring averages have changed.

19. Hypothesis test results:

$\mu_1 - \mu_2$: mean of the paired difference between cholesterol (before) and cholesterol (after)

$H_0: \mu_1 - \mu_2 = 0$

$H_a: \mu_1 - \mu_2 > 0$

Difference	Sample Diff.
Cholesterol (before) – Cholesterol (after)	2.857143

Std. Err.	DF	T-stat.	P-value
1.6822401	6	1.6984155	0.0702

$P = 0.0702 > 0.05$, so fail to reject H_0. There is not enough evidence at the 5% level of significance to support the claim that the new cereal lowers total blood cholesterol levels.

20. Hypothesis test results:

$\mu_1 - \mu_2$: mean of the paired difference between time (beginning) and time (end)

$H_0: \mu_1 - \mu_2 = 0$

$H_a: \mu_1 - \mu_2 \neq 0$

Difference	Sample Diff.
Time (beginning) – Time (end)	8.2375

Std. Err.	DF	T-stat.	P-value
1.8464191	7	4.461338	0.0029

$P = 0.0029 < 0.01$, so reject H_0. There is enough evidence at the 1% level of significance to support the claim that the contestants' times have changed.

21. Yes; $P \approx 0.0003 < 0.05$, so you reject H_0.

22. Yes; $P \approx 0.2173 > 0.10$, so you fail to reject H_0.

23. $\bar{d} \approx -1.525$ and $s_d \approx 0.542$

$$\bar{d} - t_{\alpha/2}\frac{s_d}{\sqrt{n}} < \mu_d < \bar{d} - t_{\alpha/2}\frac{s_d}{\sqrt{n}}$$

$$-1.525 - 1.753\left(\frac{0.542}{\sqrt{16}}\right) < \mu_d < -1.525 + 1.753\left(\frac{0.542}{\sqrt{16}}\right)$$

$$-1.525 - 0.238 < \mu_d < -1.525 + 0.238$$

$$-1.76 < \mu_d < -1.29$$

24. $\bar{d} \approx -0.436$ and $s_d \approx 0.677$

$$\bar{d} - t_{\alpha/2}\frac{s_d}{\sqrt{n}} < \mu_d < \bar{d} - t_{\alpha/2}\frac{s_d}{\sqrt{n}}$$

$$-0.436 - 2.160\left(\frac{0.677}{\sqrt{14}}\right) < \mu_d < -0.436 + 2.160\left(\frac{0.677}{\sqrt{14}}\right)$$

$$-0.436 - 0.391 < \mu_d < -0.436 + 0.391$$

$$-0.83 < \mu_d < -0.05$$

8.4 TESTING THE DIFFERENCE BETWEEN PROPORTIONS

8.4 Try It Yourself Solutions

1a. The claim is "there is a difference between the proportion of male high school students who smoke cigarettes and the proportion of female high school students who smoke cigarettes.

$H_0 : p_1 = p_2;\ H_a : p_1 \neq p_2$ (claim)

b. $\alpha = 0.05$

c. $z_0 = \pm 1.96$; Rejection region: $z < -1.96$, $z > 1.96$

d. $\bar{p} = \dfrac{x_1 + x_2}{n_1 + n_2} == \dfrac{1484 + 1378}{7000 + 7489} \approx 0.1975$

$\bar{q} \approx 0.8025$

e. $n_1\bar{p} \approx 1382.5 > 5$, $n_1\bar{q} \approx 5617.5 > 5$, $n_2\bar{p} \approx 1479.0775 > 5$, and $n_2\bar{q} \approx 6009.9225 > 5$.

f. $z = \dfrac{(\hat{p}_1 - \hat{p}_2) - (p_1 - p_2)}{\sqrt{\bar{p}\bar{q}\left(\dfrac{1}{n_1} + \dfrac{1}{n_2}\right)}} = \dfrac{(0.212 - 0.184) - (0)}{\sqrt{0.1975 \cdot 0.8025\left(\dfrac{1}{7000} + \dfrac{1}{7489}\right)}} \approx 4.23$

g. Reject H_0.

h. There is enough evidence at the 5% level of significance to support the claim that there is a difference between the proportion of male high school students who smoke cigarettes and the proportion of female high school students who smoke cigarettes.

2a. The claim is "the proportion of male high school students who smoke cigars is greater than the proportion of female high school students who smoke cigars."

$H_0 : p_1 \leq p_2$; $H_a : p_1 > p_2$ (claim)

b. $\alpha = 0.05$

c. $z_0 = 1.645$; Rejection region: $z > 1.645$

d. $\bar{p} = \dfrac{x_1 + x_2}{n_1 + n_2} == \dfrac{1162 + 539}{7000 + 7489} \approx 0.1174$

$\bar{q} \approx 0.8826$

e. $n_1 \bar{p} \approx 821.8 > 5$, $n_1 \bar{q} \approx 6178.2 > 5$, $n_2 \bar{p} \approx 879.2086 > 5$, and $n_2 \bar{q} \approx 6609.7914 > 5$.

f. $z = \dfrac{(\hat{p}_1 - \hat{p}_2) - (p_1 - p_2)}{\sqrt{\bar{p}\bar{q}\left(\dfrac{1}{n_1} + \dfrac{1}{n_2}\right)}} = \dfrac{(0.166 - 0.072) - (0)}{\sqrt{0.1174 \cdot 0.8826\left(\dfrac{1}{7000} + \dfrac{1}{7489}\right)}} \approx 17.565$

$\alpha = 0.05$

$z \approx 17.565$

g. Reject H_0.

h. There is enough evidence at the 5% level of significance to support the claim that the proportion of male high school students who smoke cigars is greater than the proportion of female high school students who smoke cigars.

8.4 EXERCISE SOLUTIONS

1. (1) The samples must be randomly selected.
   (2) The samples must be independent.
   (3) $n_1 \bar{p} \geq 5$, $n_1 \bar{q} \geq 5$, $n_2 \bar{p} \geq 5$, $n_2 \bar{q} \geq 5$

2. State the hypotheses and identify the claim. Specify the level of significance. Find the critical value(s) and rejection region(s). Find $\bar{p}$ and $\bar{q}$. Find the standardized test statistic. Make a decision and interpret it in the context of the claim.

3. $H_0 : p_1 = p_2$; $H_a : p_1 \neq p_2$ (claim)

   $z_0 = \pm 2.575$; Rejection regions: $z < -2.575$, $z > 2.575$

   $$\bar{p} = \frac{x_1 + x_2}{n_1 + n_2} = \frac{35 + 36}{70 + 60} \approx 0.546$$

   $\bar{q} \approx 0.454$

   $n_1 \bar{p} \approx 38.22 > 5$, $n_1 \bar{q} \approx 31.78 > 5$, $n_2 \bar{p} \approx 32.76 > 5$, and $n_2 \bar{q} \approx 27.24 > 5$.

   Can use normal sampling distribution.

   $$z = \frac{(\hat{p}_1 - \hat{p}_2) - (p_1 - p_2)}{\sqrt{\bar{p}\bar{q}\left(\dfrac{1}{n_1} + \dfrac{1}{n_2}\right)}} = \frac{(0.5 - 0.6) - (0)}{\sqrt{0.546 \cdot 0.454\left(\dfrac{1}{70} + \dfrac{1}{60}\right)}} \approx -1.142$$

   Fail to reject H_0.

4. $H_0 : p_1 \geq p_2$; $H_a : p_1 < p_2$ (claim)

   $z_0 = -1.645$; Rejection region: $z < -1.645$

   $$\bar{p} = \frac{x_1 + x_2}{n_1 + n_2} = \frac{471 + 372}{785 + 465} \approx 0.6744$$

   $\bar{q} \approx 0.3256$

   $n_1 \bar{p} \approx 529.404 > 5$, $n_1 \bar{q} \approx 255.596 > 5$, $n_2 \bar{p} \approx 313.596 > 5$, and $n_2 \bar{q} \approx 151.404 > 5$.

   Can use normal sampling distribution.

   $$z = \frac{(\hat{p}_1 - \hat{p}_2) - (p_1 - p_2)}{\sqrt{\bar{p}\bar{q}\left(\dfrac{1}{n_1} + \dfrac{1}{n_2}\right)}} = \frac{(0.600 - 0.800) - (0)}{\sqrt{0.6744 \cdot 0.3256\left(\dfrac{1}{785} + \dfrac{1}{465}\right)}} \approx -7.293$$

   Reject H_0.

5. $H_0 : p_1 = p_2$ (claim); $H_a : p_1 \neq p_2$

   $z_0 = \pm 1.645$; Rejection regions: $z < -1.645$, $z > 1.645$

   $$\bar{p} = \frac{x_1 + x_2}{n_1 + n_2} = \frac{42 + 76}{150 + 200} \approx 0.337$$

   $\bar{q} \approx 0.663$

   $n_1 \bar{p} \approx 50.55 > 5$, $n_1 \bar{q} \approx 99.45 > 5$, $n_2 \bar{p} \approx 67.4 > 5$, and $n_2 \bar{q} \approx 132.6 > 5$.

   Can use normal sampling distribution.

$$z = \frac{(\hat{p}_1 - \hat{p}_2) - (p_1 - p_2)}{\sqrt{\overline{pq}\left(\dfrac{1}{n_1} + \dfrac{1}{n_2}\right)}} = \frac{(0.28 - 0.38) - (0)}{\sqrt{(0.337)(0.663)\left(\dfrac{1}{150} + \dfrac{1}{200}\right)}} \approx -1.96$$

Reject H_0.

6. $H_0 : p_1 \le p_2$; $H_a : p_1 > p_2$ (claim)

   $z_0 = 2.33$; Rejection region: $z > 2.33$

   $$\overline{p} = \frac{x_1 + x_2}{n_1 + n_2} = \frac{6 + 4}{20 + 30} \approx 0.2$$

   $\overline{q} \approx 0.8$

   Because $n_1 \overline{p} = 4 < 5$, cannot use normal sampling distribution.

7. $H_0 : p_1 \le p_2$ (claim); $H_a : p_1 > p_2$

   $z_0 = 1.28$; Rejection region: $z > 1.28$

   $$\overline{p} = \frac{x_1 + x_2}{n_1 + n_2} = \frac{344 + 304}{860 + 800} \approx 0.390$$

   $\overline{q} \approx 0.610$

   $n_1 \overline{p} \approx 335.4 > 5$, $n_1 \overline{q} \approx 524.6 > 5$, $n_2 \overline{p} \approx 312 > 5$, and $n_2 \overline{q} \approx 488 > 5$.

   Can use normal sampling distribution.

   $$z = \frac{(\hat{p}_1 - \hat{p}_2) - (p_1 - p_2)}{\sqrt{\overline{pq}\left(\dfrac{1}{n_1} + \dfrac{1}{n_2}\right)}} = \frac{(0.400 - 0.380) - (0)}{\sqrt{(0.390)(0.610)\left(\dfrac{1}{860} + \dfrac{1}{800}\right)}} \approx 0.835$$

   Fail to reject H_0.

8. $H_0 : p_1 = p_2$ (claim); $H_a : p_1 \ne p_2$

   $z_0 = \pm 1.96$; Rejection regions: $z < -1.96$, $z > 1.96$

   $$\overline{p} = \frac{x_1 + x_2}{n_1 + n_2} = \frac{29 + 25}{45 + 30} \approx 0.72$$

   $\overline{q} \approx 0.28$

   $n_1 \overline{p} \approx 32.4 > 5$, $n_1 \overline{q} \approx 12.6 > 5$, $n_2 \overline{p} \approx 21.6 > 5$, and $n_2 \overline{q} \approx 8.4 > 5$.

   Can use normal sampling distribution.

$$z = \frac{(\hat{p}_1 - \hat{p}_2) - (p_1 - p_2)}{\sqrt{\overline{pq}\left(\dfrac{1}{n_1} + \dfrac{1}{n_2}\right)}} = \frac{(0.644 - 0.833) - (0)}{\sqrt{(0.72)(0.28)\left(\dfrac{1}{45} + \dfrac{1}{30}\right)}} \approx -1.786$$

Fail to reject H_0.

9a. The claim is "there is a difference in the proportion of subjects who feel all or mostly better after 4 weeks between subjects who used magnetic insoles and subjects who used nonmagnetic insoles."

$H_0 : p_1 = p_2$ (claim); $H_a : p_1 \neq p_2$

b. $z_0 = 2.575$; Rejection regions: $z < -2.575$; $z > 2.575$

c. $\overline{p} = \dfrac{x_1 + x_2}{n_1 + n_2} = \dfrac{17 + 18}{54 + 41} \approx 0.368$

$\overline{q} \approx 0.632$

$$z = \frac{(\hat{p}_1 - \hat{p}_2) - (p_1 - p_2)}{\sqrt{\overline{pq}\left(\dfrac{1}{n_1} + \dfrac{1}{n_2}\right)}} = \frac{(0.315 - 0.439) - (0)}{\sqrt{(0.368)(0.632)\left(\dfrac{1}{54} + \dfrac{1}{41}\right)}} \approx -1.24$$

d. Fail to reject H_0.

e. There is not enough evidence at the 1% level of significance to support the claim that there is a difference in the proportion of subjects who feel all or mostly better after 4 weeks between subjects who used magnetic insoles and subjects who used nonmagnetic insoles.

10a. The claim is "the proportion of subjects who are cancer-free after one year is greater for subjects who took the drug than for subjects who took a placebo."

$H_0 : p_1 \leq p_2$; $H_a : p_1 > p_2$ (claim)

b. $z_0 = 1.28$; Rejection region: $z > 1.28$

c. $\overline{p} = \dfrac{x_1 + x_2}{n_1 + n_2} = \dfrac{291 + 249}{300 + 300} \approx 0.9$

$\overline{q} \approx 0.1$

$$z = \frac{(\hat{p}_1 - \hat{p}_2) - (p_1 - p_2)}{\sqrt{\overline{pq}\left(\dfrac{1}{n_1} + \dfrac{1}{n_2}\right)}} = \frac{(0.97 - 0.83) - (0)}{\sqrt{(0.9)(0.1)\left(\dfrac{1}{300} + \dfrac{1}{300}\right)}} \approx 5.72$$

d. Reject H_0.

e. There is enough evidence at the 10% level of significance to support the claim that the proportion of subjects who are cancer-free after one year is greater for subjects who took the drug than for subjects who took a placebo.

11a. The claim is "the proportion of males who enrolled in college is less than the proportion of females who enrolled in college."

$$H_0 : p_1 \geq p_2; \quad H_a : p_1 < p_2 \text{ (claim)}$$

b. $z_0 = -1.645$; Rejection region: $z < -1.645$

c. $\bar{p} = \dfrac{x_1 + x_2}{n_1 + n_2} = \dfrac{575{,}750 + 595{,}561}{875{,}000 + 901{,}000} \approx 0.660$

$\bar{q} \approx 0.340$

$$z = \frac{(\hat{p}_1 - \hat{p}_2) - (p_1 - p_2)}{\sqrt{\bar{p}\bar{q}\left(\dfrac{1}{n_1} + \dfrac{1}{n_2}\right)}} = \frac{(0.658 - 0.661) - (0)}{\sqrt{(0.660)(0.340)\left(\dfrac{1}{875{,}000} + \dfrac{1}{901{,}000}\right)}} \approx -4.22$$

d. Reject H_0.

e. There is enough evidence at the 5% level of significance to support the claim that the proportion of males who enrolled in college is less than the proportion of females who enrolled in college.

12a. The claim is "there is no difference in the proportion of females who have reduced the amount they spend on eating out and the proportion of males who have reduced the amount they spend on eating out."

$$H_0 : p_1 = p_2 \text{ (claim)}; \quad H_a : p_1 \neq p_2$$

b. $z_0 = \pm 2.575$; Rejection region: $z < -2.575$, $z > 2.575$

c. $\bar{p} = \dfrac{x_1 + x_2}{n_1 + n_2} = \dfrac{312 + 375}{433 + 577} \approx 0.680$

$\bar{q} \approx 0.320$

$$z = \frac{(\hat{p}_1 - \hat{p}_2) - (p_1 - p_2)}{\sqrt{\bar{p}\bar{q}\left(\dfrac{1}{n_1} + \dfrac{1}{n_2}\right)}} = \frac{(0.72 - 0.65) - (0)}{\sqrt{(0.680)(0.320)\left(\dfrac{1}{433} + \dfrac{1}{577}\right)}} \approx 2.36$$

d. Fail to reject H_0.

e. There is not enough evidence at the 1% level of significance to reject the claim that there is no difference in the proportion of females who have reduced the amount they spend on eating out and the proportion of males who have reduced the amount they spend on eating out.

13a. The claim is "the proportion of subjects who are pain-free is the same for the two groups."

$$H_0 : p_1 = p_2 \text{ (claim)}; \quad H_a : p_1 \neq p_2$$

b. $z_0 = \pm 1.96$; Rejection region: $z < -1.96$, $z > 1.96$

c. $\bar{p} = \dfrac{x_1 + x_2}{n_1 + n_2} = \dfrac{100 + 41}{400 + 407} \approx 0.175$

$\bar{q} \approx 0.825$

$$z = \frac{(\hat{p}_1 - \hat{p}_2) - (p_1 - p_2)}{\sqrt{\bar{p}\bar{q}\left(\dfrac{1}{n_1} + \dfrac{1}{n_2}\right)}} = \frac{(0.25 - 0.10) - (0)}{\sqrt{(0.175)(0.825)\left(\dfrac{1}{400} + \dfrac{1}{407}\right)}} \approx 5.61$$

d. Reject H_0.

e. There is enough evidence at the 5% level of significance to reject the claim that the proportion of subject who are pain-free is the same for the two groups.

14a. The claim is "the proportion of subjects who are free of nausea is greater for subjects who took the drug than for subjects who took placebo."
$H_0 : p_1 \le p_2; H_a : p_1 > p_2$ (claim)

b. $z_0 = 1.28$; Rejection region: $z > 1.28$

c. $\bar{p} = \dfrac{x_1 + x_2}{n_1 + n_2} = \dfrac{260 + 216}{400 + 407} \approx 0.590$

$\bar{q} \approx 0.410$

$z = \dfrac{(\hat{p}_1 - \hat{p}_2) - (p_1 - p_2)}{\sqrt{\bar{p}\bar{q}\left(\dfrac{1}{n_1} + \dfrac{1}{n_2}\right)}} = \dfrac{(0.65 - 0.53) - (0)}{\sqrt{(0.590)(0.410)\left(\dfrac{1}{400} + \dfrac{1}{407}\right)}} \approx 3.47$

d. Reject H_0.

e. There is enough evidence at the 10% level of significance to support the claim that the proportion of subjects who are free of nausea is greater for subjects who took the drug than for subjects who took placebo."

15a. The claim is "the proportion of motorcyclists who wear a helmet is now greater."
$H_0 : p_1 \le p_2; H_a : p_1 > p_2$ (claim)

b. $z_0 = 1.645$; Rejection region: $z > 1.645$

c. $\bar{p} = \dfrac{x_1 + x_2}{n_1 + n_2} = \dfrac{404 + 317}{600 + 500} \approx 0.655$

$\bar{q} \approx 0.345$

$z = \dfrac{(\hat{p}_1 - \hat{p}_2) - (p_1 - p_2)}{\sqrt{\bar{p}\bar{q}\left(\dfrac{1}{n_1} + \dfrac{1}{n_2}\right)}} = \dfrac{(0.673 - 0.634) - (0)}{\sqrt{(0.655)(0.345)\left(\dfrac{1}{600} + \dfrac{1}{500}\right)}} \approx 1.37$

d. Fail to reject H_0.

e. There is not enough evidence at the 5% level of significance to support the claim that the proportion of motorcyclists who wear a helmet is now greater.

16a. The claim is "the proportion of motorcyclists who wear a helmet in the Northeast is less than the proportion of motorcyclists who wear helmet in the Midwest."
$H_0 : p_1 \ge p_2; H_a : p_1 < p_2$ (claim)

b. $z_0 = -1.28$; Rejection region: $z < -1.28$

c. $\bar{p} = \dfrac{x_1 + x_2}{n_1 + n_2} = \dfrac{183 + 201}{300 + 300} \approx 0.64$

$\bar{q} \approx 0.36$

$z = \dfrac{(\hat{p}_1 - \hat{p}_2) - (p_1 - p_2)}{\sqrt{\bar{p}\bar{q}\left(\dfrac{1}{n_1} + \dfrac{1}{n_2}\right)}} = \dfrac{(0.61 - 0.67) - (0)}{\sqrt{(0.64)(0.36)\left(\dfrac{1}{300} + \dfrac{1}{300}\right)}} \approx -1.53$

d. Reject H_0.

e. There is enough evidence at the 10% level of significance to support the claim that the proportion of motorcyclists who wear a helmet in the Northeast is less than the proportion of motorcyclists who wear helmet in the Midwest.

17a. The claim is "the proportion of Internet users is the same for the two age groups."
$H_0 : p_1 = p_2$ (claim); $H_a : p_1 \neq p_2$

b. $z_0 = \pm 2.575$; Rejection region: $z < -2.575$, $z > 2.575$

c. $\bar{p} = \dfrac{x_1 + x_2}{n_1 + n_2} = \dfrac{419 + 324}{450 + 400} \approx 0.874$

$\bar{q} \approx 0.126$

$z = \dfrac{(\hat{p}_1 - \hat{p}_2) - (p_1 - p_2)}{\sqrt{\bar{p}\bar{q}\left(\dfrac{1}{n_1} + \dfrac{1}{n_2}\right)}} = \dfrac{(0.931 - 0.81) - (0)}{\sqrt{(0.874)(0.126)\left(\dfrac{1}{450} + \dfrac{1}{400}\right)}} \approx 5.31$

d. Reject H_0.

e. There is enough evidence at the 1% level of significance to reject the claim that the proportion of Internet users is the same for the two age groups.

18a. The claim is "the proportion of adults who use the Internet is greater for adults who live in an urban area than for adults who live in a rural area."
$H_0 : p_1 \leq p_2$; $H_a : p_1 > p_2$ (claim)

b. $z_0 = 1.28$; Rejection region: $z > 1.28$

c. $\bar{p} = \dfrac{x_1 + x_2}{n_1 + n_2} = \dfrac{359 + 221}{485 + 315} \approx 0.725$

$\bar{q} \approx 0.275$

$z = \dfrac{(\hat{p}_1 - \hat{p}_2) - (p_1 - p_2)}{\sqrt{\bar{p}\bar{q}\left(\dfrac{1}{n_1} + \dfrac{1}{n_2}\right)}} = \dfrac{(0.740 - 0.702) - (0)}{\sqrt{(0.725)(0.275)\left(\dfrac{1}{485} + \dfrac{1}{315}\right)}} \approx 1.20$

d. Fail to reject H_0.

e. There is not enough evidence at the 10% level of significance to support the claim that the proportion of adults who use the Internet is greater for adults who live in an urban area than for adults who live in a rural area."

19. $H_0 : p_1 = p_2$ (claim); $H_a : p_1 \neq p_2$

$z_0 = 1.96$; Rejection regions: $z < -1.96$, $z > 1.96$

$\bar{p} = \dfrac{x_1 + x_2}{n_1 + n_2} = \dfrac{240 + 204}{400 + 400} \approx 0.555$

$\bar{q} \approx 0.445$

$z = \dfrac{(\hat{p}_1 - \hat{p}_2) - (p_1 - p_2)}{\sqrt{\bar{p}\bar{q}\left(\dfrac{1}{n_1} + \dfrac{1}{n_2}\right)}} = \dfrac{(0.60 - 0.51) - (0)}{\sqrt{(0.555)(0.445)\left(\dfrac{1}{400} + \dfrac{1}{400}\right)}} \approx 2.56$

Reject H_0.

There is enough evidence at the 5% level of significance to reject the claim that the proportion of customers who wait 20 minutes or less is the same at the Fairfax North and Fairfax South offices.

20. $H_0 : p_1 \le p_2; H_a : p_1 > p_2$ (claim)

$z_0 = 2.33$; Rejection region: $z > 2.33$

$$\bar{p} = \frac{x_1 + x_2}{n_1 + n_2} = \frac{252 + 204}{400 + 400} \approx 0.57$$

$\bar{q} \approx 0.43$

$$z = \frac{(\hat{p}_1 - \hat{p}_2) - (p_1 - p_2)}{\sqrt{\bar{p}\bar{q}\left(\frac{1}{n_1} + \frac{1}{n_2}\right)}} = \frac{(0.63 - 0.51) - (0)}{\sqrt{(0.57)(0.43)\left(\frac{1}{400} + \frac{1}{400}\right)}} \approx 3.43$$

Reject H_0.

There is evidence at the 1% level of significance to support the claim that the proportion of customers who wait 20 minutes or less is greater at the Staunton office that it is at the Fairfax South office.

21. $H_0 : p_1 \ge p_2; H_a : p_1 < p_2$ (claim)

$z_0 = -1.28$; Rejection region: $z < -1.28$

$$\bar{p} = \frac{x_1 + x_2}{n_1 + n_2} = \frac{224 + 252}{400 + 400} \approx 0.595$$

$\bar{q} \approx 0.405$

$$z = \frac{(\hat{p}_1 - \hat{p}_2) - (p_1 - p_2)}{\sqrt{\bar{p}\bar{q}\left(\frac{1}{n_1} + \frac{1}{n_2}\right)}} = \frac{(0.56 - 0.63) - (0)}{\sqrt{(0.595)(0.405)\left(\frac{1}{400} + \frac{1}{400}\right)}} \approx -2.02$$

Reject H_0.

There is enough evidence at the 10% level of significance to support the claim that the proportion of customers who wait 20 minutes or less at the Roanoke office is less than the proportion of customers who wait 20 minutes or less at the Staunton office.

22. $H_0 : p_1 = p_2; H_a : p_1 \ne p_2$ (claim)

$z_0 = \pm 1.96$; Rejection regions: $z < -1.96, z > 1.96$

$$\bar{p} = \frac{x_1 + x_2}{n_1 + n_2} = \frac{224 + 240}{400 + 400} \approx 0.58$$

$\bar{q} \approx 0.42$

$$z = \frac{(\hat{p}_1 - \hat{p}_2) - (p_1 - p_2)}{\sqrt{\overline{pq}\left(\frac{1}{n_1} + \frac{1}{n_2}\right)}} = \frac{(0.56 - 0.60) - (0)}{\sqrt{(0.58)(0.42)\left(\frac{1}{400} + \frac{1}{400}\right)}} \approx -1.15$$

Fail to reject H_0.

There is not enough evidence at the 5% level of significance to support the claim that there is a difference between the proportion of customers who wait 20 minutes or less at the Roanoke office and the proportion of customers who wait 20 minutes or less at the Fairfax North office.

23. No; When $\alpha = 0.01$, the rejection region becomes $z < -2.33$. Because $-2.02 > -2.33$, you fail to reject H_0.

24. Yes; When $\alpha = 0.10$, the rejection regions become $z < -1.645$ and $z > 1.645$. Because $-1.645 < -1.15 < 1.645$, you still fail to reject H_0.

25. **Hypothesis test results:**

p_1 : proportion of successes for population 1

p_2 : proportion of successes for population 2

$p_1 - p_2$: difference in proportions

$H_0 : p_1 - p_2 = 0$

$H_A : p_1 - p_2 > 0$

Difference	Count 1	Total 1	Count 2	Total 2
$p_1 - p_2$	7501	13300	8120	14500

Sample Diff.	Std. Err.	Z-Stat	P-value
0.0039849626	0.0059570055	0.66895396	0.2518

$P = 0.2518 > 0.05$, so fail to reject H_0.

There is not enough evidence at the 5% level of significance to support the claim that the proportion of men ages 18–24 living in their parents' homes was greater in 2000 than in 2009.

26. **Hypothesis test results:**

p_1 : proportion of successes for population 1

p_2 : proportion of successes for population 2

$p_1 - p_2$: difference in proportions

$H_0 : p_1 - p_2 = 0$

$H_A : p_1 - p_2 > 0$

Difference	Count1	Total1	Count2	Total2
$p_1 - p_2$	5610	13200	6362	14200

Sample Diff.	Std. Err.	Z-Stat	P-value
−0.023028169	0.005996968	−3.8399684	0.9999

$P = 0.9999 > 0.05$, so fail to reject H_0.

There is not enough evidence at the 5% level of significance to support the claim that the proportion of women ages 18 to 24 living in their parents' homes was greater in 2000 than in 2009.

27. Hypothesis test results:

p_1 : proportion of successes for population 1

p_2 : proportion of successes for population 2

$p_1 - p_2$: difference in proportions

$H_0 : p_1 - p_2 = 0$

$H_A : p_1 - p_2 \neq 0$

Difference	Count1	Total1	Count2	Total2
$p_1 - p_2$	7501	13300	5610	13200

Sample Diff.	Std. Err.	Z-Stat	P-value
0.13898496	0.006142657	22.626196	<0.0001

$P < 0.0001 < 0.01$, so reject H_0.

There is enough evidence at the 1% level of significance to reject the claim that the proportion of 18 to 24-year olds living in their parents' homes in 2000 was the same for men and women.

28. Hypothesis test results:

p_1 : proportion of successes for population 1

p_2 : proportion of successes for population 2

$p_1 - p_2$: difference in proportions

$H_0 : p_1 - p_2 = 0$

$H_A : p_1 - p_2 \neq 0$

Difference	Count1	Total1	Count2	Total2
$p_1 - p_2$	8120	14500	6362	14200

Sample Diff.	Std. Err.	Z-Stat	P-value
0.11197183	0.005902886	18.968998	<0.0001

$P = 0.0001 < 0.01$, so reject H_0.

There is enough evidence at the 10% level of significance to reject the claim that the proportion of 18 to 24-year olds living in their parents' homes in 2009 was the same for men and women.

29.

$$(\hat{p}_1 - \hat{p}_2) - z_c \sqrt{\frac{\hat{p}_1 \hat{q}_1}{n_1} + \frac{\hat{p}_2 \hat{q}_2}{n_2}} < p_1 - p_2 < (\hat{p}_1 - \hat{p}_2) + z_c \sqrt{\frac{\hat{p}_1 \hat{q}_1}{n_1} + \frac{\hat{p}_2 \hat{q}_2}{n_2}}$$

$$(0.07 - 0.09) - 1.96 \sqrt{\frac{(0.07)(0.93)}{10,000} + \frac{(0.09)(0.91)}{8000}} < p_1 - p_2 < (0.07 - 0.09) + 1.96 \sqrt{\frac{(0.07)(0.93)}{10,000} + \frac{(0.09)(0.91)}{8000}}$$

$$-0.02 - 0.008 < p_1 - p_2 < -0.02 + 0.008$$

$$-0.028 < p_1 - p_2 < -0.012$$

30.

$$(\hat{p}_1 - \hat{p}_2) - z_c\sqrt{\frac{\hat{p}_1\hat{q}_1}{n_1} + \frac{\hat{p}_2\hat{q}_2}{n_2}} < p_1 - p_2 < (\hat{p}_1 - \hat{p}_2) + z_c\sqrt{\frac{\hat{p}_1\hat{q}_1}{n_1} + \frac{\hat{p}_2\hat{q}_2}{n_2}}$$

$$(0.19 - 0.16) - 1.645\sqrt{\frac{(0.19)(0.81)}{10,000} + \frac{(0.16)(0.84)}{8000}} < p_1 - p_2 < (0.19 - 0.16) + 1.645\sqrt{\frac{(0.19)(0.81)}{10,000} + \frac{(0.16)(0.84)}{8000}}$$

$$0.03 - 0.009 < p_1 - p_2 < -0.03 + 0.009$$

$$-0.021 < p_1 - p_2 < -0.039$$

CHAPTER 8 REVIEW EXERCISE SOLUTIONS

1. Dependent because the same cities were sampled.

2. Dependent because the same runners were sampled.

3. $H_0 : \mu_1 \geq \mu_2$ (claim); $H_a : \mu_1 < \mu_2$

    $z_0 = -1.645$; Rejection region: $z < -1.645$

    $$z = \frac{(\bar{x}_1 - \bar{x}_2) - (\mu_1 - \mu_2)}{\sqrt{\frac{s_1^2}{n_1} + \frac{s_2^2}{n_2}}} = \frac{(1.28 - 1.34) - (0)}{\sqrt{\frac{(0.30)^2}{96} + \frac{(0.23)^2}{85}}} \approx -1.519$$

    Fail to reject H_0. There is not enough evidence at the 5% level of significance to support the claim.

4. $H_0 : \mu_1 = \mu_2$ (claim); $H_a : \mu_1 \neq \mu_2$

    $z_0 = \pm 2.575$; Rejection region: $z < -2.575$, $z > 2.575$

    $$z = \frac{(\bar{x}_1 - \bar{x}_2) - (\mu_1 - \mu_2)}{\sqrt{\frac{s_1^2}{n_1} + \frac{s_2^2}{n_2}}} = \frac{(5595 - 5575) - (0)}{\sqrt{\frac{(52)^2}{156} + \frac{(68)^2}{216}}} \approx 3.213$$

    Reject H_0. There is enough evidence at the 1% level of significance to reject the claim.

5. $H_0 : \mu_1 \geq \mu_2$; $H_a : \mu_1 < \mu_2$ (claim)

    $z_0 = -1.28$; Rejection regions: $z < -1.28$

    $$z = \frac{(\bar{x}_1 - \bar{x}_2) - (\mu_1 - \mu_2)}{\sqrt{\frac{s_1^2}{n_1} + \frac{s_2^2}{n_2}}} = \frac{(0.28 - 0.33) - (0)}{\sqrt{\frac{(0.11)^2}{41} + \frac{(0.10)^2}{34}}} \approx -2.060$$

    Reject H_0. There is enough evidence at the 10% level of significance to support the claim.

6. $H_0 : \mu_1 = \mu_2$; $H_a : \mu_1 \neq \mu_2$ (claim)

$z_0 = \pm 1.96$; Rejection regions: $z < -1.96$, $z > 1.96$

$$z = \frac{(\bar{x}_1 - \bar{x}_2) - (\mu_1 - \mu_2)}{\sqrt{\dfrac{s_1^2}{n_1} + \dfrac{s_2^2}{n_2}}} = \frac{(87 - 85) - (0)}{\sqrt{\dfrac{(14)^2}{410} + \dfrac{(15)^2}{340}}} \approx 1.87$$

Fail to reject H_0. There is not enough evidence at the 5% level of significance to support the claim.

7. (a) $H_0 : \mu_1 \geq \mu_2$; $H_a : \mu_1 < \mu_2$ (claim)

(b) $z_0 = -1.645$; Rejection region: $z < -1.645$

(c) $z = \dfrac{(\bar{x}_1 - \bar{x}_2) - (\mu_1 - \mu_2)}{\sqrt{\dfrac{s_1^2}{n_1} + \dfrac{s_2^2}{n_2}}} = \dfrac{(1010 - 1180) - (0)}{\sqrt{\dfrac{(75)^2}{42} + \dfrac{(90)^2}{39}}} \approx -9.20$

(d) Reject H_0.

(e) There is enough evidence at the 5% level of significance to support the claim that the Wendy's fish sandwich has less sodium than the Long John Silver's fish sandwich.

8. (a) The claim is "the mean annual salary of civilian federal employees in California is the same as those in Illinois."

$H_0 : \mu_1 = \mu_2$ (claim); $H_a : \mu_1 \neq \mu_2$

(b) $z_0 = -1.645$; Rejection regions: $z < -1.645$, $z > 1.645$

(c) $z = \dfrac{(\bar{x}_1 - \bar{x}_2) - (\mu_1 - \mu_2)}{\sqrt{\dfrac{s_1^2}{n_1} + \dfrac{s_2^2}{n_2}}} = \dfrac{(66,210 - 67,390) - (0)}{\sqrt{\dfrac{(6385)^2}{180} + \dfrac{(5998)^2}{180}}} \approx -1.81$

(d) Reject H_0.

(e) There is enough evidence at the 10% level of significance to reject the claim that the mean annual salary of civilian federal employees in California is the same as those in Illinois.

9. Yes; The new rejection region is $z < -2.33$, which contains $z = -9.20$, so you still reject H_0.

10. No; The new rejection regions are $z < -1.96$ and $z > 1.96$, which does not contain $z = -1.81$, so you fail to reject H_0.

11. $H_0 : \mu_1 = \mu_2$ (claim); $H_a : \mu_1 \neq \mu_2$

d.f. $= n_1 + n_2 - 2 = 31$

$t_0 = \pm 1.96$; Rejection regions: $t < -1.96$, $t > 1.96$

$$t = \frac{(\bar{x}_1 - \bar{x}_2) - (\mu_1 - \mu_2)}{\sqrt{\dfrac{(n_1 - 1)s_1^2 + (n_2 - 1)s_2^2}{n_1 + n_2 - 2}} \sqrt{\dfrac{1}{n_1} + \dfrac{1}{n_2}}} = \frac{(228 - 207) - (0)}{\sqrt{\dfrac{(20 - 1)(27)^2 + (13 - 1)(25)}{20 + 13 - 2}} \sqrt{\dfrac{1}{20} + \dfrac{1}{13}}} \approx 2.25$$

Reject H_0. There is not enough evidence at the 5% level of significance to support the claim.

12. $H_0 : \mu_1 = \mu_2$ (claim); $H_a : \mu_1 \neq \mu_2$

d.f. $= \min\{n_1 - 1, \ n_2 - 1\} = 5$

$t_0 = \pm 2.015$; Rejection regions: $t < -2.015, \ t > 2.015$

$$t = \frac{(\bar{x}_1 - \bar{x}_2) - (\mu_1 - \mu_2)}{\sqrt{\dfrac{s_1^2}{n_1} + \dfrac{s_2^2}{n_2}}} = \frac{(0.015 - 0.019) - (0)}{\sqrt{\dfrac{(0.011)^2}{8} + \dfrac{(0.004)^2}{6}}} \approx -0.948$$

Fail to reject H_0. There is not enough evidence at the 10% level of significance to reject the claim.

13. $H_0 : \mu_1 \leq \mu_2$ (claim); $H_a : \mu_1 > \mu_2$

d.f. $= \min\{n_1 - 1, \ n_2 - 1\} = 24$

$t_0 = 1.711$; Rejection regions: $t > 1.711$

$$t = \frac{(\bar{x}_1 - \bar{x}_2) - (\mu_1 - \mu_2)}{\sqrt{\dfrac{s_1^2}{n_1} + \dfrac{s_2^2}{n_2}}} = \frac{(183.5 - 184.7) - (0)}{\sqrt{\dfrac{(1.3)^2}{25} + \dfrac{(3.9)^2}{25}}} \approx -1.460$$

Fail to reject H_0. There is not enough evidence at the 5% level of significance to reject the claim.

14. $H_0 : \mu_1 \geq \mu_2$ (claim); $H_a : \mu_1 < \mu_2$

d.f. $= n_1 + n_2 - 2 = 33$

$t_0 = -2.326$; Rejection region: $t < -2.326$

$$t = \frac{(\bar{x}_1 - \bar{x}_2) - (\mu_1 - \mu_2)}{\sqrt{\dfrac{(n-1)s_1^2 + (n_2-1)s_2^2}{n_1 + n_2 - 2}}\sqrt{\dfrac{1}{n_1} + \dfrac{1}{n_2}}} = \frac{(44.5 - 49.1) - (0)}{\sqrt{\dfrac{(17-1)(5.85)^2 + (18-1)(5.25)^2}{17+18-2}}\sqrt{\dfrac{1}{17} + \dfrac{1}{18}}} \approx -2.45$$

Reject H_0. There is enough evidence at the 1% level of significance to reject the claim.

15. $H_0 : \mu_1 = \mu_2$; $H_a : \mu_1 \neq \mu_2$ (claim)

d.f. $= n_1 + n_2 - 2 = 10$

$t_0 = \pm 3.169$; Rejection regions: $t < -3.169, \ t > 3.169$

$$t = \frac{(\bar{x}_1 - \bar{x}_2) - (\mu_1 - \mu_2)}{\sqrt{\dfrac{(n-1)s_1^2 + (n_2-1)s_2^2}{n_1 + n_2 - 2}} \cdot \sqrt{\dfrac{1}{n_1} + \dfrac{1}{n_2}}} = \frac{(61 - 55) - (0)}{\sqrt{\dfrac{(5-1)(3.3)^2 + (7-1)(1.2)^2}{5+7-2}} \cdot \sqrt{\dfrac{1}{5} + \dfrac{1}{7}}} \approx 4.484$$

Reject H_0. There is enough evidence at the 1% level of significance to support the claim.

16. $H_0 : \mu_1 \geq \mu_2$ (claim); $H_a : \mu_1 < \mu_2$

d.f. $= \min\{n_1 - 1, \ n_2 - 1\} = 5$

$t_0 = -1.476$; Rejection region: $t < -1.476$

$$t = \frac{(\bar{x}_1 - \bar{x}_2) - (\mu_1 - \mu_2)}{\sqrt{\dfrac{s_1^2}{n_1} + \dfrac{s_2^2}{n_2}}} = \frac{(520 - 500) - (0)}{\sqrt{\dfrac{(25)^2}{7} + \dfrac{(55)^2}{6}}} \approx 0.821$$

Fail to reject H_0. There is not enough evidence at the 10% level of significance to reject the claim.

17. (a) The claim is "third graders taught with the directed reading activities scored higher than those taught without the activities."

$H_0 : \mu_1 \leq \mu_2; H_a : \mu_1 > \mu_2$ (claim)

(b) d.f. $= n_1 + n_2 - 2 = 42$

$t_0 = 1.645$; Rejection region: $t > 1.645$

(c) $\bar{x}_1 \approx 51.476$, $s_1 \approx 11.007$, $n_1 = 21$

$\bar{x}_2 \approx 41.522$, $s_2 \approx 17.149$, $n_2 = 23$

$$t = \frac{(\bar{x}_1 - \bar{x}_2) - (\mu_1 - \mu_2)}{\sqrt{\dfrac{(n-1)s_1^2 + (n_2 - 1)s_2^2}{n_1 + n_2 - 2}}} \approx \frac{(51.476 - 41.522) - (0)}{\sqrt{\dfrac{(21-1)(11.007)^2 + (23-1)(17.149)^2}{21 + 23 - 2}} \sqrt{\dfrac{1}{21} + \dfrac{1}{23}}} \approx 2.266$$

(d) Reject H_0.

(e) There is enough evidence at the 5% level of significance to support the claim that third graders taught with the directed reading activities scored higher than those taught without the activities.

18. (a) The claim is "there is no difference between the mean household incomes of two neighborhoods."

$H_0 : \mu_1 = \mu_2$ (claim); $H_a : \mu_1 \neq \mu_2$

(b) d.f. $= n_1 + n_2 - 2 = 20$

$t_0 = \pm 2.845$; Rejection regions: $t < -2.845$, $t > 2.845$

(c) $t = \dfrac{(\bar{x}_1 - \bar{x}_2) - (\mu_1 - \mu_2)}{\sqrt{\dfrac{(n-1)s_1^2 + (n_2 - 1)s_2^2}{n_1 + n_2 - 2}} \sqrt{\dfrac{1}{n_1} + \dfrac{1}{n_2}}} \approx \dfrac{(32,750 - 31,200) - (0)}{\sqrt{\dfrac{(12-1)(1900)^2 + (10-1)(1825)^2}{12 + 10 - 2}} \sqrt{\dfrac{1}{12} + \dfrac{1}{10}}} \approx 1.939$

(d) Fail to reject H_0.

(e) There is enough evidence at the 1% level of significance to reject the claim that there is no difference between the mean household incomes of two neighborhoods.

19. $H_0 : \mu_d = 0$ (claim); $H_a : \mu_d \neq 0$

$\alpha = 0.01$ and d.f. $= n - 1 = 15$

$t_0 = \pm 2.947$ (Two-tailed test); Rejection regions: $t < -2.947$, $t > 2.947$

$$t = \frac{\bar{d} - \mu_d}{\frac{s_d}{\sqrt{n}}} = \frac{85 - 0}{\frac{10.7}{\sqrt{16}}} \approx 3.178$$

Reject H_0.

20. $H_0 : \mu_d \geq 0$; $H_a : \mu_d < 0$ (claim)

$\alpha = 0.10$ and d.f. $= n - 1 = 24$

$t_0 = -1.318$ (Left-tailed test); Rejection regions: $t < -1.318$

$$t = \frac{\bar{d} - \mu_d}{\frac{s_d}{\sqrt{n}}} = \frac{3.2 - 0}{\frac{5.68}{\sqrt{25}}} \approx 2.817$$

Fail to reject H_0.

21. $H_0 : \mu_d \leq 0$ (claim); $H_a : \mu_d > 0$

$\alpha = 0.10$ and d.f. $= n - 1 = 32$

$t_0 = 1.282$ (Right-tailed test); Rejection region: $t > 1.282$

$$t = \frac{\bar{d} - \mu_d}{\frac{s_d}{\sqrt{n}}} = \frac{10.3 - 0}{\frac{18.19}{\sqrt{33}}} \approx 3.253$$

Reject H_0.

22. $H_0 : \mu_d = 0$; $H_a : \mu_d \neq 0$ (claim)

$\alpha = 0.05$ and d.f. $= n - 1 = 36$

$t_0 = \pm 1.96$ (Two-tailed test); Rejection regions: $t < -1.960$, $t > 1.960$

$$t = \frac{\bar{d} - \mu_d}{\frac{s_d}{\sqrt{n}}} = \frac{17.5 - 0}{\frac{4.05}{\sqrt{37}}} \approx 26.284$$

Reject H_0.

23. (a) The claim is "the men's systolic blood pressure decreased."
$H_0 : \mu_d \leq 0$; $H_a : \mu_d > 0$ (claim)

(b) $t_0 = 1.383$; Rejection region: $t > 1.383$

(c) $\bar{d} = 5$ and $s_d \approx 8.743$

(d) $t = \dfrac{\bar{d} - \mu_d}{\dfrac{s_d}{\sqrt{n}}} = \dfrac{5 - 0}{\dfrac{8.743}{\sqrt{10}}} \approx 1.808$

(e) Reject H_0.

(f) There is enough evidence at the 10% level of significance to support the claim that the man's systolic blood pressure decreased.

24. (a) The claim is "the weight loss supplement will help users lose weight after two weeks."

$H_0 : \mu_d \le 0; H_a : \mu_d > 0$ (claim)

(b) $t_0 = 1.860$; Rejection region: $t > 1.860$

(c) $\bar{d} \approx 1.444$ and $s_d \approx 2.744$

(d) $t = \dfrac{\bar{d} - \mu_d}{\dfrac{s_d}{\sqrt{n}}} = \dfrac{1.444 - 0}{\dfrac{2.744}{\sqrt{9}}} \approx 1.579$

(e) Fail to reject H_0.

(f) There is enough evidence at the 5% level of significance to support the claim that the weight loss supplement will help users lose weight after two weeks.

25. $H_0 : p_1 = p_2$ (claim); $H_a : p_1 \ne p_2$

$z_0 = \pm 1.96$; Rejection regions: $z < -1.96$, $z > 1.96$

$\bar{p} = \dfrac{x_1 + x_2}{n_1 + n_2} = \dfrac{425 + 410}{840 + 760} \approx 0.522$

$\bar{q} \approx 0.478$

$n_1 \bar{p} \approx 438.48 > 5$, $n_1 \bar{q} \approx 401.52 > 5$, $n_2 \bar{p} \approx 396.72 > 5$, and $n_2 \bar{q} \approx 363.28 > 5$.

Can use normal sampling distribution.

$z = \dfrac{(\hat{p}_1 - \hat{p}_2) - (p_1 - p_2)}{\sqrt{\bar{p}\bar{q}\left(\dfrac{1}{n_1} + \dfrac{1}{n_2}\right)}} = \dfrac{(0.506 - 0.539) - (0)}{\sqrt{0.522 \cdot 0.478 \left(\dfrac{1}{840} + \dfrac{1}{760}\right)}} \approx -1.320$

Fail to reject H_0.

26. $H_0 : p_1 \le p_2$ (claim): $H_a : p_1 > p_2$

$z_0 = 2.33$; Rejection region: $z > 2.33$

$\bar{p} = \dfrac{x_1 + x_2}{n_1 + n_2} = \dfrac{36 + 46}{100 + 200} \approx 0.273$

$\bar{q} \approx 0.727$

$n_1 \bar{p} \approx 27.3 > 5$, $n_1 \bar{q} \approx 72.7 > 5$, $n_2 \bar{p} \approx 54.6 > 5$, and $n_2 \bar{q} \approx 145.4 > 5$.

Can use normal sampling distribution.

$$z = \frac{(\hat{p}_1 - \hat{p}_2) - (p_1 - p_2)}{\sqrt{\overline{pq}\left(\frac{1}{n_1} + \frac{1}{n_2}\right)}} = \frac{(0.36 - 0.23) - (0)}{\sqrt{0.273 \cdot 0.727\left(\frac{1}{100} + \frac{1}{200}\right)}} \approx 2.383$$

Reject H_0.

27. $H_0 : p_1 \leq p_2$; $H_a : p_1 > p_2$ (claim)

$z_0 = 1.28$; Rejection region: $z > 1.28$

$$\overline{p} = \frac{x_1 + x_2}{n_1 + n_2} = \frac{261 + 207}{556 + 483} \approx 0.450$$

$\overline{q} \approx 0.550$

$n_1\overline{p} \approx 250.2 > 5$, $n_1\overline{q} \approx 305.8 > 5$, $n_2\overline{p} \approx 217.35 > 5$, and $n_2\overline{q} \approx 265.65 > 5$.

Can use normal sampling distribution.

$$z = \frac{(\hat{p}_1 - \hat{p}_2) - (p_1 - p_2)}{\sqrt{\overline{pq}\left(\frac{1}{n_1} + \frac{1}{n_2}\right)}} = \frac{(0.469 - 0.429) - (0)}{\sqrt{0.450 \cdot 0.550\left(\frac{1}{556} + \frac{1}{483}\right)}} \approx 1.293$$

Reject H_0.

28. $H_0 : p_1 \geq p_2$; $H_a : p_1 < p_2$ (claim)

$z_0 = -1.645$; Rejection region: $z < -1.645$

$$\overline{p} = \frac{x_1 + x_2}{n_1 + n_2} = \frac{86 + 107}{900 + 1200} \approx 0.092$$

$\overline{q} \approx 0.908$

$n_1\overline{p} \approx 82.8 > 5$, $n_1\overline{q} \approx 817.2 > 5$, $n_2\overline{p} \approx 110.4 > 5$, and $n_2\overline{q} \approx 1089.6 > 5$.

Can use normal sampling distribution.

$$z = \frac{(\hat{p}_1 - \hat{p}_2) - (p_1 - p_2)}{\sqrt{\overline{pq}\left(\frac{1}{n_1} + \frac{1}{n_2}\right)}} = \frac{(0.096 - 0.089) - (0)}{\sqrt{0.092 \cdot 0.908\left(\frac{1}{900} + \frac{1}{1200}\right)}} \approx 0.549$$

Fail to reject H_0.

29. (a) The claim is "the proportions of U.S. adults who considered the amount of federal income tax they had to pay to be too high were the same for the two years."

$H_0 : p_1 = p_2$ (claim); $H_a : p_1 \neq p_2$

(b) $z_0 = \pm 2.575$; Rejection regions: $z < -2.575$, $z > 2.575$

(c) $\bar{p} = \dfrac{x_1 + x_2}{n_1 + n_2} = \dfrac{468 + 472}{900 + 1027} \approx 0.488$

$\bar{q} \approx 0.512$

$z = \dfrac{(\hat{p}_1 - \hat{p}_2) - (p_1 - p_2)}{\sqrt{\overline{pq}\left(\dfrac{1}{n_1} + \dfrac{1}{n_2}\right)}} = \dfrac{(0.520 - 0.460) - (0)}{\sqrt{0.488 \cdot 0.512\left(\dfrac{1}{900} + \dfrac{1}{1027}\right)}} \approx 2.63$

(d) Reject H_0.

(e) There is enough evidence at the 1% level of significance to reject the claim that the proportions of U.S. adults who considered the amount of federal income tax they had to pay to be too high were the same for the two years.

30. (a) The claim is "the proportion of U.S. adults who believe it is likely that life exists on other planets is less now than in 2007."

$H_0 : p_1 \le p_2$; $H_a : p_1 > p_2$ (claim)

(b) $z_0 = 1.645$; Rejection region: $z > 1.645$

(c) $\bar{p} = \dfrac{x_1 + x_2}{n_1 + n_2} = \dfrac{570 + 530}{1000 + 1000} \approx 0.55$

$\bar{q} \approx 0.45$

$z = \dfrac{(\hat{p}_1 - \hat{p}_2) - (p_1 - p_2)}{\sqrt{\overline{pq}\left(\dfrac{1}{n_1} + \dfrac{1}{n_2}\right)}} = \dfrac{(0.57 - 0.53) - (0)}{\sqrt{0.55 \cdot 0.45\left(\dfrac{1}{1000} + \dfrac{1}{1000}\right)}} \approx 1.80$

(d) Reject H_0.

(e) There is enough evidence at the 5% level of significance to accept the claim that the proportion of U.S. adults who believe it is likely that life exists on other planets is less now than in 2007.

31. Yes; When $\alpha = 0.05$, the rejection regions become $z < -1.96$ and $z > 1.96$. Because $2.65 > 1.96$, you still reject H_0.

32. No; When $\alpha = 0.01$, the rejection region becomes $z > 2.33$. Because $1.80 < 2.33$, you fail to reject H_0.

CHAPTER 8 QUIZ SOLUTIONS

1. (a) $H_0 : \mu_1 \le \mu_2$; $H_a : \mu_1 > \mu_2$ (claim)

(b) One-tailed because H_a contains >; z-test because n_1 and n_2 are each greater than 30.

(c) $z_0 = 1.645$; Rejection region: $z > 1.645$

(d) $z = \dfrac{(\bar{x}_1 - \bar{x}_2) - (\mu_1 - \mu_2)}{\sqrt{\dfrac{s_1^2}{n_1} + \dfrac{s_2^2}{n_2}}} = \dfrac{(149 - 145) - (0)}{\sqrt{\dfrac{(35)^2}{49} + \dfrac{(33)^2}{50}}} \approx 0.585$

(e) Fail to reject H_0.

(f) There is not enough evidence at the 5% level of significance to support the claim that the mean score on the science assessment for male high school students was higher than for the female high school students.

2. (a) $H_0 : \mu_1 = \mu_2$ (claim); $H_a : \mu_1 \neq \mu_2$

(b) Two-tailed because H_a contains $\neq$; t-test because n_1 and n_2 are less than 30, the samples are independent, and the population are normally distributed.

(c) d.f. $= n_1 + n_2 - 2 = 26$

$t_0 = \pm 2.779$; Rejection regions: $t < -2.779$, $t > 2.779$

(d) $t = \dfrac{(\bar{x}_1 - \bar{x}_2) - (\mu_1 - \mu_2)}{\sqrt{\dfrac{(n-1)s_1^2 + (n_2 - 1)s_2^2}{n_1 + n_2 - 2}} \cdot \sqrt{\dfrac{1}{n_1} + \dfrac{1}{n_2}}} = \dfrac{(153 - 149) - (0)}{\sqrt{\dfrac{(13-1)(32)^2 + (15-1)(30)^2}{13 + 15 - 2}} \cdot \sqrt{\dfrac{1}{13} + \dfrac{1}{15}}} \approx 0.341$

(e) Fail to reject H_0.

(f) There is not enough evidence at the 1% level of significance to reject the claim that the mean score on the science assessment test are the same for fourth grade boys and girls.

3. (a) $H_0 : p_1 = p_2$ (claim); $H_a : p_1 \neq p_2$

(b) Two-tailed because H_a contains $\neq$; z-test because you are testing proportions and $n_1\bar{p}$, $n_1\bar{q}$, $n_2\bar{p}$, and $n_2\bar{q} \geq 5$.

(c) $z_0 = 1.645$; Rejection region: $z < -1.645$, $z > 1.645$

(d) $\bar{p} = \dfrac{x_1 + x_2}{n_1 + n_2} = \dfrac{336 + 429}{800 + 1100} \approx 0.403$

$\bar{q} \approx 0.597$

$z = \dfrac{(\hat{p}_1 - \hat{p}_2) - (p_1 - p_2)}{\sqrt{\bar{p}\bar{q}\left(\dfrac{1}{n_1} + \dfrac{1}{n_2}\right)}} = \dfrac{(0.42 - 0.39) - (0)}{\sqrt{0.403 \cdot 0.597\left(\dfrac{1}{800} + \dfrac{1}{1100}\right)}} \approx 1.32$

(e) Fail to reject H_0.

(f) There is not enough evidence at the 10% level of significance to reject the claim that the proportion of U.S. adults who are worried that their family will become a victim of terrorism has not changed.

4. (a) $H_0 : \mu_d \geq 0$; $H_a : \mu_d < 0$ (claim)

(b) One-tailed because H_a contains $<$; t-test because both populations are normally distributed and the samples are dependent.

(c) $t_0 = -2.718$; Rejection region: $t < -2.718$

(d) $\bar{d} \approx -51.17$ and $s_d \approx 34.94$

$$t = \frac{\bar{d} - \mu_d}{\frac{s_d}{\sqrt{n}}} = \frac{-51.17 - 0}{\frac{34.94}{\sqrt{12}}} \approx -5.07$$

(e) Reject H_0.

(f) There is enough evidence at the 1% level of significance to support the claim that the seminar helps adults increase their credit scores.

CUMULATIVE REVIEW, CHAPTERS 6–8

1. (a) $\hat{p} = 0.13$, $\hat{q} = 0.87$

$$\hat{p} \pm z_c \sqrt{\frac{\hat{p}\hat{q}}{n}} = 0.13 \pm 1.96 \sqrt{\frac{(0.13)(0.87)}{1000}} \approx 0.13 \pm 0.021 = (0.109,\ 0.151)$$

(b) $H_0 : p \le 0.10$; $H_a : p > 0.10$ (claim)

$z_0 = 1.645$; Rejection region: $z > 1.645$

$$z = \frac{\hat{p} - p}{\sqrt{\frac{pq}{n}}} = \frac{0.13 - 0.10}{\sqrt{\frac{(0.10)(0.90)}{1000}}} \approx 3.16$$

Reject H_0.

There is enough evidence at the 5% level of significance to support the claim that more than 10% of people who attend community college are age 40 or older.

2. $H_0 : \mu_d \ge 0$; $H_a : \mu_d < 0$ (claim)

$\alpha = 0.10$ d.f. $= n - 1 = 7$

$t_0 = -1.415$; Rejection region: $t < -1.415$

$\bar{d} = -1.575$ and $s_d \approx 0.803$

$$t = \frac{\bar{d} - \mu_d}{\frac{s_d}{\sqrt{n}}} \approx \frac{-1.575 - 0}{\frac{0.803}{\sqrt{8}}} \approx -5.548$$

Reject H_0.

There is enough evidence at the 10% level of significance to support the claim that the fuel additive improved gas mileage.

3. $\bar{x} \pm z_c \dfrac{s}{\sqrt{n}} = 26.97 \pm 1.96 \dfrac{3.4}{\sqrt{42}} \approx 26.97 \pm 1.03 = (25.94,\ 28.00)$; z-distribution

4. $\bar{x} \pm t_c \dfrac{s}{\sqrt{n}} = 3.46 \pm 1.753 \dfrac{1.63}{\sqrt{16}} \approx 3.46 \pm 0.71 = (2.75,\ 4.17)$; t-distribution

5. $\bar{x} \pm t_c \dfrac{s}{\sqrt{n}} = 12.1 \pm 2.787 \dfrac{2.64}{\sqrt{26}} \approx 12.1 \pm 1.4 = (10.7,\ 13.5)$; t-distribution

6. $\bar{x} \pm t_c \dfrac{s}{\sqrt{n}} = 8.21 \pm 2.365 \dfrac{0.62}{\sqrt{8}} \approx 8.21 \pm 0.52 = (7.69,\ 8.73)$; t-distribution

7. $H_0 : \mu_1 \le \mu_2$; $H_a : \mu_1 > \mu_2$ (claim)

$z_0 = 1.28$; Rejection region: $z > 1.28$

$$z = \frac{(\bar{x}_1 - \bar{x}_2) - 0}{\sqrt{\dfrac{s_1^2}{n_1} + \dfrac{s_2^2}{n_2}}} = \frac{(3086 - 2263) - (0)}{\sqrt{\dfrac{(563)^2}{85} + \dfrac{(624)^2}{68}}} \approx 8.464$$

Reject H_0. There is enough evidence at the 10% level of significance to support the claim that the mean birth weight of a single-birth baby is greater than the mean birth weight of a baby that has a twin.

8. $H_0 : \mu \ge 33$

$H_a : \mu < 33$ (claim)

9. $H_0 : p \ge 0.19$ (claim)

$H_a : p < 0.19$

10. $H_0 : \sigma = 0.63$ (claim)

$H_a : \sigma \ne 0.63$

11. $H_0 : \mu = 2.28$

$H_a : \mu \ne 2.28$ (claim)

12. (a) $\left(\dfrac{(n-1)s^2}{\chi_R^2},\ \dfrac{(n-1)s^2}{\chi_L^2} \right) = \left(\dfrac{(26-1)(3.1)^2}{46.928},\ \dfrac{(26-1)(3.1)^2}{10.520} \right) \approx (5.1,\ 22.8)$

(b) $\left(\sqrt{5.1},\ \sqrt{22.8} \right) \approx (2.3,\ 4.8)$

(c) $H_0 : \sigma \ge 2.5$; $H_a : \sigma < 2.5$ (claim)

$\chi_0^2 = 11.524$; Rejection region: $\chi^2 < 11.524$

$$\chi^2 = \frac{(n-1)s^2}{\sigma^2} = \frac{(25)(3.1)}{(2.5)^2} = 38.44$$

Fail to reject H_0.

There is not enough evidence at the 1% level of significance to support the claim that the standard deviation of the mean number of chronic medications taken by elderly adults in the community is less than 2.5 medications.

13. $H_0 : \mu_1 = \mu_2$; $H_a : \mu_1 \ne \mu_2$ (claim)

d.f. $= n_1 + n_2 - 2 = 26 + 18 - 2 = 42$

$t_0 = \pm 1.96$; Rejection regions: $t < -1.960$, $t > 1.960$

$$t = \frac{(\bar{x}_1 - \bar{x}_2) - (0)}{\sqrt{\dfrac{(n_1-1)s_1^2 + (n_2-1)s_2^2}{n_1 + n_2 - 2}} \sqrt{\dfrac{1}{n_1} + \dfrac{1}{n_2}}} = \frac{1783 - 2064}{\sqrt{\dfrac{(26-1)(218)^2 + (18-1)(186)^2}{26 + 18 - 2}} \sqrt{\dfrac{1}{20} + \dfrac{1}{18}}} \approx -4.456$$

Reject H_0. There is enough evidence at the 5% level of significance to support the claim that the mean SAT scores for male athletes and male non-athletes at a college are different.

14. (a) $\bar{x} \approx 38{,}896.46$

$s \approx 2881.83$

$$\bar{x} \pm t_c \frac{s}{\sqrt{n}} \approx 38{,}896.46 \pm 2.060\frac{2881.83}{\sqrt{26}}$$

$$\approx 38{,}896.46 \pm 1164.26$$

$$\approx (37{,}732.2,\ 40{,}060.7)$$

(b) $H_0 : \mu = 40{,}000$ (claim); $H_a : \mu \neq 40{,}000$

$t_0 = \pm 2.060$; Rejection regions: $t < -2.060, t > 2.060$

$$t = \frac{\bar{x} - \mu}{\dfrac{s}{\sqrt{n}}} \approx \frac{38{,}896.46 - 40{,}000}{\dfrac{2881.83}{\sqrt{26}}} = -1.95$$

Fail to reject H_0. There is not enough evidence at the 5% level of significance to reject the claim that the mean annual earnings for translators is $40,000.

15. $H_0 : p_1 = p_2$ (claim); $H_a : p_1 \neq p_2$

$$\bar{p} = \frac{x_1 + x_2}{n_1 + n_2} = \frac{195 + 204}{319 + 323} \approx 0.621$$

$$\bar{q} \approx 0.379$$

$z_0 = \pm 1.645$; Rejection regions: $z < -1.645, z > 1.645$

$$z_0 = \frac{(\hat{p}_1 - \hat{p}_2) - 0}{\sqrt{\bar{p}\bar{q}\left(\dfrac{1}{n_1} + \dfrac{1}{n_2}\right)}} = \frac{(0.611 - 0.632)}{\sqrt{(0.621)(0.379)\left(\dfrac{1}{319} + \dfrac{1}{323}\right)}} \approx -0.548$$

Fail to reject H_0. There is not enough evidence at the 10% level of significance to reject the claim that the proportions of players sustaining head and neck injuries are the same for the two groups.

16. (a) $\bar{x} \pm z\dfrac{s}{\sqrt{n}} = 42 \pm 1.96\dfrac{1.6}{\sqrt{40}} \approx 42 \pm 0.496 \approx (41.5,\ 42.5)$

(b) $H_0 : \mu \geq 45$ (claim); $H_a : \mu < 45$

$z_0 = -1.96$; Rejection region: $z < -1.96$

$$z = \frac{\bar{x} - \mu}{\dfrac{s}{\sqrt{n}}} = \frac{42 - 45}{\dfrac{1.6}{\sqrt{40}}} \approx -11.86$$

Reject H_0. There is enough evidence at the 5% level of significance to reject the claim that the mean incubation period for ostriches is at least 45 days.

9.1 CORRELATION

9.1 Try It Yourself Solutions

1ab.

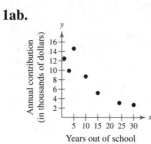

c. Yes, it appears that there is a negative linear correlation. As the number of years out of school increases, the annual contribution decreases.

2ab.

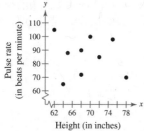

c. No, it appears that there is no linear correlation between height and pulse rate.

3ab.

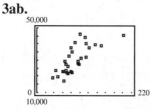

c. Yes, it appears that there is a positive linear correlation. As the team salary increases, the average attendance per home game increases.

4. (a)

x	y	xy	x^2	y^2
1	12.5	12.5	1	156.25
10	8.7	87.0	100	75.69
5	14.6	73.0	25	213.16
15	5.2	78.0	225	27.04
3	9.9	29.7	9	98.01
24	3.1	74.4	576	9.61
30	2.7	81.0	900	7.29
$\sum x = 88$	$\sum y = 56.7$	$\sum xy = 435.6$	$\sum x^2 = 1836$	$\sum y^2 = 587.05$

353

(b) $r = \dfrac{n\sum xy - (\sum x)(\sum y)}{\sqrt{n\sum x^2 - (\sum x)^2}\sqrt{n\sum y^2 - (\sum y)^2}}$

$= \dfrac{(7)(435.6) - (88)(56.7)}{\sqrt{(7)(1836) - (88)^2}\sqrt{(7)(587.05) - (56.7)^2}}$

$= \dfrac{-1940.4}{\sqrt{5108}\sqrt{894.46}} \approx -0.908$

(c) Because r is close to -1, this suggests a strong negative linear correlation between years out of school and annual contribution.

5ab. $r \approx 0.750$

   c. Because r is close to 1, this suggests a strong positive linear correlation between the salaries and the average attendances at home games.

6a. $n = 7$

   b. $\alpha = 0.01$

   c. 0.875

   d. $|r| \approx |0.908| > 0.875$; The correlation is significant.

   e. There is enough evidence at the 1% level of significance to conclude that there is a significant linear correlation between the number of years out of school and the annual contribution.

7a. $H_0 : \rho = 0$; $H_a : \rho \neq 0$

   b. $\alpha = 0.01$

   c. d.f. $= n - 2 = 28$

   d. $t_0 = \pm 2.763$; Rejection regions: $t < -2.763$ or $t > 2.763$

   e. $t = \dfrac{r}{\sqrt{\dfrac{1 - r^2}{n - 2}}} = \dfrac{0.74972}{\sqrt{\dfrac{1 - (0.74972)^2}{30 - 2}}} \approx 5.995$

   f. Reject H_0.

   g. There is enough evidence at the 1% level of significance to conclude that there is a significant linear correlation between the salaries and the average attendances at home games for the teams in Major League Baseball.

9.1 EXERCISE SOLUTIONS

1. Increase

2. Decrease

3. The range of values for the correlation coefficient is -1 to 1.

4. The sample correlation coefficient r measures the strength and direction of a linear relationship between two variables; $r = -0.932$ indicates a stronger correlation because $|-0.932| = 0.932$ is closer to 1 than $|0.918| = 0.918$.

5. Answers will vary. Sample answer:
    Perfect positive linear correlation: price per gallon of gasoline and total cost of gasoline
    Perfect negative linear correlation: distance from door and height of wheelchair ramp

6. A table can be used to compare r with a critical value, or a hypothesis test can be performed using a t-test.

7. r is the sample correlation coefficient, while ρ is the population correlation coefficient.

8. Answers will vary. Sample answer: The fact that two variables have a linear relationship does not necessarily imply that one variable is the cause of the other.

9. Negative linear correlation

10. No linear correlation

11. Perfect negative linear correlation

12. No linear correlation

13. Positive linear correlation

14. Perfect positive linear correlation

15. (c), You would expect a positive linear correlation between age and income.

16. (d), You would not expect age and height to be correlated.

17. (b), You would expect a negative linear correlation between age and balance on student loans.

18. (a), You would expect the relationship between age and body temperature to be fairly constant.

19. Explanatory variable: Amount of water consumed
    Response variable: Weight loss

20. Explanatory variable: Hours of safety classes
    Response variable: Number of accidents

21. (a)

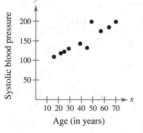

(b)

x	y	xy	x^2	y^2
16	109	1744	256	11,881
25	122	3050	625	14,884
39	143	5577	1521	20,449
45	132	5940	2025	17,424
49	199	9751	2401	39,601
64	185	11,840	4096	34,225
70	199	13,930	4900	39,601
29	130	3770	841	16,900
57	175	9975	3249	30,625
22	118	2596	484	13,924
$\sum x = 416$	$\sum y = 1512$	$\sum xy = 68{,}173$	$\sum x^2 = 20{,}398$	$\sum y^2 = 239{,}514$

$$r = \frac{n\sum xy - (\sum x)(\sum y)}{\sqrt{n\sum x^2 - (\sum x)^2}\sqrt{n\sum y^2 - (\sum y)^2}}$$

$$= \frac{10(68{,}173) - (416)(1512)}{\sqrt{10(20{,}398) - (416)^2}\sqrt{10(239{,}514) - (1512)^2}}$$

$$= \frac{52{,}738}{\sqrt{30{,}924}\sqrt{108{,}996}} \approx 0.908$$

(c) Strong positive linear correlation

22. (a)

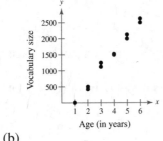

(b)

x	y	xy	x^2	y^2
1	3	3	1	9
2	400	880	4	193,600
3	1200	3600	9	1,440,000
4	1500	6000	16	2,250,000
5	2100	10,500	25	4,410,000
6	2600	15,600	36	6,760,000
3	1100	3300	9	1,210,000
5	2000	10,000	25	4,000,000
2	500	1000	4	250,000
4	1525	6100	16	2,325,625
6	2500	15,000	36	6,250,000
$\sum x = 41$	$\sum y = 15{,}468$	$\sum xy = 71{,}983$	$\sum x^2 = 181$	$\sum y^2 = 29{,}089{,}234$

$$r = \frac{n\sum xy - (\sum x)(\sum y)}{\sqrt{n\sum x^2 - (\sum x)^2}\sqrt{n\sum y^2 - (\sum y)^2}}$$

$$= \frac{11(71,983) - (41)(15,468)}{\sqrt{11(181) - (41)^2}\sqrt{11(29,089,234) - (15,468)^2}}$$

$$= \frac{157,625}{\sqrt{310}\sqrt{80,722,550}} \approx 0.996$$

(c) Strong positive linear correlation

23. (a)

Hours studying

(b)

x	y	xy	x^2	y^2
0	40	0	0	1600
1	41	41	1	1681
2	51	102	4	2601
4	48	192	16	2304
4	64	256	16	4096
5	69	345	25	4761
5	73	365	25	5329
5	75	375	25	5625
6	68	408	36	4624
6	93	558	36	8649
7	84	588	49	7056
7	90	630	49	8100
8	95	760	64	9025
$\sum x = 60$	$\sum y = 891$	$\sum xy = 4620$	$\sum x^2 = 346$	$\sum y^2 = 65,451$

$$r = \frac{n\sum xy - (\sum x)(\sum y)}{\sqrt{n\sum x^2 - (\sum x)^2}\sqrt{n\sum y^2 - (\sum y)^2}}$$

$$= \frac{13(4620) - (60)(891)}{\sqrt{13(346) - (60)^2}\sqrt{13(65,451) - (891)^2}}$$

$$= \frac{6600}{\sqrt{898}\sqrt{56,982}} \approx 0.923$$

(c) Strong positive linear correlation

24. (a)

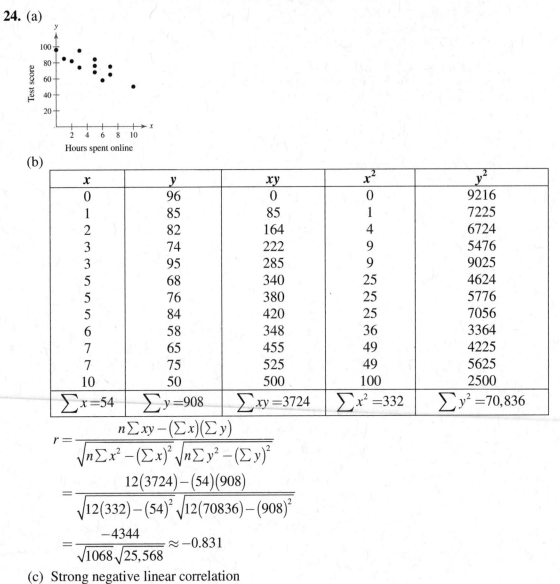

(b)

x	y	xy	x^2	y^2
0	96	0	0	9216
1	85	85	1	7225
2	82	164	4	6724
3	74	222	9	5476
3	95	285	9	9025
5	68	340	25	4624
5	76	380	25	5776
5	84	420	25	7056
6	58	348	36	3364
7	65	455	49	4225
7	75	525	49	5625
10	50	500	100	2500
$\sum x = 54$	$\sum y = 908$	$\sum xy = 3724$	$\sum x^2 = 332$	$\sum y^2 = 70{,}836$

$$r = \frac{n\sum xy - \left(\sum x\right)\left(\sum y\right)}{\sqrt{n\sum x^2 - \left(\sum x\right)^2}\sqrt{n\sum y^2 - \left(\sum y\right)^2}}$$

$$= \frac{12(3724) - (54)(908)}{\sqrt{12(332) - (54)^2}\sqrt{12(70836) - (908)^2}}$$

$$= \frac{-4344}{\sqrt{1068}\sqrt{25{,}568}} \approx -0.831$$

(c) Strong negative linear correlation

25. (a)

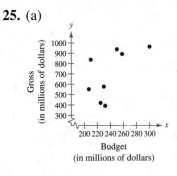

(b)

x	y	xy	x^2	y^2
300	961	288,300	90,000	923,521
258	891	229,878	66,564	793,881
250	937	234,250	62,500	877,969
210	836	175,560	44,100	698,896
232	391	90,712	53,824	152,881
230	576	132,480	52,900	331,776
225	419	94,275	50,625	175,561
207	551	114,057	42,849	303,601
$\sum x = 1912$	$\sum y = 5562$	$\sum xy = 1,359,512$	$\sum x^2 = 463,362$	$\sum y^2 = 4,258,086$

$$r = \frac{n\sum xy - (\sum x)(\sum y)}{\sqrt{n\sum x^2 - (\sum x)^2}\sqrt{n\sum y^2 - (\sum y)^2}}$$

$$= \frac{8(1,359,512) - (1912)(5562)}{\sqrt{8(463,362) - (1912)^2}\sqrt{8(4,258,086) - (5562)^2}}$$

$$= \frac{241,552}{\sqrt{51,152}\sqrt{3,128,844}} \approx 0.604$$

(c) Weak positive linear correlation

26. (a)

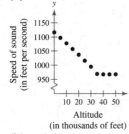

Altitude
(in thousands of feet)

(b)

x	y	xy	x^2	y^2
0	1116.3	0.000	0	1.25×10^6
5	1096.9	5484.5	25	1.2×10^6
10	1077.3	10,773	100	1.16×10^6
15	1057.2	15,858	225	1.12×10^6
20	1036.8	20,736	400	1.07×10^6
25	1015.8	25,395	625	1.03×10^6
30	994.5	29,835	900	989,030
35	969.0	33,915	1225	938,961
40	967.7	38,708	1600	936,443
45	967.7	43,547	2025	936,443
50	967.7	48,385	2500	936,443
$\sum x = 275$	$\sum y = 11,266.9$	$\sum xy = 272,636$	$\sum x^2 = 9625$	$\sum y^2 = 11,571,687.43$

$$r = \frac{n\sum xy - (\sum x)(\sum y)}{\sqrt{n\sum x^2 - (\sum x)^2}\sqrt{n\sum y^2 - (\sum y)^2}}$$

$$= \frac{11(272,636) - (275)(11,266.9)}{\sqrt{11(9625) - (275)^2}\sqrt{11(11,571,687.43) - (11,266.9)^2}}$$

$$= \frac{-99,401.5}{\sqrt{30,250}\sqrt{345,526.12}} \approx -0.972$$

(c) Strong negative linear correlation

27. (a)

Earnings per share

(b)

x	y	xy	x^2	y^2
6.00	2.45	14.7000	36.0000	6.0025
1.44	0.15	0.2160	2.0736	0.0225
4.44	0.62	2.7528	19.7136	0.3844
3.38	0.91	3.0758	11.4244	0.8281
3.63	0.68	2.4684	13.1769	0.4624
4.46	1.14	5.0844	19.8916	1.2996
3.80	0.52	1.9760	14.4400	0.2704
1.43	0.06	0.0858	2.0449	0.0036
1.88	0.19	0.3572	3.5344	0.0361
4.57	1.80	8.2260	20.8849	3.2400
4.28	0.48	2.0544	18.3184	0.2304
2.92	0.63	1.8396	8.5264	0.3969
$\sum x = 42.23$	$\sum y = 9.63$	$\sum xy = 42.8364$	$\sum x^2 = 170.0291$	$\sum y^2 = 13.1769$

$$r = \frac{n\sum xy - (\sum x)(\sum y)}{\sqrt{n\sum x^2 - (\sum x)^2}\sqrt{n\sum y^2 - (\sum y)^2}}$$

$$= \frac{12(42.8364) - (42.23)(9.63)}{\sqrt{12(170.0291) - (42.23)^2}\sqrt{12(13.1769) - (9.63)^2}}$$

$$= \frac{107.3619}{\sqrt{256.9763}\sqrt{65.3859}} \approx 0.828$$

(c) Strong positive linear correlation

28. (a)

(b)

x	y	xy	x^2	y^2
1.60	0.78	1.2480	2.5600	0.6084
1.55	0.80	1.2400	2.4025	0.6400
1.44	0.73	1.0512	2.0736	0.5329
1.40	0.72	1.0080	1.9600	0.5184
1.32	0.68	0.8976	1.7424	0.4624
1.23	0.64	0.7872	1.5129	0.4096
1.22	0.63	0.7686	1.4884	0.3969
1.23	0.63	0.7749	1.5129	0.3969
1.22	0.62	0.7564	1.4884	0.3844
1.18	0.60	0.7080	1.3924	0.3600
1.16	0.59	0.6844	1.3456	0.3481
1.19	0.60	0.7140	1.4161	0.3600
1.21	0.61	0.7381	1.4641	0.3720
1.20	0.58	0.6960	1.4400	0.3364
$\sum x = 18.15$	$\sum y = 9.21$	$\sum xy = 12.0724$	$\sum x^2 = 23.7993$	$\sum y^2 = 6.1265$

$$r = \frac{n\sum xy - \left(\sum x\right)\left(\sum y\right)}{\sqrt{n\sum x^2 - \left(\sum x\right)^2}\sqrt{n\sum y^2 - \left(\sum y\right)^2}}$$

$$= \frac{14(12.0724) - (18.15)(9.21)}{\sqrt{14(23.7993) - (18.15)^2}\sqrt{14(6.1265) - (9.21)^2}}$$

$$= \frac{1.8521}{\sqrt{3.7677}\sqrt{0.9469}} \approx 0.981$$

(c) Strong positive linear correlation

29. The correlation coefficient becomes $r \approx 0.621$. The new data entry is an outlier, so the linear correlation is weaker.

30. The correlation coefficient becomes $r \approx -0.343$. The new data entry is an outlier, so the linear correlation is weaker.

31. $r \approx 0.623$

$n = 8$ and $\alpha = 0.01$

critical value $= 0.834$

$|r| \approx 0.623 < 0.834 \Rightarrow$ The correlation is not significant.

or

$H_0: \rho = 0; \ H_a: \rho \neq 0$

$\alpha = 0.01$

d.f. $= n - 2 = 6$

$t_0 = \pm 3.703$; Rejection regions: $t < -3.707$ or $t > 3.707$.

$$t = \frac{r}{\sqrt{\dfrac{1-r^2}{n-2}}} = \frac{0.623}{\sqrt{\dfrac{1-(0.623)^2}{8-2}}} \approx 1.951$$

Fail to reject H_0. There is not enough evidence at the 1% level of significance to conclude that there is a significant linear correlation between vehicle weight and the variability in braking distance.

32. $r \approx 0.955$

$n = 8$ and $\alpha = 0.05$

critical value $= 0.707$

$|r| = 0.955 > 0.707 \Rightarrow$ The correlation is significant.

or

$H_0: \rho = 0; \ H_a: \rho \neq 0$

$\alpha = 0.05$

d.f. $= n - 2 = 6$

$t_0 = \pm 2.447$; Rejection regions: $t < -2.447$ or $t > 2.447$.

$$t = \frac{r}{\sqrt{\dfrac{1-r^2}{n-2}}} = \frac{0.955}{\sqrt{\dfrac{1-(0.955)^2}{8-2}}} \approx 7.887$$

Reject H_0. There is enough evidence at the 5% level of significance to conclude that there is a significant linear correlation between vehicle weight and the variability in braking distance.

33. $r \approx 0.923$

$n = 13$ and $\alpha = 0.01$

critical value $= 0.684$

$|r| = 0.923 > 0.684 \Rightarrow$ The correlation is significant.

or

$H_0 : \rho = 0; H_a : \rho \neq 0$

$\alpha = 0.01$

d.f. $= n - 2 = 11$

$t_0 = \pm 3.106$; Rejection regions: $t < -3.106$ or $t > 3.106$.

$r \approx 0.923$

$$t = \frac{r}{\sqrt{\dfrac{1-r^2}{n-2}}} = \frac{0.923}{\sqrt{\dfrac{1-(0.923)^2}{13-2}}} \approx 7.955$$

Reject H_0. There is enough evidence at the 1% level of significance to conclude that a significant linear correlation exists.

34. $r \approx -0.831$

$n = 12$ and $\alpha = 0.05$

critical value $= 0.576$

$|r| = 0.831 > 0.576 \Rightarrow$ The correlation is significant.

or

$H_0 : \rho = 0; H_a : \rho \neq 0$

$\alpha = 0.05$

d.f. $= n - 2 = 10$

$t_0 = \pm 2.228$; Rejection regions: $t < -2.228$ or $t > 2.228$.

$r \approx -0.831$

$$t = \frac{r}{\sqrt{\dfrac{1-r^2}{n-2}}} = \frac{-0.831}{\sqrt{\dfrac{1-(-0.831)^2}{12-2}}} \approx -4.724$$

Reject H_0. There is enough evidence at the 5% level of significance to conclude that there is a significant linear correlation between the data.

35. $r \approx 0.828$

$n = 12$ and $\alpha = 0.01$

critical value $= 0.708$

$|r| \approx 0.828 > 0.708 \Rightarrow$ The correlation is significant.

or

$H_0 : \rho = 0; \ H_a : \rho \neq 0$

$\alpha = 0.01$

d.f. $= n - 2 = 10$

$t_0 = \pm 3.169$; Rejection regions: $t < -3.169$ or $t > 3.169$.

$r \approx 0.828$

$$t = \frac{r}{\sqrt{\dfrac{1-r^2}{n-2}}} = \frac{0.828}{\sqrt{\dfrac{1-(0.828)^2}{12-2}}} \approx 4.670$$

Reject H_0. There is enough evidence at the 1% level of significance to conclude that there is a significant linear correlation between earnings per share and dividends per share.

36. $r \approx 0.981$

$n = 14$ and $\alpha = 0.05$

critical value $= 0.532$

$|r| \approx 0.981 > 0.532 \Rightarrow$ The correlation is significant.

or

$H_0 : \rho = 0; \ H_a : \rho \neq 0$

$\alpha = 0.05$

d.f. $= n - 2 = 12$

$t_0 = \pm 2.179$; Rejection regions: $t < -2.179$ or $t > 2.179$.

$r \approx 0.981$

$$t = \frac{r}{\sqrt{\dfrac{1-r^2}{n-2}}} = \frac{0.981}{\sqrt{\dfrac{1-(0.981)^2}{14-2}}} \approx 17.516$$

Reject H_0. There is enough evidence at the 5% level of significance to conclude that there is a significant linear correlation between crimes and arrests.

37. (a)

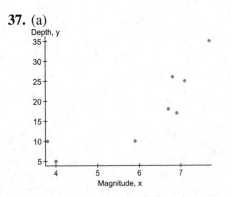

(b) 0.848

(c) Reject H_0. There is enough evidence at the 1% level of significance to conclude that there is a significant linear correlation between the magnitudes of earthquakes and their depths below the surface at the epicenter.

38. (a)

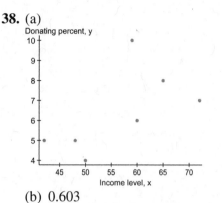

(b) 0.603

(c) Fail to reject H_0. There is not enough evidence at the 5% level of significance to conclude that there is a significant linear correlation between family income level and percent of income donated to charities.

39. The correlation coefficient becomes $r \approx 0.085$. The new rejection regions are $t < -3.499$ and $t > 3.499$ and the new standardized test statistic is $t \approx 0.227$. So, now you fail to reject H_0.

40. The correlation coefficient becomes $r \approx -0.042$. The new rejection regions are $t < -2.447$ and $t > 2.447$ and the new standardized test statistic is $t \approx -0.102$. So, you still fail to reject H_0.

41. 0.883; 0.883; The correlation coefficient remains unchanged when the x-values and y-values are switched.

42. -0.779; -0.779; The correlation coefficient remains unchanged when the x-values and y-values are switched.

43. Answers will vary.

9.2 LINEAR REGRESSION

9.2 Try It Yourself Solutions

1a. $n = 7$

$$\sum x = 88$$
$$\sum y = 56.7$$
$$\sum xy = 435.6$$
$$\sum x^2 = 1836$$

b. $m = \dfrac{n\sum xy - (\sum x)(\sum y)}{n\sum x^2 - (\sum x)^2}$

$= \dfrac{(7)(435.6) - (88)(56.7)}{(7)(1836) - (88)^2}$

$= \dfrac{-1940.4}{5108} \approx -0.379875$

$b = \bar{y} - m\bar{x} = \dfrac{\sum y}{n} - m\dfrac{\sum x}{n}$

$\approx \dfrac{(56.7)}{7} - (-0.379875)\dfrac{(88)}{7}$

≈ 12.8756

c. $\hat{y} = -0.380x + 12.876$

2a. Enter the data.

b. $m \approx 189.038015$

$b \approx 13,497.9583$

c. $\hat{y} = 189.038x + 13,497.958$

3a. (1) $\hat{y} = 12.481(2) + 33.683$ (2) $\hat{y} = 12.481(3.32) + 33.683$

b. (1) 58.645   (2) 75.120

c. (1) 58.645 minutes   (2) 75.120 minutes

9.2 EXERCISE SOLUTIONS

1. A residual is the difference between the observed y-value of a data point and the predicted y-value on the regression line for the x-coordinate of the data point. A residual is positive when the data point is above the line, negative when the point is below the line, and zero when the observed y-value equals the predicted y-value.

2. Positive

3. Substitute a value of x into the equation of a regression line and solve for y.

4. Prediction values are meaningful only for x-values in (or close to) the range of the original data.

5. The correlation between variables must be significant.

6. Answers will vary. Sample answer: Because the regression line models the trend of the given data, and it is not known if the trend continues beyond the range of those data.

7. b   **8.** a   **9.** e   **10.** c   **11.** f

12. d   **13.** c   **14.** b   **15.** a   **16.** d

17.

x	y	xy	x^2
869	60	52,140	755,161
820	50	41,000	672,400
771	50	38,550	594,441
696	52	36,192	484,416
692	40	27,680	478,864
676	47	31,772	456,976
656	41	26,896	430,336
492	39	19,188	242,064
486	26	12,636	236,196
$\sum x = 6158$	$\sum y = 405$	$\sum xy = 286,054$	$\sum x^2 = 4,350,854$

$$m = \frac{n\sum xy - (\sum x)(\sum y)}{n\sum x^2 - (\sum x)^2}$$

$$= \frac{(9)(286,054) - (6158)(405)}{(9)(4,350,854) - (6158)^2}$$

$$= \frac{80,496}{1,236,722} \approx 0.065088$$

$$b = \overline{y} - m\overline{x} = \frac{\sum y}{n} - m\frac{\sum x}{n}$$

$$\approx \frac{405}{9} - (0.065088)\left(\frac{6158}{9}\right)$$

$$\approx 0.4653$$

$$\hat{y} = mx + b = 0.065x + 0.465$$

(a) $\hat{y} = 0.065(800) + 0.465 \approx 52$

(b) $\hat{y} = 0.065(750) + 0.465 \approx 49$

(c) It is not meaningful to predict the value of y for $x = 400$ because $x = 400$ is outside the range of the original data.

(d) $\hat{y} = 0.065(625) + 0.465 \approx 41$

18.

x	y	xy	x^2
1924	174.9	336,507.6	3,701,776
1592	136.9	217,944.8	2,534,464
2413	275.0	663,575.0	5,822,569
2332	219.9	512,806.8	5,438,224
1552	120.0	186,240.0	2,408,704
1312	99.9	131,310.0	1,721,344
1278	145.0	185,310.0	1,633,284
$\sum x = 12,403$	$\sum y = 1171.6$	$\sum xy = 2,233,453$	$\sum x^2 = 23,260,365$

$$m = \frac{n\sum xy - (\sum x)(\sum y)}{n\sum x^2 - (\sum x)^2}$$

$$= \frac{(7)(2,233,453) - (12,403)(1171.6)}{(7)(23,260,365) - (12,403)^2}$$

$$= \frac{1,102,816}{8,988,146} \approx 0.122697$$

$$b = \bar{y} - m\bar{x} = \frac{\sum y}{n} - m\frac{\sum x}{n}$$

$$\approx \frac{1171.6}{7} - (0.122697)\left(\frac{12,403}{7}\right)$$

$$\approx -50.0301$$

$$\hat{y} = 0.123x - 50.030$$

(a) $\hat{y} = 0.123(1450) - 50.030 = 128.32$

(b) It is not meaningful to predict the value of y for $x = 2720$ because $x = 2720$ is outside the range of the original data.

(c) $\hat{y} = 0.123(2175) - 50.030 = 217.495$

(d) $\hat{y} = 0.123(1890) - 50.030 = 182.44$

19.

x	y	xy	x^2
0	40	0	0
1	41	41	1
2	51	102	4
4	48	192	16
4	64	256	16
5	69	345	25
5	73	365	25
5	75	375	25
6	68	408	36
6	93	558	36
7	84	588	49
7	90	630	49
8	95	760	64
$\sum x = 60$	$\sum y = 891$	$\sum xy = 4620$	$\sum x^2 = 346$

$$m = \frac{n\sum xy - \left(\sum x\right)\left(\sum y\right)}{n\sum x^2 - \left(\sum x\right)^2}$$

$$= \frac{(13)(4620) - (60)(891)}{(13)(346) - (60)^2}$$

$$= \frac{6600}{898} \approx 7.349666$$

$$b = \overline{y} - m\overline{x} \approx \left(\frac{891}{13}\right) - (7.349666)\left(\frac{60}{13}\right) \approx 34.6169$$

$$\hat{y} = 7.350x + 34.617$$

(a) $\hat{y} = 7.350(3) + 34.617 \approx 57$

(b) $\hat{y} = 7.350(6.5) + 34.617 \approx 82$

(c) It is not meaningful to predict the value of y for $x = 13$ because $x = 13$ is outside the range of the original data.

(d) $\hat{y} = 7.350(4.5) + 34.617 \approx 68$

20.

x	y	xy	x^2
0	96	0	0
1	85	85	1
2	82	164	4
3	74	222	9
3	95	285	9
5	68	340	25
5	76	380	25
5	84	420	25
6	58	348	36
7	65	455	49
7	75	525	49
10	50	500	100
$\sum x = 54$	$\sum y = 908$	$\sum xy = 3724$	$\sum x^2 = 332$

$$m = \frac{x\sum xy - (\sum x)(\sum y)}{n\sum x^2 - (\sum x)^2}$$

$$= \frac{(12)(3724) - (54)(908)}{(12)(332) - (54)^2}$$

$$= \frac{-4344}{1068} \approx -4.067416$$

$$b = \overline{y} - m\overline{x} \approx \left(\frac{908}{12}\right) - (-4.067416)\left(\frac{54}{12}\right) \approx 93.9700$$

$$\hat{y} = -4.067x + 93.970$$

(a) $\hat{y} = -4.067(4) + 93.970 \approx 78$

(b) $\hat{y} = -4.067(8) + 93.970 \approx 61$

(c) $\hat{y} = -4.067(9) + 93.970 \approx 57$

(d) It is not meaningful to predict the value of y for $x = 15$ because $x = 15$ is outside the range of the original data.

21.

x	y	xy	x^2
150	420	63,000	22,500
170	470	79,900	28,900
120	350	42,000	14,400
120	360	43,200	14,400
90	270	24,300	8,100
180	550	99,000	32,400
170	530	90,100	28,900
140	460	64,400	19,600
90	380	34,200	8,100
110	330	36,300	12,100
$\sum x = 1340$	$\sum y = 4120$	$\sum xy = 576,400$	$\sum x^2 = 189,400$

$$m = \frac{x\sum xy - (\sum x)(\sum y)}{n\sum x^2 - (\sum x)^2}$$

$$= \frac{(10)(576,400) - (1340)(4120)}{(10)(189,400) - (1340)^2}$$

$$= \frac{243,200}{98,400} \approx 2.471545$$

$$b = \bar{y} - m\bar{x} \approx \left(\frac{4120}{10}\right) - (2.471545)\left(\frac{1340}{10}\right) \approx 80.8130$$

$$\hat{y} = 2.472x + 80.813$$

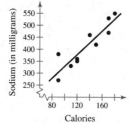

(a) $\hat{y} = 2.472(170) + 80.813 = 501.053$ milligrams

(b) $\hat{y} = 2.472(100) + 80.813 = 328.013$ milligrams

(c) $\hat{y} = 2.472(140) + 80.813 = 426.893$ milligrams

(d) It is not meaningful to predict the value of y for $x = 210$ because $x = 210$ is outside the range of the original data.

22.

x	y	xy	x^2
140	6	840	19,600
200	9	1800	40,000
160	6	960	25,600
170	9	1530	28,900
170	10	1700	28,900
190	17	3230	36,100
190	13	2470	36,100
210	18	3780	44,100
190	19	3610	36,100
170	10	1700	28,900
160	10	1600	25,600
$\sum x = 1950$	$\sum y = 127$	$\sum xy = 23,220$	$\sum x^2 = 349,900$

$$m = \frac{x\sum xy - (\sum x)(\sum y)}{n\sum x^2 - (\sum x)^2}$$

$$= \frac{(11)(23,220) - (1950)(127)}{(11)(349,900) - (1950)^2}$$

$$= \frac{7770}{46,400} \approx 0.167457$$

$$b = \bar{y} - m\bar{x} \approx \left(\frac{127}{11}\right) - (0.167457)\left(\frac{1950}{10}\right) \approx -18.1400$$

$$\hat{y} = 0.167x - 18.140$$

(a) $\hat{y} = 0.167(150) - 18.140 = 6.91$ grams

(b) It is not meaningful to predict the value of y for $x = 90$ because $x = 90$ is outside the range of the original data.

(c) $\hat{y} = 0.167(175) - 18.140 = 11.085$ grams

(d) $\hat{y} = 0.167(208) - 18.140 = 16.596$ grams

23.

x	y	xy	x^2
8.5	66.0	561.00	72.25
9.0	68.5	616.50	81.00
9.0	67.5	607.50	81.00
9.5	70.0	665.00	90.25
10.0	70.0	700.00	100.00
10.0	72.0	720.00	100.00
10.5	71.5	750.75	110.25
10.5	69.5	729.75	110.25
11.0	71.5	786.50	121.00
11.0	72.0	792.00	121.00
11.0	73.0	803.00	121.00
12.0	73.5	882.00	144.00
12.0	74.0	888.00	144.00
12.5	74.0	925.00	156.25
$\sum x = 146.5$	$\sum y = 993.0$	$\sum xy = 10,427.0$	$\sum x^2 = 1552.25$

$$m = \frac{x\sum xy - (\sum x)(\sum y)}{n\sum x^2 - (\sum x)^2}$$

$$= \frac{(14)(10,427.0) - (146.5)(993.0)}{(14)(1552.25) - (146.5)^2}$$

$$= \frac{503.5}{269.25} \approx 1.870009$$

$$b = \overline{y} - m\overline{x} \approx \left(\frac{993.0}{14}\right) - (1.870)\left(\frac{146.5}{14}\right) \approx 51.3603$$

$$\hat{y} = 1.870x + 51.360$$

(a) $\hat{y} = 1.870(11.5) + 51.360 = 72.865$ inches

(b) $\hat{y} = 1.870(8.0) + 51.360 = 66.32$ inches

(c) It is not meaningful to predict the value of y for $x = 15.5$ because $x = 15.5$ is outside the range of the original data.

(d) $\hat{y} = 1.870(10.0) + 51.360 = 70.06$ inches

24.

x	y	xy	x^2
0.1	14.9	1.49	0.01
0.2	14.5	2.90	0.04
0.4	13.9	5.56	0.16
0.7	14.1	9.87	0.49
0.6	13.9	8.34	0.36
0.9	13.7	12.33	0.81
0.1	14.3	1.43	0.01
0.2	13.9	2.78	0.04
0.4	14.0	5.60	0.16
0.9	14.1	12.69	0.81
$\sum x = 4.5$	$\sum y = 141.3$	$\sum xy = 62.99$	$\sum x^2 = 2.89$

$$m = \frac{x\sum xy - (\sum x)(\sum y)}{n\sum x^2 - (\sum x)^2}$$

$$= \frac{(10)(62.99) - (4.5)(141.3)}{(10)(2.89) - (4.5)^2}$$

$$= \frac{-5.95}{8.65} \approx -0.687861$$

$$b = \bar{y} - m\bar{x} \approx \left(\frac{141.3}{10}\right) - (-0.687861)\left(\frac{4.5}{10}\right) \approx 14.4395$$

$$\hat{y} = -0.688x + 14.440$$

Age (in years)

(a) $\hat{y} = -0.688(0.3) + 14.440 = 14.234$ hours

(b) It is not meaningful to predict the value of y for $x = 3.9$ because $x = 3.9$ is outside the range of the original data.

(c) $\hat{y} = -0.688(0.6) + 14.440 = 14.027$ hours

(d) $\hat{y} = -0.688(0.8) + 14.440 = 13.89$ hours

25. Strong positive linear correlation; As the years of experience of registered nurses increase. their salaries tend to increase.

26.

$\hat{y} = 43.214 - 0.9976x$

27. No, it is not meaningful to predict a salary for a registered nurse with 28 years of experience because $x = 28$ is outside the range of the original data.

28. $|r| \approx 0.880 > 0.661$ (the critical value), so the population has a significant correlation.

29. Answers will vary. Sample answer: Although it is likely that there is a cause-and-effect relationship between a registered nurse's years of experience and salary, the relationship between variables may also be influenced by other factors, such as work performance, level of education, or the number of years with an employer.

30a. $\hat{y} = 0.024x + 0.181$

  b. $r \approx 0.773$

  c.

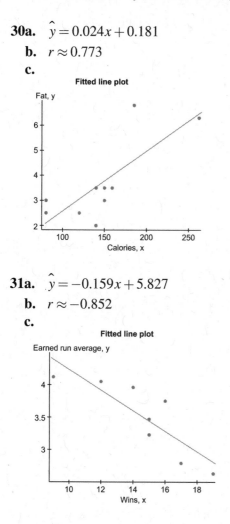

31a. $\hat{y} = -0.159x + 5.827$

  b. $r \approx -0.852$

  c.

Fitted line plot

Earned run average, y

Wins, x

32. (a) $\hat{y} = 1.724x + 79.733$ (b) $\hat{y} = 0.453x - 26.448$

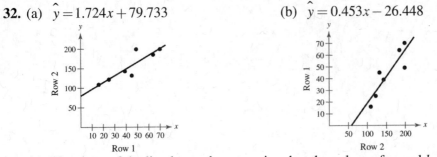

(c) The slope of the line keeps the same sign, but the values of m and b change.

33. (a)   (b)

$\hat{y} = -4.297x + 94.200$ $\hat{y} = -0.1413x + 14.763$

(c) The slope of the line keeps the same sign, but the values of m and b change.

34. (a) $m \approx 1.711$ (b)

$b \approx 3.912$

$\hat{y} = 1.711x + 3.912$

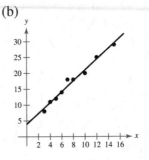

(c)

x	y	$\hat{y} = 1.711x + 3.912$	$y - \hat{y}$
8	18	17.600	0.400
4	11	10.756	0.244
15	29	29.577	−0.577
7	18	15.889	2.111
6	14	14.178	−0.178
3	8	9.045	−1.045
12	25	24.444	0.556
10	20	21.022	−1.022
5	12	12.467	−0.467

(d) The residual plot shows no pattern in the residuals because the residuals fluctuate about 0. This suggests that the regression line is a good representation of the data.

35. (a) $m \approx 0.139$

$b \approx 21.024$

$\hat{y} = 0.139x + 21.024$

(b)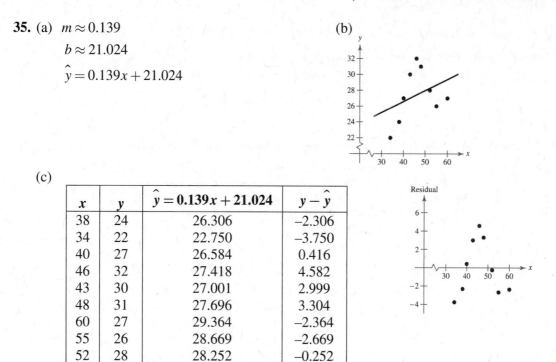

(c)

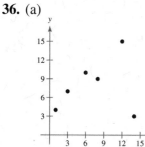

x	y	$\hat{y} = 0.139x + 21.024$	$y - \hat{y}$
38	24	26.306	−2.306
34	22	22.750	−3.750
40	27	26.584	0.416
46	32	27.418	4.582
43	30	27.001	2.999
48	31	27.696	3.304
60	27	29.364	−2.364
55	26	28.669	−2.669
52	28	28.252	−0.252

(d) The residual plot shows a pattern because the residuals do not fluctuate about 0. This implies that the regression line is not a good representation of the relationship between the variables.

36. (a)

(b) The point (14, 3) may be an outlier.

(c) The point (14, 3) is influential because using all 6 points $\Rightarrow \hat{y} = 0.212x + 6.445$.

However, excluding the point (14, 3) $\Rightarrow \hat{y} = 0.905x + 3.568$

The slopes and y-intercepts of the regression lines with the point included and without the point included are significantly different.

37. (a)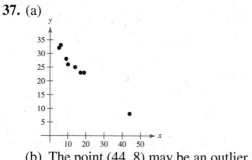

(b) The point (44, 8) may be an outlier.

(c) Excluding the point (44, 8) $\Rightarrow \hat{y} = -0.711x + 35.263$. The point (44, 8) is not influential because using all 8 points $\Rightarrow \hat{y} = -0.607x + 34.160$.

The slopes and y-intercepts with the point included and without the point are not significantly different.

38. The point (201.4, 45,364) is an outlier because it is far removed from the other entries in the data set; The point (201.4, 45,364) is influential because using all 30 points $\Rightarrow \hat{y} = 189.038x + 13,497.958$. However, excluding the point (201.4, 45,364) $\Rightarrow \hat{y} = 225.022x + 10,653.695$. The slopes and y-intercepts of the regression lines with the point included and without the point included are significantly different.

39. $m \approx 654.536$

$b \approx -1214.857$

$\hat{y} = 654.536x - 1214.857$

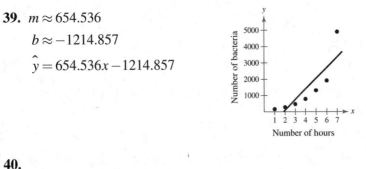

40.

x	y	$\log y$
1	165	2.218
2	280	2.447
3	468	2.670
4	780	2.892
5	1310	3.117
6	1920	3.283
7	4900	3.690

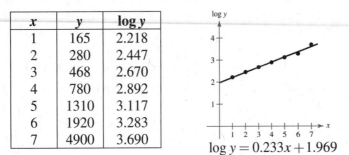

$\log y = 0.233x + 1.969$

41. Using a technology tool $\Rightarrow y = 93.028(1.712)^x$.

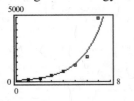

42. The exponential equation is a much better model for the data. The graph of the exponential equation fits the data better than the regression line.

43. $m = -78.929$

$b = 576.179$

$\hat{y} = -78.929x + 576.179$

44.

x	y	$\log x$	$\log y$
1	695	0	2.842
2	410	0.301	2.613
3	256	0.477	2.408
4	110	0.602	2.041
5	80	0.699	1.903
6	75	0.778	1.875
7	68	0.845	1.833
8	74	0.903	1.869

$$\log y = m(\log x) + b \Rightarrow \log y = -1.251 \, \log x + 2.893$$

A linear model is more appropriate for the transformed data.

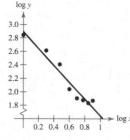

45. Using a technology tool $\Rightarrow y = 782.300x^{-1.251}$.

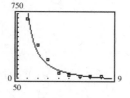

46. The power equation is a much better model for the data. The graph of the power equation fits the data much better than the regression line.

47. $y = a + b \ln x = 25.035 + 19.599 \ln x$ **48.** $\hat{y} = a + b \ln x = 13.8116 - 0.2966 \ln x$

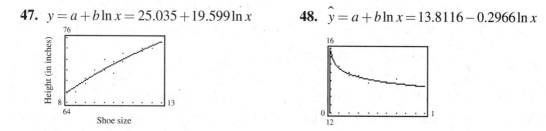

49. The logarithmic equation is a better model for the data. The graph of the logarithmic equation fits the data better than the regression line.

50. The logarithmic equation is a better model for the data. The graph of the logarithmic equation fits the data better than the regression line.

9.3 MEASURES OF REGRESSION AND PREDICTION INTERVALS

9.3 Try It Yourself Solutions

1a. $r \approx 0.979$ **b.** $r^2 \approx (0.979)^2 \approx 0.958$

c. About 95.8% of the variation in the times is explained.
About 4.2% of the variation is unexplained.

2a.

x_i	y_i	$\hat{y}_i$	$y_i - \hat{y}_i$	$\left(y_i - \hat{y}_i\right)^2$
15	26	28.386	−2.386	5.693
20	32	35.411	−3.411	11.635
20	38	35.411	2.589	6.703
30	56	49.461	6.539	42.759
40	54	63.511	−9.511	90.459
45	78	70.536	7.464	55.711
50	80	77.561	2.439	5.949
60	88	91.611	−3.611	13.039
				$\sum = 231.948$

b. $n = 8$

c. $s_e = \sqrt{\dfrac{\sum\left(y_i - \hat{y}_i\right)^2}{n-2}} = \sqrt{\dfrac{231.948}{6}} \approx 6.218$

d. The standard error of estimate of the weekly sales for a specific radio ad time is about $621.80.

3a. $n = 10$, d.f. $= 8$, $t_c = 2.306$, $s_e \approx 138.255$

b. $\hat{y} = 196.152(4.0) + 102.289 = 886.897$

c. $E = t_c s_e \sqrt{1 + \dfrac{1}{n} + \dfrac{n\left(x - \overline{x}\right)^2}{n\left(\sum x^2\right) - \left(\sum x\right)^2}}$

$\approx (2.306)(138.255)\sqrt{1 + \dfrac{1}{10} + \dfrac{10(4.0 - 2.31)^2}{10(67.35) - (23.1)^2}}$

≈ 364.088

d. $\hat{y} + E \rightarrow (522.809,\ 1250.985)$

e. You can be 95% confident that when the gross domestic product is $4 trillion, the carbon dioxide emissions will be between 522.809 and 1250.985 million metric tons.

9.3 EXERCISE SOLUTIONS

1. Total variation $= \sum \left(y_i - \overline{y} \right)^2$; the sum of the squares of the differences between the y-values of each ordered pair and the mean of the y-values of the ordered pairs.

2. Explained variation $= \sum \left(\hat{y}_i - \overline{y} \right)^2$; the sum of the squares of the differences between the predicted y-values and the mean of the y-values of the ordered pairs.

3. Unexplained variation $= \sum \left(y_i - \hat{y}_i \right)^2$; the sum of the squares of the differences between the observed y-values and the predicted y-values.

4. Coefficient of determination: $r^2 = \dfrac{\sum \left(\hat{y}_i - \overline{y} \right)^2}{\sum \left(y_i - \overline{y} \right)^2}$

   r^2 is the ratio of the explained variation to the total variation and is the percent of variation of y that is explained by the relationship between x and y. $1 - r^2$ is the percent of variation that is unexplained.

5. Two variables that have perfect positive or perfect negative linear correlation have a correlation coefficient of 1 or -1, respectively. In either case, the coefficient of determination is 1, which means that 100% of the variation in the response variable is explained by the variation in the explanatory variable.

6. Two variables have a bivariate normal distribution when, for any fixed values of either variable, the corresponding values of the other variable are normally distributed.

7. $r^2 = (0.465)^2 \approx 0.216$; About 21.6% of the variation is explained. About 78.4% of the variation is unexplained.

8. $r^2 = (-0.328)^2 \approx 0.108$; About 10.8% of the variation is explained. About 89.2% of the variation is unexplained.

9. $r^2 = (-0.957)^2 \approx 0.916$; About 91.6% of the variation is explained. About 8.4% of the variation is unexplained.

10. $r^2 = (0.881)^2 \approx 0.776$; About 77.6% of the variation is explained. About 22.4% of the variation is unexplained.

11. (a) $r^2 = \dfrac{\sum \left(\hat{y}_i - \overline{y} \right)^2}{\sum \left(y_i - \overline{y} \right)^2} \approx 0.798$

    About 79.8% of the variation in proceeds can be explained by the variation in the number of issues, and about 20.2% of the variation is unexplained.

(b) $s_e = \sqrt{\dfrac{\sum\left(y_i - \widehat{y}_i\right)^2}{n-2}} = \sqrt{\dfrac{650,383,054}{10}} \approx 8064.633$

The standard error of estimate of the proceeds for a specific number of issues is about $8,064,633,000.

12. (a) $r^2 = \dfrac{\sum\left(\widehat{y}_i - \overline{y}\right)^2}{\sum\left(y_i - \overline{y}\right)^2} \approx 0.909$

About 90.9% of the variation in the amount of crude oil imported can be explained by the variation in the amount of crude oil produced, and about 9.1% of the variation is unexplained.

(b) $s_e = \sqrt{\dfrac{\sum\left(y_i - \widehat{y}_i\right)^2}{n-2}} = \sqrt{\dfrac{454,987.745}{5}} \approx 301.658$

The standard error of estimate of the amount of crude oil imported for a specific amount of crude oil produced is about 301,658 barrels per day.

13. (a) $r^2 = \dfrac{\sum\left(\widehat{y}_i - \overline{y}\right)^2}{\sum\left(y_i - \overline{y}\right)^2} \approx 0.981$

About 98.1% of the variation in sales can be explained by the variation in the total square footage, and about 1.9% of the variation is unexplained.

(b) $s_e = \sqrt{\dfrac{\sum\left(y_i - \widehat{y}_i\right)^2}{n-2}} = \sqrt{\dfrac{8413.958}{9}} \approx 30.576$

The standard error of estimate of the sales for a specific total square footage is about 30,576,000,000.

14. (a) $r^2 = \dfrac{\sum\left(\widehat{y}_i - \overline{y}\right)^2}{\sum\left(y_i - \overline{y}\right)^2} \approx 0.578$

About 57.8% of the variation in the median number of leisure hours per week can be explained by the variation in the median number of work hours per week, and about 42.2% of the variation is unexplained.

(b) $s_e = \sqrt{\dfrac{\sum\left(y_i - \widehat{y}_i\right)^2}{n-2}} = \sqrt{\dfrac{32.419}{8}} \approx 2.013$

The standard error of estimate of the median number of leisure hours per week for a specific median number of hours per week is about 2.013 hours.

15. (a) $r^2 = \dfrac{\sum\left(\widehat{y}_i - \overline{y}\right)^2}{\sum\left(y_i - \overline{y}\right)^2} \approx 0.963$

About 96.3% of the variation in wages for federal government employees can be explained by the variation in wages for state government employees, and about 3.7% of the variation is unexplained.

(b) $s_e = \sqrt{\dfrac{\sum(y_i - \hat{y}_i)^2}{n-2}} = \sqrt{\dfrac{1614.4324}{4}} \approx 20.090$

The standard error of estimate of the average weekly wages for federal government employees for a specific average weekly wage for state government employees is about 20.09.

16. (a) $r^2 = \dfrac{\sum(\hat{y}_i - \bar{y})^2}{\sum(y_i - \bar{y})^2} \approx 0.919$

About 91.9% of the variation in the turnout for federal elections can be explained by the variation in the voting age population, and about 8.1% of the variation is unexplained.

(b) $s_e = \sqrt{\dfrac{\sum(y_i - \hat{y}_i)^2}{n-2}} = \sqrt{\dfrac{31.933}{6}} \approx 2.307$

The standard error of estimate of the turnout in a federal election for a specific voting age population is about 2,307,000.

17. (a) $r^2 = \dfrac{\sum(\hat{y}_i - \bar{y})^2}{\sum(y_i - \bar{y})^2} \approx 0.790$

About 79.0% of the variation in the gross collection of corporate income taxes can be explained by the variation in the gross collections of individual income taxes, and about 21.0% of the variation is unexplained.

(b) $s_e = \sqrt{\dfrac{\sum(y_i - \hat{y}_i)^2}{n-2}} = \sqrt{\dfrac{8982.865}{5}} \approx 42.386$

The standard error of estimate of the gross collections of corporate income taxes for a specific gross collection of individual income taxes is about \$42,386,000,000.

18. (a) $r^2 = \dfrac{\sum(\hat{y}_i - \bar{y})^2}{\sum(y_i - \bar{y})^2} \approx 0.7704$

About 77.04% of the variation in assets in federal pension plans can be explained by the variation in IRAs, and about 22.96% of the variation is unexplained.

(b) $s_e = \sqrt{\dfrac{\sum(y_i - \hat{y}_i)^2}{n-2}} = \sqrt{\dfrac{42,262.56}{7}} \approx 77.70$

The standard error of estimate of assets in federal pension plans for a specific total of IRA assets is about \$77,700,000,000.

19. $n = 12$, d.f. $= 10$, $t_c = 2.228$, $s_e \approx 8064.633$

$$\hat{y} = 104.982x + 14,128.671 = 104.982(450) + 14,128.671 = 61,370.571$$

$$E = t_c s_e \sqrt{1 + \frac{1}{n} + \frac{n(x - \bar{x})^2}{n(\sum x^2) - (\sum x)^2}}$$

$$\approx (2.228)(8064.633)\sqrt{1 + \frac{1}{12} + \frac{12(450 - 2142/12)^2}{12(615,732) - (2142)^2}}$$

$$\approx 21,253.747$$

$$\hat{y} + E \rightarrow (40,116.824, \ 82,624.318) \rightarrow (40,116,824,000, \ 82,624,318,000)$$

You can be 95% confident that the proceeds will be between 40,116,824,000 and 82,624,318,000 when the number of initial offerings is 450.

20. $n = 7$, d.f. $= 5$, $t_c = 2.571$, $s_e \approx 301.658$

$$\hat{y} = -2.735x + 27,657.823 = -2.735(5500) + 27,657.823 = 12,615.323$$

$$E = t_c s_e \sqrt{1 + \frac{1}{n} + \frac{n(x - \bar{x})^2}{n(\sum x^2) - (\sum x)^2}}$$

$$\approx (2.571)(301.658)\sqrt{1 + \frac{1}{7} + \frac{7(5500 - 37991/7)^2}{7(206,793,623) - (37,991)^2}}$$

$$\approx 832.272$$

$$\hat{y} + E \rightarrow (11,783.051, \ 13,447.595) \rightarrow (11,783,051, \ 13,447,595)$$

You can be 95% confident that the amount of crude oil imported by the United States will be between 11,783,051 and 13,447,595 when the amount of crude oil produced by the United States is 5,500,000 barrels per day.

21. $n = 11$, d.f. $= 9$, $t_c = 1.833$, $s_e \approx 30.576$

$$\hat{y} = 549.448x - 1881.694 = -549.448(5.75) - 1881.694 \approx 1277.632$$

$$E = t_c s_e \sqrt{1 + \frac{1}{n} + \frac{n(x - \bar{x})^2}{n(\sum x^2) - (\sum x)^2}}$$

$$\approx (1.833)(30.576)\sqrt{1 + \frac{1}{11} + \frac{11(5.75 - 61.2/11)^2}{11(341.9) - (61.2)^2}}$$

$$\approx 59.197$$

$$\hat{y} + E \rightarrow (1218.435, \ 1336.829) \rightarrow (1,218,435,000,000, \ 1,336,829,000,000)$$

You can be 90% confident that the shopping center sales will be between \$1,218,435,000,000 and \$1,336,829,000,000 when the total square footage is 5.75 billion.

22. $n = 10$, d.f. $= 8$, $t_c = 1.860$, $s_e \approx 2.013$

$$\hat{y} = -0.646x + 50.734 = -0.646(45.1) + 50.734 \approx 21.599$$

$$E = t_c s_e \sqrt{1 + \frac{1}{n} + \frac{n(x - \bar{x})^2}{n(\sum x^2) - (\sum x)^2}}$$

$$\approx (1.860)(2.013)\sqrt{1 + \frac{1}{10} + \frac{10(45.1 - 475.5/10)^2}{10(22,716.29) - (475.5)^2}}$$

$$\approx 4.026$$

$$\hat{y} + E \rightarrow (17.573,\ 25.625)$$

You can be 90% confident that the median number of leisure hours per week will be between 17.573 and 25.625 when the median number of work hours per week is 45.1.

23. $n = 6$, d.f. $= 4$, $t_c = 4.604$, $s_e \approx 20.090$

$$\hat{y} = 1.900x - 411.976 = 1.900(800) - 411.976 = 1108.024$$

$$E = t_c s_e \sqrt{1 + \frac{1}{n} + \frac{n(x - \bar{x})^2}{n(\sum x^2) - (\sum x)^2}}$$

$$\approx (4.604)(20.090)\sqrt{1 + \frac{1}{6} + \frac{6(800 - 4854/6)^2}{6(3,938,466) - (4854)^2}}$$

$$\approx 100.204$$

$$\hat{y} + E \rightarrow (1007.82,\ 1208.228)$$

You can be 99% confident that the average weekly wages of federal government employees will be between 1007.82 and 1208.23 when the average weekly wage of state government employees is $800.

24. $n = 8$, d.f. $= 6$, $t_c = 3.707$, $s_e \approx 2.307$

$$\hat{y} = 0.333x + 7.580 = 0.333(210) + 7.580 = 77.51$$

$$E = t_c s_e \sqrt{1 + \frac{1}{n} + \frac{n(x - \bar{x})^2}{n(\sum x^2) - (\sum x)^2}}$$

$$\approx (3.707)(2.307)\sqrt{1 + \frac{1}{8} + \frac{8(210 - 1523.4/8)^2}{8(293,361.28) - (1523.4)^2}}$$

$$\approx 9.532$$

$$\hat{y} + E \rightarrow (67.978,\ 87.042)$$

You can be 99% confident that the voter turnout in federal election will be between 67.978 million and 87.042 million when the voting age population is 210 million.

25. $n = 7$, d.f. $= 5$, $t_c = 2.571$, $s_e \approx 42.386$

$$\hat{y} = 0.415x - 186.626 \overset{!}{=} 0.415(1250) - 186.626 \approx 332.124$$

$$E = t_c s_e \sqrt{1 + \frac{1}{n} + \frac{n(x - \bar{x})^2}{n(\sum x^2) - (\sum x)^2}}$$

$$\approx (2.571)(42.386)\sqrt{1 + \frac{1}{7} + \frac{7(1250 - 8151/7)^2}{7(9,686,505) - (8151)^2}}$$

$$\approx 118.395$$

$$\hat{y} + E \rightarrow (213.729,\ 450.519)$$

You can be 95% confident that the corporate income taxes collected by the U.S. Internal Revenue Service for a given year will be between $213.729 million and $450.519 million when the U.S. Internal Revenue Service collects $1.250 million in individual income taxes that year.

26. $n = 9$, d.f. $= 7$, $t_c = 1.895$, $s_e \approx 77.70$

$$\hat{y} = 0.174x + 432.225 = 0.174(3800) + 432.225 = 1093.425$$

$$E = t_c s_e \sqrt{1 + \frac{1}{n} + \frac{n(x - \bar{x})^2}{n(\sum x^2) - (\sum x)^2}}$$

$$\approx (1.895)(77.70)\sqrt{1 + \frac{1}{9} + \frac{9(3800 - 30,253/9)^2}{9(106,362,725) - (30,253)^2}}$$

$$\approx 158.057$$

$$\hat{y} + E \rightarrow (935.368,\ 1251.482)$$

You can be 90% confident that the total assets in federal pension plans will be between $935.368 billion and $1251.482 billion when the total assets in IRAs is $3800 billion.

27.

28. $\hat{y} = 0.258x + 4.700$

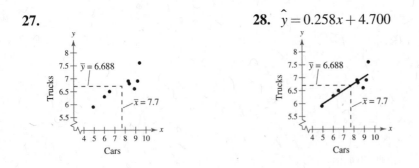

29.

x_i	y_i	$\hat{y}_i$	$\hat{y}_i - \overline{y}$	$y_i - \hat{y}_i$	$y_i - \overline{y}$
9.4	7.6	7.1252	0.4372	0.4748	0.912
9.2	6.9	7.0736	0.3856	−0.1736	0.212
8.9	6.6	6.9962	0.3082	−0.3962	−0.088
8.4	6.8	6.8672	0.1792	−0.0672	0.112
8.3	6.9	6.8414	0.1534	0.0586	0.212
6.5	6.5	6.377	−0.311	0.123	−0.188
6	6.3	6.248	−0.44	0.052	−0.388
4.9	5.9	5.9642	−0.7238	−0.0642	−0.788

30. (a) Explained variation $= \sum\left(\hat{y}_i - \overline{y}\right)^2 \approx 1.305$

   (b) Unexplained variation $= \sum\left(y_i - \hat{y}_i\right)^2 \approx 0.442$

   (c) Total variation $= \sum\left(y_i - \overline{y}\right)^2 \approx 1.749$

31. $r^2 \approx 0.746$; About 74.6% of the variation in the median age of trucks can be explained by the variation in the median age of cars, and about 25.4% of the variation is unexplained.

32. $s_e \approx 0.272$; The standard error of estimate of the median age of trucks for a specific median age of cars is about 0.272 year.

33. $\hat{y} = 0.258x + 4.700 = 0.258(7.0) + 4.700 = 6.506$

$$E = t_c s_e \sqrt{1 + \frac{1}{n} + \frac{n\left(x - \overline{x}\right)^2}{n\left(\sum x^2\right) - \left(\sum x\right)^2}}$$

$$\approx (2.447)(0.272)\sqrt{1 + \frac{1}{8} + \frac{8(7.0 - 61.6/8)^2}{8(493.92) - (61.6)^2}}$$

$$\approx 0.723$$

$$\hat{y} + E \rightarrow (5.783,\ 7.229)$$

34. The slope and correlation coefficient will have the same sign because the denominators of both formulas are always positive while the numerators are always equal.

35a. $r^2 \approx 0.671$
  b. $s_e \approx 1.780$
  c. $9.537 < y < 19.010$

36a. $r^2 \approx 0.522$
  b. $s_e \approx 2.371$
  c. $5.954 < y < 20.470$

37. critical value $= \pm 3.707$

$m \approx -0.205$

$s_e \approx 0.554$

$$t = \frac{m}{s_e}\sqrt{\sum x^2 - \frac{(\sum x)^2}{n}} \approx \frac{-0.205}{0.554}\sqrt{838.55 - \frac{(79.5)^2}{8}} \approx -2.578$$

Fail to reject $H_0 : M = 0$.

38. critical value $= \pm 2.306$

$m \approx 1.328$

$s_e \approx 5.086$

$$t = \frac{m}{s_e}\sqrt{\sum x^2 - \frac{(\sum x)^2}{n}} \approx \frac{1.328}{5.086}\sqrt{14,660 - \frac{(374)^2}{10}} \approx 6.771$$

Reject $H_0 : M = 0$.

39. $E = t_c s_e \sqrt{\dfrac{1}{n} + \dfrac{\overline{x}^2}{\sum x^2 - \left[(\sum x)^2/n\right]}} \approx (2.306)(138.255)\sqrt{\dfrac{1}{10} + \dfrac{\left(\dfrac{23.1}{10}\right)^2}{(67.35) - \dfrac{(23.1)^2}{10}}} \approx 221.216$

$b \pm E \Rightarrow 102.289 \pm 221.216 = (-118.927,\ 323.505)$

$E = \dfrac{t_c s_e}{\sqrt{\sum x^2 - \dfrac{(\sum x)^2}{n}}} \approx \dfrac{2.306(138.255)}{\sqrt{67.35 - \dfrac{(23.1)^2}{10}}} \approx 85.241$

$m \pm E \Rightarrow 196.152 \pm 85.241 \Rightarrow (110.911,\ 281.393)$

40. $E = t_c s_e \sqrt{\dfrac{1}{n} + \dfrac{\overline{x}^2}{\sum x^2 - \left[(\sum x)^2/n\right]}} \approx (3.355)(138.255)\sqrt{\dfrac{1}{10} + \dfrac{\left(\dfrac{23.1}{10}\right)^2}{(67.35) - \dfrac{(23.1)^2}{10}}} \approx 321.847$

$b \pm E \Rightarrow 102.289 \pm 321.847 = (-219.558,\ 424.136)$

$E = \dfrac{t_c s_e}{\sqrt{\sum x^2 - \dfrac{(\sum x)^2}{n}}} \approx \dfrac{3.355(138.255)}{\sqrt{67.35 - \dfrac{(23.1)^2}{10}}} \approx 124.017$

$m \pm E \Rightarrow 196.152 \pm 124.017 \Rightarrow (72.135,\ 320.169)$

9.4 MULTIPLE REGRESSION

9.4 Try It Yourself Solutions

1a. Enter the data.

b. $\hat{y} = 46.385 + 0.540x_1 - 4.897x_2$

2ab. (1) $\hat{y} = 46.385 + 0.540(89) - 4.897(1)$

  (2) $\hat{y} = 46.385 + 0.540(78) - 4.897(3)$

  (3) $\hat{y} = 46.385 + 0.540(83) - 4.897(2)$

c. (1) $\hat{y} = 89.548$ (2) $\hat{y} = 73.814$ (3) $\hat{y} = 81.411$

d. (1) 90 (2) 74 (3) 81

9.4 EXERCISE SOLUTIONS

1. $\hat{y} = 61,298 + 57.56x_1 - 78.45x_2$

  (a) $\hat{y} = 61,298 + 57.56(1100) - 78.45(1090) = 39,103.5$ pounds per acre

  (b) $\hat{y} = 61,298 + 57.56(1060) - 78.45(1050) = 39,939.1$ pounds per acre

  (c) $\hat{y} = 61,298 + 57.56(1300) - 78.45(1250) = 38,063.5$ pounds per acre

  (d) $\hat{y} = 61,298 + 57.56(1140) - 78.45(1120) = 39,052.4$ pounds per acre

2. $\hat{y} = 22 - 0.027x_1 + 0.156x_2$

  (a) $\hat{y} = 22 - 0.027(1250) + 0.156(250) = 27.25$ bushels per acre

  (b) $\hat{y} = 22 - 0.027(1400) + 0.156(275) = 27.1$ bushels per acre

  (c) $\hat{y} = 22 - 0.027(1425) + 0.156(300) = 30.325$ bushels per acre

  (d) $\hat{y} = 22 - 0.027(1300) + 0.156(250) = 25.9$ bushels per acre

3. $\hat{y} = -52.2 - 0.3x_1 + 4.5x_2$

  (a) $\hat{y} = -52.2 - 0.3(70) + 4.5(8.6) = 7.5$ cubic feet

  (b) $\hat{y} = -52.2 - 0.3(65) + 4.5(11.0) = 16.8$ cubic feet

  (c) $\hat{y} = -52.2 - 0.3(83) + 4.5(17.6) = 51.9$ cubic feet

  (d) $\hat{y} = -52.2 - 0.3(87) + 4.5(19.6) = 62.1$ cubic feet

4. $\hat{y} = -4016 + 11.5x_1 + 7.55x_2 + 12.5x_3$

(a) $\hat{y} = -4016 + 11.5(421) + 7.55(224) + 12.5(144) = 4316.7$ kilograms

(b) $\hat{y} = -4016 + 11.5(311) + 7.55(171) + 12.5(102) = 2126.55$ kilograms

(c) $\hat{y} = -4016 + 11.5(376) + 7.55(226) + 12.5(124) = 3564.3$ kilograms

(d) $\hat{y} = -4016 + 11.5(231) + 7.55(135) + 12.5(86) = 734.75$ kilograms

5. $\hat{y} = -2518.364 + 126.822x_1 + 66.360x_2$

(a) $s_e = 28.489$; The standard error of estimate of the predicted sales given a specific total square footage and number of shopping centers is $28.489 billion.

(b) $r^2 = 0.985$; The multiple regression model explains 98.5% of the variation in y.

6. $\hat{y} = -16.984 - 0.007x_1 + 0.524x_2$

(a) $s_e = 1.756$; The standard error of estimate of the predicted equity given a specific net sales and total assets is $1.756 billion.

(b) $r^2 = 0.963$; The multiple regression model explains 96.3% of the variation in y.

7. $\hat{y} = -2518.364 + 126.822x_1 + 66.360x_2$

The equation is the same.

8. $\hat{y} = -16.984 - 0.007x_1 + 0.524x_2$

The equation is the same.

9. $n = 11$, $k = 2$, $r^2 = 0.985$

$$r_{adj}^2 = 1 - \left[\frac{\left(1 - r^2\right)(n-1)}{n - k - 1} \right] \approx 0.981$$

About 98.1% of the variation in y can be explained by the relationships between variables.
$r_{adj}^2 < r^2$

10. $n = 5$, $k = 2$, $r^2 = 0.963$

$$r_{adj}^2 = 1 - \left[\frac{\left(1 - r^2\right)(n-1)}{n - k - 1} \right] \approx 0.925$$

About 92.5% of the variation in y can be explained by the relationships between variables.
$r_{adj}^2 < r^2$

CHAPTER 9 REVIEW EXERCISE SOLUTIONS

1.

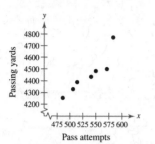

$r \approx 0.912$; strong positive linear correlation; the number of passing yards increases as the number of pass attempts increases.

2.

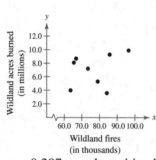

$r \approx 0.297$; weak positive linear correlation; the number of wildland acres burned increases as the number of wildland fires increases.

3.

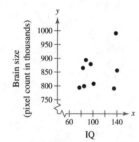

$r \approx 0.338$; weak positive linear correlation; brain size increases as IQ increases.

4.

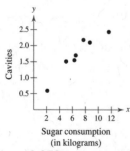

$r \approx 0.979$; strong positive linear correlation; the number of cavities increases as the annual per capita sugar consumption increases.

5. $H_0: \rho = 0; H_a: \rho \neq 0$

   $\alpha = 0.01$, d.f. $= n - 2 = 24$

   $t_0 = 2.797$

   $t = \dfrac{r}{\sqrt{\dfrac{1-r^2}{n-2}}} = \dfrac{0.24}{\sqrt{\dfrac{1-(0.24)^2}{26-2}}} \approx 1.211$

   Fail to reject H_0. There is not enough evidence at the 1% level of significance to conclude that a significant linear correlation exists.

6. $H_0: \rho = 0; H_a: \rho \neq 0$

   $\alpha = 0.05$, d.f. $= n - 2 = 20$

   $t_0 = \pm 2.086$

   $t = \dfrac{r}{\sqrt{\dfrac{1-r^2}{n-2}}} = \dfrac{-0.55}{\sqrt{\dfrac{1-(-0.55)^2}{22-2}}} \approx -2.945$

   Reject H_0. There is enough evidence at the 5% level of significance to conclude that a significant linear correlation exists.

7. $H_0: \rho = 0; H_a: \rho \neq 0$

   $\alpha = 0.05$, d.f. $= n - 2 = 5$

   $t_0 = \pm 2.571$

   $t = \dfrac{r}{\sqrt{\dfrac{1-r^2}{n-2}}} = \dfrac{0.912}{\sqrt{\dfrac{1-(0.912)^2}{7-2}}} \approx 4.972$

   Reject H_0. There is enough evidence at the 5% level of significance to conclude that a significant linear correlation exists between passing attempts and passing yards.

8. $H_0: \rho = 0; H_a: \rho \neq 0$

   $\alpha = 0.05$, d.f. $= n - 2 = 6$

   $t_0 = \pm 2.447$

   $t = \dfrac{r}{\sqrt{\dfrac{1-r^2}{n-2}}} = \dfrac{0.297}{\sqrt{\dfrac{1-(0.297)^2}{8-2}}} \approx 0.762$

   Fail to reject H_0. There is not enough evidence at the 5% level of significance to conclude that a significant linear correlation exists between number of wildland fires and number of wildland acres burned.

9. $H_0: \rho = 0; H_a: \rho \neq 0$

$\alpha = 0.01, \text{ d.f.} = n - 2 = 7$

$t_0 = \pm 3.499$

$t = \dfrac{r}{\sqrt{\dfrac{1-r^2}{n-2}}} \approx \dfrac{0.338}{\sqrt{\dfrac{1-(0.338)^2}{9-2}}} \approx 0.950$

Fail to reject H_0. There is not enough evidence at the 1% level of significance to conclude that a significant linear correlation exists between brain size and IQ.

10. $H_0: \rho = 0; H_a: \rho \neq 0$

$\alpha = 0.01, \text{ d.f.} = n - 2 = 5$

$t_0 = \pm 4.032$

$t = \dfrac{r}{\sqrt{\dfrac{1-r^2}{n-2}}} \approx \dfrac{0.979}{\sqrt{\dfrac{1-(0.979)^2}{7-2}}} \approx 10.738$

Reject H_0. There is enough evidence at the 1% level of significance to conclude that there is a linear correlation between sugar consumption and tooth decay.

11. $\hat{y} = 0.038x - 3.529$

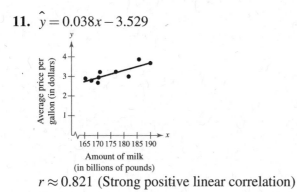

$r \approx 0.821$ (Strong positive linear correlation)

12. $\hat{y} = 1.076x + 0.299$

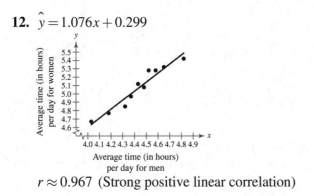

$r \approx 0.967$ (Strong positive linear correlation)

13. $\hat{y} = -0.086x + 10.450$

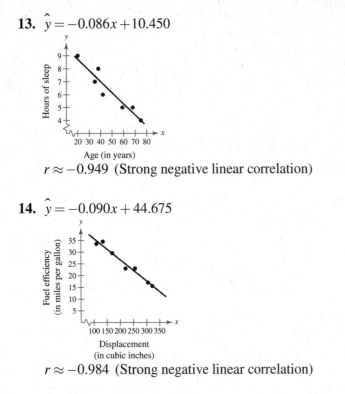

$r \approx -0.949$ (Strong negative linear correlation)

14. $\hat{y} = -0.090x + 44.675$

$r \approx -0.984$ (Strong negative linear correlation)

15. (a) It is not meaningful to predict the value of y for $x = 160$ because $x = 160$ is outside the range of the original data.

(b) $\hat{y} = 0.038(175) - 3.529 \approx \$3.12$

(c) $\hat{y} = 0.038(180) - 3.529 \approx \$3.31$

(d) It is not meaningful to predict the value of y for $x = 200$ because $x = 200$ is outside the range of the original data.

16. (a) $\hat{y} = 1.076(4.2) + 0.299 = 4.818$ hours

(b) $\hat{y} = 1.076(4.5) + 0.299 = 5.141$ hours

(c) $\hat{y} = 1.076(4.75) + 0.299 = 5.41$ hours

(d) It is not meaningful to predict the value of y for $x = 5$ because $x = 5$ is outside the range of the original data.

17. (a) It is not meaningful to predict the value of y for $x = 18$ because $x = 18$ is outside the range of the original data.

(b) $\hat{y} = 10.450 - 0.086x = 10.450 - 0.086(25) = 8.3$ hours

(c) It is not meaningful to predict the value of y for $x = 85$ because $x = 85$ is outside the range of the original data.

(d) $\hat{y} = 10.450 - 0.086x = 10.450 - 0.086(50) = 6.15$ hours

18. (a) It is not meaningful to predict the value of y for $x = 86$ because $x = 86$ is outside the range of the original data.

(b) $\hat{y} = -0.090(198) + 44.675 \approx 26.86$ miles per gallon

(c) $\hat{y} = -0.090(289) + 44.675 \approx 18.67$ miles per gallon

(d) It is not meaningful to predict the value of y for $x = 407$ because $x = 407$ is outside the range of the original data.

19. $r^2 = (-0.450)^2 \approx 0.203$

About 20.3% of the variation in y is explained.
About 79.7% of the variation in y is unexplained.

20. $r^2 = (-0.937)^2 \approx 0.878$

About 87.8% of the variation in y is explained.
About 12.2% of the variation in y is unexplained.

21. $r^2 = (0.642)^2 \approx 0.412$

About 41.2% of the variation in y is explained.
About 58.8% of the variation in y is unexplained.

22. $r^2 = (0.795)^2 \approx 0.632$

About 63.2% of the variation in y is explained.
About 36.8% of the variation in y is unexplained.

23. (a) $r^2 \approx 0.679$

About 67.9% of the variation in y is explained.
About 32.1% of the variation in y is unexplained.

(b) $s_e \approx 1.138$

The standard error of estimate of the fuel efficiency of compact sports sedans for a specific price of compact sports sedan is about 1.138 miles per gallon.

24. (a) $r^2 \approx 0.446$

About 44.6% of the variation in y is explained.
About 55.4% of the variation in y is unexplained.

(b) $s_e \approx 235.079$

The standard error of the price for a specific area is about $235.08.

25. $\hat{y} = 0.038(185) - 3.529 = 3.501$

$$E = t_c s_e \sqrt{1 + \frac{1}{n} + \frac{n(x - \bar{x})^2}{n(\sum x^2) - (\sum x)^2}} \approx (1.895)(0.246)\sqrt{1 + \frac{1}{9} + \frac{9(185 - 1578.8/9)^2}{9(277,555.56) - (1578.8)^2}}$$

$$\approx 0.524$$

$$\hat{y} - E < y < \hat{y} + E$$

$$3.501 - 0.524 < y < 3.501 + 0.524$$

$$2.997 < y < 4.025$$

You can be 90% confident that the price per gallon of milk will be between $3.00 and $4.03 when 185 billion pounds of milk is produced.

26. $\hat{y} = 1.076(4.25) + 0.299 = 4.872$

$$E = t_c s_e \sqrt{1 + \frac{1}{n} + \frac{n(x - \bar{x})^2}{n(\sum x^2) - (\sum x)^2}} \approx (1.860)(0.069)\sqrt{1 + \frac{1}{10} + \frac{10(4.25 - 44.38/10)^2}{10(197.4296) - (44.38)^2}}$$

$$\approx 0.139$$

$$\hat{y} - E < y < \hat{y} + E$$

$$4.872 - 0.139 < y < 4.872 + 0.139$$

$$4.733 < y < 5.011$$

You can be 90% confident that the average time women spend per day watching television will be between 4.733 hours and 5.011 hours when the average time men spend per day watching television is 4.25 hours.

27. $\hat{y} = -0.086(45) + 10.450 = 6.580$

$$E = t_c s_e \sqrt{1 + \frac{1}{n} + \frac{n(x - \bar{x})^2}{n(\sum x^2) - (\sum x)^2}} \approx (2.571)(0.622)\sqrt{1 + \frac{1}{7} + \frac{7(45 - 337/7)^2}{7(18,563) - (337)^2}}$$

$$\approx 1.7127$$

$$\hat{y} - E < y < \hat{y} + E$$

$$6.580 - 1.7127 < y < 6.580 + 1.7127$$

$$4.867 < y < 8.293$$

You can be 95% confident that the hours slept will be between 4.867 and 8.293 hours for a person who is 45 years old.

28. $\hat{y} = -0.090(265) + 44.675 = 20.825$

$$E = t_c s_e \sqrt{1 + \frac{1}{n} + \frac{n(x - \bar{x})^2}{n(\sum x^2) - (\sum x)^2}} \approx (2.571)(1.476)\sqrt{1 + \frac{1}{7} + \frac{7(265 - 1516/7)^2}{7(369,382) - (1516)^2}}$$

$$\approx 4.157$$

$$\hat{y} - E < y < \hat{y} + E$$

$$20.825 - 4.157 < y < 20.825 + 4.157$$

$$16.668 < y < 24.982$$

You can be 95% confident that the fuel efficiency will be between 16.668 miles per gallon and 24.982 miles per gallon when the engine displacement is 265 cubic inches.

29. $\hat{y} = -0.414(39.9) + 37.147 \approx 20.628$

$$E = t_c s_e \sqrt{1 + \frac{1}{n} + \frac{n(x - \bar{x})^2}{n(\sum x^2) - (\sum x)^2}} \approx (3.499)(1.138)\sqrt{1 + \frac{1}{9} + \frac{9(39.9 - 319.7/9)^2}{9(11,468.29) - (319.7)^2}}$$

$$\approx 4.509$$

$$\hat{y} - E < y < \hat{y} + E$$

$$20.628 - 4.509 < y < 20.628 + 4.509$$

$$16.119 < y < 25.137$$

You can be 99% confident that the fuel efficiency of the compact sports sedan that costs \$39,900 will be between 16.119 and 25.137 miles per gallon.

30. $\hat{y} = 1.454(900) - 532.053 = 776.547$

$$E = t_c s_e \sqrt{1 + \frac{1}{n} + \frac{n(x - \bar{x})^2}{n(\sum x^2) - (\sum x)^2}} \approx (2.921)(235.079)\sqrt{1 + \frac{1}{18} + \frac{18(900 - 13,203/18)^2}{18(10,021,083) - (13,203)^2}}$$

$$\approx 732.481$$

$$\hat{y} - E < y < \hat{y} + E$$

$$776.547 - 732.481 < y < 776.547 + 732.481$$

$$44.066 < y < 1509.028$$

You can be 99% confident that the price will be between \$44.07 and \$1509.03 when the cooking area is 900 square inches.

31. $\hat{y} = 3.674 + 1.287x_1 + (-7.531)x_2$

32. $s_e \approx 0.710$; $r^2 \approx 0.943$

About 94.3% of the variation in y can be explained by the model.

33. (a) 21.705   (b) 25.21   (c) 30.1   (d) 25.86

34. (a) 11.272   (b) 14.695   (c) 14.380   (d) 9.232

CHAPTER 9 QUIZ SOLUTIONS

1.

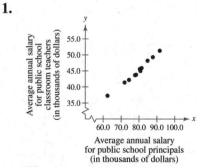

The data appear to have a positive linear correlation. As x increases, y tends to increase.

2. $r \approx 0.993$; Strong positive linear correlation; public school classroom teachers' salaries increase as public school principals' salaries increase.

3. $H_0 : \rho = 0$; $H_a : \rho \neq 0$

$\alpha = 0.05$, d.f. $= n - 2 = 9$

$t_0 = \pm 2.262$

$$t = \frac{r}{\sqrt{\dfrac{1-r^2}{n-2}}} \approx \frac{0.993}{\sqrt{\dfrac{1-(0.993)^2}{11-2}}} \approx 25.22$$

Reject H_0. There is enough evidence at the 5% level of significance to conclude that a significant correlation exists.

4.

x	y	xy	x^2
62.5	37.3	2331.25	3906.25
71.9	41.4	2976.66	5169.61
74.4	42.2	3139.68	5535.36
77.8	43.7	3399.86	6052.84
78.4	43.8	3433.92	6146.56
80.8	45.0	3636.00	6528.64
80.5	45.6	3670.80	6480.25
81.5	45.9	3740.85	6642.25
84.8	48.2	4087.36	7191.04
87.7	49.3	4323.61	7691.29
91.6	51.3	4699.08	8390.56
$\sum x = 871.9$	$\sum y = 493.7$	$\sum xy = 39.439.08$	$\sum x^2 = 69,734.65$

$$m = \frac{n\sum xy - (\sum x)(\sum y)}{n\sum x^2 - (\sum x)^2} = \frac{11(39,439.08) - (871.9)(493.7)}{11(69,734.65) - (871.9)^2} = \frac{3372.74}{6871.54} \approx 0.490827$$

$$b = \bar{y} - m\bar{x} = \frac{\sum y}{n} - m\left(\frac{\sum x}{n}\right) \approx \frac{493.7}{11} - (0.490827)\left(\frac{871.9}{11}\right) \approx 5.9771$$

$$\hat{y} = mx + b = 0.491x + 5.977$$

Average annual salary for public school classroom teachers (in thousands of dollars) vs. Average annual salary for public school principals (in thousands of dollars)

5. $\hat{y} = 0.491(90.5) + 5.977 = 50.4125 \Rightarrow \$50,412.50$

6. $r^2 \approx (0.993)^2 \approx 0.986$

About 98.6% of the variation in the average annual salaries of public school classroom teachers can be explained by the average annual salaries of public school principals, and about 1.4% of the variation is unexplained.

7. $s_e \approx 0.490$; The standard error of the estimate of the average annual salary of public school classroom teachers for a specific average annual salary of public school principals is about $490.

8. $\hat{y} = 0.491(85.75) + 5.977 \approx 48.080$

$$E = t_c s_e \sqrt{1 + \frac{1}{n} + \frac{n(x - \bar{x})^2}{n(\sum x^2) - (\sum x)^2}} \approx (2.262)(0.490)\sqrt{1 + \frac{1}{11} + \frac{11(85.75 - 871.9/11)^2}{11(69,734.65) - (871.9)^2}}$$

$$\approx 1.193$$

$$\hat{y} - E < y < \hat{y} + E$$

$$48.080 - 1.193 < y < 48.080 + 1.193$$

$$46.887 < y < 49.273$$

You can be 95% confident that the average annual salary of public school classroom teacher will be between $46,887 and $49,273 when the average annual salary of public school principals is $85,750.

9. (a) $\hat{y} = -47 + 5.91(22.7) - 1.99(14.0) = \$59.30$

(b) $\hat{y} = -47 + 5.91(17.9) - 1.99(14.2) = \$30.53$

(c) $\hat{y} = -47 + 5.91(20.9) - 1.99(15.5) = \$45.67$

(d) $\hat{y} = -47 + 5.91(19.1) - 1.99(15.1) = \$35.83$

10.1 GOODNESS OF FIT TEST

10.1 Try It Yourself Solutions

1.

Tax Preparation Method	% of people	Expected frequency
Accountant	25%	$500(0.25) = 125$
By hand	20%	$500(0.20) = 100$
Computer software	35%	$500(0.35) = 175$
Friend/family	5%	$500(0.05) = 25$
Tax preparation service	15%	$500(0.15) = 75$

2a. The expected frequencies are 64, 80, 32, 56, 60, 48, 40, and 20, all of which are at least 5.

b. Claimed distribution:

Ages	Distribution
0–9	16%
10–19	20%
20–29	8%
30–39	14%
40–49	15%
50–59	12%
60–69	10%
70+	5%

H_0 : The distribution of ages is as shown in table above.

H_a : The distribution of ages differs from the claimed distribution. (claim)

c. $\alpha = 0.05$ **d.** d.f. $= n - 1 = 7$

e. $\chi_0^2 = 14.067$; ion region: $\chi^2 > 14.067$

f.

Ages	Distribution	Observed	Expected	$\dfrac{(O - E)^2}{E}$
0–9	16%	76	64	2.250
10–19	20%	84	80	0.200
20–29	8%	30	32	0.125
30–39	14%	60	56	0.286
40–49	15%	54	60	0.600
50–59	12%	40	48	1.333
60–69	10%	42	40	0.100
70+	5%	14	20	1.800

$\chi^2 \approx 6.694$

g. Fail to reject H_0.

h. There is not enough evidence at the 5% level of significance to support the sociologist's claim that the distribution of ages differs from the age distribution 10 years ago.

401

3a. The expected frequency for each category is 30 which is at least 5.

b. Claimed distribution:

Color	Distribution
Brown	$16.\overline{6}\%$
Yellow	$16.\overline{6}\%$
Red	$16.\overline{6}\%$
Blue	$16.\overline{6}\%$
Orange	$16.\overline{6}\%$
Green	$16.\overline{6}\%$

H_0 : The distribution of colors is uniform, as shown in the table above. (claim)

H_a : The distribution of colors is not uniform.

c. $\alpha = 0.05$

d. d.f. $= n - 1 = 5$

e. $\chi_0^2 = 11.071$; Rejection region: $\chi^2 > 11.071$

f.

Color	Distribution	Observed	Expected	$\dfrac{(O - E)^2}{E}$
Brown	16.6%	22	30	$2.1\overline{33}$
Yellow	16.6%	27	30	0.300
Red	16.6%	22	30	$2.1\overline{33}$
Blue	16.6%	41	30	$4.0\overline{33}$
Orange	16.6%	41	30	$4.0\overline{33}$
Green	16.6%	27	30	0.300
				12.933

$\chi^2 \approx 12.933$

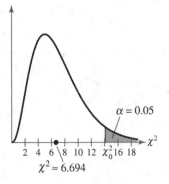

$\alpha = 0.05$

$\chi^2 \approx 6.694$

g. Reject H_0.

h. There is enough evidence at the 5% level of significance to dispute the claim that the distribution of different colored candies in bags of peanut M&M's is uniform.

10.1 EXERCISE SOLUTIONS

1. A multinomial experiment is a probability experiment consisting of a fixed number of independent trials in which there are more than two possible outcomes for each trial. The probability of each outcome is fixed, and each outcome is classified into categories.

2. The observed frequencies must be obtained using a random sample, and each expected frequency must be greater than or equal to 5.

3. $E_1 = np_1 = (150)(0.3) = 45$

4. $E_1 = np_1 = (500)(0.9) = 450$

5. $E_1 = np_1 = (230)(0.25) = 57.5$

6. $E_1 = np_1 = (415)(0.08) = 33.2$

7a. Claimed Distribution:

Age	Distribution
2–17	26.7%
18–24	19.8%
25–39	19.7%
40–49	14%
50+	19.8%

H_0 : The distribution of the ages of moviegoers is 26.7% ages 2–17, 19.8% ages 18–24, 19.7% ages 25–39, 14% ages 40–49, and 19.8% ages 50+ (claim)

H_a : The distribution of the ages differs from the claimed or expected distribution.

b. $\chi_0^2 = 7.779$, Rejection region: $\chi^2 > 7.779$

c.

Age	Distribution	Observed	Expected	$\dfrac{(O - E)^2}{E}$
2–17	26.7%	240	267	2.730
18–24	19.8%	214	198	1.293
25–39	19.7%	183	197	0.995
40–49	14%	156	140	1.829
50+	19.8%	207	198	0.409
				7.256

$\chi^2 \approx 7.256$

d. Fail to reject H_0.

e. There is not enough evidence at the 10% level of significance to conclude that the distribution of the ages of movie goers has changed.

8a. Claimed distribution:

Response	Distribution
2 cups a week	15%
1 cup a week	13%
1 cup a day	27%
2 or more cups a day	45%

H_0 : The distribution of the amounts of coffee people drink is 15% 2 cups a week, 13% 1 cup a week, 27%, 1 cup c day, and 45% 2 or more cups a day. (claim)

H_a : The distribution of amounts differs from the claimed or expected distribution.

b. $\chi_0^2 = 7.815$, Rejection region: $\chi^2 > 7.815$

c.

Response	Distribution	Observed	Expected	$\dfrac{(O-E)^2}{E}$
2 cups a week	15%	206	240	4.817
1 cup a week	13%	193	208	1.082
1 cup a day	27%	462	432	2.083
2 or more cups a day	45%	739	720	0.501
				8.483

$\chi^2 \approx 8.483$

d. Reject H_0.

e. There is enough evidence at the 5% level of significance to conclude that the distribution of the amounts of coffee people drink differs from the claimed distribution.

9a. Claimed distribution:

Day	Distribution
Sunday	7%
Monday	4%
Tuesday	6%
Wednesday	13%
Thursday	10%
Friday	36%
Saturday	24%

H_0 : The distribution of the days people order food for delivery is 7% Sunday, 4% Monday, 6% Tuesday, 13% Wednesday, 10% Thursday, 36% Friday, and 24% Saturday.

H_a : The distribution of days differs from the claimed or expected distribution.

b. $\chi_0^2 = 16.812$, Rejection region: $\chi^2 > 16.812$

c.

	Distribution	Observed	Expected	$\frac{(O-E)^2}{E}$
Sunday	7%	43	35	1.829
Monday	4%	16	20	0.800
Tuesday	6%	25	30	0.833
Wednesday	13%	49	65	3.938
Thursday	10%	46	50	0.320
Friday	36%	168	180	0.800
Saturday	24%	153	120	9.075
				17.595

$\chi^2 \approx 17.595$

d. Reject H_0.

e. There is enough evidence at the 1% level of significance to conclude that the distribution of delivery days has changed.

10a. Claimed distribution:

Response	Distribution
Limited advancement	41%
Lack of recognition	25%
Low salary	15%
Unhappy with mgmt.	10%
Bored/don't know	9%

H_0 : The distribution of responses is as shown in the table above.

H_a : The distribution of responses differs from the claimed or expected distribution. (claim)

b. $\chi_0^2 = 13.277$, Rejection region: $\chi^2 > 13.277$

c.

Response	Distribution	Observed	Expected	$\frac{(O-E)^2}{E}$
Limited advancement	41%	78	82.00	0.195
Lack of recognition	25%	52	50.00	0.080
Low salary	15%	30	30.00	0.000
Unhappy with mgmt.	10%	25	20.00	1.250
Bored/don't know	9%	15	18.00	0.500
				2.025

$\chi^2 \approx 2.025$

d. Fail to reject H_0.

e. There is not enough evidence at the 1% significance level to conclude that the distribution of the responses differs from the claimed or expected distribution.

11a. Claimed distribution:

Season	Distribution
Spring	25%
Summer	25%
Fall	25%
Winter	25%

H_0 : The number of homicide crimes in California by season is uniform.

H_a : The number of homicide crimes in California by season is not uniform. (claim)

b. $\chi_0^2 = 7.815$, Rejection region: $\chi^2 > 7.815$

c.

Season	Distribution	Observed	Expected	$\dfrac{(O-E)^2}{E}$
Spring	25%	312	300	0.480
Summer	25%	299	300	$0.00\overline{3}$
Fall	25%	297	300	0.030
Winter	25%	292	300	$0.21\overline{3}$
				0.727

$\chi^2 \approx 0.727$

d. Fail to reject H_0.

e. There is not enough evidence at the 5% level of significance to reject the claim that the distribution of the number of homicide crimes in California by season is uniform.

12a. Claimed distribution:

Month	Distribution	Month	Distribution
January	$8.\overline{33}\%$	July	$8.\overline{33}\%$
February	$8.\overline{33}\%$	August	$8.\overline{33}\%$
March	$8.\overline{33}\%$	September	$8.\overline{33}\%$
April	$8.\overline{33}\%$	October	$8.\overline{33}\%$
May	$8.\overline{33}\%$	November	$8.\overline{33}\%$
June	$8.\overline{33}\%$	December	$8.\overline{33}\%$

H_0 : The distribution of the number of homicide crimes in California by month is uniform. (claim)

H_a : The distribution of homicides by month is not uniform.

b. $\chi_0^2 = 17.275$, Rejection region: $\chi^2 > 17.275$

c.

Month	Distribution	Observed	Expected	$\dfrac{(O-E)^2}{E}$
January	$8.\overline{33}\%$	98	100	0.040
February	$8.\overline{33}\%$	103	100	0.090
March	$8.\overline{33}\%$	114	100	1.960
April	$8.\overline{33}\%$	92	100	0.640
May	$8.\overline{33}\%$	106	100	0.360
June	$8.\overline{33}\%$	106	100	0.360
July	$8.\overline{33}\%$	84	100	2.560
August	$8.\overline{33}\%$	109	100	0.810
September	$8.\overline{33}\%$	112	100	1.440
October	$8.\overline{33}\%$	95	100	0.250
November	$8.\overline{33}\%$	91	100	0.810
December	$8.\overline{33}\%$	90	100	1.000
				10.320

$\chi^2 \approx 10.320$

d. Fail to reject H_0.

e. There is not enough evidence at the 10% level of significance to reject the claim that the distribution of the number of homicide crimes in California by month is uniform.

13a. Claimed distribution:

Month	Distribution
Strongly agree	55%
Somewhat agree	30%
Neither agree or disagree	5%
Somewhat disagree	6%
Strongly disagree	4%

H_0 : The distribution of the opinions of U.S. parents on whether a college education is worth the expense is 55% strongly agree, 70% somewhat agree, 5% neither agree or disagree, 6% somewhat disagree, 4% strongly disagree.

H_a : The distribution of opinions differs from the claimed or expected distribution. (claim)

b. $\chi_0^2 = 9.488$, Rejection region: $\chi^2 > 9.488$

c.

Month	Distribution	Observed	Expected	$\dfrac{(O-E)^2}{E}$
Strongly agree	55%	86	110	5.236
Somewhat agree	30%	62	60	0.067
Neither agree or disagree	5%	34	10	57.600
Somewhat disagree	6%	14	12	0.333
Strongly disagree	4%	4	8	2.000
				65.236

$\chi^2 \approx 65.236$

d. Reject H_0.

e. There is enough evidence at the 5% level of significance to conclude that the distribution of opinions of U.S. parents on whether a college education is worth the expense differs from the claimed or expected distribution.

14a. Claimed distribution:

Response	Distribution
Saving for your child's college education	50%
Saving for your own retirement	37%
Not sure	13%

H_0 : The distribution of the opinions of U.S. female adults on which is more important to save for, your child's college education or your own retirement, is 50% child's education, 37% retirement, and 13% not sure. (claim)

H_a : The distribution of the opinions of U.S. female adults differs from the distribution of the opinions of U.S. male adults.

b. $\chi_0^2 = 4.605$, Rejection region: $\chi^2 > 4.605$

c.

Response	Distribution	Observed	Expected	$\dfrac{(O - E)^2}{E}$
Saving for your child's college education	50%	180	200	2.000
Saving for your own retirement	37%	172	148	3.892
Not sure	13%	48	52	0.308
				6.200

$\chi^2 \approx 6.200$

d. Reject H_0.

e. There is enough evidence at the 10% level of significance to conclude that the distribution of opinions of U.S. female adults on which is more important to save for, your child's college education or your own retirement, differs from the distribution of the opinions of U.S. male adults.

15a. Claimed distribution:

Response	Distribution
Larger	33.3%
Same size	$33.\overline{3}\%$
Smaller	$33.\overline{3}\%$

H_0 : The distribution of prospective home buyers by the size they want their next house to be is uniform. (claim)

H_a : The distribution of prospective home buyers by the size they want their next house to be is not uniform. (claim)

b. $\chi_0^2 = 5.991$, Rejection region: $\chi^2 > 5.991$

c.

Response	Distribution	Observed	Expected	$\dfrac{(O-E)^2}{E}$
Larger	33.3%	285	$266.\overline{66}$	1.260
Same size	$33.\overline{3}\%$	224	$266.\overline{66}$	6.827
Smaller	$33.\overline{3}\%$	291	$266.\overline{66}$	2.220
				10.308

$\chi^2 \approx 10.308$

d. Reject H_0.

e. There is enough evidence at the 5% level of significance to reject the claim that the distribution of prospective home buyers by the size they want their next house to be is uniform.

16a. Claimed distribution:

Day	Distribution
Sunday	$14\frac{2}{7}\%$
Monday	$14\frac{2}{7}\%$
Tuesday	$14\frac{2}{7}\%$
Wednesday	$14\frac{2}{7}\%$
Thursday	$14\frac{2}{7}\%$
Friday	$14\frac{2}{7}\%$
Saturday	$14\frac{2}{7}\%$

H_0 : The distribution of the number of births by day of the week is uniform. (claim)

H_a : The distribution of the number of births is not uniform.

b. $\chi_0^2 = 16.812$, Rejection region: $\chi^2 > 16.812$

c.

Day	Distribution	Observed	Expected	$\dfrac{(O-E)^2}{E}$
Sunday	$14\frac{2}{7}\%$	65	100	12.250
Monday	$14\frac{2}{7}\%$	103	100	0.090
Tuesday	$14\frac{2}{7}\%$	114	100	1.960
Wednesday	$14\frac{2}{7}\%$	116	100	2.560
Thursday	$14\frac{2}{7}\%$	115	100	2.250
Friday	$14\frac{2}{7}\%$	112	100	1.440
Saturday	$14\frac{2}{7}\%$	75	100	6.250
				26.800

$\chi^2 \approx 26.800$

d. Reject H_0.

e. There is enough evidence at the 1% level of significance to reject the claim that the distribution of the number of births by day of the week is uniform.

17. Chi-Square goodness-of-fit results:

Observed: Recent survey
Expected: Previous survey

N	DF	Chi-Square	P-Value
400	9	18.637629	0.0285

Reject H_0. There is enough evidence at the 10% level of significance to conclude that there has been a change in the claimed or expected distribution of U.S. adults' favorite sports.

18. Chi-Square goodness-of-fit results:

Observed: Not married
Expected: Married

N	DF	Chi-Square	P-Value
250	7	9.523134	0.2172

Fail to reject H_0. There is not enough evidence at the 1% level of significance to conclude that the distribution of the opinions of U.S. adults who are not married differs from the opinions of U.S. adults who are married.

19a. Frequency distribution: $\mu = 69.435$; $\sigma \approx 8.337$

Lower Boundary	Upper Boundary	Lower z-score	Upper z-score	Area
49.5	58.5	−2.39	−1.31	0.0867
58.5	67.5	−1.31	−0.23	0.3139
67.5	76.5	−0.23	0.85	0.3933
76.5	85.5	0.85	1.93	0.1709
85.5	94.5	1.93	3.01	0.0255

Class Boundaries	Distribution	Frequency	Expected	$\dfrac{(O-E)^2}{E}$
49.5–58.5	8.67%	19	17	0.2353
58.5–67.5	31.39%	61	63	0.0635
67.5–76.5	39.33%	82	79	0.1139
76.5–85.5	17.09%	34	34	0
85.5–94.5	2.55%	4	5	0.2000
		200		0.613

H_0 : Test scores have a normal distribution. (claim)

H_a : Test scores do not have a normal distribution.

b. $\chi_0^2 = 13.277$; Rejection region . $\chi^2 > 13.277$

c. $\chi^2 = 0.613$

d. Fail to reject H_0.

e. There is not enough evidence at the 1% level of significance to reject the claim that the test scores are normally distributed.

20a. Frequency distribution: $\mu = 74.775$; $\sigma \approx 9.822$

Lower Boundary	Upper Boundary	Lower z-score	Upper z-score	Area
50.5	60.5	−2.47	−1.45	0.0668
60.5	70.5	−1.45	−0.44	0.2564
70.5	80.5	−0.44	0.58	0.3891
80.5	90.5	0.58	1.60	0.2262
90.5	100.5	1.60	2.62	0.0504

Class Boundaries	Distribution	Frequency	Expected	$\dfrac{(O-E)^2}{E}$
50.5–60.5	6.68%	28	27	0.0370
60.5–70.5	25.64%	106	103	0.0874
70.5–80.5	38.91%	151	156	0.1603
80.5–90.5	22.62%	97	90	0.5444
90.5–100.5	5.04%	18	20	0.2000
		400		1.029

H_0 : Test scores have a normal distribution. (claim)

H_a : Test scores do not have a normal distribution.

b. $\chi_0^2 = 9.488$; Rejection region . $\chi^2 > 9.488$

c. $\chi^2 = 1.029$

d. Fail to reject H_0.

e. There is not enough evidence at the 5% level of significance to reject the claim that the test scores are normally distributed.

10.2 INDEPENDENCE

10.2 Try It Yourself Solutions

1a.

	Hotel	Leg Room	Rental Size	Other	Total
Business	36	108	14	22	180
Leisure	38	54	14	14	120
Total	74	162	28	36	300

b. $n = 300$

c.

	Hotel	Leg Room	Rental Size	Other
Business	44.4	97.2	16.8	21.6
Leisure	29.6	64.8	11.2	14.4

2a. The claim is that "the travel concerns depend on the purpose of travel."

H_0 : Travel concern is independent of travel purpose.

H_a : Travel concern is dependent on travel purpose. (claim)

b. $\alpha = 0.01$ **c.** $(r-1)(c-1) = 3$

d. $\chi_0^2 = 11.345$; Rejection region: $\chi^2 > 11.345$

e.

O	E	$O-E$	$(O-E)^2$	$\dfrac{(O-E)^2}{E}$
36	44.4	−8.4	70.56	1.5892
108	97.2	10.8	116.64	1.2000
14	16.8	−2.8	7.84	0.4667
22	21.6	0.4	0.16	0.0074
38	29.6	8.4	70.56	2.3838
54	64.8	−10.8	116.64	1.8000
14	11.2	2.8	7.84	0.7000
14	14.4	−0.4	0.16	0.0111
				8.1582

$\chi^2 \approx 8.158$

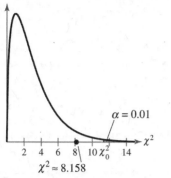

$\chi^2 \approx 8.158$

f. Fail to reject H_0.

g. There is not enough evidence to conclude that travel concern is dependent on travel purpose.

3a. H_0 : Whether or not a tax cut would influence an adult to purchase a hybrid vehicle is independent of age.

   H_a : Whether or not a tax cut would influence an adult to purchase a hybrid vehicle is dependent on age. (claim)

b. Enter the data.

c. $\chi_0^2 = 9.210$; Rejection region: $\chi^2 > 9.210$

d. $\chi^2 \approx 15.306$

e. Reject H_0.

f. There is enough evidence at the 1% level of significance to conclude that whether or not a tax cut would influence an adult to purchase a hybrid vehicle is dependent on age.

10.2 EXERCISE SOLUTIONS

1. Find the sum of the row and the sum of the column in which the cell is located. Find the product of these sums. Divide the product by the sample size.

2. In a contingency table, a marginal frequency is the frequency an entire category of a variable occurs, whereas a joint frequency is a frequency from a cell in the interior of a contingency table.

3. Answer will vary. *Sample answer:* For both the chi-square test for independence and the chi-square goodness-of-fit test, you are testing a claim about data that are in categories. However, the chi-square goodness-of-fit test has only one data value per category, while the chi-square test for independence has multiple data values per category.

   Both tests compare observed and expected frequencies. However, the chi-square goodness-of-fit test simply compares the distributions, whereas the chi-square test for independence compares them and then draws a conclusion about the dependence or independence of the variables.

4. A chi-square independence test is always a right-tailed test because if the variables are dependent, then the chi-square test statistic will be large, which is evidence for rejecting the null hypothesis.

5. False. If the two variables of a chi-square test for independence are dependent, then you can expect a large difference between the observed frequencies and the expected frequencies.

6. True.

7a.

Result	Athlete has		
	Stretched	Not stretched	Total
Inquiry	18	22	40
No Inquiry	211	189	400
	229	211	440

b.

Result	Athlete has	
	Stretched	Not stretched
Inquiry	20.82	19.18
No Inquiry	208.18	191.82

8a.

Result	Athlete has		
	Drug	Placebo	Total
Nausea	36	13	49
No Nausea	254	262	516
Total	290	275	565

b.

Result	Athlete has	
	Drug	Placebo
Nausea	25.15	23.85
No Nausea	264.85	251.15

9a.

Bank employee	Preference			
	New procedure	Old Procedure	No preference	Total
Teller	92	351	50	493
Customer service	76	42	8	126
Total	168	393	58	619

b.

Bank employee	Preference		
	New procedure	Old Procedure	No preference
Teller	133.80	313.00	46.19
Customer service	34.20	80.00	11.81

10a.

Size	Rating			
	Excellent	Fair	Poor	Total
Seats 100 or fewer	182	203	165	550
Seats over 100	180	311	159	650
	362	514	324	1200

b.

	Rating		
Size	**Excellent**	**Fair**	**Poor**
Seats 100 or fewer	165.92	235.58	148.50
Seats over 100	196.08	278.42	175.50

11a.

	Type of car				
Gender	**Compact**	**Full-size**	**SUV**	**Truck/Van**	**Total**
Male	28	39	21	22	110
Female	24	32	20	14	90
	52	71	41	36	200

b.

	Type of car			
Gender	**Compact**	**Full-size**	**SUV**	**Truck/Van**
Male	28.6	39.05	22.55	19.8
Female	23.4	31.95	18.45	16.2

12a.

	Age					
Type of movie rented	**18–24**	**25–34**	**35–44**	**45–64**	**65 and older**	**Total**
Comedy	38	30	24	10	8	110
Action	15	17	16	9	5	62
Drama	12	11	19	25	13	80
Total	65	58	59	44	26	252

b.

	Age				
Type of movie rented	**18–24**	**25–34**	**35–44**	**45–64**	**65 and older**
Comedy	28.37	25.32	25.75	19.21	11.35
Action	15.99	14.27	14.52	10.83	6.40
Drama	20.63	18.41	18.73	13.97	8.25

13a. The claim is "achieving a basic skill level is related to the location of the school."

H_0 : Skill level in a subject is independent of location. (claim)

H_a : Skill level in a subject is dependent on location.

b. d.f. $= (r - 1)(c - 1) = 2$

$\chi_0^2 = 9.210$; Rejection region: $\chi^2 > 9.210$

c.

O	E	$O-E$	$(O-E)^2$	$\dfrac{(O-E)^2}{E}$
43	41.129	1.871	3.500641	0.0851
42	41.905	0.095	0.009025	0.0002
38	39.965	−1.965	3.861225	0.0966
63	64.871	−1.871	3.500641	0.0540
66	66.095	−0.095	0.009025	0.0001
65	63.035	1.965	3.861225	0.0613
				0.2973

$\chi^2 \approx 0.297$

d. Fail to reject H_0. There is not enough evidence at the 1% level of significance to reject the claim that skill level in a subject is independent of location.

14a. The claim is "attitudes about the safety steps taken by the school staff are related to the type of school."

H_0 : Attitudes about safety are independent of the type of school.

H_a : Attitudes about safety are dependent on the type of school. (claim)

b. d.f. $= (r-1)(c-1) = 1$

$\chi_0^2 = 6.635$; Rejection region: $\chi^2 > 6.635$

c.

O	E	$O-E$	$(O-E)^2$	$\dfrac{(O-E)^2}{E}$
41	50.074	−10.074	101.4855	2.0267
51	40.926	10.074	101.4855	2.4797
64	53.926	10.074	101.4855	1.8819
34	44.074	−10.074	101.4855	2.3026
				8.6909

$\chi^2 \approx 8.691$

d. Reject H_0. There is enough evidence at the 1% level of significance to conclude that attitudes about safety are dependent on the type of school.

15a. The claim is "the number of times former smokers tried to quit before they were habit-free is related to gender."

H_0 : The number of times former smokers tried to quit is independent of gender.

H_a : The number of times former smokers tried to quit is dependent of gender. (claim)

b. d.f. $= (r-1)(c-1) = 2$

$\chi_0^2 = 5.991$; Rejection region: $\chi^2 = 5.991$

c.

O	E	$O - E$	$(O - E)^2$	$\dfrac{(O - E)^2}{E}$
271	270.930	0.070	0.004900	0
257	257.286	−0.286	0.081796	0.0003
149	148.784	0.216	0.046656	0.0003
146	146.070	−0.070	0.004900	0
139	138.714	0.286	0.081796	0.0006
80	80.216	−0.216	0.046656	0.0006
				0.0018

$\chi^2 \approx 0.002$

d. Fail to reject H_0. There is not enough evidence at the 5% level of significance to conclude that the number of times former smokers tried to quit is dependent on gender.

16a. The claim is "the adults' ratings of the movie are independent of gender."

H_0 : The adults' ratings of the movie are independent of gender.

H_a : The adults' ratings of the movie are dependent on gender. (claim)

b. d.f. $= (r - 1)(c - 1) = 3$

$\chi_0^2 = 7.815$; Rejection region: $\chi^2 = 7.815$

c.

O	E	$O - E$	$(O - E)^2$	$\dfrac{(O - E)^2}{E}$
97	99.0	−2.0	4.00	0.0404
42	37.5	4.5	20.25	0.5400
26	25.5	0.5	0.25	0.0098
5	8.0	−3.0	9.00	1.1250
101	99.0	2.0	4.00	0.0404
33	37.5	−4.5	20.25	0.5400
25	25.5	−0.5	0.25	0.0098
11	8.0	3.0	9.00	1.1250
				3.4304

$\chi^2 \approx 3.430$

d. Fail to reject H_0. There is not enough evidence at the 5% level of significance to conclude that the adults' rating of the movie are dependent on gender.

17a. The claim is "the treatment. is related to the result"

H_0 : Results are independent of the type of treatment.

H_a : Results are dependent on the type of treatment. (claim)

b. d.f. $= (r - 1)(c - 1) = 1$

$\chi_0^2 = 2.706$; Rejection region: $\chi^2 > 2.706$

c.

O	E	$O - E$	$(O - E)^2$	$\dfrac{(O - E)^2}{E}$
39	31.660	7.34	53.8756	1.7017
25	32.340	−7.34	53.8756	1.6659
54	61.340	−7.34	53.8756	0.8783
70	62.660	7.34	53.8756	0.8598
				5.1057

$\chi^2 \approx 5.106$

d. Reject H_0. There is enough evidence at the 10% level of significance to conclude that results are dependent on the type of treatment.

Sample answer: Because the results are significant at the 10% level of significance, you may consider recommending the drug. However, you may want to perform more tests before recommending the drug.

18a. The claim is "the treatment is related to the result."

H_0 : The result is independent of the type of treatment.

H_a : The result is dependent on the type of treatment. (claim)

b. d.f. $= (r - 1)(c - 1) = 2$

$\chi_0^2 = 4.605$; Rejection region: $\chi^2 > 4.605$

c.

O	E	$O - E$	$(O - E)^2$	$\dfrac{(O - E)^2}{E}$
58	66.667	−8.667	75.116889	1.1267
81	66.667	14.333	205.434889	3.0815
61	66.667	−5.667	32.114889	0.4817
42	33.333	8.667	75.116889	2.2535
19	33.333	−14.333	205.434889	6.1631
39	33.333	5.667	32.114889	0.9635
				14.0700

$\chi^2 \approx 14.070$

d. Reject H_0. There is enough evidence at the 10% level of significance to conclude that the result is dependent on the type of treatment.

19a. The claim is "the reason and the type of worker are dependent."

H_0 : Reasons are independent of the type of worker.

H_a : Reasons are dependent on the type of worker. (claim)

b. d.f. $= (r - 1)(c - 1) = 2$

$\chi_0^2 = 9.210$; Rejection region: $\chi^2 = 9.210$

c.

O	E	$O - E$	$(O - E)^2$	$\dfrac{(O - E)^2}{E}$
30	39.421	−9.421	88.755241	2.2515
36	31.230	4.770	22.752900	0.7286
41	36.349	4.651	21.631801	0.5951
47	37.579	9.421	88.755241	2.3618
25	29.770	−4.770	22.752900	0.7643
30	34.651	−4.651	21.631801	0.6243
				7.3256

$\chi^2 \approx 7.326$

d. Fail to reject H_0. There is not enough evidence at the 1% level of significance to conclude that the reason(s) for continuing education are dependent on the type or worker. Based on these results, marketing strategies should not differ between technical and non-technical audiences in regard to reason(s) for continuing education.

20a. The claim is "age is related to which aspect of career development is considered to be most important."

H_0 : The aspect of career development that is considered to be the most important is independent of age.

H_a : The aspect of career development that is considered to be the most important is independent of age. (claim)

b. d.f. $= (r - 1)(c - 1) = 4$

$\chi_0^2 = 13.277$; Rejection region: $\chi^2 > 13.277$

c.

O	E	$O - E$	$(O - E)^2$	$\dfrac{(O - E)^2}{E}$
31	27.6602	3.3398	11.154264	0.4033
22	24.0680	−2.0680	4.276624	0.1777
21	22.2718	−1.2718	1.617475	0.0726
27	34.0146	−7.0146	49.204613	1.4466
31	29.5971	1.4029	1.968128	0.0665
33	27.3883	5.6117	31.491177	1.1498
19	15.3252	3.6748	13.504155	0.8812
14	13.3350	0.6650	0.442225	0.0332
8	12.3398	−4.3398	18.833864	1.5263
				5.7572

$\chi^2 \approx 5.757$

d. Fail to reject H_0. There is not enough evidence at the 1% level of significance to conclude that age is related to which aspect of career development is considered to be most important.

21a. The claim is "the type of crash depends on the type of vehicle."

H_0 : The type of crash is independent of the type of vehicle.

H_a : The type of crash is dependent on the type of vehicle. (claim)

b. d.f. $= (r-1)(c-1) = 2$

$\chi_0^2 = 5.991$; Rejection region: $\chi^2 > 5.991$

c.

O	E	$O - E$	$(O - E)^2$	$\dfrac{(O - E)^2}{E}$
1,237	1425.637	−188.637	35,583.917770	24.9600
547	452.600	94.400	8,911.360000	19.6893
479	384.763	94.237	8,880.612169	23.0807
1,453	1264.363	188.637	35,583.917770	28.1438
307	401.400	−94.400	8,911.360000	22.2007
247	341.237	−94.237	8,800.612169	26.0248
				144.0990

$\chi^2 \approx 144.099$

d. Reject H_0. There is enough evidence at the 5% level of significance to conclude that the type of crash is dependent on the type of vehicle.

22a. The claim is "the metropolitan status of libraries and Internet access speed are related."

H_0 : Metropolitan status of libraries and Internet access speed are independent..

H_a : Metropolitan status of libraries and Internet access speed are dependent (claim)

b. d.f. $= (r-1)(c-1) = 4$

$\chi_0^2 = 13.277$; Rejection region: $\chi^2 > 13.277$

c.

O	E	$O - E$	$(O - E)^2$	$\dfrac{(O - E)^2}{E}$
5	14.4921	−9.4921	90.099962	6.2172
20	27.4471	−7.4471	55.459298	2.0206
58	41.0608	16.9392	286.936497	6.9881
24	23.5714	0.4826	0.183698	0.0078
46	44.6429	1.3571	1.841720	0.0413
65	66.7857	−1.7857	3.188724	0.0477
37	27.9365	9.0365	82.147032	2.9405
59	52.9101	6.0899	37.086882	0.7009
64	79.1534	−15.1534	229.625532	2.9010
				21.8651

$\chi^2 \approx 21.865$

d. Reject H_0. There is enough evidence at the 1% level of significance to conclude that the metropolitan status of libraries and Internet access speed are related.

23a–b. Contingency table results:

Rows: Expected income

Columns: None

Cell format
Count
Expected count

	More Likely	Less Likely	Did not make a difference
Less than $35,000	37 33.33	10 6.836	22 27.99
35,000 to $50,000	28 25.17	12 5.164	15 21.14
$50,000 to $100,000	55 62.75	9 12.87	65 52.7
Greater than $100,000	36 34.75	1 7.127	29 29.18
Total	156	32	131

	Did not consider it	Total
Less than $35,000	25 25.85	94
35,000 to $50,000	16 19.52	71
$50,000 to $100,000	48 48.68	177
Greater than $100,000	32 26.95	98
Total	121	440

Statistic	DF	Value	P-value
Chi-square	9	26.22966	0.0019

c. Reject H_0. There is enough evidence at the 1% level of significance to conclude that the decision to borrow money is dependent on the child's expected income after graduation.

24a–b. Contingency table results:

Rows: Expected income

Columns: None

Cell format
Count
Expected count

	16–20	21–30	31–40	41–50
Male	45	170	90	72
	44.8	165.9	92.09	73.84
Female	9	30	21	17
	9.2	34.07	18.91	15.16
Total	54	200	111	89

	51–60	61 and older	Total
Male	45	26	448
	45.63	25.72	
Female	10	5	92
	9.37	5.281	
Total	55	31	540

Statistic	DF	Value	P-value
Chi-square	5	1.2078544	0.9441

c. Fail to reject H_0. There is not enough evidence at the 5% level of significance to conclude that age is related to gender in fatal alcohol-related accidents of passenger vehicle drivers with blood alcohol concentrations greater than or equal to 0.08.

25. The claim is "the proportions of motor vehicle crash deaths involving males or females are the same for each age group."

H_0 : The proportions are equal. (claim)

H_a : At least one of the proportions is different from the others.

d.f. $= (r - 1)(c - 1) = 7$

$\chi_0^2 = 14.067$; Rejection region: $\chi^2 > 14.067$

O	E	$O - E$	$(O - E)^2$	$\dfrac{(O - E)^2}{E}$
123	121.632	1.368	1.871424	0.01539
97	89.965	7.035	49.491225	0.55012
82	79.169	2.831	8.014561	0.10123
82	82.048	−0.048	0.002304	0.00003
56	56.138	−0.138	0.109044	0.00034
31	35.266	−4.266	18.198756	0.51604
26	31.668	−5.668	32.126224	1.01447
14	15.114	−1.114	1.240996	0.08211
46	47.368	−1.368	1.871424	0.03951
28	35.035	−7.035	49.491225	1.41262
28	30.831	−2.831	8.014561	0.25995
32	31.952	0.048	0.002304	0.00007
22	21.862	0.138	0.019044	0.00087
18	13.734	4.266	18.198756	1.32509
18	12.332	5.668	32.126224	2.60511
7	5.886	1.114	1.240996	0.21084
				8.13379

$\chi^2 \approx 8.134$

Fail to reject H_0. There is not enough evidence at the 5% level of significance to reject the claim that the proportions of motor vehicle crash deaths involving males or females are the same for each age group.

26. The claim is "the proportions of the results for drug and placebo treatments or the same."

H_0 : The proportions are equal. (claim)

H_a : At least one of proportion is different from the others.

d.f. $= (r - 1)(c - 1) = 1$

$\chi_0^2 = 2.706$; Rejection region: $\chi^2 > 2.706$

O	E	$O - E$	$(O - E)^2$	$\dfrac{(O - E)^2}{E}$
39	31.66	7.34	53.8756	1.7017
25	32.34	−7.34	53.8756	1.6659
54	61.34	−7.34	53.8756	0.8783
70	62.66	7.34	53.8756	0.8598
				5.1057

$\chi^2 \approx 5.106$

Reject H_0. There is enough evidence at the 10% level of significance to reject the claim that the proportions of the results for drug and placebo treatments or the same.

27. Right-tailed

28. Answers will vary. *Sample answer:* Both tests are very similar, but the chi-square test for independence tests whether the occurrence of one variable affects the probability of the occurrence of another variable, while the chi-square homogeneity of proportions test determines whether the proportions for categories from a population follow the same distribution as another population.

29.

Status	Educational attainment			
	Not a high school graduate	**High school graduate**	**Some college, no degree**	**Associate's, bachelor's, or advanced degree**
Employed	0.055	0.183	0.114	0.290
Unemployed	0.006	0.011	0.005	0.007
Not in the labor force	0.073	0.118	0.053	0.085

30a. 0.7%
  b. 5.3%
  c. 18.3%
  d. 32.9%
  e. 31.2%

31. Several of the expected frequencies are less than 5.

32.

Status	Educational attainment			
	Not a high school graduate	High school graduate	Some college, no degree	Associate's, bachelor's, or advanced degree
Employed	0.086	0.285	0.177	0.452
Unemployed	0.207	0.379	0.172	0.241
Not in the labor force	0.221	0.358	0.163	0.259

33. 45.2%

34. 16.3%

35.

Status	Educational attainment			
	Not a high school graduate	High school graduate	Some college, no degree	Associate's, bachelor's, or advanced degree
Employed	0.411	0.587	0.660	0.759
Unemployed	0.046	0.036	0.030	0.019
Not in the labor force	0.544	0.377	0.311	0.223

36. 22.3%

37. 4.6%

38.

39. Answers will vary. *Sample answer:* As educational attainment increases, employment increases.

10.3 COMPARING TWO VARIANCES

10.3 Try It Yourself Solutions

1a. $\alpha = 0.05$ **b.** $F_0 = 2.45$

2a. $\alpha = 0.01$ **b.** $F_0 = 18.31$

3a. The claim is "the variance of the time required for nutrients to enter the bloodstream is less with the specially treated intravenous solution than the variance of the time without the solution."
   $H_0 : \sigma_1^2 \le \sigma_2^2 ; \ H_a : \sigma_1^2 > \sigma_2^2$ (claim)
  b. $\alpha = 0.01$
  c. d.f.$_N = n_1 - 1 = 24$
    d.f.$_D = n_2 - 1 = 19$
  d. $F_0 = 2.92$; Rejection region: $F > 2.92$
  e. $F = \dfrac{s_1^2}{s_2^2} = \dfrac{180}{56} \approx 3.21$
  f. Reject H_0.
  g. There is enough evidence at the 1% level of significance to support the researcher's claim that a specially treated intravenous solution decreases the variance of the time required for nutrients to enter the bloodstream.

4a. The claim is "the pH levels of the soil in two geographic regions have equal standard deviations."
  b. $\alpha = .01$
  c. d.f.$_N = n_1 - 1 = 15$
    d.f.$_D = n_2 - 1 = 21$
  d. $F_0 = 3.43$; Rejection region: $F > 3.43$
  e. $F = \dfrac{s_1^2}{s_2^2} = \dfrac{(0.95)^2}{(0.78)^2} \approx 1.48$
  f. Fail to reject H_0.
  g. There is not enough evidence at the 1% level of significance to reject the biologist's claim that the pH levels of the soil in the two geographic regions have equal standard deviations.

10.3 EXERCISE SOLUTIONS

1. Specify the level of significance α. Determine the degrees of freedom for the numerator and denominator. Use Table 7 in Appendix B to find the critical value F.

2. (1) The F-distribution is a family of curves determined by two types of degrees of freedom, d.f.$_N$ and d.f.$_D$.
    (2) F-distributions are positively skewed.
    (3) The area under the F-distribution curve is equal to 1.
    (4) F-values are always greater than or equal to 0.

(5) For all *F*-distributions, the mean value of *F* is approximately equal to 1.

3. (1) The samples must be randomly selected, (2) the samples must be independent, and (3) each population must have a normal distribution.

4. Determine the sample whose variance is greater. Use the size of this sample n_1 to find $\text{d.f.}_N = n_1 - 1$. Use the size of the other sample n_2 to find $\text{d.f.}_D = n_2 - 1$.

5. $F_0 = 2.54$ **6.** $F_0 = 7.21$ **7.** $F_0 = 2.06$

8. $F_0 = 14.62$ **9.** $F_0 = 9.16$ **10.** $F_0 = 1.91$

11. $F_0 = 1.80$ **12.** $F_0 = 2.42$

13. $H_0 : \sigma_1^2 \leq \sigma_2^2$; $H_a : \sigma_1^2 > \sigma_2^2$ (claim)
$\text{d.f.}_N = 4$
$\text{d.f.}_D = 5$
$F_0 = 3.52$; Rejection region: $F > 3.52$
$$F = \frac{s_1^2}{s_2^2} = \frac{773}{765} \approx 1.010$$

Fail to reject H_0. There is not enough evidence at the 10% level of significance to support the claim.

14. $H_0 : \sigma_1^2 = \sigma_2^2$ (claim); $H_a : \sigma_1^2 \neq \sigma_2^2$
$\text{d.f.}_N = 6$
$\text{d.f.}_D = 7$
$F_0 = 5.12$; Rejection region: $F > 5.12$
$$F = \frac{s_1^2}{s_2^2} = \frac{310}{297} \approx 1.044$$

Fail to reject H_0. There is not enough evidence at the 5% level of significance to reject the claim.

15. $H_0 : \sigma_1^2 \leq \sigma_2^2$ (claim); $H_a : \sigma_1^2 > \sigma_2^2$
$\text{d.f.}_N = 10$
$\text{d.f.}_D = 9$
$F_0 = 5.26$; Rejection region: $F > 5.26$
$$F = \frac{s_1^2}{s_2^2} = \frac{842}{836} \approx 1.007$$

Fail to reject H_0. There is not enough evidence at the 1% level of significance to reject the claim.

16. $H_0 : \sigma_1^2 = \sigma_2^2$; $H_a : \sigma_1^2 \neq \sigma_2^2$ (claim)

d.f.$_N = 30$

d.f.$_D = 27$

$F_0 = 2.13$; Rejection region: $F > 2.13$

$F = \dfrac{s_1^2}{s_2^2} = \dfrac{245}{112} \approx 2.188$

Reject H_0. There is enough evidence at the 5% level of significance to reject the claim.

17. $H_0 : \sigma_1^2 = \sigma_2^2$ (claim); $H_a : \sigma_1^2 \neq \sigma_2^2$

d.f.$_N = 12$

d.f.$_D = 19$

$F_0 = 3.76$; Rejection region: $F > 3.76$

$F = \dfrac{s_1^2}{s_2^2} = \dfrac{9.8}{2.5} \approx 3.920$

Reject H_0. There is enough evidence at the 1% level of significance to reject the claim.

18. $H_0 : \sigma_1^2 \leq \sigma_2^2$; $H_a : \sigma_1^2 > \sigma_2^2$ (claim)

d.f.$_N = 15$

d.f.$_D = 11$

$F_0 = 2.72$; Rejection region: $F > 2.72$

$F = \dfrac{s_1^2}{s_2^2} = \dfrac{44.6}{39.3} \approx 1.135$

Fail to reject H_0. There is not enough evidence at the 5% level of significance to reject the claim.

19.   Population 1: Company B
Population 2: Company A

a. The claim is "the variance of the life of Company A's appliances is less than the variance of the life of Company B's appliances."

$H_0 : \sigma_1^2 \leq \sigma_2^2$; $H_a : \sigma_1^2 > \sigma_2^2$ (claim)

b. d.f.$_N = 24$

d.f.$_D = 19$

$F_0 = 2.11$; Rejection region: $F > 2.11$

c. $F = \dfrac{s_1^2}{s_2^2} = \dfrac{2.8}{2.6} \approx 1.08$

d. Fail to reject H_0.

e. There is not enough evidence at the 5% level of significance to support Company A's claim that the variance of life of its appliances is less than the variance of life of Company B appliances.

20. Population 1: Competitor
Population 2: Auto Manufacturer

a. The claim is "the variance of the life of the fuel consumption for the company's hybrid vehicles is less than that of the competitor's hybrid vehicles."

$$H_0 : \sigma_1^2 \le \sigma_2^2 ; \ H_a : \sigma_1^2 > \sigma_2^2 \ \text{(claim)}$$

b. $\text{d.f.}_N = 20$

$\text{d.f.}_D = 18$

$F_0 = 3.08$; Rejection region: $F > 3.08$

c. $F = \dfrac{s_1^2}{s_2^2} = \dfrac{0.77}{0.24} \approx 3.21$

d. Reject H_0.

e. There is enough evidence at the 1% level of significance to conclude that the variance of the fuel consumption for the company's hybrid vehicles is less than that of the competitor's hybrid vehicles.

21. Population 1: Company B
Population 2: Company A

a. The claim is "the variance of the prices differ between the two companies."

$$H_0 : \sigma_1^2 = \sigma_2^2 ; \ H_a : \sigma_1^2 \ne \sigma_2^2 \ \text{(claim)}$$

b. $\text{d.f.}_N = 4$

$\text{d.f.}_D = 6$

$F_0 = 6.23$; Rejection region: $F > 6.23$

c. $F = \dfrac{s_1^2}{s_2^2} = \dfrac{30,445}{14,490.48} \approx 2.10$

d. Fail to reject H_0.

e. There is not enough evidence at the 5% level of significance to conclude that the variances of the prices differ between the two companies.

22. Population 1: Brand B
Population 2: Brand A

a. The claim is "the variance of the numbers of calories differ between the two brands."

$$H_0 : \sigma_1^2 = \sigma_2^2 ; \ H_a : \sigma_1^2 \ne \sigma_2^2 \ \text{(claim)}$$

b. $\text{d.f.}_N = 9$

$\text{d.f.}_D = 9$

$F_0 = 3.18$; Rejection region: $F > 3.18$

c. $F = \dfrac{s_1^2}{s_2^2} = \dfrac{982.22}{284.44} \approx 3.45$

d. Reject H_0.

e. There is enough evidence at the 10% level of significance to conclude that the variances of the numbers of calories differ between the two brands.

23. Population 1: District 1

  Population 2: District 2

  a. The claim is "the standard deviations of science achievement test scores for eighth grade students are the same in Districts 1 and 2."

  $$H_0 : \sigma_1^2 = \sigma_2^2 \text{(claim)}; \ H_a : \sigma_1^2 \neq \sigma_2^2$$

  b. d.f.$_N = 11$

  d.f.$_D = 13$

  $F_0 = 2.635$; Rejection region: $F > 2.635$

  c. $F = \dfrac{s_1^2}{s_2^2} = \dfrac{(36.8)^2}{(32.5)^2} \approx 1.282$

  d. Fail to reject H_0.

  e. There is not enough evidence at the 10% level of significance to reject the administrator's claim that the standard deviations of science assessment test scores for eighth grade students are the same in Districts 1 and 2.

24. Population 1: District 1

  Population 2: District 2

  a. The claim is "the standard deviations of U.S. history assessment scores for eighth grade students are the same in Districts 1 and 2."

  $$H_0 : \sigma_1^2 = \sigma_2^2 \text{(claim)}; \ H_a : \sigma_1^2 \neq \sigma_2^2$$

  b. d.f.$_N = 9$

  d.f.$_D = 12$

  $F_0 = 5.20$ Rejection region: $F > 5.20$

  c. $F = \dfrac{s_1^2}{s_2^2} = \dfrac{(33.9)^2}{(30.2)^2} \approx 1.26$

  d. Fail to reject H_0.

  e. There is not enough evidence at the 1% level of significance to reject that the standard deviations of U.S. history assessment test scores for eighth grade students are the same in Districts 1 and 2.

25. Population 1: New York

  Population 2: California

  a. The claim is "the standard deviation of the annual salaries for actuaries is greater in New York than in California."

  $$H_0 : \sigma_1^2 \leq \sigma_2^2; \ H_a : \sigma_1^2 > \sigma_2^2 \ \text{(claim)}$$

  b. d.f.$_N = 15$

  d.f.$_D = 16$

  $F_0 = 2.35$; Rejection region: $F > 2.35$

  c. $F = \dfrac{s_1^2}{s_2^2} = \dfrac{(14,900)^2}{(9,600)^2} \approx 2.41$

  d. Reject H_0.

  e. There is enough evidence at the 5% level of significance to conclude the standard deviation of the annual salaries for actuaries is greater in New York than in California.

26. Population 1: Florida
   Population 2: Louisiana

 a. The claim is "the standard deviations of the annual salaries for public relations managers is greater in Florida than in Louisiana."

$$H_0 : \sigma_1^2 \le \sigma_2^2; \ H_a : \sigma_1^2 > \sigma_2^2 \text{ (claim)}$$

 b. $\text{d.f.}_N = 27$

   $\text{d.f.}_D = 23$

   $F_0 = 1.985;$ Rejection region: $F > 1.985$

 c. $F = \dfrac{s_1^2}{s_2^2} = \dfrac{(10,100)^2}{(6,400)^2} \approx 2.490$

 d. Reject H_0.

 e. There is enough evidence at the 5% level of significance to support the claim that the standard deviation of the annual salaries for public relations managers is greater in Florida than in Louisiana.

27. Hypothesis test results:

   σ_1^2 : variance of population 1

   σ_2^2 : variance of population 2

   σ_1^2 / σ_2^2 : variance ratio

   $H_0 : \sigma_1^2 / \sigma_2^2 = 1$

   $H_A : \sigma_1^2 / \sigma_2^2 \ne 1$

Ratio	n1	n2	Sample Ratio	F-Stat	P-value
σ_1^2 / σ_2^2	15	18	0.5281571	0.5281571	0.2333

   $P \approx 0.2333 > 0.10$, so fail to reject H_0. There is not enough evidence at the 10% level of significance to reject the claim.

28. Hypothesis test results:

   σ_1^2 : variance of population 1

   σ_2^2 : variance of population 2

   σ_1^2 / σ_2^2 : variance ratio

   $H_0 : \sigma_1^2 / \sigma_2^2 = 1$

   $H_A : \sigma_1^2 / \sigma_2^2 \ne 1$

Ratio	n1	n2	Sample Ratio	F-Stat	P-value
σ_1^2 / σ_2^2	24	20	2.712803	2.712803	0.0308

   $P \approx 0.0308 < 0.05$, so reject H_0. There is enough evidence at the 5% level of significance to support the claim.

29. Hypothesis test results:

σ_1^2 : variance of population 1

σ_2^2 : variance of population 2

σ_1^2 / σ_2^2 : variance ratio

$H_0 : \sigma_1^2 / \sigma_2^2 = 1$

$H_A : \sigma_1^2 / \sigma_2^2 > 1$

Ratio	n1	n2	Sample Ratio	F-Stat	P-value
σ_1^2 / σ_2^2	22	29	2.153926	2.153926	0.0293

$P \approx 0.0293 < 0.05$, so reject H_0. There is enough evidence at the 5% level of significance to reject the claim.

30. Hypothesis test results:

σ_1^2 : variance of population 1

σ_2^2 : variance of population 2

σ_1^2 / σ_2^2 : variance ratio

$H_0 : \sigma_1^2 / \sigma_2^2 = 1$

$H_A : \sigma_1^2 / \sigma_2^2 > 1$

Ratio	n1	n2	Sample Ratio	F-Stat	P-value
σ_1^2 / σ_2^2	7	13	1.1879483	1.1879483	0.3751

$P \approx 0.3751 > 0.01$, so fail to reject H_0. There is not enough evidence at the 1% level of significance to support the claim.

31. Right-tailed: $F_R = 14.73$

Left-tailed:

(1) d.f.$_N$ = 3 and d.f.$_D$ = 6

(2) $F = 6.60$

(3) Critical value is $\dfrac{1}{F} = \dfrac{1}{6.60} \approx 0.15$.

32. Right-tailed: $F_R = 2.33$

Left-tailed:

(1) d.f.$_N$ = 15 and d.f.$_D$ = 20

(2) $F = 2.20$

(3) Critical value is $\dfrac{1}{F} = \dfrac{1}{2.20} \approx 0.45$.

33. $\dfrac{s_1^2}{s_2^2} F_L < \dfrac{\sigma_1^2}{\sigma_2^2} < \dfrac{s_1^2}{s_2^2} F_R \rightarrow \left(\dfrac{10.89}{9.61} \right)(0.331) < \dfrac{\sigma_1^2}{\sigma_2^2} < \left(\dfrac{10.89}{9.61} \right)(3.33) \rightarrow 0.375 < \dfrac{\sigma_1^2}{\sigma_2^2} < 3.774$

34. $\dfrac{s_1^2}{s_2^2} F_L < \dfrac{\sigma_1^2}{\sigma_2^2} < \dfrac{s_1^2}{s_2^2} F_R \rightarrow \left(\dfrac{5.29}{3.61}\right)(0.331) < \dfrac{\sigma_1^2}{\sigma_2^2} < \left(\dfrac{5.29}{3.61}\right)(3.33) \rightarrow 0.485 < \dfrac{\sigma_1^2}{\sigma_2^2} < 4.880$

10.4 ANALYSIS OF VARIANCE

10.4 Try It Yourself Solutions

1a. The claim is "there is a difference in the mean a monthly sales among the sales regions."

$H_0 : \mu_1 = \mu_2 = \mu_3 = \mu_4$

H_a : At least one mean is different from the others. (claim)

b. $\alpha = 0.05$

c. d.f.$_N$ = 3

d.f.$_D$ = 14

d. F_0 = 3.34; Rejection region: $F > 3.34$

e.

Variation	Sum of Squares	Degrees of Freedom	Mean Squares	F
Between	549.8	3	183.3	4.22
Within	608.0	14	43.4	

$F \approx 4.22$

f. Reject H_0.

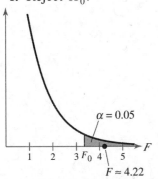

$\alpha = 0.05$

$F \approx 4.22$

g. There is enough evidence at the 5% level of significance to conclude that there is a difference in the mean monthly sales among the sales regions.

2a. Enter the data.

b. $H_0 : \mu_1 = \mu_2 = \mu_3 = \mu_4$

H_a : At least one mean is different from the others. (claim)

Variation	Sum of Squares	Degrees of Freedom	Mean Squares	F
Between	0.584	3	0.195	1.34
Within	4.360	30	0.145	

$F = 1.34 \rightarrow P\text{-value} = 0.280$

c. $0.280 > 0.05$

d. Fail to reject H_0. There is not enough evidence to conclude that at least one mean is different from the others.

10.4 EXERCISE SOLUTIONS

1. $H_0 : \mu_1 = \mu_2 = \ldots = \mu_4$
    H_a : At least one mean is different from the others.

2. Each sample must be randomly selected from a normal, or approximately normal, population. The samples must be independent of each other. Each population must have the same variance.

3. The MS_B measures the differences related to the treatment given to each sample.
    The MS_W measures the differences related to entries within the same sample.

4. H_{0A} : There is no difference among the treatment means of Factor *A*.
    H_{aA} : There is at least one difference among the treatment means of Factor *A*.

    H_{0B} : There is no difference among the treatment means of Factor *B*.
    H_{aB} : There is at least one difference among the treatment means of Factor *A*.

    H_{0AB} : There is no interaction between Factor *A* and Factor *B*.
    H_{aAB} : There is interaction between Factor *A* and Factor *B*.

5a. The claim is that "the mean costs per ounce are different."
    $H_0 : \mu_1 = \mu_2 = \mu_3$
    H_a : At least one mean is different from the others. (claim)

   b. d.f.$_N = k - 1 = 2$
    d.f.$_D = N - k = \mathbf{26}$
    $F_0 = 3.37$; Rejection region: $F > 3.37$

   c.

Variation	Sum of Squares	Degrees of Freedom	Mean Squares	F
Between	0.518	2	0.259	1.02
Within	6.629	26	0.255	

   $F \approx 1.02$

   d. Fail to reject H_0.

   e. There is not enough evidence at the 5% level of significance to conclude that the mean costs per ounce are different.

6a. The claim is that "at least one of the mean battery prices is different from the others."
    $H_0 : \mu_1 = \mu_2 = \mu_3$
    H_a : At least one mean is different from the others. (claim)

   b. d.f.$_N = k - 1 = 2$
    d.f.$_D = N - k = 14$
    $F_0 = 3.74$; Rejection region: $F > 3.74$

c.

Variation	Sum of Squares	Degrees of Freedom	Mean Squares	F
Between	198.529	2	99.265	0.418
Within	33.25	14	237.5	

$F \approx 0.42$

d. Fail to reject H_0.

e. There is not enough evidence at the 5% level of significance to conclude that at least one of the mean battery prices is different from the others.

7a. The claim is "at least one mean salary is different."

$H_0 : \mu_1 = \mu_2 = \mu_3$

$H_a :$ At least one mean is different from the others. (claim)

b. d.f.$_N = k - 1 = 2$

d.f.$_D = N - k = 27$

$F_0 = 5.49$; Rejection region: $F > 5.49$

c.

Variation	Sum of Squares	Degrees of Freedom	Mean Squares	F
Between	3125.521	2	1562.761	21.99
Within	1918.441	27	71.053	

$F \approx 21.99$

d. Reject H_0.

e. There is enough evidence at the 1% level of significance to conclude that at least one mean is different.

8a. The claim is "at least one mean age is different."

$H_0 : \mu_1 = \mu_2 = \mu_3 = \mu_4 = \mu_5$

$H_a :$ At least one mean is different from the others. (claim)

b. d.f.$_N = k - 1 = 4$

d.f.$_D = N - k = 60$

$F_0 = 2.53$; Rejection region: $F > 2.53$

c.

Variation	Sum of Squares	Degrees of Freedom	Mean Squares	F
Between	266	4	66.5	0.27
Within	14559.846	60	242.664	

$F \approx 0.27$

d. Fail to reject H_0.

e. There is not enough evidence at the 5% level of significance to conclude that at least one mean is different.

9a. The claim is "at least one mean cost is different."

$H_0 : \mu_1 = \mu_2 = \mu_3 = \mu_4 = \mu_5$

$H_a :$ At least one mean is different from the others. (claim)

b. $\text{d.f.}_N = k - 1 = 4$

$\text{d.f.}_D = N - k = 21$

$F_0 = 4.37$; Rejection region: $F > 4.37$

c.

Variation	Sum of Squares	Degrees of Freedom	Mean Squares	F
Between	2841.1	4	710.275	12.61
Within	1182.9	21	56.329	

$F \approx 12.61$

d. Reject H_0.

e. There is enough evidence at the 1% level of significance to conclude that at least one mean cost per miles is different.

10a. The claim is "at least one mean well-being index score is different."

$H_0 : \mu_1 = \mu_2 = \mu_3 = \mu_4$ (claim)

H_a : At least one mean is different from the others.

b. $\text{d.f.}_N = k - 1 = 3$

$\text{d.f.}_D = N - k = 30$

$F_0 = 2.28$; Rejection region: $F > 2.28$

c.

Variation	Sum of Squares	Degrees of Freedom	Mean Squares	F
Between	22.811	3	7.604	2.55
Within	89.448	30	2.982	

$F \approx 2.55$

d. Reject H_0.

e. There is enough evidence at the 10% level of significance to reject the claim that the mean scores are the same for all regions.

11a. The claim is "the mean number of days patients spend at the hospital is the same for all four regions."

$H_0 : \mu_1 = \mu_2 = \mu_3 = \mu_4$ (claim)

H_a : At least one mean is different from the others. (claim)

b. $\text{d.f.}_N = k - 1 = 3$

$\text{d.f.}_D = N - k = 29$

$F_0 = 4.54$; Rejection region: $F > 4.54$

c.

Variation	Sum of Squares	Degrees of Freedom	Mean Squares	F
Between	5.608	3	1.869	0.56
Within	97.302	29	3.355	

$F \approx 0.56$

d. Fail to reject H_0.

e. There is not enough evidence at the 1% level of significance for the company to reject the claim that the mean number of days patients spend at the hospital is the same for all four regions.

12a. The claim is "the mean salary is different in at least one of the areas."

$H_0 : \mu_1 = \mu_2 = \mu_3 = \mu_4 = \mu_5 = \mu_6$

H_a : At least one mean is different from the others. (claim)

b. d.f.$_N$ = $k - 1 = 5$

d.f.$_D$ = $N - k = 30$

$F_0 = 2.53$; Rejection region: $F > 2.53$

c.

Variation	Sum of Squares	Degrees of Freedom	Mean Squares	F
Between	274,390,504	5	54,878,100.8	1.63
Within	1,007,909,953	30	33,596,998.4	

$F \approx 1.63$

d. Fail to reject H_0.

e. There is not enough evidence at the 5% level of significance to conclude that the mean salary is different in at least one of the areas.

13a. The claim is "the mean energy consumption in at least one region is different from the others."

$H_0 : \mu_1 = \mu_2 = \mu_3 = \mu_4$

H_a : At least one mean is different from the others. (claim)

b. d.f.$_N$ = $k - 1 = 3$

d.f.$_D$ = $N - k = 35$

$F_0 = 2.247$; Rejection region: $F > 2.247$

c.

Variation	Sum of Squares	Degrees of Freedom	Mean Squares	F
Between	15,340.657	3	5113.552	3.107
Within	57,609.672	35	1645.991	

$F \approx 3.107$

d. Reject H_0.

e. There is enough evidence at the 10% level of significance to conclude that the mean energy consumption of at least one region is different from the others.

14a. The claim is "the mean amounts spent are equal for all regions."

$H_0 : \mu_1 = \mu_2 = \mu_3 = \mu_4$

H_a : At least one mean is different from the others. (claim)

b. d.f.$_N$ = $k - 1 = 3$

d.f.$_D$ = $N - k = 29$

$F_0 = 2.93$; Rejection region: $F > 2.93$

c.

Variation	Sum of Squares	Degrees of Freedom	Mean Squares	F
Between	3,112,137.05	3	1,037,379.02	4.29
Within	7,017,376.29	29	241,978.49	

$F \approx 4.29$

d. Reject H_0.

e. There is enough evidence at the 5% level of significance to reject the claim that the mean amounts spent are equal for all regions.

15. Analysis of Variance results:
Data stored in separate columns.

Column means

Column	N	Means	Std. Error
Grade 9	8	84.375	9.531784
Grade 10	8	79.25	9.090321
Grade 11	8	76.625	7.648383
Grade 12	8	70.75	6.9224014

ANOVA table

Source	df	SS	MS	F-stat	P-value
Treatments	3	771.25	257.08334	0.45923114	0.7129
Error	28	15674.675	559.8125		
Total	31	16446			

Fail to reject H_0. There is not enough evidence at the 1% level of significance to reject the claim that the mean numbers of female students who played on a sports team are equal for all grades.

16. Analysis of Variance results:
Data stored in separate columns.

Column means

Column	N	Means	Std. Error
Gainesville	11	188.67273	12.685002
Orlando	10	209.56	11.292428
Tampa	10	173.96	14.59111

ANOVA table

Source	df	SS	MS	F-stat	P-value
Treatments	2	6404.441	3202.2205	1.8549093	0.1752
Error	28	48337.77	1726.3489		
Total	30	54742.21			

Fail to reject H_0. There is not enough evidence at the 10% level of significance to conclude that at least one mean sale price is different.

17. H_0 : Advertising medium has to effect on mean ratings.
H_a : Advertising medium has an effect on mean ratings.

H_0 : Length of ad has no effect on mean ratings.
H_a : Length of ad has an effect on mean ratings.

H_0 : There is no interaction effect between advertising medium and length of ad on mean ratings.
H_a : There is an interaction effect between advertising medium and length of ad on mean ratings.

Source	d.f.	SS	MS	F	P
Ad medium	1	1.25	1.25	0.57	0.459
Length of ad	1	0.45	0.45	0.21	0.655
Interaction	1	0.45	0.45	0.21	0.655
Error	16	34.80	2.17		
Total	19	36.95			

None of the null hypotheses can be rejected at the 10% level of significance.

18. H_0 : Type of vehicle has no effect on the mean number of vehicles sold.

H_a : Type of vehicle has an effect on the mean number of vehicles sold.

H_0 : Gender has no effect on the mean number of vehicles sold.

H_a : Gender has an effect on the mean number of vehicles sold.

H_0 : There is no interaction effect between type of vehicle and gender on the mean number of vehicles sold.

H_a : There is an interaction effect between type of vehicle and gender on the mean number of vehicles sold.

Source	d.f.	SS	MS	F	P
Type of vehicle	2	84.08	42.04	34.01	0.000
Gender	1	0.38	0.38	0.30	0.589
Interaction	2	12.25	6.12	4.96	0.019
Error	18	22.25	1.24		
Total	23	118.96			

There appears to be an interaction effect between type of vehicle and gender on the mean number of vehicles sold. Also, it appears that type of vehicle has an effect on the mean number of vehicles sold.

19. H_0 : Age has no effect on mean GPA.

H_a : Age has an effect on mean GPA.

H_0 : Gender has no effect on mean GPA.

H_a : Gender has an effect on mean GPA.

H_0 : There is no interaction effect between age and gender on mean GPA.

H_a : There is no interaction effect between age and gender on mean GPA.

Source	d.f.	SS	MS	F	P
Age	3	0.41	0.14	0.12	0.948
Gender	1	00.18	0.18	0.16	0.697
Interaction	3	0.29	0.10	0.08	0.968
Error	16	18.66	1.17		
Total	23	19.55			

None of the null hypotheses can be rejected at the 10% level of significance.

20. H_0 : Technicians have no effect on mean repair time.

H_a : Technicians have an effect on mean repair time.

H_0 : Brand has no effect on mean repair time.

H_a : Brand has an effect on mean repair time.

H_0 : There is no interaction effect between technicians and brand on mean repair time.

H_a : There is interaction effect between technicians and brand on mean repair time.

Source	d.f.	SS	MS	F	P
Technicians	3	714	238	1.74	0.185
Brand	2	382	191	1.40	0.266
Interaction	6	2007	334	2.45	0.054
Error	24	3277	137		
Total	35	6381			

There appears to be an of interaction effect between technicians and brand on the mean repair time at the 10% level of significance

21.

	Mean	Size
Pop 1	66.36	10
Pop2	48.52	10
Pop3	42.27	10

$SS_W = 1918.441$

$\sum (n_i - 1) = N - k = 27$

$F_0 = 5.49 \rightarrow CV_{\text{Scheffe}'} = 5.49(3 - 1) = 10.98$

$$\frac{(\overline{x}_1 - \overline{x}_2)^2}{\dfrac{SS_W}{\sum (n_i - 1)}\left[\dfrac{1}{n_1} + \dfrac{1}{n_2}\right]} \approx 23.396 \rightarrow \text{Significant difference}$$

$$\frac{(\overline{x}_1 - \overline{x}_3)^2}{\dfrac{SS_W}{\sum (n_i - 1)}\left[\dfrac{1}{n_1} + \dfrac{1}{n_3}\right]} \approx 40.837 \rightarrow \text{Significant difference}$$

$$\frac{(\overline{x}_2 - \overline{x}_3)^2}{\dfrac{SS_W}{\sum (n_i - 1)}\left[\dfrac{1}{n_2} + \dfrac{1}{n_3}\right]} \approx 2.749 \rightarrow \text{No difference}$$

22.

	Mean	Size
Pop 1	43.6	5
Pop2	54.0	6
Pop3	69.5	6
Pop 4	73.5	4
Pop 5	61.4	5

$SS_W = 1182.900$

$\sum (n_i - 1) = N - k = 21$

$F_0 = 4.37 \rightarrow CV_{\text{Scheffe}'} = 4.37(5 - 1) = 17.48$

$$\frac{(\bar{x}_1 - \bar{x}_2)^2}{\dfrac{SS_W}{\sum (n_i - 1)}\left[\dfrac{1}{n_1} + \dfrac{1}{n_2}\right]} \approx 5.237 \rightarrow \text{No difference}$$

$$\frac{(\bar{x}_1 - \bar{x}_3)^2}{\dfrac{SS_W}{\sum (n_i - 1)}\left[\dfrac{1}{n_1} + \dfrac{1}{n_3}\right]} \approx 32.479 \rightarrow \text{Significant difference}$$

$$\frac{(\bar{x}_1 - \bar{x}_4)^2}{\dfrac{SS_W}{\sum (n_i - 1)}\left[\dfrac{1}{n_1} + \dfrac{1}{n_4}\right]} \approx 35.270 \rightarrow \text{Significant difference}$$

$$\frac{(\bar{x}_1 - \bar{x}_5)^2}{\dfrac{SS_W}{\sum (n_i - 1)}\left[\dfrac{1}{n_1} + \dfrac{1}{n_5}\right]} \approx 14.062 \rightarrow \text{No difference}$$

$$\frac{(\bar{x}_2 - \bar{x}_3)^2}{\dfrac{SS_W}{\sum (n_i - 1)}\left[\dfrac{1}{n_2} + \dfrac{1}{n_3}\right]} \approx 12.795 \rightarrow \text{No difference}$$

$$\frac{(\bar{x}_2 - \bar{x}_4)^2}{\dfrac{SS_W}{\sum (n_i - 1)}\left[\dfrac{1}{n_2} + \dfrac{1}{n_4}\right]} \approx 16.201 \rightarrow \text{No difference}$$

$$\frac{(\bar{x}_2 - \bar{x}_5)^2}{\dfrac{SS_W}{\sum (n_i - 1)}\left[\dfrac{1}{n_2} + \dfrac{1}{n_5}\right]} \approx 2.651 \rightarrow \text{No difference}$$

$$\frac{(\overline{x}_3 - \overline{x}_4)^2}{\dfrac{SS_W}{\sum (n_i - 1)}\left[\dfrac{1}{n_3} + \dfrac{1}{n_4}\right]} \approx 0.682 \rightarrow \text{No difference}$$

$$\frac{(\overline{x}_3 - \overline{x}_5)^2}{\dfrac{SS_W}{\sum (n_i - 1)}\left[\dfrac{1}{n_3} + \dfrac{1}{n_5}\right]} \approx 3.177 \rightarrow \text{No difference}$$

$$\frac{(\overline{x}_4 - \overline{x}_5)^2}{\dfrac{SS_W}{\sum (n_i - 1)}\left[\dfrac{1}{n_4} + \dfrac{1}{n_5}\right]} \approx 5.776 \rightarrow \text{No difference}$$

23.

	Mean	Size
Pop 1	$65.9\overline{3}$	6
Pop2	66.1	8
Pop3	$64.8\overline{63}$	11
Pop 4	$66.9\overline{8}$	9

$SS_W = 89.448$

$\sum (n_i - 1) = N - k = 30$

$F_0 = 2.28 \rightarrow CV_{\text{Scheffe'}} = 2.28(4 - 1) = 6.84$

$$\frac{(\overline{x}_1 - \overline{x}_2)^2}{\dfrac{SS_W}{\sum (n_i - 1)}\left[\dfrac{1}{n_1} + \dfrac{1}{n_2}\right]} \approx 0.032 \rightarrow \text{No difference}$$

$$\frac{(\overline{x}_1 - \overline{x}_3)^2}{\dfrac{SS_W}{\sum (n_i - 1)}\left[\dfrac{1}{n_1} + \dfrac{1}{n_3}\right]} \approx 1.490 \rightarrow \text{No difference}$$

$$\frac{(\overline{x}_1 - \overline{x}_4)^2}{\dfrac{SS_W}{\sum (n_i - 1)}\left[\dfrac{1}{n_1} + \dfrac{1}{n_4}\right]} \approx 1.345 \rightarrow \text{No difference}$$

$$\frac{(\overline{x}_2 - \overline{x}_3)^2}{\dfrac{SS_W}{\sum (n_i - 1)}\left[\dfrac{1}{n_2} + \dfrac{1}{n_3}\right]} \approx 2.374 \rightarrow \text{No difference}$$

$$\frac{(\overline{x}_2 - \overline{x}_4)^2}{\dfrac{SS_w}{\sum(n_i - 1)}\left[\dfrac{1}{n_2} + \dfrac{1}{n_4}\right]} \approx 1.122 \rightarrow \text{No difference}$$

$$\frac{(\overline{x}_3 - \overline{x}_4)^2}{\dfrac{SS_w}{\sum(n_i - 1)}\left[\dfrac{1}{n_3} + \dfrac{1}{n_4}\right]} \approx 7.499 \rightarrow \text{Significant difference}$$

24.

	Mean	Size
Pop 1	2312	10
Pop 2	1786	9
Pop 3	$1755.\overline{142857}$	7
Pop 4	$1491.\overline{285714}$	7

$SS_W = 7,017,376.286$

$F_0 = 2.93 \rightarrow \text{CV}_{\text{Scheffe}'} = 2.93(4 - 1) = 8.79$

$$\frac{(\overline{x}_1 - \overline{x}_2)^2}{\dfrac{SS_W}{\sum(n_i - 1)}\left[\dfrac{1}{n_1} + \dfrac{1}{n_2}\right]} \approx 5.416 \rightarrow \text{No difference}$$

$$\frac{(\overline{x}_1 - \overline{x}_3)^2}{\dfrac{SS_W}{\sum(n_i - 1)}\left[\dfrac{1}{n_1} + \dfrac{1}{n_3}\right]} \approx 5.277 \rightarrow \text{No difference}$$

$$\frac{(\overline{x}_1 - \overline{x}_4)^2}{\dfrac{SS_W}{\sum(n_i - 1)}\left[\dfrac{1}{n_1} + \dfrac{1}{n_4}\right]} \approx 11.462 \rightarrow \text{Significant difference}$$

$$\frac{(\overline{x}_2 - \overline{x}_3)^2}{\dfrac{SS_W}{\sum(n_i - 1)}\left[\dfrac{1}{n_2} + \dfrac{1}{n_3}\right]} \approx 0.015 \rightarrow \text{No difference}$$

$$\frac{(\overline{x}_2 - \overline{x}_4)^2}{\dfrac{SS_w}{\sum(n_i - 1)}\left[\dfrac{1}{n_2} + \dfrac{1}{n_4}\right]} \approx 1.413 \rightarrow \text{No difference}$$

$$\frac{(\overline{x}_3 - \overline{x}_4)^2}{\dfrac{SS_w}{\sum(n_i - 1)}\left[\dfrac{1}{n_3} + \dfrac{1}{n_4}\right]} \approx 1.007 \rightarrow \text{No difference}$$

CHAPTER 10 REVIEW EXERCISE SOLUTIONS

1a.

Response	Distribution
Less than $10	29%
$10 to $20	16%
More than $21	9%
Don't give one/other	46%

H_0 : The distribution of the allowance amounts is 29% less than $10, 16% $10 to $20, 9% more than $21, and 46% don't give one/other.

H_a : The distribution of amounts differ from the claimed or expected distribution. (claim)

b. $\chi_0^2 = 6.251$; Rejection region: $\chi^2 > 6.251$

c.

Response	Distribution	Observed	Expected	$\dfrac{(O - E)^2}{E}$
Less than $10	29%	353	319.87	3.431
$10 to $20	16%	167	176.48	0.509
More than $21	9%	94	99.27	0.280
Don't give one/other	46%	489	507.38	0.666
				4.886

$\chi^2 \approx 4.886$

d. Fail to reject H_0.

e. There is not enough evidence at the 10% level of significance to conclude that there has been a change in the claimed or expected distribution.

2a.

Response	Distribution
1–5	4%
6–10	24%
11–15	34%
16–30	31%
31–60	6%
61 and over	1%

H_0 : The distribution of the lengths of office visits is 4% 1–5 minutes, 24%. 6–10 minutes 34% 11–15 minutes, 6% 31–60 minutes, and 1% 61 minutes and over.

H_a : The distribution of lengths differs from the claimed or expected distribution. (claim)

b. $\chi_0^2 = 15.086$; Rejection region: $\chi^2 > 15.086$

c.

Response	Distribution	Observed	Expected	$\dfrac{(O-E)^2}{E}$
1–5	4%	9	14	1.786
6–10	24%	62	84	5.762
11–15	34%	126	119	0.412
16–30	31%	129	108.5	3.873
31–60	6%	23	21	0.190
61 and over	1%	1	3.5	1.786
				13.809

$\chi^2 \approx 13.809$

d. Fail to reject H_0.

e. There is not enough evidence at the 1% level of significance to conclude that there has been a change in the claimed or expected distribution.

3a.

Response	Distribution
Short-game shots	65%
Approach and swing	22%
Driver shots	9%
Putting	4%

H_0 : The distribution of responses from golf students about what they need the most help with is 22% approach and swing, 9% driver shots, 4% putting and 65% short-game shots. (claim)

H_a : The distribution of responses differs from the claimed or expected distribution.

b. $\chi^2_0 = 7.815$; Rejection region: $\chi^2 > 7.815$

c.

Response	Distribution	Observed	Expected	$\dfrac{(O-E)^2}{E}$
Short-game shots	65%	276	282.75	0.161
Approach and swing	22%	99	95.70	0.114
Driver shots	9%	42	39.15	0.207
Putting	4%	18	17.40	0.021
				0.503

$\chi^2 \approx 0.503$

d. Fail to reject H_0.

e. There is not enough evidence at the 5% level of significance to conclude that the distribution of golf students' responses is the same as the claimed or expected distribution.

4a.

Response	Distribution
Auto companies	20%
Fast food companies	20%
Financial services companies	20%
Pharmaceutical companies	20%
Soft drink companies	20%

H_0 : The distribution of the thoughts of adults ages 55 and over on which industry has the most trustworthy advertising is uniformly distributed. (claim)

H_a : The distribution of responses differs from the claimed or expected distribution.

b. $\chi_0^2 = 9.488$; Rejection region: $\chi^2 > 9.488$

c.

Response	Distribution	Observed	Expected	$\dfrac{(O-E)^2}{E}$
Auto companies	20%	128	160	6.400
Fast food companies	20%	192	160	6.400
Financial services companies	20%	112	160	14.400
Pharmaceutical companies	20%	152	160	0.400
Soft drink companies	20%	216	160	19.600
				47.200

$\chi^2 \approx 47.200$

d. Reject H_0.

e. There is enough evidence at the 5% level of significance to reject the claim that the distribution of responses about which industry has the most trustworthy advertising is uniform.

5a. Expected frequencies:

Gender	Years of full-time teaching experience				
	Less than 3 years	3–9 years	10–20 years	20 years or more	Total
Male	63	356.4	319.8	310.8	1050
Female	147	831.6	746.2	725.2	2450
Total	210	1188	1066	1036	3500

b. H_0 : Years of full-time teaching experience is independent of gender.

H_a : Years of full-time teaching experience is dependent on gender.

$\chi_0^2 = 11.345$

O	E	$O - E$	$(O - E)^2$	$\dfrac{(O-E)^2}{E}$
58	63.0	−5.0	25.00	0.3968
377	356.4	20.6	424.36	1.1907
280	319.8	−39.8	1584.04	4.9532
335	310.8	24.2	585.64	1.8843
152	147	5.0	25.00	0.1701
811	831.6	−20.6	424.36	0.5103
786	746.2	39.8	1584.04	2.1228
701	725.2	−24.2	585.64	0.8076
				12.0358

$\chi^2 \approx 12.036$

Reject H_0.

c. There is enough evidence at the 1% level of significance to conclude that public school teachers' genders and years of full-time teaching experience are related.

6a. Expected frequencies:

Gender	Type of vehicles owned				
	Car	Truck	SUV	Van	Total
Male	94.25	82.65	50.75	4.35	232
Female	100.75	88.35	54.25	4.65	248
Total	195	171	105	9	480

b. H_0 : Type of vehicle is independent of gender.

H_a : Type of vehicle is dependent on gender.

$\chi_0^2 = 7.815$

O	E	$O - E$	$(O - E)^2$	$\dfrac{(O - E)^2}{E}$
85	94.25	−9.25	85.5625	0.9078
96	82.65	13.35	178.2225	2.1564
45	50.75	−5.75	33.0625	0.6515
6	4.35	1.65	2.7225	0.6259
110	100.75	9.25	85.5625	0.8493
75	88.35	−13.35	178.2225	2.1072
60	54.25	5.75	33.0625	0.6094
3	4.65	−1.65	2.7225	0.5855
				8.4029

$\chi^2 \approx 8.403$

Reject H_0.

c. There is enough evidence at the 5% level of significance to conclude that type of vehicle owned is dependent on gender.

7a. Expected frequencies:

Status	Vertebrae Group					
	Mammals	Birds	Reptiles	Amphibians	Fish	Total
Endangered	54.86	40.38	22.10	16.00	26.67	160.01
Threatened	17.14	12.62	6.90	5.00	8.33	49.99
Total	72	53	29	21	35	210

b. H_0 : Species' status (endangered or threatened) is independent of vertebrate group.

H_a : Species' status (endangered or threatened) is dependent on vertebrate group.

$\chi_0^2 = 13.277$

O	E	$O - E$	$(O - E)^2$	$\dfrac{(O - E)^2}{E}$
62	54.857	7.143	51.022449	0.9301
48	40.381	7.619	58.049161	1.4375
17	22.095	5.095	25.959025	1.1749
12	16.000	−4.000	16.000000	1.0000
21	26.667	−5.667	32.114889	1.2043
10	17.143	−7.143	51.022449	2.9763
5	12.619	−7.619	58.049161	4.6001
12	6.905	5.095	25.959025	3.7595
9	5.000	4.000	16.000000	3.2000
14	8.333	5.667	32.114889	3.8539
				24.1366

$\chi^2 \approx 24.154$

Reject H_0.

c. There is enough evidence at the 1% level of significance to conclude that species' status (endangered or threatened) is dependent on vertebrate group.

8a. Expected frequencies:

Gender	Time of day				
	12 AM– 5:59 AM	**6 AM– 11:59 AM**	**12 PM– 5:59 PM**	**6 PM – 11:59 PM**	**Total**
	582.68	612.81	967.93	918.57	3082
	326.32	343.19	542.07	514.43	1726
Total	909	956	1510	1433	4808

b. H_0 : Fatal pedestrian motor vehicle collisions by time of day is independent of gender.

H_a : Fatal pedestrian motor vehicle collisions by time of day is dependent on gender..

$\chi_0^2 = 6.251$

O	E	$O - E$	$(O - E)^2$	$\dfrac{(O - E)^2}{E}$
654	582.683	71.317	5086.114489	8.7289
591	612.810	−21.810	475.676100	0.7762
909	967.933	−58.933	3473.098489	3.5882
928	918.574	9.426	88.849476	0.0967
255	326.317	−71.317	5086.114489	15.5864
365	343.190	21.810	475.676100	1.386
601	542.067	58.933	3473.098489	6.4071
505	514.426	−9.426	88.849476	0.1727
				36.7421

$\chi^2 \approx 36.742$

Reject H_0.

c. There is enough evidence at the 10% level of significance to conclude that the time of day of a collision is dependent on gender.

9. $F_0 \approx 2.286$ **10.** $F_0 = 4.71$ **11.** $F_0 = 2.39$ **12.** $F_0 = 2.01$

13. $F_0 \approx 2.06$ **14.** $F_0 = 4.36$ **15.** $F_0 = 2.08$ **16.** $F_0 = 4.73$

17. $H_0 : \sigma_1^2 \leq \sigma_2^2$(claim); $H_a : \sigma_1^2 > \sigma_2^2$

d.f.$_N = 15$

d.f.$_D = 20$

$F_0 = 3.09$; Rejection region: $F > 3.09$

$$F = \frac{s_1^2}{s_2^2} = \frac{653}{270} \approx 2.419$$

Fail to reject H_0. There is not enough evidence at the 1% level of significance to reject the claim.

18. $H_0 : \sigma_1^2 = \sigma_2^2$; $H_a : \sigma_1^2 \neq \sigma_2^2$ (claim)

d.f.$_N = 30$

d.f.$_D = 28$

$F_0 = 1.87$; Rejection region: $F > 1.87$

$$F = \frac{s_1^2}{s_2^2} = \frac{87.3}{45.5} \approx 1.919$$

Reject H_0. There is enough evidence at the 10% level of significance to support the claim.

19. Population 1: Garfield County

Populations 2: Kay County

The claim is "the variation in wheat production is greater in Garfield County than in Kay County."

$H_0 : \sigma_1^2 \leq \sigma_2^2$; $H_a : \sigma_1^2 > \sigma_2^2$ (claim)

d.f.$_N = 20$

d.f.$_D = 15$

$F_0 = 1.92$; Rejection region: $F > 1.92$

$$F = \frac{s_1^2}{s_2^2} = \frac{(0.76)^2}{(0.58)^2} \approx 1.717$$

Fail to reject H_0. There is not enough evidence at the 10% level of significance to support the claim that the variation in wheat production is greater in Garfield County than in Kay County.

20. Population 1: San Francisco $\rightarrow s_1 = \$44$

Population 2: Sacramento $\rightarrow s_2 = \$44$

The claim is "the standard deviations of hotel rooms rates for San Francisco. (A and Sacramento, CA are the same."

$H_0 : \sigma_1^2 = \sigma_2^2$(claim); $H_a : \sigma_1^2 \neq \sigma_2^2$

d.f.$_N = 35$

d.f.$_D = 30$

$F_0 = 2.569$; Rejection region: $F > 2.569$

$$F = \frac{s_1^2}{s_2^2} = \frac{(75)^2}{(44)^2} \approx 2.905$$

Reject H_0.

There is enough evidence at the 1% level of significance to reject the claim that the standard deviations of hotel room rates for San Francisco, CA and Sacramento, CA are the same.

21. Population 1: Male $\rightarrow s_1^2 = 20{,}002.56$

Population 2: Female $\rightarrow s_2^2 = 17{,}136.11$

$H_0 : \sigma_1^2 = \sigma_2^2$; $H_a : \sigma_1^2 \neq \sigma_2^2$ (claim)

d.f.$_N = 12$

d.f.$_D = 8$

$F_0 = 7.015$; Rejection region: $F > 7.015$

$F = \dfrac{s_1^2}{s_2^2} = \dfrac{20{,}002.56}{17{,}136.11} \approx 1.167$

Fail to reject H_0. There is not enough evidence at the 1% level of significance to support the claim that the test score variance for females is different than that for males.

22. Population 1: Current $\rightarrow s_1^2 = 0.00146$

Population 2: New $\rightarrow s_2^2 = 0.00050$

The claim is "the new mold produces inserts that are less variable in diameter than the inserts the current mold produces."

$H_0 : \sigma_1^2 \leq \sigma_2^2$; $H_a : \sigma_1^2 > \sigma_2^2$ (claim) $H_0 : \sigma_1^2 \leq \sigma_2^2$; $H_a : \sigma_1^2 > \sigma_2^2$ (claim)

d.f.$_N = 11$

d.f.$_D = 11$

$F_0 = 2.82$; Rejection region: $F > 2.82$

$F = \dfrac{s_1^2}{s_2^2} = \dfrac{0.00146}{0.00050} \approx 2.92$

Reject H_0. There is enough evidence at the 5% level of significance to support the claim that the new mold produces inserts that are less variable in diameter than the inserts the current mold produces.

23. The claim is "the mean energy consumption in at least one region is different from the others."

$H_0 : \mu_1 = \mu_2 = \mu_3 = \mu_4$

$H_a :$ At least one mean is different from the others. (claim)

d.f.$_N = k - 1 = 3$

d.f.$_D = N - k = 28$

$F_0 = 2.29$; Rejection region: $F > 2.29$

Variation	Sum of Squares	Degrees of Freedom	Mean Squares	F
Between	512.457	3	170.819	8.51
Within	562.162	28	20.077	

$F \approx 8.508$

Reject H_0. There is enough evidence at the 10% level of significance to conclude that at least one of the mean costs is different from the others.

24. The claim is "at least one of the mean incomes is different from the others."

$H_0 : \mu_1 = \mu_2 = \mu_3 = \mu_4$

H_a : At least one mean is different from the others. (claim)

d.f.$_N$ $= k - 1 = 3$

d.f.$_D$ $= N - k = 20$

$F_0 = 3.10$; Rejection region: $F > 3.10$

Variation	Sum of Squares	Degrees of Freedom	Mean Squares	F
Between	462,902,041	3	154,300,680	1.09
Within	2,826,753,458	20	141,337,673	

$F \approx 1.092$

Fail to reject H_0. There is not enough evidence at the 5% level of significance to conclude that at least one of the mean incomes is different from the others.

CHAPTER 10 QUIZ SOLUTIONS

1. Population 1: San Francisco $\rightarrow s_1^2 = 88.664$

Population 2: Baltimore $\rightarrow s_2^2 = 41.792$

a. $H_0 : \sigma_1^2 = \sigma_2^2$; $H_a : \sigma_1^2 \neq \sigma_2^2$ (claim)

b. $\alpha = 0.01$

c. d.f.$_N$ $= 12$, d.f.$_D$ $= 14 \Rightarrow F_0 = 4.43$

d. Rejection region: $F > 4.43$

e. $F = \dfrac{s_1^2}{s_2^2} = \dfrac{88.644}{41.792} \approx 2.12$

f. Fail to reject H_o.

g. There is not enough evidence at the 1% level of significance to conclude the variances in annual wages for San Francisco, CA and Baltimore, MD are different.

2a. $H_0 : \mu_1 = \mu_2 = \mu_3 = \mu_4$

H_a : At least one mean is different from the others. (claim)

b. $\alpha = 0.10$

c. d.f.$_N$ $= 2$, d.f.$_D$ $= 40 \Rightarrow F_0 = 2.44$

d. Rejection region: $F > 2.44$

e.

Variation	Sum of Squares	Degrees of Freedom	Mean Squares	F
Between	3423.12	2	1711.56	27.48
Within	2491.79	40	62.29	

$F \approx 27.48$

f. Reject H_o.

g. There is enough evidence at the 10% level of significance to reject the claim that the mean annual wages are equal for all three cities.

3a. H_0 : The distribution of educational achievement for people in the United States ages 35–44 is 13.4% not a high school graduate, 31.2% high school graduate, 17.2% some college, no degree; 8.8% associate's degree, 19.1% bachelor's degree, and 10.3% advanced degree.

  H_a : The distribution of educational achievement for people in the United States ages 35–44 differs from the claimed distribution. (claim)

b. $\alpha = 0.05$

c. $\chi_0^2 = 11.071$

d. Rejection region: $\chi^2 > 11.071$

e.

	Distribution	Observed	Expected	$\dfrac{(O - E)^2}{E}$
Not a H.S. graduate	13.4%	36	43.014	1.144
H.S. graduate	31.2%	92	100.152	0.664
Some college no degree	17.2%	55	55.212	0.001
Associate's degree	8.8%	32	28.248	0.498
Bachelor's degree	19.1%	70	61.311	1.231
Advanced degree	10.3%	36	33.063	0.261
		321		3.799

$\chi^2 \approx 3.799$

f. Fail to reject H_0.

g. There is not enough evidence at the 5% level of significance to conclude that the distribution for people in the United States ages 35–44 differs from the distribution for ages 25 and older.

4a. H_0 : The distribution of educational achievement for people in the United States ages 65–74 is 13.4% not a high school graduate, 31.2% high school graduate, 17.2% some college, no degree; 8.8% associate's degree, 19.1% bachelor's degree, and 19.1% advanced degree.

  H_a : The distribution of educational achievement for people in the United States ages 65–74 differs from the claimed distribution. (claim)

b. $\alpha = 0.01$

c. $\chi_0^2 = 15.086$

d. Rejection region: $\chi^2 > 15.086$

e.

	Distribution	Observed	Expected	$\dfrac{(O - E)^2}{E}$
Not a H.S. graduate	13.4%	86	60.434	10.8154
H.S. graduate	31.2%	161	140.712	2.9251
Some college no degree	17.2%	72	77.572	0.4002
Associate's degree	8.8%	27	39.688	4.0563
Bachelor's degree	19.1%	60	86.141	7.9329
Advanced degree	10.3%	45	46.453	0.0454
		451		26.175

$\chi^2 \approx 26.175$

f. Reject H_0.

g. There is enough evidence at the 1% level of significance to conclude that the distribution for people in the United States ages 65–74 differs from the distribution for people ages 25 and older.

11.1 THE SIGN TEST

11.1 Try It Yourself Solutions

1a. The claim is "the median number of days a home is on the market in its city is greater than 120."
  H_0 : median ≤ 120; H_a : median > 120 (claim)

b. $\alpha = 0.025$

c. $n = 24$

d. The critical value is 6.

e. $x = 6$

f. Reject H_0.

g. There is enough evidence at the 2.5% level of significance to support the agency's claim that the median number of days a home is on the market in its city is greater than 120.

2a. The claim is "the median age of automobiles in operation in the United States is 9.4 years."
  H_0 : median $= 9.4$; H_a : median > 9.4 (claim)

b. $\alpha = 0.10$

c. $n = 92$

d. The critical value is $z_0 = -1.645$.

e. $x = 41$

$$z = \frac{(x+0.5) = 0.5(n)}{\frac{\sqrt{n}}{2}} = \frac{(41+0.5) - 0.5(92)}{\frac{\sqrt{92}}{2}} \approx \frac{-4.5}{4.80} \approx -0.94$$

f. Fail to reject H_0.

g. There is not enough evidence at the 10% level of significance to reject the organization's claim that the median age of automobiles in operation in the United States is 9.4 years.

3a. The claim is "a new vaccine will decrease the number of colds in adults."
  H_0 : The number of colds will not decrease.
  H_a : The number of colds will decrease. (claim)

b. $\alpha = 0.05$

c. $n = 11$

d. The critical value is 2.

e. $x = 2$

f. Reject H_0.

g. There is enough evidence at the 5% level of significance to support the researcher's claim that the new vaccine will decrease the number of colds in adults.

11.1 EXERCISE SOLUTIONS

1. A nonparametric test is a hypothesis test that does not require any specific conditions concerning the shapes of populations or the values of any population parameters.

    A nonparametric test is usually easier to perform than its corresponding parametric test, but the nonparametric test is usually less efficient.

2. Median

3. When n is less than or equal to 25, the test statistic is equal to x (the smaller number of $+$ or $-$ signs). When n is greater than 25, the test statistic is equal to

    $$z = \frac{(x + 0.5) - 0.5n}{\frac{\sqrt{n}}{2}}.$$

4. Answers will vary. *Sample answer:* It is called the sign test because each value in a sample is compared to the hypothesized median and assigned a $+$ or $-$ sign based on whether the difference is positive or negative. The numbers of $+$ signs and $-$ signs are used to determine whether the null hypothesis should be rejected.

5. Identify the claim and state H_0 and H_a. Identify the level of significance and sample size. Find the critical value using Table 8 (if $n \leq 25$) or Table 4 ($n > 25$). Calculate the test statistic. Make a decision and interpret in the context of the problem.

6. A sample must be randomly selected from each population and the samples must be dependent.

7. (a) The claim is "the median amount of new credit card charges for the previous month was more than \$300."
       H_0 : median $\leq$ \$300; H_a : median $>$ \$300 (claim)
    (b) The critical value is 1.
    (c) $x = 5$
    (d) Fail to reject H_0.
    (e) There is not enough evidence at the 1% level of significance for the accountant to conclude that the median amount of new credit charges for the previous month was more than \$300.

8. (a) The claim is "the median daily high temperature for the month of July in Pittsburgh is 83° Fahrenheit."
       H_0 : median $=$ 83 (claim); H_a : median $\neq$ 83
    (b) The critical value is 1.
    (c) $x = 4$
    (d) Fail to reject H_0.
    (e) There is not enough evidence at the 1% level of significance to reject the Meteorologist's claim that the daily median temperature for the month of July in Pittsburgh is 83° Fahrenheit

9. (a) The claim is "the median sales price of new privately owned one-family homes sold in the past year is \$198,000 or less."

H_0 : median $\leq$ \$198,000; H_a : median > \$198,000 (claim)

(b) The critical value is 1.

(c) $x = 4$

(d) Fail to reject H_0.

(e) There is not enough evidence at the 5% level of significance to reject the claim that the median sales price of new privately owned one-family homes sold in the past year is \$198,000 or less.

10. (a) The claim is "the median daily high temperature for the month of January in San Diego is 66° Fahrenheit."

H_0 : median = 66 (claim); H_a : median $\neq$ 66

(b) The critical value is 2.

(c) $x = 0$

(d) Reject H_0.

(e) There is enough evidence at the 1% level of significance to reject the Meteorologist's claim that the median daily high temperature for the month of January in San Diego is 66° Fahrenheit.

11. (a) The claim is "the median amount of credit card debt for families holding such debt is at least \$3000."

H_0 : median $\geq$ \$3000 (claim); H_a : median < \$3000

(b) The critical value is $z_0 = -2.05$.

(c) $x = 44$

$$z = \frac{(x + 0.5) - 0.5(n)}{\dfrac{\sqrt{n}}{2}} = \frac{(44 + 0.5) - 0.5(104)}{\dfrac{\sqrt{104}}{2}} \approx \frac{-7.5}{5.099} \approx -1.47$$

(d) Fail to reject H_0.

(e) There is not enough evidence at the 2% level of significance to reject the institution's claim that the median amount of credit card debt for families holding such debts is at least \$3000.

12. (a) The claim is "the median amount of financial debt for families holding such debt is less than \$65,000."

H_0 : median $\geq$ \$65,000; H_a : median < \$65,000 (claim)

(b) The critical value is $z_0 = -1.96$.

(c) $x = 24$

$$z = \frac{(x + 0.5) - 0.5(n)}{\dfrac{\sqrt{n}}{2}} = \frac{(24 + 0.5) - 0.5(70)}{\dfrac{\sqrt{70}}{2}} \approx \frac{-10.5}{4.183} \approx -2.51$$

(d) Reject H_0.

(e) There is enough evidence at the 2.5% level of significance to support the accountant's claim that the median amount of financial debt for families holding such debts is less than \$65,000.

13. (a) The claim is "the median age of Twitter® users is greater than 30 years old."

H_0 : median ≤ 30; H_a : median > 30 (claim)

(b) The critical value is 4.

(c) $x = 10$

(d) Fail to reject H_0.

(e) There is not enough evidence at the 1% level of significance to support the research group's claim that the median age of Twitter users is greater than 30 years old.

14. (a) The claim is "the median age of Facebook® users is less than 32 years old."

H_0 : median ≥ 32; H_a : median < 32 (claim)

(b) The critical value is 5.

(c) $x = 5$

(d) Reject H_0.

(e) There is enough evidence at the 5% level of significance to support the research group's claim that the median age of Facebook® users is less than 32 years old.

15. (a) The claim is "the median number of rooms in renter-occupied units is four."

H_0 : median $= 4$; (claim) H_a : median $\neq 4$

(b) The critical value is $z_0 = -1.96$.

(c) $x = 31$

$$z = \frac{(x+0.5) - 0.5(n)}{\dfrac{\sqrt{n}}{2}} = \frac{(31+0.5) - 0.5(80)}{\dfrac{\sqrt{80}}{2}} \approx \frac{-8.5}{4.47} \approx -1.90$$

(d) Fail to reject H_0.

(e) There is not enough evidence at the 5% level of significance to reject the organization's claim that the median number of rooms in renter-occupied units is 4.

16. (a) The claim is "the median square footage of renter-occupied units is 1350 square feet."

H_0 : median $= 1350$; (claim) H_a : median $\neq 1350$

(b) The critical value is 5.

(c) $x = 7$

(d) Fail to reject H_0.

(e) There is not enough evidence at the 10% level of significance to reject the organization's claim that the median square footage of renter-occupied units is 1350 square feet.

17. (a) The claim is "the median hourly wage of computer systems analysts is $37.06."

H_0 : median $= \$37.06$; (claim) H_a : median $\neq \$37.06$

(b) The critical value is $z_0 = -2.575$.

(c) $x = 18$

$$z = \frac{(x+0.5) - 0.5(n)}{\dfrac{\sqrt{n}}{2}} = \frac{(18+0.5) - 0.5(43)}{\dfrac{\sqrt{43}}{2}} \approx \frac{-3}{3.28} \approx -0.91$$

(d) Fail to reject H_0.

(e) There is not enough evidence at the 1% level of significance to reject the labor organization's claim that the median hourly earnings of computer systems analysts is $37.06.

18. (a) The claim is "the median hourly wage of podiatrists is at least $55.89."

H_0: median $\geq$ $55.89; (claim) H_a: median < $55.89

(b) The critical value is 6.

(c) $x = 5$

(d) Reject H_0.

(e) There is enough evidence at the 5% level of significance to reject the organization's claim that the median hourly wage of podiatrists is at least $55.89.

19. (a) The claim is "the lower back pain intensity scores decreased after acupuncture."

H_0: The lower back pain intensity scores have not decreased.

H_a: The lower back pain intensity scores have decreased. (claim)

(b) The critical value is 1.

(c) $x = 0$

(d) Reject H_0.

(e) There is enough evidence at the 5% level of significance to conclude that the lower back pain intensity scores were lower after acupuncture.

20. (a) The claim is "the lower back pain intensity scores decreased after taking the anti-inflammatory drugs."

H_0: The lower back pain intensity scores have not decreased.

H_a: The lower back pain intensity scores have decreased. (claim)

(b) The critical value is 2.

(c) $x = 4$

(d) Fail to reject H_0.

(e) There is not enough evidence at the 5% level of significance to conclude that the lower back pain intensity scores decreased after taking the anti-inflammatory drugs.

21. (a) The claim is "the student's critical reading SAT scores improved."

H_0: The SAT scores have not improved.

H_a: The SAT scores have improved. (claim)

(b) The critical value is 2.

(c) $x = 4$

(d) Fail to reject H_0.

(e) There is not enough evidence at the 5% level of significance to conclude that the critical reading SAT scores improved.

22. (a) The claim is "the student's critical reading SAT scores improved the second time they took the SAT."

H_0: The SAT scores have not improved.

H_a: The SAT scores have improved. (claim)

(b) The critical value is 1.

(c) $x = 3$

(d) Fail to reject H_0.

(e) There is not enough evidence at the 1% level of significance to conclude that the SAT scores have improved.

23. (a) The claim is "the proportion of adults who feel older than their real age is equal to the proportion of adults who feel younger than their real age."

H_0 : The proportion of adults who feel older than their real age is equal to the proportion of adults who feel younger than their real age. (claim)

H_a : The proportion of adults who feel older than their real age is different from the proportion of adults who feel younger than their real age.

The critical value is 3.

$x = 3$

Reject H_0.

(b) There is enough evidence at the 5% level of significance to reject the claim that the proportion of adults who feel older than their real age is equal to the proportion of adults who feel younger than their real age.

24. (a) The claim is "the proportion of adults who contact their parents by phone weekly is equal to the proportion of adults who contact their parents by phone daily."

H_0 : The proportion of adults who contact their parents by phone weekly is equal to the proportion of adults who contact their parents by phone daily. (claim)

H_a : The proportion of adults who contact their parents by phone weekly is different from the proportion of adults who contact their parents by phone daily.

The critical value is 5.

$x = 8$

Fail to reject H_0.

(b) There is not enough evidence at the 5% level of significance to reject the claim that the proportion of adults who contact their parents by phone weekly is equal to the proportion of adults who contact their parents by phone daily."

25. Hypothesis test results:

Parameter: median of variable

H_0: Parameter = 22.55

H_A: Parameter ≠ 22.55

Variable	a	n for test
Hourly wages (in dollars)	14	13

Sample Median	Below	Equal	Above	P-value
26.075	2	1	11	0.0225

$P \approx 0.0225 < 0.05$, so reject H_0. There is enough evidence at the 5% level of significance to reject the labor organization's claim that the median hourly wage of tool and die makers is $22.25.

26. Hypothesis test results:

Parameter: median of variable

H_0: Parameter ≤ 57

H_A: Parameter > 57

Variable	n	n for test	Sample Median
Age	24	21	50

Below	Equal	Above	P-value
14	3	7	0.9608

$P \approx 0.9608 > 0.01$, so fail to reject H_0. There is not enough evidence at the 1% level of significance to support the television network's claim that the median age of viewers for the Masters Golf Tournament is greater than 57 years.

27. (a) The claim is "the median weekly earnings of female workers are less than or equal to \$638."

H_0: median $\leq \$638$; (claim) H_a: median $> \$638$

(b) The critical value is $z_0 = 2.33$.

(c) $x = 29$

$$z = \frac{(x + 0.5) - 0.5(n)}{\dfrac{\sqrt{n}}{2}} = \frac{(29 + 0.5) - 0.5(47)}{\dfrac{\sqrt{47}}{2}} \approx \frac{5}{3.428} \approx 1.46$$

(d) Fail to reject H_0.

(e) There is not enough evidence at the 1% level of significance to reject the organization's claim that the median weekly earnings of female workers is less than or equal to \$638.

28. (a) The claim is "the median weekly earnings of male workers are greater than \$798."

H_0: median $\leq \$798$; H_a: median $> \$798$ (claim)

(b) The critical value is $z_0 = 2.33$.

(c) $x = 45$

$$z = \frac{(x + 0.5) - 0.5(n)}{\dfrac{\sqrt{n}}{2}} = \frac{(45 - 0.5) - 0.5(68)}{\dfrac{\sqrt{68}}{2}} \approx \frac{10.5}{4.123} \approx 2.55$$

(d) Reject H_0.

(e) There is enough evidence at the 1% level of significance to support the organization's claim that the median weekly earnings of male workers is greater than 798.

29. (a) The claim is "the median age of brides at the time of their first marriage is less than or equal to 26 years."

H_0: median ≤ 26; H_a: median > 26 (claim)

(b) The critical value is $z_0 = 1.645$.

(c) $x = 35$

$$z = \frac{(x + 0.5) - 0.5(n)}{\dfrac{\sqrt{n}}{2}} = \frac{(35 + 0.5) - 0.5(59)}{\dfrac{\sqrt{59}}{2}} \approx \frac{5}{3.841} \approx 1.302$$

(d) Fail to reject H_0.

(e) There is not enough evidence at the 5% level of significance to reject the counselor's claim that the median age of brides at the time of their first marriage is less than or equal to 26 years.

30. (a) The claim is "the median age of grooms at the time of their first marriage is greater than 28 years."

H_0: median ≤ 28; H_a: median > 28 (claim)

(b) The critical value is $z_0 = 1.645$.

(c) $x = 33$

$$z = \frac{(x + 0.5) - 0.5(n)}{\frac{\sqrt{n}}{2}} = \frac{(33 + 0.5) - 0.5(56)}{\frac{\sqrt{56}}{2}} \approx \frac{4.5}{3.742} \approx 1.203$$

(d) Fail to reject H_0.

(e) There is not enough evidence at the 5% level of significance to support the counselor's claim that the median age of grooms at the time of their first marriage is greater than 28 years.

11.2 THE WILCOXON TESTS

11.2 Try It Yourself Solutions

1a. The claim is "a spray-on water repellant is effective."

H_0: There is no difference in the amounts of water repelled.

H_a: There is a difference in the amounts of water repelled.

b. $\alpha = 0.01$

c. $n = 11$

d. The critical value is 5.

e.

No repellent	Repellent applied	Difference	Absolute value	Rank	Signed rank
8	15	−7	7	11	−11
7	12	−5	5	9	−9
7	11	−4	4	7.5	−7.5
4	6	−2	2	3.5	−3.5
6	6	0	0	—	—
10	8	2	2	3.5	3.5
9	8	1	1	1.5	1.5
5	6	−1	1	1.5	−1.5
9	12	−3	3	5.5	−5.5
11	8	3	3	5.5	5.5
8	14	−6	6	10	−10
4	8	−4	4	7.5	−7.5

Sum of negative ranks = −55.5

Sum of positive ranks = 10.5

$w_s = 10.5$

f. Fail to reject H_0.

g. There is not enough evidence at the 1% level of significance for the quality control inspector to conclude that the spray-on water repellent is effective.

2a. The claim is "there is no difference in the claims paid by paid by the companies."

H_0: There is no difference in the claims paid by paid by the companies.

H_a: There is a difference in the claims paid by paid by the companies. (claim)

b. $\alpha = 0.05$

c. The critical values are $z_0 = \pm 1.96$.

d. $n_1 = 12$ and $n_2 = 12$

e.

Ordered data	Sample	Rank	Ordered data	Sample	Rank
1.7	B	1	5.3	B	13
1.8	B	2	5.6	B	14
2.2	B	3	5.8	A	15
2.5	A	4	6.0	A	16
3.0	A	5.5	6.2	A	17
3.0	B	5.5	6.3	A	18
3.4	B	7	6.5	A	19
3.9	A	8	7.3	B	20
4.1	B	9	7.4	A	21
4.4	B	10	9.9	A	22
4.5	A	11	10.6	A	23
4.7	B	12	10.8	B	24

R = sum ranks of company B = 120.5

f. $\mu_R = \dfrac{n_1(n_1 + n_2 + 1)}{2} = \dfrac{12(12 + 12 + 1)}{2} = 150$

$\sigma_R = \sqrt{\dfrac{n_1 n_2 (n_1 + n_2 + 1)}{12}} = \sqrt{\dfrac{(12)(12)(12 + 12 + 1)}{12}} \approx 17.321$

$z = \dfrac{R - \mu_R}{\sigma_R} \approx \dfrac{120.5 - 150}{17.321} \approx -1.703$

g. Fail to reject H_0.

h. There is not enough evidence at the 5% level of significance to conclude that there is a difference in the claims paid by the companies.

11.2 EXERCISE SOLUTIONS

1. If the samples are dependent, use the Wilcoxon signed-rank test. If the samples are independent, use the Wilcoxon rank sum test.

2. The sample size of both samples must be at least 10 to use the Wilcoxon rank sum test.

3. (a) The claim is "there was no reduction in diastolic blood pressure."

H_0: There is no reduction in diastolic blood pressure. (claim)

H_a: There is a reduction in diastolic blood pressure.

(b) Wilcoxon signed-rank test

(c) The critical value is 10.

(d)

Before treatment	After treatment	Difference	Absolute difference	Rank	Signed rank
108	99	9	9	8	8
109	115	−6	6	4.5	−4.5
120	105	15	15	12	12
129	116	13	13	10.5	10.5
112	115	−3	3	2	−2
111	117	−6	6	4.5	−4.5
117	108	9	9	8	8
135	122	13	13	10.5	10.5
124	120	4	4	3	3
118	126	−8	8	6	−6
130	128	2	2	1	1
115	106	9	9	8	8

Sum of negative ranks = −17

Sum of positive ranks = 61

$w_s = 17$

(e) Fail to reject H_0.

(f) There is not enough evidence at the 1% level of significance to reject the claim that there was no reduction in diastolic blood pressure.

4. (a) The claim is "there is no difference in the salaries earned by workers in the wholesale trade and manufacturing industries."

H_0: There is no difference in salaries. (claim)

H_a: There is a difference in salaries.

(b) Wilcoxon rank sum test

(c) The critical value is $z_0 = \pm 1.645$.

(d)

Ordered data	Sample	Rank
43	M	1
45	M	2
47	M	3
49	M	4
53	WT	5
55	WT	6.5
55	M	6.5
56	WT	8.5
56	M	8.5
58	M	10
59	WT	11
62	WT	13
62	WT	13
62	M	13
64	WT	15
65	WT	16.5
65	M	16.5
67	WT	18.5
67	M	18.5
70	WT	20

R = sum ranks of Manufacturing = 83

$$\mu_R = \frac{n_1(n_1 + n_2 + 1)}{2} = \frac{10(10 + 10 + 1)}{2} = 105$$

$$\sigma_R = \sqrt{\frac{n_1 n_2 (n_1 + n_2 + 1)}{12}} = \sqrt{\frac{(10)(10)(10 + 10 + 1)}{12}} \approx 13.229$$

$$z = \frac{R - \mu_R}{\sigma_R} \approx \frac{83 - 105}{13.229} \approx -1.663$$

(e) Reject H_0.

(f) There is enough evidence at the 10% level of significance to reject the analyst's claim that there is no difference in the salaries earned by workers in the wholesale trade and manufacturing industries.

5. (a) The claim is "the cost of prescription drugs is lower in Canada than in the United States."

   H_0: The cost of prescription drugs is not lower in Canada than in the United States.

   H_a: The cost of prescription drugs is lower in Canada than in the United States. (claim)

   (b) Wilcoxon signed-rank test
   (c) The critical value is 4.

(d)

Cost in US.	Cost in Canada	Difference	Absolute difference	Rank	Signed rank
1.26	1.04	0.22	0.22	1	1
1.76	0.82	0.94	0.94	3	3
4.19	2.22	1.97	1.97	7	7
3.36	2.22	1.14	1.14	4	4
1.80	1.31	0.49	0.49	2	2
9.91	11.47	−1.56	1.56	6	−6
3.95	2.63	1.32	1.32	5	5

Sum of negative ranks = −6
Sum of positive ranks = 22
$w_s = 6$

(e) Fail to reject H_0.

(f) There is not enough evidence at the 5% level of significance for the researcher to conclude that the cost of prescription drugs is lower in Canada than in the United States.

6. (a) The claim is "there is a difference in the earnings of people with bachelor's degrees and those with associate's degrees."

H_0: There is no difference in the earnings.

H_a: There is a difference in the earnings. (claim)

(b) Wilcoxon rank sum test

(c) The critical values are $z_0 = \pm 1.96$.

(d)

Ordered data	Sample	Rank
33	A	1
34	A	2
36	A	3
38	A	4.5
38	A	4.5
39	A	6
42	A	7
44	B	8
45	A	9.5
45	A	9.5
47	A	11
50	B	12.5
50	B	12.5
52	B	14
54	B	15.5
54	B	15.5
56	B	17
60	B	18
63	B	19
70	B	20
76	B	21

R = sum ranks of associate's degree = 58

$$\mu_R = \frac{n_1(n_1 + n_2 + 1)}{2} = \frac{10(10 + 11 + 1)}{2} = 110$$

$$\sigma_R = \sqrt{\frac{n_1 n_2 (n_1 + n_2 + 1)}{12}} = \sqrt{\frac{(11)(10)(11 + 10 + 1)}{12}} \approx 14.201$$

$$z = \frac{R - \mu_R}{\sigma_R} \approx \frac{58 - 110}{14.201} \approx -3.66$$

(e) Reject H_0.

(f) There is enough evidence at the 5% level of significance to support the administrator's belief that there is a difference in the earnings.

7. (a) The claim is "there is a difference in the salaries earned by teachers in Wisconsin and Michigan."

   H_0: There is not a difference in the salaries.

   H_a: There is a difference in the salaries. (claim)

   (b) Wilcoxon rank sum test

   (c) The critical values are $z_0 = \pm 1.96$.

   (d)

Ordered data	Sample	Rank
46	WI	1
49	MI	2
50	WI	3.5
50	WI	3.5
51	WI	6.5
51	WI	6.5
51	WI	6.5
51	MI	6.5
52	WI	9
53	WI	10.5
53	MI	10.5
54	MI	12
55	WI	13.5
55	MI	13.5
57	MI	15.5
57	MI	15.5
58	MI	17
59	WI	18
61	MI	19
63	MI	20.5
63	MI	20.5
64	WI	22
72	MI	23

R = sum ranks of Wisconsin = 100.5

$$\mu_R = \frac{n_1(n_1 + n_2 + 1)}{2} = \frac{11(11 + 12 + 1)}{2} = 132$$

$$\sigma_R = \sqrt{\frac{n_1 n_2 (n_1 + n_2 + 1)}{12}} = \sqrt{\frac{(11)(12)(11 + 12 + 1)}{12}} \approx 16.248$$

$$z = \frac{R - \mu_R}{\sigma_R} \approx \frac{100.5 - 132}{16.248} \approx -1.94$$

(e) Fail to reject H_0.

(f) There is not enough evidence at the 5% level of significance to support the representative's claim that there is a difference in the salaries earned by teachers in Wisconsin and Michigan.

8. (a) The claim is "the experimental medication affects an individual's heart rate."

 H_0: The experimental medication does not affect an individual's heart rate.

 H_a: The experimental medication does affects an individual's heart rate. (claim)

(b) Wilcoxon signed-rank test

(c) The critical value is 25.

(d)

Before	After	Difference	Absolute value	Rank	Signed rank
72	73	−1	1	1.5	−1.5
81	80	1	1	1.5	1.5
75	75	0	0	—	—
76	79	−3	3	6.5	−6.5
79	74	5	5	9	9
74	76	−2	2	4	−4
65	73	−8	8	12	−12
67	67	0	0	—	—
76	74	2	2	4	4
83	77	6	6	10.5	10.5
66	70	−4	4	8	−8
75	77	−2	2	4	−4
76	76	0	0	—	—
78	75	3	3	6.5	6.5
68	74	−6	6	10.5	−10.5

Sum of negative ranks = −46.5

Sum of positive ranks = 31.5

$w_s = 31.5$

(e) Fail to reject H_0.

(f) There is not enough evidence at the 5% level of significance for the physician to conclude that the experimental medication affects an individual's heart rate.

9. The claim is "a certain fuel additive improves a car's gas mileage."

 H_0: The fuel additive does not improve gas mileage.

 H_a: The fuel additive does improve gas mileage. (claim)

The critical value is $z_0 = 1.28$.

Before	After	Difference	Absolute value	Rank	Signed rank
36.4	36.7	−0.3	0.3	4.5	−4.5
36.4	36.9	−0.5	0.5	11	−11
36.6	37.0	−0.4	0.4	7	−7
36.6	37.5	−0.9	0.9	17	−17
36.8	38.0	−1.2	1.2	19.5	−19.5
36.9	38.1	−1.2	1.2	19.5	−19.5
37.0	38.4	−1.4	1.4	25	−25
37.1	38.7	−1.6	1.6	30.5	−30.5
37.2	38.8	−1.6	1.6	30.5	−30.5
37.2	38.9	−1.7	1.7	32	−32
36.7	36.3	0.4	0.4	7	7
37.5	38.9	−1.4	1.4	25	−25
37.6	39.0	−1.4	1.4	25	−25
37.8	39.1	−1.3	1.3	21.5	−21.5
37.9	39.4	−1.5	1.5	28.5	−28.5
37.9	39.4	−1.5	1.5	28.5	−28.5
38.1	39.5	−1.4	1.4	25	−25
38.4	39.8	−1.4	1.4	25	−25
40.2	40.0	0.2	0.2	2.5	2.5
40.5	40.0	0.5	0.5	11	11
40.9	40.1	0.8	0.8	16	16
35.0	36.3	−1.3	1.3	21.5	−21.5
32.7	32.8	−0.1	0.1	1	−1
33.6	34.2	−0.6	0.6	14.5	−14.5
34.2	34.7	−0.5	0.5	11	−11
35.1	34.9	0.2	0.2	2.5	2.5
35.2	34.9	0.3	0.3	4.5	4.5
35.3	35.3	0	0	—	—
35.5	35.9	−0.4	0.4	7	−7
35.9	36.4	−0.5	0.5	11	−11
36.0	36.6	−0.6	0.6	14.5	−14.5
36.1	36.6	−0.5	0.5	11	−11
37.2	38.3	−1.1	1.1	18	−18

Sum of negative ranks = −484.5
Sum of positive ranks = 43.5
$w_s = 43.5$

$$z = \frac{w_s - \dfrac{n(n+1)}{4}}{\sqrt{\dfrac{n(n+1)(2n+1)}{24}}} = \frac{43.5 - \dfrac{32(32+1)}{4}}{\sqrt{\dfrac{32(32+1)\left[(2)32+1\right]}{24}}} = \frac{-220.5}{\sqrt{2860}} = -4.123$$

Note: $n = 32$ because one of the differences is zero and should be discarded.

Reject H_0. There is enough evidence at the 10% level of significance for the engineer to conclude that the gas mileage is improved.

10. The claim is "a fuel additive improves gas mileage."

H_0: The fuel additive does not improve gas mileage.

H_a: The fuel additive does improve gas mileage. (claim)

The critical value is $z_0 = -1.645$.

Before	After	Difference	Absolute value	Rank	Signed rank
34.0	36.6	−2.6	2.6	24.5	−24.5
34.2	36.7	−2.5	2.5	21.5	−21.5
34.4	37.2	−2.8	2.8	29.5	−29.5
34.4	37.2	−2.8	2.8	29.5	−29.5
34.6	37.3	−2.7	2.7	27.5	−27.5
34.8	37.4	−2.6	2.6	24.5	−24.5
35.6	37.6	−2	2	15.5	−15.5
35.7	37.7	−2	2	15.5	−15.5
30.2	34.2	−4	4	32	−32
31.6	34.9	−3.3	3.3	31	−31
32.3	34.9	−2.6	2.6	24.5	−24.5
33.0	34.9	−1.9	1.9	11.5	−11/5
33.1	35.7	−2.6	2.6	24.5	−24.5
33.7	36.0	−2.3	2.3	20	−20
33.7	36.2	−2.5	2.5	21.5	−21.5
33.8	36.5	−2.7	2.7	27.5	−27.5
35.7	37.8	−2.1	2.1	18.5	−18.5
36.1	38.1	−2	2	15.5	−15.5
36.1	38.2	−2.1	2.1	18.5	−18.5
36.6	38.3	−1.7	1.7	6	−6
36.6	38.3	−1.7	1.7	6	−6
36.8	38.7	−1.9	1.9	11.5	−11.5
37.1	38.8	−1.7	1.7	6	−6
37.1	38.9	−1.8	1.8	8.5	−8.5
37.2	39.1	−1.9	1.9	11.5	−11.5
37.9	39.1	−1.2	1.2	2	−2
37.9	39.2	−1.3	1.3	3	−3
38.0	39.4	−1.4	1.4	4	−4
38.0	39.8	−1.8	1.8	8.5	−8.5
38.4	40.3	−1.9	1.9	11.5	−11.5
38.8	40.8	−2	2	15.5	−15.5
42.1	43.2	−1.1	1.1	1	−1

Sum of negative ranks = −528

Sum of positive ranks = 0

$w_s = 0$

$$z = \frac{w_s - \dfrac{n(n+1)}{4}}{\sqrt{\dfrac{n(n+1)(2n+1)}{24}}} = \frac{0 - 264}{\sqrt{2860}} = -4.937$$

Reject H_0. There is enough evidence at the 5% level of significance to support the engineer's claim that the fuel additive improves gas mileage.

11.3 THE KRUSKAL-WALLIS TEST

11.3 Try It Yourself Solutions

1a. The claim is "the distribution of the veterinarians' salaries in these three states are different."

H_0: There is no difference in the salaries in the three states.

H_a: There is a difference in the salaries in the three states. (claim)

b. $\alpha = 0.05$

c. d.f. $= k - 1 = 2$

d. $\chi_0^2 = 5.991$; Rejection region: $\chi^2 > 5.991$

e.

Ordered data	State	Rank	Ordered data	State	Rank
88.28	CA	1	99.70	CA	15
88.80	PA	2	99.75	NY	16
92.50	NY	3	99.95	CA	17
93.10	NY	4	99.99	PA	18
94.40	PA	5	100.55	PA	19
95.15	CA	6	100.75	CA	20
96.25	PA	7	101.20	CA	21
97.25	PA	8	101.55	NY	22
97.44	CA	9.5	101.97	NY	23
97.50	NY	9.5	102.35	NY	24
97.50	NY	11	103.20	CA	25
97.89	CA	12	103.70	PA	26
98.85	NY	13	110.45	PA	27
99.20	PA	14	113.90	CA	28

$R_1 = 157.5$

$R_2 = 119$

$R_3 = 129$

f. $H = \dfrac{12}{N(N+1)}\left(\dfrac{R_1^2}{n_1} + \dfrac{R_2^2}{n_2} + \dfrac{R_3^2}{n_3}\right) - 3(N+1)$

$= \dfrac{12}{28(29)}\left(\dfrac{(157.5)^2}{10} + \dfrac{(129)^2}{9} + \dfrac{(119.5)^2}{9}\right) - 3(29)$

≈ 0.433

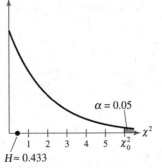

$H \approx 0.433$

g. Fail to reject H_0.

h. There is not enough evidence at the 5% level of significance to conclude that the distributions of the veterinarians' salaries in these three states are different.

11.3 EXERCISE SOLUTIONS

1. The conditions for using a Kruskal-Wallis test are that each sample must be randomly selected and the size of each sample must be at least 5.

2. The Kruskal-Wallis test is always a right-tailed test because the null hypothesis is only rejected when H is significantly large.

3. (a) The claim is "the distributions of the annual premiums in these three states are different."

   H_0: There is no difference in the premiums.

   H_a: There is a difference in the premiums. (claim)

   (b) The critical value is 5.991.

(c)

Ordered data	Sample	Rank
535	VA	1
546	VA	2
618	VA	3
625	VA	4
725	CT	5
730	VA	6
757	MA	7
806	CT	8
815	VA	9
889	MA	10
890	CT	11
912	VA	12
930	CT	13
947	CT	14
980	MA	15
1025	MA	16
1040	CT	17
1105	MA	18
1110	MA	19
1165	CT	20
1295	MA	21

$R_1 = 88,\ R_2 = 106,\ R_3 = 37$

$$H = \frac{12}{N(N+1)}\left(\frac{R_1^2}{n_1} + \frac{R_2^2}{n_2} + \frac{R_3^2}{n_3}\right) - 3(N+1)$$

$$= \frac{12}{21(21+1)}\left(\frac{(88)^2}{7} + \frac{(106)^2}{7} + \frac{(37)^2}{7}\right) - 3(21+1)$$

$$\approx 9.506$$

(d) Reject H_0.

(e) There is enough evidence at the 5% level of significance to conclude that the distributions of the annual premiums in Connecticut, Massachusetts, and Virginia are different.

4. The claim is "the distributions of the registered nurses' hourly pay rates in these three states are different."

H_0: There is no difference in the hourly pay rates.

H_a: There is a difference in the hourly pay rates. (claim)

(b) The critical value is 5.991.

(c)

Ordered data	Sample	Rank
24.6	KT	1
25.1	IN	2
25.25	OH	3
25.58	KT	4
25.75	OH	5
26.65	IN	6
26.95	KT	7
27.4	IN	8
27.8	IN	9.5
27.8	OH	9.5
28.1	KT	11
28.25	IN	12
28.55	KT	13
29.44	IN	14
30.15	OH	15
30.2	KT	16
30.24	IN	17
31.55	OH	18
31.6	KT	19
31.82	OH	20

$R_1 = 68.5$, $R_2 = 71$, $R_3 = 70.5$

$$H = \frac{12}{N(N+1)}\left(\frac{R_1^2}{n_1} + \frac{R_2^2}{n_2} + \frac{R_3^2}{n_3}\right) - 3(N+1)$$

$$= \frac{12}{20(20+1)}\left(\frac{(68.5)^2}{7} + \frac{(71)^2}{7} + \frac{(70.5)^2}{6}\right) - 3(20+1)$$

$$\approx 0.395$$

(d) Fail to reject H_0.

(e) There is not enough evidence at the 5% level of significance to conclude that the distributions of the registered nurses' hourly pay rates in the three states are different.

5. The claim is "the distributions of the annual salaries in these four states are different."

H_0: There is no difference in the salaries.

H_a: There is a difference in the salaries. (claim)

(b) The critical value is 6.251.

(c)

Ordered data	Sample	Rank
25.5	KT	1
27.1	WV	2
27.8	SC	3
28.9	WV	4
30.4	WV	5
30.9	KT	6
32.5	KT	7.5
32.5	NC	7.5
32.7	SC	9
33.6	NC	10
34.1	SC	11
34.2	KT	12
35.4	SC	13
36.6	NC	14
37.4	WV	15
38.2	WV	16
38.9	NC	17
40.5	NC	18
40.9	SC	19
41.5	SC	20
42.6	WV	21
43.1	KT	22
51.3	NC	23
54.7	KT	24

$R_1 = 72.5$, $R_2 = 89.5$, $R_3 = 75$, $R_4 = 63$

$$H = \frac{12}{N(N+1)} \left(\frac{R_1^2}{n_1} + \frac{R_2^2}{n_2} + \frac{R_3^2}{n_3} + \frac{R_4^2}{n_4} \right) - 3(N+1)$$

$$= \frac{12}{24(24+1)} \left(\frac{(72.5)^2}{6} + \frac{(89.5)^2}{6} + \frac{(75)^2}{6} + \frac{(63)^2}{6} \right) - 3(24+1)$$

$$\approx 1.202$$

$H = 1.202$

(d) Fail to reject H_0.

(e) There is not enough evidence at the 10% level of significance to conclude that the distributions of the annual salaries in the four states are different.

6. The claim is "the distributions of the amounts of caffeine in these four beverages are different."

H_0: There is no difference in the amounts of caffeine.

H_a: There is a difference in the amounts of caffeine. (claim)

(b) The critical value is 11.345.

(c)

Ordered data	Sample	Rank
10	Teas	1
15	Teas	2
32	Teas	3
42	Teas	4
47	Soft drinks	5
51	Soft drinks	6
56	Soft drinks	7
71	Soft drinks	8
72	Soft drinks	9
95	Soft drinks	10
96	Soft drinks	11
100	Teas	12
106	Teas	13
141	Energy drinks	14
150	Coffee	15
152	Energy drinks	16
154	Energy drinks	17
160	Energy drinks	18
166	Energy drinks	19
200	Energy drinks	20
206	Coffee	21
266	Coffee	22
300	Coffee	23
320	Coffee	24

$R_1 = 105,\ R_2 = 56,\ R_3 = 104,\ R_4 = 35$

$$H = \frac{12}{N(N+1)}\left(\frac{R_1^2}{n_1} + \frac{R_2^2}{n_2} + \frac{R_3^2}{n_3} + \frac{R_4^2}{n_4}\right) - 3(N+1)$$

$$= \frac{12}{24(24+1)}\left(\frac{(105)^2}{5} + \frac{(56)^2}{7} + \frac{(104)^2}{6} + \frac{(35)^2}{6}\right) - 3(24+1)$$

$$\approx 18.197$$

(d) Reject H_0.

(e) There is enough evidence at the 1% level of significance to conclude that the distributions of the amounts of caffeine are different.

7. **Kruskal-Wallis results:**
   Data stored in separate columns.
   Chi Square = 8.0965185 (adjusted for ties)
   DF = 2
   P-value = 0.0175

Column	N	Median	Ave. Rank
A	6	5	6.75
B	6	8.5	14.5
C	6	5	7.25

   $P \approx 0.0175 > 0.01$, so fail to reject H_0. There is not enough evidence at the 1% level of significance to conclude that the distributions of the number of job offers at Colleges A, B, and C are different.

8. **Kruskal-Wallis results:**
   Data stored in separate columns.
   Chi Square = 14.57108(adjusted for ties)
   DF = 3
   P-value = 0.0022

Column	N	Median	Ave. Rank
A	6	5	12.083333
B	6	8.5	20.5
C	6	5	12.333333
D	6	3	5.0833335

   $P \approx 0.0022 < 0.01$, so reject H_0. There is enough evidence at the 1% level of significance to conclude that the distributions of the number of job offers at all four colleges are different.

9. (a) The claim is "the mean number of days patients spend in a hospital differs according to the region of the United States in which the patient lives."

   H_0: There is no difference in the number of days spent in the hospital.

   H_a: There is a difference in the number of days spent in the hospital. (claim)

   The critical value is 11.345.

Ordered data	Sample	Rank
1	NE	2.5
1	MW	2.5
1	S	2.5
1	S	2.5
2	W	5
3	NE	8.5
3	NE	8.5
3	MW	8.5
3	MW	8.5
3	W	8.5
3	W	8.5
4	MW	13.5
4	MW	13.5
4	MW	13.5
4	W	13.5
5	NE	19
5	MW	19
5	S	19
5	S	19
5	S	19
5	W	19
5	W	19
6	NE	26
6	NE	26
6	NE	26
6	MW	26
6	W	26
6	W	26
6	W	26
7	MW	30.5
7	S	30.5
8	NE	33.5
8	NE	33.5
8	S	33.5
8	S	33.5
9	MW	36
11	NE	37

$R_1 = 220.5, \ R_2 = 171.5, \ R_3 = 159.5, \ R_4 = 151.5$

$$H = \frac{12}{N(N+1)} \left(\frac{R_1^2}{n_1} + \frac{R_2^2}{n_2} + \frac{R_3^2}{n_3} + \frac{R_4^2}{n_4} \right) - 3(N+1)$$

$$= \frac{12}{37(37+1)} \left(\frac{(220.5)^2}{10} + \frac{(171.5)^2}{10} + \frac{(159.5)^2}{8} + \frac{(151.5)^2}{9} \right) - 3(37+1)$$

$$\approx 1.507$$

$H \approx 1.507;$

Fail to reject H_0. There is not enough evidence at the 1% level of significance to support the underwriter's claim that there is a difference in the mean number of days spent in the hospital.

(b)

Variation	Sum of squares	Degrees of freedom	Mean squares	F
Between	9.17	3	3.06	0.52
Within	194.72	33	5.90	

Because $\alpha = 0.01$ and the test is two-tailed, use the $\frac{1}{2}\alpha = 0.005$ table. The critical value is about 5.24. Because $F \approx 0.52$ is less than the critical value, the decision is to fail to reject H_0. There is not enough evidence at the 1% level of significance to support the underwriter's claim that there is a difference in the mean number of days spent in the hospital.

10. (a) The claim is "the mean energy consumptions are different."

H_0: There is no difference in the mean energy consumptions.

H_a: There is a difference in the mean energy consumptions. (claim)

The critical value is 11.345.

Ordered data	Sample	Rank
28	W	1
32	W	2
39	W	3
40	S	4
56	W	5
62	MW	6
63	W	7
67	S	8
70	S	9.5
70	W	9.5
72	NE	11.5
72	S	11.5
74	S	13.5
74	W	13.5
78	W	15
84	MW	16
91	S	17.5
91	S	17.5
95	NE	19
97	MW	20
100	NE	21
104	NE	22
106	NE	23.5
106	W	23.5
108	NE	25
113	MW	26
118	W	27
120	MW	28
129	MW	29
134	NE	30
138	NE	21
147	S	32
148	MW	33
151	NE	34
165	MW	35
174	NE	36
183	MW	37
194	MW	38
212	MW	39

$R_1 = 253,\ R_2 = 307,\ R_3 = 113.5,\ R_4 = 106.5$

$$H = \frac{12}{N(N+1)}\left(\frac{R_1^2}{n_1} + \frac{R_2^2}{n_2} + \frac{R_3^2}{n_3} + \frac{R_4^2}{n_4}\right) - 3(N+1)$$

$$= \frac{12}{39(39+1)}\left(\frac{(253)^2}{10} + \frac{(307)^2}{11} + \frac{(113.5)^2}{8} + \frac{(106.5)^2}{10}\right) - 3(39+1)$$

$$\approx 16.26$$

$$H \approx 16.26$$

Reject H_0. There is enough evidence at the 1% level of significance to support the claim that the mean energy consumptions are different.

(b)

Variation	Sum of squares	Degrees of freedom	Mean squares	F
Between	32,116	3	10,705	8.18
Within	45,794	35	1308	

Because $\alpha = 0.01$ and the test is two-tailed, use the $\frac{1}{2}\alpha = 0.005$ table, The critical value is about 5.24. Because $F \approx 8.18$ is greater than the critical value, the decision is to reject H_0. There is enough evidence at the 1% level of significance to support the claim that the mean energy consumptions are different.

(c) Both tests come to the same decision, which is that there is enough evidence to support the claim that the mean energy consumptions.

11.4 RANK CORRELATION

11.4 Try It Yourself Solutions

1a. The claim is "there is a correlation between the number of males and females who receive doctoral degrees."

$H_0: \rho_s = 0$; $H_a: \rho_s \neq 0$ (claim)

b. $\alpha = 0.01$

c. The critical value is 0.929.

d.

Male	Rank	Female	Rank	d	d^2
25	3.5	20	1.5	2	4
24	1.5	20	1.5	0	0
24	1.5	22	3.0	−1.5	2.25
25	3.5	23	4.0	−0.5	0.25
27	5.0	26	5.0	0	0
29	6.0	27	6.0	0	0
30	7.0	30	7.0	0	0
					$\sum d^2 = 6.5$

$\sum d^2 = 6.5$

e. $r_c \approx 1 - \dfrac{6\sum d^2}{n(n^2-1)} = 1 - \dfrac{6(6.5)}{7(7^2-1)} \approx 0.884$

f. Fail to reject H_0.

g. There is not enough evidence at the 1% level of significance to conclude that a significant correlation exists between the number of males and females who received doctoral degrees.

11.4 EXERCISE SOLUTIONS

1. The Spearman rank correlation coefficient can be used to describe the relationship between linear and nonlinear data. Also, it can be used for data at the ordinal level and it is easier to calculate by hand than the Pearson correlation coefficient.

2. Both the Spearman rank correlation coefficient and the Pearson correlation coefficient range from -1 to 1, inclusive.

3. The ranks of corresponding data pairs are identical when r_s is equal to 1.

   The ranks of corresponding data pairs are in reverse order when r_s is equal to -1.

   The ranks of corresponding data pairs have no relationship when r_s is equal to 0.

4. The value of r_s represents the correlation coefficient of the sample data, whereas ρ_s represents the correlation coefficient of the entire population.

5. (a) The claim is "there is a correlation between debt and income in the farming business."

   $H_0: \rho_s = 0$; $H_a: \rho_s \neq 0$ (claim)

   (b) The critical value is 0.929.

   (c)

Debt	Rank	Income	Rank	d	d^2
19,955	7	28,926	7	0	0
10.480	4	8,630	2	2	4
14.434	6	12,942	5	1	1
9,982	2	8,807	3	-1	1
10,085	3	11,028	4	-1	1
4,235	1	7,008	1	0	0
13,286	5	15,268	6	-1	1
					$\sum d^2 = 8$

   $\sum d^2 = 8$

   $$r_c \approx 1 - \frac{6\sum d^2}{n(n^2 - 1)} \approx 0.857$$

   (d) Fail to reject H_0.

   (e) There is not enough evidence at the 1% level of significance to support the claim that there is a correlation between debt and income in the farming business.

6. (a) The claim is "there is a correlation between the overall score and the price."

   $H_0: \rho_s = 0$; $H_a: \rho_s \neq 0$ (claim)

   (b) The critical value is 0.618.

(c)

Score	Rank	Price	Rank	d	d^2
85	11	2600	9	2	4
78	10	2800	10	0	0
77	9	3700	11	−2	4
75	8	1700	7	1	1
73	7	1300	5	2	4
71	6	900	2	4	16
66	4.5	1000	3.5	1	1
66	4.5	1400	6	−1.5	2.25
64	3	1800	8	−5	25
62	2	1000	3.5	−1.5	2.25
58	1	700	1	0	0
					$\sum d^2 = 59.5$

$$\sum d^2 = 59.5$$

$$r_c \approx 1 - \frac{6\sum d^2}{n(n^2 - 1)} \approx 0.730$$

(d) Reject H_0.

(e) There is enough evidence at the 5% level of significance to conclude that there is a correlation between the overall score and price.

7. (a) The claim is "there is a correlation between wheat and oat prices."

$H_0: \rho_s = 0$; $H_a: \rho_s \neq 0$ (claim)

(b) The critical value is 0.833.

(c)

Oat	Rank	Wheat	Rank	d	d^2
1.10	1	2.62	1	0	0
1.59	4	2.78	2	2	4
1.81	6	3.56	6	0	0
1.48	2.5	3.40	3.5	−1	1
1.48	2.5	3.40	3.5	−1	1
1.63	5	3.42	5	0	0
1.87	7	4.26	7	0	0
2.63	8	6.48	8	0	0
3.10	9	6.80	9	0	0
					$\sum d^2 = 6$

$$\sum d^2 = 6$$

$$r_c \approx 1 - \frac{6\sum d^2}{n(n^2 - 1)} \approx 0.950$$

(d) Reject H_0.

(e) There is enough evidence at the 1% level of significance to conclude that there is a correlation between the oat and wheat prices.

8. (a) The claim is "there is a correlation between the overall score and the price."

$H_0: \rho_s = 0$; $H_a: \rho_s \neq 0$ (claim)

(b) The critical value is 0.497.

(c)

Score	Rank	Price	Rank	d	d^2
73	12	230	5	7	49
65	7	400	9	-2	4
60	3.5	600	10.5	-7	49
71	11	350	8	3	9
62	5	100	2	3	9
39	1	300	6.5	-5.5	30.25
67	8	600	10.5	-2.5	6.25
64	6	700	12	-6	36
68	9	140	3	6	36
60	3.5	200	4	-0.5	0.25
70	10	80	1	9	81
55	2	300	6.5	-4.5	20.25
					$\sum d^2 = 330$

$\sum d^2 = 330$

$r_c \approx 1 - \dfrac{6\sum d^2}{n(n^2-1)} \approx -0.154$

(d) Fail to reject H_0.

(e) There is not enough evidence at the 10% level of significance to conclude that there is a correlation between the overall score and the price.

9. The claim is "there is a correlation between science achievement scores and GNI."

$H_0: \rho_s = 0$; $H_a: \rho_s \neq 0$ (claim)

The critical value is 0.700.

Science average	Rank	GNI	Rank	d	d^2
534	9	1307	3	6	36
495	5	2467	6	-1	1
516	7	3207	7	0	0
475	2	1988	5	-3	9
531	8	4829	8	0	0
410	1	989	2	-1	1
488	3	1314	4	-1	1
503	6	438	1	5	25
489	4	13,886	9	-5	25
					$\sum d^2 = 98$

$\sum d^2 = 98$

$r_c \approx 1 - \dfrac{6\sum d^2}{n(n^2-1)} \approx 0.183$

Fail to reject H_0. There is not enough evidence at the 5% level of significance to conclude that there is a correlation between science achievement scores and GNI.

10. The claim is "there is a correlation between mathematics achievement scores and GNI."
$H_0: \rho_s = 0$; $H_a: \rho_s \neq 0$ (claim)
The critical value is 0.700.

Math average	Rank	GNI	Rank	d	d^2
527	9	1307	3	6	36
496	5	2467	6	−1	1
504	7	3207	7	0	0
462	2	1988	5	−3	9
523	8	4829	8	0	0
406	1	989	2	−1	1
480	4	1314	4	0	0
502	6	438	1	5	25
474	3	13,886	9	−6	36
					$\sum d^2 = 108$

$\sum d^2 = 108$

$r_c \approx 1 - \dfrac{6 \sum d^2}{n(n^2 - 1)} \approx 0.100$

Fail to reject H_0. There is not enough evidence at the 5% level of significance to conclude that there is a correlation between mathematics achievement scores and GNI.

11. The claim is "there is a correlation between science and mathematics achievement scores."
$H_0: \rho_s = 0$; $H_a: \rho_s \neq 0$ (claim)
The critical value is 0.700.

Science average	Rank	Science average	Rank	d	d^2
534	9	527	9	0	0
495	5	496	5	0	0
516	7	504	7	0	0
475	2	462	2	0	0
531	8	523	8	0	0
410	1	406	1	0	0
488	3	480	4	−1	1
503	6	502	6	0	0
489	4	474	3	1	1
					$\sum d^2 = 2$

$\sum d^2 = 2$

$r_c \approx 1 - \dfrac{6 \sum d^2}{n(n^2 - 1)} \approx 0.983$

Reject H_0. There is enough evidence at the 5% level of significance to conclude that there is a correlation between science and mathematics achievement scores.

12. Answers will vary. *Sample answer:* Although there is a strong correlation between math and science scores, there is not a significant correlation between the scores and GNI.

13. The claim is "there is a correlation between average hours worked and the number of on-the-job injuries."

$H_0: \rho_s = 0$; $H_a: \rho_s \neq 0$ (claim)

The critical values are $\dfrac{\pm z}{\sqrt{n-1}} = \dfrac{\pm 1.96}{\sqrt{33-1}} \approx \pm 0.346$.

Hours worked	Rank	Injuries	Rank	D	D^2
47.6	31	16	2	29	841
44.1	11	33	31.5	−20.5	420.25
45.6	24	25	17.5	6.5	42.25
45.5	21.5	33	31.5	−10	100
44.5	14	18	3.5	10.5	110.25
47.3	30	20	7	23	529
44.6	16	21	10	6	36
45.9	25	18	3.5	21.5	462.25
45.5	21.5	21	10	11.5	132.25
43.7	9.5	28	26	−16.5	272.25
44.8	17.5	15	1	16.5	272.25
42.5	3	26	21	−18	324
46.5	26	34	33	−7	49
42.3	2	32	30	−28	784
45.5	21.5	26	21	0.5	0.25
41.8	1	28	26	−25	625
43.1	5.5	22	12	−6.5	42.25
44.4	12	19	5	7	49
44.5	14	23	13.5	0.5	0.25
43.7	9.5	20	7	2.5	6.25
44.9	19	28	26	−7	49
47.8	32	24	15.5	16.5	272.25
46.6	27	26	21	6	36
45.5	21.5	29	29	−7.5	56.25
43.5	7.5	21	10	−2.5	6.25
42.8	4	28	26	−22	484
44.8	17.5	23	13.5	4	16
43.5	7.5	26	21	−13.5	182.25
47.0	29	24	15.5	13.5	182.25
44.5	14	20	7	7	49
50.1	33	28	26	7	49
46.7	28	26	21	7	49
43.1	5.5	25	17.5	−12	144
					$\sum d^2 = 6673$

$\sum d^2 = 6673$

$r_c \approx 1 - \dfrac{6\sum d^2}{n(n^2-1)} \approx -0.115$

Fail to reject H_0. There is not enough evidence at the 5% level of significance to conclude that there is a correlation between average hours worked and the number of on-the-job injuries.

14. The claim is "there is a correlation between average hours worked and the number of on-the-job injuries."

$H_0: \rho_s = 0$; $H_a: \rho_s \neq 0$ (claim)

The critical values are $\dfrac{\pm z}{\sqrt{n-1}} = \dfrac{\pm 1.96}{\sqrt{34-1}} \approx \pm 0.341$.

Hours worked	Rank	Injuries	Rank	D	D²
40.5	26	12	6	20	400
38.3	14	13	10.5	3.5	12.25
37.8	8	19	26.5	−18.5	342.25
38.2	12	18	23.5	−11.5	132.25
38.6	15	22	28.5	−13.5	182.25
41.2	30.5	22	28.5	2	4
39	17.5	17	21	−3.5	12.25
41	28	13	10.5	17.5	305.25
40.6	27	15	17.5	9.5	90.25
44.1	34	10	2.5	31.5	992.25
39.7	24	18	23.5	0.5	0.25
41.2	30.5	19	26.5	4	16
41.1	29	13	10.5	18.5	342.25
38.2	12	24	33.5	−21.5	462.25
42.3	32.5	12	6	26.5	702.25
39.2	21	12	6	15	225
36.1	3	13	10.5	−7.5	56.25
36.2	4	15	17.5	−13.5	182.25
38.7	16	18	23.5	−7.5	56.25
36	2	11	4	−2	4
37.3	7	24	33.5	−26.5	702.25
36.5	5	16	20	−15	225
37.9	9	13	10.5	−1.5	2.25
38	10	23	31	−21	441
36.7	6	14	14.5	−8.5	72.25
40.1	25	10	2.5	22.5	506.25
35.5	1	5	1	0	0
38.2	12	14	14.5	−2.5	6.25
42.3	32.5	13	10.5	22	484
39	17.5	18	23.5	−6	36
39.6	22.5	15	17.5	5	25
39.1	19.5	23	31	−11.5	132.25
39.6	22.5	15	17.5	5	25
39.1	19.5	23	31	−11.5	132.25
					$\sum d^2 = 7310.5$

$$\sum d^2 = 7310.5$$

$$r_c \approx 1 - \frac{6\sum d^2}{n(n^2 - 1)} \approx -0.117$$

Fail to reject H_0. There is not enough evidence at the 5% level of significance to conclude that there is a correlation between average hours worked and the number of on-the-job injuries.

11.5 THE RUNS TEST

11.5 Try It Yourself Solutions

1a. *PPP F P F PPPP FF P F PP FFF PPP F PPP*

  b. 13 groups $\Rightarrow$ 13 runs

  c. 3, 1, 1, 1, 4, 2, 1, 1, 2, 3, 3, 1, 3

2a. The claim is "the sequence of genders is not random."

   H_0: The sequence of genders is random.

   H_a: The sequence of genders is not random. (claim)

  b. $\alpha = 0.05$

  c. *M FFF MM FF M F MM FFF*

   n_1 = number of *F*'s = 9

   n_2 = number of *M*'s = 6

   G = number of runs = 8

  d. lower critical value = 4

   upper critical value = 13

  e. $G = 8$

  f. Fail to reject H_0.

  g. There is not enough evidence at the 5% level of significance to support the claim that the sequence of genders is not random.

3a. The claim is "the sequence of weather conditions is not random."

   H_0: The sequence of weather conditions is random.

   H_a: The sequence of weather conditions is not random. (claim)

  b. $\alpha = 0.05$

  c. n_1 = number of *N*'s = 21

   n_2 = number of *S*'s = 10

   G = number of runs = 17

  d. critical values = ± 1.96

  e. $\mu_G = \dfrac{2n_1 n_2}{n_1 + n_2} + 1 = \dfrac{2(21)(10)}{21 + 10} + 1 = 14.55$

   $\sigma_G = \sqrt{\dfrac{2n_1 n_2 (2n_1 n_2 - n_1 - n_2)}{(n_1 + n_2)^2 (n_1 + n_2 - 1)}} = \sqrt{\dfrac{2(21)(10)(2(21)(10) - 21 - 10)}{(21 + 10)^2 (21 + 10 - 1)}} \approx 2.4$

$$z = \frac{G - \mu_G}{\sigma_G} \approx \frac{17 - 14.55}{2.38} \approx 1.03$$

f. Fail to reject H_0.

g. There is not enough evidence at the 5% level of significance to support the claim that the sequence of weather conditions is not random.

11.5 EXERCISE SOLUTIONS

1. Answers will vary. *Sample answer:* It is called the runs test because it considers the number of runs of data in a sample to determine whether the sequence of data was randomly selected.

2. When both n_1 and n_2 are less than or equal to 20, the test statistic is equal to the number of runs G. When either n_1 or n_2 is greater than 20, the test statistic is equal to

$$\frac{G - \mu_G}{\sigma_G}.$$

3. Number of runs = 8
   Run lengths = 1, 1, 1, 1, 3, 3, 1, 1

4. Number of runs = 9
   Run lengths = 2, 2, 1, 1, 2, 2, 1, 1, 2

5. Number of runs = 9
   Run lengths = 1, 1, 1, 1, 1, 6, 3, 2, 4

6. Number of runs = 10
   Run lengths = 3, 3, 1, 2, 6, 1, 2, 1, 1, 2

7. n_1 = number of T's = 6
   n_2 = number of F's = 6

8. n_1 = number of U's = 8
   n_2 = number of D's = 6

9. n_1 = number of M's = 10
   n_2 = number of F's = 10

10. n_1 = number of A's = 13
    n_2 = number of B's = 9

11. n_1 = number of T's = 6
    n_1 = number of F's = 6
    too high: 11; too low: 3

12. n_1 = number of M's = 9
    n_2 = number of F's = 3
    too high: 8; too low: 2

13. n_1 = number of N's = 11
    n_1 = number of S's = 7
    too high: 14; too low: 5

14. n_1 = number of X's = 7
    n_2 = number of Y's = 14
    too high: 15; too low: 5

15. (a) The claim is "the tosses were not random."
    H_0: The coin tosses were random.
    H_a: The coin tosses were not random. (claim)
    (b) n_1 = number of H's = 7
    n_2 = number of T's = 9
    lower critical value = 4
    upper critical value = 14
    (c) $G = 9$ runs

(d) Fail to reject H_0.

(e) There is not enough evidence at the 5% level of significance to support the claim that the coin tosses were not random.

16. (a) The claim is "the sequence of majority parties is not random."

H_0: The sequence of majority parties is random.

H_a: The sequence of majority parties is not random. (claim)

(b) n_1 = number of R's = 18

n_2 = number of D's = 32

$z_0 = \pm 1.96$

(c) $G = 14$ runs

$$M_G = \frac{2n_1 n_2}{n_1 + n_2} + 1 = \frac{2(18)(32)}{18 + 32} + 1 = 24.04$$

$$\sigma_G = \sqrt{\frac{2n_1 n_2 (2n_1 n_2 - n_1 - n_2)}{(n_1 + n_2)^2 (n_1 + n_2 - 1)}} = \sqrt{\frac{2(18)(32)(2(18)(32) - 18 - 32)}{(18 + 32)^2 (18 + 32 - 1)}} \approx 3.22$$

$$z = \frac{G - \mu_G}{\sigma_G} \approx \frac{14 - 24.04}{3.22} \approx -3.12$$

(d) Reject H_0.

(e) There is enough evidence at the 5% level of significance to conclude that the sequence is not random.

17. (a) The claim is "the sequence of World Series winning teams is not random."

H_0: The sequence of leagues of winning teams is random.

H_a: The sequence of leagues of winning teams is not random. (claim)

(b) n_1 = number of N's = 17

n_2 = number of A's = 23

$z_0 = \pm 1.96$

(c) $G = 26$ runs

$$\mu_G = \frac{2n_1 n_2}{n_1 + n_2} + 1 = \frac{2(17)(23)}{17 + 23} + 1 = 20.55$$

$$\sigma_G = \sqrt{\frac{2n_1 n_2 (2n_1 n_2 - n_1 - n_2)}{(n_1 + n_2)^2 (n_1 + n_2 - 1)}} = \sqrt{\frac{2(17)(23)(2(17)(23) - 17 - 23)}{(17 + 23)^2 (78 + 23 - 1)}} \approx 3.05$$

$$z = \frac{G - \mu_G}{\sigma_G} \approx \frac{26 - 20.55}{3.05} \approx 1.79$$

(d) Fail to reject H_0.

(e) There is not enough evidence at the 5% level of significance to conclude that the sequence of leagues of World Series winning teams is not random.

18. (a) The claim is "the digits were not randomly generated."

H_0: The sequence of digits was randomly generated.

H_a: The sequence of digits was not randomly generated. (claim)

(b) n_1 = number of O's = 16

n_2 = number of E's = 16

lower critical value = 11; upper critical value = 23

(c) $G = 9$ runs

(d) Reject H_0.

(e) There is enough evidence at the 5% level of significance to support the claim that the sequence of digits was not randomly generated.

19. (a) The claim is "the microchips are random by gender."

H_0: The microchips are random by gender.

H_a: The microchips are not random by gender. (claim)

(b) n_1 = number of M's = 9

n_2 = number of F's = 20

lower critical value = 8; upper critical value = 18

(c) $G = 12$ runs

(d) Fail to reject H_0.

(e) There is not enough evidence at the 5% level of significance to reject the claim that the microchips are random by gender.

20. (a) The claim is "the sequence of past winners is not random."

H_0: The sequence of past winners is random.

H_a: The sequence of past winners is not random. (claim)

(b) n_1 = number of F's = 42

n_2 = number of A's = 16

$z_0 = \pm 1.96$

(c) $G = 32$ runs

$$\mu_G = \frac{2n_1 n_2}{n_1 + n_2} + 1 = \frac{2(42)(16)}{42+16} + 1 \approx 24.2$$

$$\sigma_G = \sqrt{\frac{2n_1 n_2 (2n_1 n_2 - n_1 - n_2)}{(n_1 + n_2)^2 (n_1 + n_2 - 1)}} = \sqrt{\frac{2(42)(16)(2(42)(16) - 42 - 16)}{(42+16)^2 (42+16-1)}} \approx 3.0$$

$$z = \frac{G - \mu_G}{\sigma_G} \approx \frac{32 - 24.17}{3.00} \approx 2.61$$

(d) Reject H_0.

(e) There is enough evidence at the 5% level of significance to support the claim that the sequence is not random.

21. The claim is "the daily high temperatures do not occur randomly."

H_0: Daily high temperatures occur randomly.

H_a: Daily high temperatures do not occur randomly. (claim)

median = 87

n_1 = number of F's = 15

n_2 = number of A's = 13

lower critical value = 9

upper critical value = 21

$G = 11$ runs

Fail to reject H_0,

There is not enough evidence at the 5% level of significance to support the claim that the daily high temperatures do not occur randomly.

22. The claim is "the scores occur randomly."

H_0: The sequence of exam scores is random. (claim)

H_a: The sequence of exam scores is not random.

median = 87

n_1 = number above median = 14

n_2 = number below median = 15

lower critical value = 9

upper critical value = 22

$G = 15$ runs

Fail to reject H_0,

There is not enough evidence at the 5% level of significance to reject the claim that the sequence of exam scores is random.

23. Answers will vary.

CHAPTER 11 REVIEW EXERCISE SOLUTIONS

1. (a) The claim is "the median number of customers per day is not more than 650."

H_0: median ≤ 650 (claim); H_a: median > 650

(b) The critical value is 2.

(c) $x = 7$

(d) Fail to reject H_0.

(e) There is not enough evidence at the 1% level of significance to reject the bank manager's claim that the median number of customers per day is no more than 650.

2. (a) The claim is "median credit score for U.S. adults is at least 710."

H_0: median ≥ 710 (claim); H_a: median < 710

(b) The critical value is 2.

(c) $x = 5$

(d) Fail to reject H_0.

(e) There is not enough evidence at the 5% level of significance to reject the company's claim that the median credit score for U.S. adults is at least 710.

3. (a) The claim is "median sentence length for all federal prisoners is 2 years."

   H_0: median = 2 (claim); $\qquad$ H_a: median ≠ 2

   (b) The critical value is $z_0 = -1.645$..

   (c) $x = 65$

   $$z = \frac{(x+0.5) - 0.5(n)}{\dfrac{\sqrt{n}}{2}} = \frac{(65+0.5) - 0.5(174)}{\dfrac{\sqrt{174}}{2}} \approx \frac{-21.5}{6.595} \approx -3.26$$

   (d) Reject H_0.

   (e) There is enough evidence at the 10% level of significance to reject the agency's claim that the median sentence length for all federal prisoner's is 2 years.

4. (a) The claim is "there was no reduction in diastolic blood pressure."

   H_0: There is no reduction in diastolic blood pressure. (claim)

   H_a: There is a reduction in diastolic blood pressure.

   (b) The critical value is 1.

   (c) $x = 4$

   (d) Fail to reject H_0.

   (e) There is not enough evidence at the 5% level of significance to reject the claim that there was no reduction in diastolic blood pressure.

5. (a) The claim is "there was no reduction in diastolic blood pressure."

   H_0: There is no reduction in diastolic blood pressure. (claim)

   H_a: There is a reduction in diastolic blood pressure.

   (b) The critical value is 2.

   (c) $x = 3$

   (d) Fail to reject H_0.

   (e) There is not enough evidence at the 5% level of significance to reject the claim that there was no reduction in diastolic blood pressure.

6. (a) The claim is "the median salary of lawyers 9 months after graduation from law school is $68,500.

   (b) The critical value is $z_0 = -1.96$.

   (c) $x = 49$

   $$z = \frac{(x+0.5) - 0.5(n)}{\dfrac{\sqrt{n}}{2}} = \frac{(49+0.5) - 0.5(125)}{\dfrac{\sqrt{125}}{2}} \approx \frac{-13}{5.59} \approx -2.33$$

   (d) Reject H_0.

   (e) There is enough evidence at the 5% level of significance to reject the claim that the median starting salary is $68,500.

7. (a) Independent; Wilcoxon rank sum test

(b) The claim is "there is a difference in the total times required to earn a doctorate degree by female and male graduate students."

H_0: There is no difference in the total times to earn a doctorate degree by female and male graduate students.

H_a: There is a difference in the total times to earn a doctorate degree by female and male graduate students.

(c) The critical values are $z_0 \pm 2.575$.

(d)

Ordered data	Sample	Rank
7	F	1.5
7	F	1.5
8	M	4.5
8	M	4.5
8	M	4.5
8	M	4.5
9	F	8.5
9	F	8.5
9	M	8.5
9	M	8.5
10	F	13
10	F	13
10	M	13
10	M	13
10	M	13
11	F	17.5
11	M	17.5
11	M	17.5
11	M	17.5
12	F	20.5
12	F	20.5
13	F	22.5
13	F	22.5
14	F	24

$$\mu_R = \frac{n_1(n_1 + n_2 + 1)}{2} = \frac{12(12 + 12 + 1)}{2} = 150$$

$$\sigma_R = \sqrt{\frac{n_1 n_2 (n_1 + n_2 + 1)}{12}} \sqrt{\frac{(12)(12)(12 + 12 + 1)}{12}} \approx 17.321$$

$$z = \frac{R - \mu_R}{\sigma_R} \approx \frac{126.5 - 150}{17.321} \approx -1.357$$

(e) Fail to reject H_0.

(f) There is not enough evidence at the 1% level of significance to support the claim that there is a difference in the total times to earn a doctorate degree by female and male graduate students.

8. (a) Dependent; Wilcoxon signed-rant test
    (b) The claim is "a new drug affects the number of headache hours experienced by headache sufferers."

    H_0: The new drug does not affect the number of headache hours experienced.

    H_a: The new drug does affect the number of headache hours experienced. (claim)
    (c) The critical value is 4.
    (d)

Before	After	Difference	Absolute value	Rank	Signed rank
0.9	1.4	−0.5	0.5	1.5	−1.5
2.3	1.5	0.8	0.8	4	4
2.7	1.4	1.3	1.3	6.5	6.5
2.4	1.8	0.6	0.6	3	3
2.9	1.3	1.6	1.6	8	8
1.9	0.6	1.3	1.3	6.5	6.5
1.2	0.7	0.5	0.5	1.5	1.5
3.1	1.9	1.2	1.2	5	5

Sum of negative ranks $= -1.5$
Sum of positive ranks $= 34.5$
$w_s = 1.5$

    (e) Reject H_0.
    (f) There is enough evidence at the 5% level of significance to support the claim that the new drug does affect the number of headache hours experienced.

9. (a) The claim is "the distributions of the ages of the doctorate recipients in these three fields of study are different."

    H_0: There is no difference in ages of doctorate recipients among the fields of study.

    H_a: There is a difference in ages of doctorate recipients among the fields of study. (claim)
    (b) The critical value is 9.210.

(c)

Ordered data	Sample	Rank
29	L	1.5
29	P	1.5
30	L	5.5
30	P	5.5
30	P	5.5
30	P	5.5
30	P	5.5
30	S	5.5
31	L	12.5
31	L	12.5
31	L	12.5
31	P	12.5
31	P	12.5
31	P	12.5
31	S	12.5
31	S	12.5
32	L	20
32	L	20
32	L	20
32	P	20
32	P	20
32	S	20
32	S	20
33	P	25
33	S	25
33	S	25
34	L	28
34	L	28
34	S	28
35	L	31
35	S	31
35	S	31
36	S	33

$R_1 = 191.5$, $R_2 = 126$, $R_3 = 243.5$

$$H = \frac{12}{N(N+1)} \left(\frac{R_1^2}{n_1} + \frac{R_2^2}{n_2} + \frac{R_3^2}{n_3} \right) - 3(N+1)$$

$$= \frac{12}{33(33+1)} \left(\frac{(191.5)^2}{11} + \frac{(126)^2}{11} + \frac{(243.5)^2}{11} \right) - 3(33+1)$$

$$\approx 6.741$$

(d) Fail to reject H_0.

(e) There is not enough evidence at the 1% level of significance to conclude that the distributions of ages of the doctorate recipients in these three fields are different.

10. (a) The claim is "the distributions of the starting salaries in these four fields of engineering are different."

H_0: There is no difference in the starting salaries among the fields of engineering.

H_a: There is a difference in the starting salaries among the fields of engineering. (claim)

(b) The critical value is 7.815.

(c)

Ordered data	Sample	Rank
56.1	Mech	1
56.8	Elec	2
57.1	Mech	3
57.9	Elec	4
58.2	Mech	5
58.3	Mech	6
58.5	Elec	7
58.7	Comp	8.5
58.7	Mech	8.5
58.9	Mech	10
59	Mech	11.5
59	Mech	11.5
59.3	Comp	14
59.3	Comp	14
59.3	Elec	14
59.5	Elec	16
59.7	Elec	17
59.8	Elec	18
59.9	Comp	19
60	Elec	20
60.5	Comp	21.5
60.5	Elec	21.5
61.1	Comp	23
61.3	Elec	24
61.4	Comp	25
61.5	Mech	26
62	Mech	27
62.3	Chem	28
62.4	Comp	29
63.1	Comp	30
63.7	Chem	31
63.9	Chem	32
65.5	Chem	33.5
65.5	Comp	33.5
66.4	Chem	35
67.4	Chem	36
67.9	Chem	37
68.5	Chem	38
69.1	Chem	39
69.7	Chem	40

$$R_1 = 349.5, \ R_2 = 217.5, \ R_3 = 143.5, \ R_4 = 109.5$$

$$H = \frac{12}{N(N+1)} \left(\frac{R_1^2}{n_1} + \frac{R_2^2}{n_2} + \frac{R_3^2}{n_3} + \frac{R_4^2}{n_4} \right) - 3(N+1)$$

$$= \frac{12}{40(40+1)} \left(\frac{(349.5)^2}{10} + \frac{(217.5)^2}{10} + \frac{(143.5)^2}{10} + \frac{(109.5)}{10} \right) - 3(40+1)$$

$$\approx 24.833$$

(d) Reject H_0.

(e) There is enough evidence at the 5% level of significance to conclude that the distributions of the starting salaries in the four fields of engineering are different.

11. (a) The claim is "there is a correlation between overall score and price."
$H_0: \rho_s = 0$; $H_a: \rho_s \neq 0$ (claim)

(b) The critical value is 0.786.

(c)

Score	Rank	Price	Rank	d	d^2
93	7	500	6.5	0.5	0.25
91	6	300	5	1	1
90	5	500	6.5	−1.5	2.25
87	4	150	2	2	4
85	2	250	4	−1	1
74	3	200	3	−1	1
69	1	130	1	0	0
					$\sum d^2 = 9.5$

$$\sum d^2 = 9.5$$

$$r_s = 1 - \frac{6\sum d^2}{n(n^2-1)} = 1 - \frac{6(9.5)}{7(7^2-1)} = 0.8301$$

(d) Reject H_0.

(e) There is enough evidence at the 5% level of significance to conclude that there is a correlation between overall score and price.

12. (a) The claim is "there is a correlation between overall score and price."
$H_0: \rho_s = 0$; $H_a: \rho_s \neq 0$ (claim)

(b) The critical value is 0.600.

(c)

Score	Rank	Price	Rank	d	d^2
86	9	33	7	2	4
84	8	32	6	2	4
82	7	20	3	4	16
81	6	45	9	−3	9
75	5	19	2	3	9
74	4	25	4.5	−0.5	0.25
71	3	25	4.5	−1.5	2.25
69	2	18	1	1	1
62	1	37	8	−7	49
					$\sum d^2 = 94.5$

$$\sum d^2 = 94.5$$

$$r_s = 1 - \frac{6\sum d^2}{n(n^2-1)} = 1 - \frac{6(94.5)}{9(9^2-1)} = 0.2125$$

(d) Fail to reject H_0.

(e) There is not enough evidence at the 10% level of significance to conclude that there is a correlation between overall score and price.

13. (a) The claim is "the stops were not random by gender."

   H_0: The traffic stops were random by gender.

   H_a: The traffic stops were not random by gender. (claim)

   (b) n_1 = number of F's = 12

   n_2 = number of M's = 13

   lower critical value = 8
   upper critical value = 19

   (c) $G = 14$ runs

   (d) Fail to reject H_0.

   (e) There is not enough evidence at the 5% level of significance support the claim that the traffic stops were not random by gender.

14. (a) The claim is "the departure status of the buss is not random."

   H_0: The departure status of buses is random.

   H_a: The departure status of buses is not random. (claim)

   (b) n_1 = number of T's = 11

   n_2 = number of L's = 7

   lower critical value = 5
   upper critical value = 14

   (c) $G = 5$ runs

   (d) Reject H_0.

   (e) There is enough evidence at the 5% level of significance support the claim that the departure status of the buses is not random.

CHAPTER 11 QUIZ SOLUTIONS

1. (a) The claim is "there is a difference in the hourly earnings of union and nonunion workers in state and local governments."

    H_0: There is no difference in the hourly earnings.

    H_a: There is a difference in the hourly earnings. (claim)

    (b) Wilcoxon rank sum test

    (c) The critical values are $z_0 \pm 1.645$.

    (d)

Ordered data	Sample	Rank
19.10	N	1
19.85	N	2
20.05	N	3
20.70	N	4
20.90	N	5
21.15	N	6
21.75	N	7
23.40	N	8
24.20	U	9
24.80	U	10.5
24.80	N	10.5
25.05	U	12
25.30	U	13
25.60	U	14.5
25.60	N	14.5
26.50	U	16
27.20	U	17
29.75	U	18
30.33	U	19
32.97	U	20

    R = sum ranks of nonunion workers = 61

    $$\mu_R = \frac{n_1(n_1 + n_2 + 1)}{2} = \frac{10(10 + 10 + 1)}{2} = 105$$

    $$\sigma_R = \sqrt{\frac{n_1 n_2 (n_1 + n_2 + 1)}{12}} \sqrt{\frac{(10)(10)(10 + 10 + 1)}{12}} \approx 13.229$$

    $$z = \frac{R - \mu_R}{\sigma_R} \approx \frac{61 - 105}{13.229} \approx -3.33$$

    (e) Reject H_0.

    (f) There is enough evidence at the 10% level of significance to support the claim that there is a difference in the hourly earnings of union and nonunion workers in state and local governments.

2. (a) The claim is "the median number of annual volunteer hours is 52."

H_0: median is 52 (claim); H_a: median $\neq$ 52

(b) Sign test

(c) The critical values are ± 1.96.

(d) $x = 23$

$$z = \frac{(x+0.5)-0.5n}{\frac{\sqrt{n}}{2}}$$

$$= \frac{(23+0.5)-0.5(70)}{\frac{\sqrt{70}}{2}} = -2.75$$

(e) Reject H_0.

(f) There is enough evidence at the 5% level of significance to reject the organization's claim that the median number of annual volunteer hours is 52.

3. (a) The claim is "the distributions of sales prices in these four regions are different."

H_0: There is no difference in sales prices among the regions.

H_a: There is a difference in sales prices among the regions. (claim)

(b) Kruskal-Wallis test

(c) The critical value is 11.345.

(d)

Ordered data	Sample	Rank
149.8	S	1
150.9	S	2
161	S	3
164.6	S	4
169.5	S	5
170.5	MW	6
172.6	S	7
175.5	S	8
175.9	MW	9
185.3	MW	10
187.1	MW	11
188.9	MW	12
189.9	W	13
190.5	S	14
191.9	MW	15
200.9	MW	16
201.9	W	17
205.1	MW	18
206.3	W	19
218.5	W	20
220	W	21
225.7	W	22
230	W	23
237.9	NE	24
238.6	NE	25
245.5	NE	26
250	NE	27
252.5	NE	28
255.7	W	29
259.4	NE	30
265.9	NE	31
270.2	NE	32

$R_1 = 223, \; R_2 = 97, \; R_3 = 44, \; R_4 = 164$

$$H = \frac{12}{N(N+1)} \left(\frac{R_1^2}{n_1} + \frac{R_2^2}{n_2} + \frac{R_3^2}{n_3} + \frac{R_4^2}{n_4} \right) - 3(N+1)$$

$$= \frac{12}{32(32+1)} \left(\frac{(223)^2}{8} + \frac{(97)^2}{8} + \frac{(44)^2}{8} + \frac{(164)}{8} \right) - 3(32+1)$$

$$\approx 25.957$$

(e) Reject H_0.

(f) There is enough evidence at the level of significance to conclude that the distributions of the sales prices in these regions are different.

4. (a) The claim is "days with rain are not random."

H_0: The days with rain are random.

H_a: The rains with rain are not random. (claim)

(b) Runs test

(c) n_1 = number of N's = 15

n_2 = number of R's = 15

lower critical value = 10

upper critical value = 22

(d) $G = 16$ runs

(e) Fail to reject H_0.

(f) There is not enough evidence at the 5% level of significance for the meteorologist to conclude that days with rain are not random.

5. (a) $H_0: \rho_s = 0$; $H_a: \rho_s \neq 0$ (claim)

(b) Spearman rank correlation coefficient.

(c) The critical value is 0.829.

Larceny	Rank	Motor vehicle	Rank	d	d^2
1403	1	161	1	0	0
1506	2	608	2	0	0
2937	4	659	3	1	1
3449	6	897	4	1	1
2728	3	774	5	−1	1
3042	5	945	6	−1	1
					$\sum d^2 = 4$

$$\sum d^2 = 4$$

$$r_c = 1 - \frac{6\sum d^2}{n(n^2 - 1)} = 1 - \frac{6(4)}{6(6^2 - 1)} \approx 0.886$$

(e) Reject H_0.

(f) There is enough evidence at the 10% level of significance to conclude that there is a correlation between the number of larceny-thefts and the number of motor vehicle thefts.

CUMULATIVE REVIEW FOR CHAPTERS 9–11

1. (a)

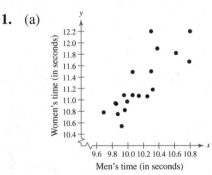

$r \approx 0.815$

There is a strong positive linear correlation.

(b) $H_0: \rho = 0$

$H_a: \rho \neq 0$ (claim)

$t_0 = 2.110$

$$t = \frac{r}{\sqrt{\dfrac{1-r^2}{n-2}}} \approx \frac{0.815}{\sqrt{\dfrac{1-(0.815)^2}{19-2}}} \approx 5.799$$

Reject H_0. There is enough evidence at the 5% level of significance to conclude that there is a significant linear correlation between the men's and women's winning 100-meter times.

(c) $\hat{y} = 1.264x - 1.581$

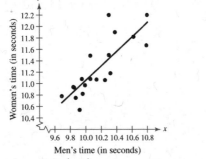

(d) $\hat{y} = 1.264(9.9) - 1.581 = 10.93$ seconds

2. The claim is "there is a difference in the weekly earnings of workers who are union members and workers who are not union members."

H_0: Median (Union) = Median (Nonunion)

H_a: Median (Union) $\neq$ Median (Nonunion) (claim)

The critical values are $z_0 = \pm 1.96$.

Ordered data	Sample	Rank
557	N	1
638	N	2
655	N	3
691	N	4
692	U	5
758	N	6
800	U	7
803	N	8
814	N	9
855	U	10
862	N	11
884	U	12
904	U	13
930	U	14
991	U	15
994	U	16
1040	U	17

R = sum ranks of nonunion workers = 44

$$\mu_R = \frac{n_1(n_1 + n_2 + 1)}{2} = \frac{8(8 + 9 + 1)}{2} = 72$$

$$\sigma_R = \sqrt{\frac{n_1 n_2 (n_1 + n_2 + 1)}{12}} \sqrt{\frac{8(9)(8 + 9 + 1)}{12}} \approx 10.392$$

$$z = \frac{R - \mu_R}{\sigma_R} \approx \frac{44 - 72}{10.392} \approx -2.69$$

Reject H_0. There is enough evidence at the 5% level of significance to support the agency's claim that there is a difference in the weekly earnings of workers who are union members and workers who are not union members.

3. The claim is "the median age of people with mutual funds is 50 years."

    H_0: Median = 50 (claim)

    H_a: Median $\neq$ 50

    The critical value is 3.

    $x = 6$

    Fail to reject H_0. There is not enough evidence at the 1% level of significance to reject the company's claim that the median age of people with mutual funds is 50 years.

4. The claim is "the mean expenditures are equal for all four regions."

    H_0: $\mu_1 = \mu_2 = \mu_3 = \mu_4$ (claim)

    H_a: At least one μ is different.

    $F_0 = 2.29$

Variation	Sum of squares	Degrees of freedom	Mean squares	F
Between	1,028,888.6	3	342,962.88	4.119
Within	2,331,130.2	28	83,254.65	

    $F = 4.119$

    Reject H_0. There is enough evidence at the 10% level of significance to reject the claim that the expenditures are equal for all four regions.

5. (a) $\hat{y} = 11,182 + 174.53(91) - 104.41(88) = 17,876.15$ pounds per ounce.

    (b) $\hat{y} = 11,182 + 174.53(110) - 104.41(98) = 20,148.12$ pounds per ounce.

6. The claim is "the standard deviations reading test scores for eigth grade students are the same in Colorado and Utah."

    H_0: $\sigma_1^2 = \sigma_2^2$ (claim)

    H_a: $\sigma_1^2 \neq \sigma_2^2$

    $F_0 = 2.46$

    $$F = \frac{s_1^2}{s_2^2} = \frac{34.6^2}{33.2^2} = 1.086$$

    Fail to reject H_0. There is not enough evidence at the 10% level of significance to reject the claim that the standard deviations of reading test scores for eighth grade students are the same in Colorado and Utah.

7. The claim is "the distributions of the annual household incomes in these regions are different."

H_0: The medians are all equal.

H_a: The medians are not all equal. (claim)

The critical value is 11.345.

Ordered data	Sample	Rank
41.5	S	1
44.4	S	2
45.2	MW	3
45.6	S	4
46.4	S	5
47.0	S	6
47.1	NE	7
48.5	MW	8
49.2	S	9.5
49.2	S	9.5
49.3	MW	11
50.0	NE	12
50.7	MW	13
51.4	W	14
51.6	NE	15
51.8	MW	16
52.0	MW	17
52.4	W	18
52.5	NE	19
53.5	W	20
54.0	W	21
54.3	NE	22
54.4	MW	23
54.7	W	24
54.8	NE	25
55.7	NE	26
55.9	W	27
56.8	W	28

$R_1 = 126$, $R_2 = 91$, $R_3 = 37$, $R_4 = 152$

$$H = \frac{12}{N(N+1)}\left(\frac{R_1^2}{n_1} + \frac{R_2^2}{n_2} + \frac{R_3^2}{n_3} + \frac{R_4^2}{n_4}\right) - 3(N+1)$$

$$= \frac{12}{28(28+1)}\left(\frac{(126)^2}{7} + \frac{(91)^2}{7} + \frac{(37)^2}{7} + \frac{(152)}{7}\right) - 3(28+1)$$

$$\approx 15.671$$

Reject H_0. There is enough evidence at the 1% level of significance to support the claim to conclude that the distributions of annual household incomes in these regions are different.

8. Claimed distributions:

Response	Distribution
None	5%
Little	16%
Half	31%
Most	33%
All	15%

H_0: The distribution is as claimed. (claim)

H_a: The distribution is not as claimed.

Response	Distribution	Observed	Expected	$\dfrac{(O-E)^2}{E}$
None	5%	31	45	4.356
Little	16%	164	144	2.778
Half	31%	277	279	0.014
Most	33%	305	297	0.215
All	15%	123	135	1.067
		900		$x^2 \approx 8.430$

$\chi_0^2 = 9,488$

$\chi \approx 8.430$

Fail to reject H_0. There is not enough evidence at the 5% level of significance to conclude that the distribution of how much parents intend to contribute to their children's college costs differs from the claimed or expected distribution.

9. (a) $r^2 \approx 0.733$

   Metacarpal bone length explains about 73.3% of the variability in height. About 26.7% of the variation is unexplained.

   (b) $s_e \approx 4.255$

   The standard error of estimate of the height for a specific metacarpal bone length is about 4.255 centimeters.

   (c) $\hat{y} = 94.428 + 1.700(50) = 179.428$

   $$E = t_c S_e \sqrt{1 + \frac{1}{n} + \frac{n(x_0 - \overline{x})^2}{n\sum x^2 - \left(\sum x\right)^2}} \approx 2.365(4.255)\sqrt{1 + \frac{1}{9} + \frac{9(50 - 45.444)^2}{9(18,707) - (409)^2}} \approx 11.402$$

   $\hat{y} \pm E \Rightarrow (168.026,\ 190.83)$

   You can be 95% confident that the height will be between 168.026 centimeters and 190.83 centimeters when the metacarpal bone length is 50 centimeters.

10. The claim is "there is a correlation between overall score and the price."

$H_0: \rho_s = 0$; $H_a: \rho_s \neq 0$ (claim)

The critical value is 0.643.

Score	Rank	Price	Rank	d	d^2
74	3.5	77	3.5	0	0
82	7	96	6	1	1
78	5	77	3.5	1.5	2.25
84	8	116	8	0	0
80	6	98	7	−1	1
64	1	67	1	0	0
70	2	70	2	0	0
74	3.5	81	5	−1.5	2.25
					$\sum d^2 = 6.5$

$$r_c = 1 - \frac{6\sum d^2}{n(n^2 - 1)} \approx 0.923$$

Reject H_0.

There is enough evidence at the 10% level of significance to conclude that there is a correlation between the overall score and the price.

Alternative Presentation of the Standard Normal Distribution

Try It Yourself Solutions

1. (1) 0.4857
    (2) $z = \pm 2.17$

2a.

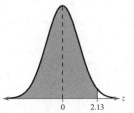

b. 0.4834

c. Area $= 0.5 + 0.4834 = 0.9834$

3a.

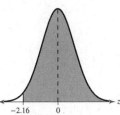

b. 0.4846

c. Area $= 0.50 + 00.4846 = 0.9846$

4a.

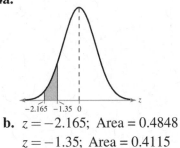

b. $z = -2.165$; Area $= 0.4848$

    $z = -1.35$; Area $= 0.4115$

c. Area $= 0.4848 - 0.4115 = 0.0733$

Normal Probability Plots and Their Graphs

Try It Yourself Solutions

1a.

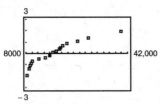

The points do not appear to be approximately linear.

b. 39,860 is a possible outlier because it is far removed from the other entries in the data set.

c. Because the points do not appear to be approximately linear and there is an outlier, you can conclude that the sample data do not come from a population that has a normal distribution.

ACTIVITY 1.3

1. {1, 17, 17, 17, 14, 10, 15, 6}
    Answers will vary. This list is a random sample taken with replacement because 17 appears three
    times.

2. Min = 1
    Max = 731
    Number of samples = 8
    {565, 718, 305, 75, 364, 221, 230, 231}
    Answers will vary. The random number generator is easier to use than the random number table.

ACTIVITY 2.3

1. When the mean is equal to the median, the shape of the distribution will be symmetric.
    When a few points are added that are less than 10, the mean and median both decrease slightly.
    As you continue to add points that are less than 10, the median will decrease dramatically and the
    mean will also decrease, but to a lesser degree.

2. Neither the mean nor the median can be any of the points that were plotted. Because there are 10
    points in each output region, the mean will fall somewhere between the two regions. By the same
    logic, the median will be the average of the greatest point between 0 and 0.75 and the least point
    between 20 and 25.

ACTIVITY 2.4

1. When a point with a value of 15 is added, the mean remains constant and the standard deviation
    decreases. When a point with a value of 20 is added, the mean is raised and the standard deviation
    increases. (Answers will vary.)

2. To get the largest standard deviation, plot four of the points at 30 and four of the points at 40. To
    get the smallest standard deviation, plot all of the points at the same number.

ACTIVITY 3.1

1. Answers will vary.

2. Answers will vary. P(market goes up on day 36) = 0.5

ACTIVITY 3.3

1. $P(3 \text{ or } 4) = \dfrac{1}{6} + \dfrac{1}{6} = \dfrac{1}{3}$

2. Answers will vary.

3. The green line will increase to 0.5.

ACTIVITY 4.2

1. Answers will vary. $\{7, 8, 7, 7, 7, 7, 8, 8, 9, 10\}$

   (a) $P(x = 5) = \dfrac{0}{10}$

   (b) $P(x \geq 8) = \dfrac{5}{10}$

   (c) $P(x \leq 7) = \dfrac{5}{10}$

2. Answers will vary. $\{3, 1, 2, 2, 1, 2, 2, 2, 5, 3\}$

   (a) $P(x = 4) = \dfrac{0}{10}$

   (b) $P(x \geq 5) = \dfrac{1}{10}$

   (c) $P(x < 4) = \dfrac{9}{10}$

3. Answers will vary. $\{7, 8, 7, 7, 7, 7, 8, 8, 9, 10\}$

   (a) $P(x = 5) \approx 0.103$

   When using $N = 100$, the estimated probability of exactly five is closer to 0.103.

ACTIVITY 5.4

1. The mean of the sampling distribution of a uniform, bell-shaped, and skewed distribution will be approximately 25.

2. The estimated standard deviation of the sampling distribution will be approximately $\dfrac{\sigma}{\sqrt{50}}$.

ACTIVITY 6.2

1. Approximately 95% of the z and t confidence intervals will contain the mean of 25.

2. Approximately 95% of the z and t confidence intervals will contain the mean of 7.26. Because $n = 24$, we should use a t-CI.

ACTIVITY 6.3

1. Approximately 95% and 99% of the CI's will contain 0.6.

2. Approximately 95% and 99% of the CI's will contain 0.4.

ACTIVITY 7.3

1. At $\alpha = 0.05$, approximately 50 of the 1000 null hypotheses will be rejected. At $\alpha = 0.01$, approximately 10 of the 1000 null hypotheses will be rejected.

2. If the null hypothesis is rejected at the 0.01 level, the P-value will be smaller than 0.01. So, it would also be rejected at the 0.05 level.
Suppose a null hypothesis is rejected at the 0.05 level. It will not necessarily be rejected at the 0.01 level because $0.01 < P$-value < 0.05.

3. $H_0 : \mu \geq 27$
The proportion of rejected null hypotheses will be larger than 0.05 and 0.01 because the true mean is 25 (i.e. $\mu < 27$).

ACTIVITY 7.4

1. Approximately 50 null hypotheses will be rejected at the 0.05 level while approximately 10 null hypotheses will be rejected at the 0.01 level.

2. $H_0 : p \geq 0.4$
The proportion of null hypotheses rejected will be less than 0.05 and 0.01 because the true $p = 0.6$.

ACTIVITY 9.1

1. If the scatter plot is linear with a positive slope, $r \approx 1$. If the scatter plot is linear with a negative slope, $r \approx -1$.

2. Create a data set that is linear with a positive slope.

3. Create a data set that is nonlinear.

4. $r \approx -0.9$ has a negative slope while using $r \approx 0.9$ will have a positive slope.

ACTIVITY 9.2

1. Answers will vary.

2. The regression line is influenced by the new point.

3. The regression line is not as influenced by the new point due to more points being used to calculate the regression line.

4. As the sample size increases, the slope changes less.

CHAPTER 1

CASE STUDY: *RATING TELEVISION SHOWS IN THE UNITED STATES*

1. Yes. A rating of 8.4 is equivalent to 9,618,000 households which is twice the number of households at a rating of 4.2.

2. $\dfrac{20,000}{114,500,000} \approx 0.000175 \Rightarrow 0.0175\%$

3. Program Name and Network

4. Rank and Rank Last Week
   Data can be arranged in increasing or decreasing order.

5. Day, Time
   Data can be chronologically ordered.
   Hours or minutes

6. Rating, Share, and Audience

7. Shows are ranked by rating. Share is not arranged in decreasing order.

8. A decision of whether a program should be cancelled or not can be made based on the Nielsen ratings.

CHAPTER 2

CASE STUDY: *EARNINGS OF ATHLETES*

1. The NFL because it has a lot more players than the other organizations.

2. MLB:

Midpoint, x	f	xf
250,000.0	353	88,250,000.0
1,250,000.5	182	227,500,091.0
4,000,000.5	164	656,000,082.0
8,000,000.5	85	680,000,042.5
19,000,000.0	74	1,406,000,000.0
	$N = 858$	$\sum xf = 3,057,750,215.5$

$\mu = \dfrac{\sum xf}{N} = \dfrac{3,057,750,215.5}{858} \approx \$3,563,811.44$

MLS:

Midpoint, x	f	xf
250,000.0	403	100,750,000.0
1,250,000.5	5	6,250,002.5
4,000,000.5	1	4,000,000.5
8,000,000.5	1	8,000,000.5
19,000,000.0	0	0.0
	$N = 410$	$\sum xf = 119,000,003.5$

$$\mu = \frac{\sum xf}{N} = \frac{119,000,003.5}{410} \approx \$290,243.91$$

NBA:

Midpoint, x	f	xf
250,000.0	35	8,750,000.0
1,250,000.5	157	196,250,078.5
4,000,000.5	137	548,000,068.5
8,000,000.5	77	616,000,038.5
19,000,000.0	57	1,083,000,000.0
	$N = 463$	$\sum xf = 2,452,000,185.5$

$$\mu = \frac{\sum xf}{N} = \frac{2,452,000,185.5}{463} \approx \$5,295,896.73$$

NFL:

Midpoint, x	f	xf
250,000.0	554	138,500,000.0
1,250,000.5	746	932,500,373.0
4,000,000.5	438	1,752,000,219.0
8,000,000.5	85	680,000,042.5
19,000,000.0	38	722,000,000.0
	$N = 1861$	$\sum xf = 4,225,000,592.5$

$$\mu = \frac{\sum xf}{N} = \frac{4,225,000,592.5}{1861} \approx \$2,270,285.11$$

NHL:

Midpoint, x	f	xf
250,000.0	42	10,500,000.0
1,250,000.5	406	507,500,203.0
4,000,000.5	237	948,000,118.5
8,000,000.5	37	296,000,018.5
19,000,000.0	0	0.0
	$N = 722$	$\sum xf = 1,762,000,340$

$$\mu = \frac{\sum xf}{N} = \frac{1,762,000,340}{722} \approx \$2,440,443.68$$

NASCAR:

Midpoint, x	f	xf
250,000.0	23	5,750,000.0
1,250,000.5	16	20,000,008.0
4,000,000.5	31	124,000,015.5
8,000,000.5	6	48,000,003.0
19,000,000.0	0	0.0
	$N = 76$	$\sum xf = 197,750,026.5$

$$\mu = \frac{\sum xf}{N} = \frac{197,750,026.5}{76} \approx \$2,601,974.03$$

PGA:

Midpoint, x	f	xf
250,000.0	110	27,500,000.0
1,250,000.5	115	143,750,057.5
4,000,000.5	36	144,000,018.0
8,000,000.5	1	8,000,000.5
19,000,000.0	0	0.0
	$N = 262$	$\sum xf = 323,250,076$

$$\mu = \frac{\sum xf}{N} = \frac{323,250,076}{262} \approx \$1,233,778.92$$

3. The NBA had the greatest earnings per player ($5,295,896.73).

4. MLB: $\mu \approx \$3,563,811.44$

Midpoint, x	$x - \mu$	$(x - \mu)^2$	$(x - \mu)^2 f$
250,000.0	–3,313,811.44	1.0981×10^{13}	3.8764×10^{15}
1,250,000.5	–2,313,810.94	5.3537×10^{12}	9.7438×10^{14}
4,000,000.5	436,189.06	1.9026×10^{11}	3.1203×10^{13}
8,000,000.5	4,436,189.06	1.9680×10^{13}	1.6728×10^{15}
19,000,000.0	15,436,188.56	2.3828×10^{14}	1.7632×10^{16}
			$\sum (x - \mu)^2 f = 2.4187 \times 10^{16}$

$$s = \sqrt{\frac{\sum (x - \mu)^2 f}{N}} = \sqrt{\frac{2.4187 \times 10^{16}}{858}} \approx \$5,309,423.39$$

MLS: $\mu \approx \$290,243.91$

Midpoint, x	$x - \mu$	$(x - \mu)^2$	$(x - \mu)^2 f$
250,000.0	–40,243.91	1.6196×10^9	6.5269×10^{11}
1,250,000.5	959,756.59	9.2113×10^{11}	4.6057×10^{12}
4,000,000.5	3,709,756.59	1.3762×10^{13}	1.3762×10^{13}
8,000,000.5	7,709,756.59	5.9440×10^{13}	5.9440×10^{13}
19,000,000.0	18,709,756.09	3.5005×10^{14}	0
			$\sum (x - \mu)^2 f = 7.8460 \times 10^{13}$

$$s = \sqrt{\frac{\sum (x - \mu)^2 f}{N}} = \sqrt{\frac{7.8460 \times 10^{13}}{410}} \approx \$437,453.83$$

NBA: $\mu \approx \$5,295,896.73$

Midpoint, x	$x - \mu$	$(x - \mu)^2$	$(x - \mu)^2 f$
250,000.0	–5,045,896.73	2.5461×10^{13}	8.9114×10^{14}
1,250,000.5	–4,045,896.23	1.6369×10^{13}	2.5700×10^{15}
4,000,000.5	–1,295,896.23	1.6793×10^{12}	2.3007×10^{14}
8,000,000.5	2,704,103.77	7.3122×10^{12}	5.6304×10^{14}
19,000,000.0	13,704,103.27	1.8780×10^{14}	1.0705×10^{16}
			$\sum (x - \mu)^2 f = 1.4959 \times 10^{16}$

$$s = \sqrt{\frac{\sum (x - \mu)^2 f}{N}} = \sqrt{\frac{1.4959 \times 10^{16}}{463}} \approx \$5,684,087.90$$

NFL: $\mu \approx \$2,270,285.11$

Midpoint, x	$x - \mu$	$(x - \mu)^2$	$(x - \mu)^2 f$
250,000.0	–2,020,285.11	4.0816×10^{12}	2.2612×10^{15}
1,250,000.5	–1,020,284.61	1.0410×10^{12}	7.7657×10^{14}
4,000,000.5	1,729,715.39	2.9919×10^{12}	1.3105×10^{15}
8,000,000.5	5,729,715.39	3.2830×10^{13}	2.7905×10^{15}
19,000,000.0	16,729,714.89	2.7988×10^{14}	1.0636×10^{16}
			$\sum (x - \mu)^2 f = 1.7775 \times 10^{16}$

$$s = \sqrt{\frac{\sum (x - \mu)^2 f}{N}} = \sqrt{\frac{1.7775 \times 10^{16}}{1861}} \approx \$3,090,520.42$$

NHL: $\mu \approx \$2,440,443.68$

Midpoint, x	$x - \mu$	$(x-\mu)^2$	$(x-\mu)^2 f$
250,000.0	−2,190,443.68	4.7980×10^{12}	2.0152×10^{14}
1,250,000.5	−1,190,443.18	1.4172×10^{12}	5.7536×10^{14}
4,000,000.5	1,559,556.82	2.4322×10^{12}	5.7644×10^{14}
8,000,000.5	5,559,556.82	3.0909×10^{13}	1.1436×10^{15}
19,000,000.0	16,559,556.32	2.7422×10^{14}	0
			$\sum (x-\mu)^2 f = 2.4969 \times 10^{15}$

$$s = \sqrt{\frac{\sum (x-\mu)^2 f}{N}} = \sqrt{\frac{2.4969 \times 10^{15}}{722}} \approx \$1,859,653.26$$

NASCAR: $\mu \approx \$2,601,974.03$

Midpoint, x	$x - \mu$	$(x-\mu)^2$	$(x-\mu)^2 f$
250,000.0	−2,351,974.03	5.5318×10^{12}	1.2723×10^{14}
1,250,000.5	−1,351,973.53	1.8278×10^{12}	2.9245×10^{13}
4,000,000.5	1,398,026.47	1.9545×10^{12}	6.0589×10^{13}
8,000,000.5	5,398,026.47	2.9139×10^{13}	1.7483×10^{14}
19,000,000.0	16,398,025.97	2.6890×10^{14}	0
			$\sum (x-\mu)^2 f = 3.9189 \times 10^{14}$

$$s = \sqrt{\frac{\sum (x-\mu)^2 f}{N}} = \sqrt{\frac{3.9189 \times 10^{14}}{76}} \approx \$2,270,781.22$$

PGA: $\mu \approx \$1,233,778.92$

Midpoint, x	$x - \mu$	$(x-\mu)^2$	$(x-\mu)^2 f$
250,000.0	−983,778.92	9.6782×10^{11}	1.0646×10^{14}
1,250,000.5	16,221.58	2.6314×10^{8}	3.0261×10^{10}
4,000,000.5	2,766,221.58	7.6520×10^{12}	2.7547×10^{14}
8,000,000.5	6,766,221.58	4.5782×10^{13}	4.5782×10^{13}
19,000,000.0	17,766,221.08	3.1564×10^{14}	0
			$\sum (x-\mu)^2 f = 4.2774 \times 10^{14}$

$$s = \sqrt{\frac{\sum (x-\mu)^2 f}{N}} = \sqrt{\frac{4.2774 \times 10^{14}}{262}} \approx \$1,277,730.57$$

5. The NBA has the greatest standard deviation ($5,684,087.40).

6. By examining the frequency distributions, the NBA is most bell-shaped.

CHAPTER 3

CASE STUDY: *UNITED STATES CONGRESS*

1. $P(\text{female representative}) = \dfrac{76}{433} = 0.176$

   $P(\text{female senator}) = \dfrac{17}{100} = 0.17$

2. The probabilities are very close, but there is a slightly higher probability of selecting a female from the House of Representatives than from the Senate.

3. (a) $P(\text{male representative}) = \dfrac{357}{433} = 0.824$

   (b) $P(\text{Republican}) = \dfrac{178}{433} = 0.411$

   (c) $P\big(\text{male}\,|\,\text{Republican}\big) = \dfrac{161}{178} = 0.904$

   (d) $P(\text{female and Democrat}) = P(\text{female}) \cdot P(\text{Democrat}\,|\,\text{female}) = \dfrac{76}{433} \cdot \dfrac{59}{76} = 0.136$

   (e) Dependent. The outcome of selecting a female affects the outcome of selecting a Democrat.

4. (a) $P(\text{male senator}) = \dfrac{83}{100} = 0.83$

   (b) $P(\text{senator is not a Democrat}) = \dfrac{43}{100} = 0.43$

   (c) $P(\text{female or Republican}) = P\big(\text{female}\big) + P\big(\text{Republican}\big) - P\big(\text{female and Republican}\big)$

   $$= \dfrac{17}{100} + \dfrac{41}{100} - \dfrac{4}{100} = 0.54$$

   (d) $P(\text{male or Democrat}) = P\big(\text{male}\big) + P\big(\text{Democrat}\big) - P\big(\text{male and Democrat}\big)$

   $$= \dfrac{83}{100} + \dfrac{57}{100} - \dfrac{44}{100} = 0.96$$

   (e) Mutually exclusive. In the 111th Congress, a senator cannot be both female and Independent because there are no female Independent senators.

5. U.S. Congress

		Political Party			
		Republican	**Democrat**	**Independent**	**Total**
	Male	198	240	2	440
Gender	**Female**	21	72	0	93
	Total	219	312	2	533

   (a) $P(\text{Independent}) = \dfrac{2}{533} \approx 0.004$

(b) P(female and Republican) $= P$(female) $\cdot$ P(Republican|female)

$$= \frac{93}{533} \cdot \frac{21}{93} \approx 0.039$$

(c) P(male or Democrat) $= P\left(\text{male}\right) + P\left(\text{Democrat}\right) - P\left(\text{male and Democrat}\right)$

$$= \frac{440}{533} + \frac{312}{533} - \frac{240}{533} \approx 0.961$$

CHAPTER 4

CASE STUDY: *BINOMIAL DISTRIBUTION OF AIRPLANE ACCIDENTS*

1. P(crash in 2006) $= \dfrac{2}{11,000,000} \approx 0.00000018$

2. (a) $P(x = 4) = 0.192$

   (b) $P(x = 10) = 0.009$

   (c) $P(1 \le x \le 5) = P(x = 1) + P(x = 2) + P(x = 3) + P(x = 4) + P(x = 5)$
   $= 0.054 + 0.119 = 0.174 + 0.192 + 0.169 = 0.708$

3. $n = 11,000,000, p = 0.0000008$

   (a) $P(x = 4) \approx 0.0376641$

   (b) $P(x = 10) \approx 0.1156838$

   (c) $P(1 \le x \le 5) \approx 0.1282358$

x	$P(x)$
0	0.0001507
1	0.0013264
2	0.0058364
3	0.0171200
4	0.0376641
5	0.0662889
6	0.0972237
7	0.1222241
8	0.1344465
9	0.1314588
10	0.1156838
11	0.0925470
12	0.0678678

4. No, because each flight is not an independent trial. There are no flights that use the same plane.

5. Assume $p = 0.0000004$. The number of flights would be 64,000 years × 365 days per year = 23,360,000 flights. The average number of fatal accidents for that number of flights would be 9.344. So, the claim cannot be justified.

CHAPTER 5

CASE STUDY: *BIRTH WEIGHTS IN AMERICA*

1. (a) 42 weeks and over $(\mu = 7.57)$

    (b) 32 to 33 weeks $(\mu = 5.14)$

    (c) 41 weeks $(\mu = 7.75)$

2. (a) $P(x < 5.5) = P(z < 2.95) = 0.9984 \rightarrow 99.84\%$

    (b) $P(x < 5.5) = P(z < 0.23) = 0.5910 \rightarrow 59.10\%$

    (c) $P(x < 5.5) = P(z < -2.08) = 0.0188 \rightarrow 1.88\%$

    (d) $P(x < 5.5) = P(z < -1.86) = 0.0314 \rightarrow 3.14\%$

3. (a) Top 10% $\Rightarrow$ 90th percentile $\Rightarrow z = 1.28$
       $x = \mu + z\sigma = 1.90 + (1.28)(1.22) = 3.46$
       Birth weights must be at least 3.46 pounds to be in the top 10%.

    (b) Top 10% $\Rightarrow$ 90th percentile $\Rightarrow z = 1.28$
       $x = \mu + z\sigma = 6.19 + (1.28)(1.29) = 7.84$
       Birth weights must be at least 7.84 pounds to be in the top 10%.

    (c) Top 10% $\Rightarrow$ 90th percentile $\Rightarrow z = 1.28$
       $x = \mu + z\sigma = 7.75 + (1.28)(1.07) = 9.12$
       Birth weights must be at least 9.09 pounds to be in the top 10%.

    (d) Top 10% $\Rightarrow$ 90th percentile $\Rightarrow z = 1.28$
       $x = \mu + z\sigma = 7.57 + (1.28)(1.11) = 8.99$
       Birth weights must be at least 8.99 pounds to be in the top 10%.

4. (a) $P(6 < x < 9) = P(3.36 < z < 5.82) \approx 1 - 0.9996 = 0.0004$

    (b) $P(6 < x < 9) = P(1.01 < z < 2.61) = 0.9955 - 0.8438 = 0.1517$

    (c) $P(6 < x < 9) = P(-0.15 < z < 2.18) = 0.9854 - 0.4404 = 0.5450$

    (d) $P(6 < x < 9) = P(-1.19 < z < 1.58) = 0.9429 - 0.1170 = 0.8259$

5. (a) $P(x < 3.25) = P(z < 1.11) = 0.8665$

    (b) $P(x < 3.25) = P(z < -0.47) = 0.3192$

    (c) $P(x < 3.25) = P(z < -1.20) = 0.1151$

    (d) $P(x < 3.25) = P(z < -3.74) \approx 0.0001$ (using technology)

CHAPTER 6

CASE STUDY: *MARATHON TRAINING*

1. (a) $\bar{x} = 167.9$ male
    (b) $\bar{x} = 189.0$ Female

2. (a) ~~$\sigma \approx 8.36$~~ $S \cong 8.4$
    (b) ~~$\sigma \approx 7.90$~~ $s \cong 7.9$

3. (a) $\bar{x} \pm z_c \dfrac{\sigma}{\sqrt{n}} \approx 167.9 \pm 1.96 \dfrac{8.36}{\sqrt{30}} \approx 167.9 \pm 2.99 \approx (164.9,\ 170.9)$ male

    (b) $\bar{x} \pm z_c \dfrac{\sigma}{\sqrt{n}} \approx 189.0 \pm 1.96 \dfrac{7.90}{\sqrt{70}} \approx 189.0 \pm 2.83 \approx (186.2,\ 191.8)$ Female

4. (a) With 95% confidence, you can say the mean male training time is between 164.9 and 170.9 minutes.

    (b) With 95% confidence, you can say the mean female training time is between 186.2 and 191.8 minutes.

5. $\bar{x} = 178.45$
    $S\ \sigma \approx 13.35$

    $\bar{x} \pm z_c \dfrac{\sigma}{\sqrt{n}} \approx 178.45 \pm 1.96 \dfrac{13.35}{\sqrt{60}} \approx 178.45 \pm 3.38 \approx (175.07,\ 181.83)$

    With 95% confidence, you can say the mean training time for all runners is between 175.07 and 181.83 minutes. The confidence interval is in between the confidence intervals of the male and female runners.

6. (a) $n = \left(\dfrac{z_c \sigma}{E}\right)^2 = \left(\dfrac{(2.575)(8.4)}{2}\right)^2$ 116.96 117 male $\approx 131.3 \rightarrow 132$ runners   assume $\sigma = 8.9$ min

    (b) $n = \left(\dfrac{z_c \sigma}{E}\right)^2 = \left(\dfrac{(2.575)(7.9)}{2}\right)^2$ 103.45 104 female $\approx 117.0 \rightarrow 117$ runners   assume $\sigma = 8.4$ min

CHAPTER 7

CASE STUDY: *HUMAN BODY TEMPERATURE: WHAT'S NORMAL?*

1. (a) (see part d)
    (b) $z_0 = \pm 1.96$ (see part d)
    (c) Rejection regions: $z < -1.96$ and $z > 1.96$ (see part d)

(d) $\bar{x} \approx 98.25,$ $s \approx 0.73$

$$z = \dfrac{\bar{x} - \mu}{\dfrac{s}{\sqrt{n}}} = \dfrac{98.25 - 98.6}{\dfrac{0.73}{\sqrt{130}}} = \dfrac{-0.35}{0.0640} \approx -5.469$$

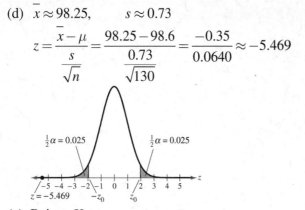

$\frac{1}{2}\alpha = 0.025$ $\frac{1}{2}\alpha = 0.025$

$z = -5.469$ $-z_0$ z_0

(e) Reject H_0.

(f) There is sufficient evidence at the 5% level to reject the claim that the mean body temperature of adult humans is $98.6°$ F.

2.   No, $\alpha = 0.01 \rightarrow z_0 = \pm 2.575 \rightarrow$ Reject H_0

3. $H_0 : \mu_m = 98.6$ and $H_a : \mu_m \neq 98.6$
     $\alpha = 0.01 \rightarrow z_0 = \pm 2.575$
     $\bar{x} \approx 98.105,$ $s \approx 0.699$

$$z = \dfrac{\bar{x} - \mu}{\dfrac{s}{\sqrt{n}}} = \dfrac{98.105 - 98.6}{\dfrac{0.699}{\sqrt{65}}} = \dfrac{-0.495}{0.0867} \approx -5.709$$

Reject H_0. There is sufficient evidence to reject the claim.

4. $H_0 : \mu_w = 98.6$ and $H_a : \mu_w \neq 98.6$
     $\alpha = 0.01 \rightarrow z_0 = \pm 2.575$
     $\bar{x} \approx 98.394,$ $s \approx 0.743$

$$z = \dfrac{\bar{x} - \mu}{\dfrac{s}{\sqrt{n}}} = \dfrac{98.394 - 98.6}{\dfrac{0.743}{\sqrt{65}}} = \dfrac{-0.206}{0.0922} \approx -2.234$$

Fail to reject H_0. There is insufficient evidence to reject the claim.

5. $\bar{x} \approx 98.25,$ $s \approx 0.73$

$$\bar{x} \pm z_c \dfrac{s}{\sqrt{n}} = 98.25 \pm 2.575 \dfrac{0.73}{\sqrt{130}} 98.25 \pm 0.165 \approx (98.05,\ 98.415)$$

6.   Wunderlich may have sampled more women than men, thus causing an overestimated body temperature.

CHAPTER 8

CASE STUDY: *READABILITY OF PATIENT EDUCATION MATERIALS*

1. $H_0 : \mu_1 = \mu_2$; $H_A : \mu_1 \neq \mu_2$ (claim)

   $z_0 = \pm 1.96$; Rejection regions: $z < -1.96, z > 1.96$

   $$z = \frac{(\bar{x}_1 - \bar{x}_2) - (\mu_1 - \mu_2)}{\sqrt{\dfrac{s_1^2}{n_1} + \dfrac{s_2^2}{n_2}}} = \frac{(11.9 - 11.84) - (0)}{\sqrt{\dfrac{(2.2)^2}{51} + \dfrac{(0.94)^2}{52}}} \approx 0.18$$

   Fail to reject H_0. There is not enough evidence at the 5% level of significance to support the claim that there is a difference in the mean readability levels of PEMs in Study 1 and Study 2.

2. $H_0 : \mu_1 = \mu_3$; $H_A : \mu_1 \neq \mu_3$ (claim)

   $z_0 = \pm 1.96$; Rejection regions: $z < -1.96, z > 1.96$

   $$z = \frac{(\bar{x}_1 - \bar{x}_3) - (\mu_1 - \mu_3)}{\sqrt{\dfrac{s_1^2}{n_1} + \dfrac{s_3^2}{n_3}}} = \frac{(11.9 - 9.43) - (0)}{\sqrt{\dfrac{(2.2)^2}{51} + \dfrac{(1.31)^2}{52}}} \approx 7.62$$

   Reject H_0. There is enough evidence at the 5% level of significance to support the claim that there is a difference in the mean readability levels of PEMs in Study 1 and Study 3.

3. $H_0 : \mu_2 = \mu_3$; $H_A : \mu_2 \neq \mu_3$ (claim)

   $z_0 = \pm 1.96$; Rejection regions: $z < -1.96, z > 1.96$

   $$z = \frac{(\bar{x}_2 - \bar{x}_3) - (\mu_2 - \mu_3)}{\sqrt{\dfrac{s_2^2}{n_2} + \dfrac{s_3^2}{n_3}}} = \frac{(11.84 - 9.43) - (0)}{\sqrt{\dfrac{(0.94)^2}{52} + \dfrac{(1.31)^2}{171}}} \approx 14.66$$

   Reject H_0. There is enough evidence at the 5% level of significance to support the claim that there is a difference in the mean readability levels of PEMs in Study 2 and Study 3.

4. There is not a difference in mean readability levels for Study 1 and Study 2, but there is a difference for Study 1 and Study 3, and for Study 2 and Study 3.

5.

$$(\bar{x}_1 - \bar{x}_2) - z_c \sqrt{\frac{s_1^2}{n_1} + \frac{s_2^2}{n_2}} < \mu_1 - \mu_2 < (\bar{x}_1 - \bar{x}_2) + z_c \sqrt{\frac{s_1^2}{n_1} + \frac{s_2^2}{n_2}}$$

$$(11.9 - 11.84) - 1.96\sqrt{\frac{(2.2)^2}{51} + \frac{(0.94)^2}{52}} < \mu_1 - \mu_2 < (11.9 - 11.84) + 1.96\sqrt{\frac{(2.2)^2}{51} + \frac{(0.94)^2}{52}}$$

$$0.06 - 1.96\sqrt{0.112} < \mu_1 - \mu_2 < 0.06 + 1.96\sqrt{0.112}$$

$$-0.6 < \mu_1 - \mu_2 < 0.7$$

Because the CI contains zero, there is not a difference in the mean readability levels of PEMs in Study 1 and Study 2.

6. (a) $H_0 : \mu_1 = \mu_4$; $H_A : \mu_1 \neq \mu_4$ (claim)

$z_0 = \pm 2.575$; Rejection regions: $z < -2.575, z > 2.575$

$$z = \frac{(\bar{x}_1 - \bar{x}_4) - (\mu_1 - \mu_4)}{\sqrt{\frac{(s_1)^2}{n_1} + \frac{(s_4)^2}{n_4}}} = \frac{(11.9 - 11.1) - (0)}{\sqrt{\frac{(2.2)^2}{51} + \frac{(1.67)^2}{137}}} \approx 2.36$$

Fail to reject H_0. There is enough evidence at the 1% level of significance to support the claim that there is a difference in the mean readability levels of PEMs in Study 1 and Study 4.

(b) $H_0 : \mu_2 = \mu_4$; $H_A : \mu_2 \neq \mu_4$ (claim)

$z_0 = \pm 2.575$; Rejection regions: $z < -2.575, z > 2.575$

$$z = \frac{(\bar{x}_2 - \bar{x}_4) - (\mu_1 - \mu_4)}{\sqrt{\frac{s_2^2}{n_2} + \frac{s_4^2}{n_4}}} = \frac{(11.84 - 11.1) - (0)}{\sqrt{\frac{(0.94)^2}{52} + \frac{(1.67)^2}{137}}} \approx 3.83$$

Reject H_0. There is enough evidence at the 1% level of significance to support the claim that there is a difference in the mean readability levels of PEMs in Study 2 and Study 4.

CHAPTER 9

CASE STUDY: *CORRELATION OF BODY MEASUREMENTS*

1. Answers will vary.

2.

	r
a	0.698
b	0.746
c	0.351
d	0.953
e	0.205
f	0.580
g	0.844
h	0.798
i	0.116
j	0.954
k	0.710
l	0.710

3. d, g, and j have strong correlations ($r > 0.8$).

(d) $\hat{y} = 1.129x - 8.817$

(g) $\hat{y} = 1.717x + 23.144$

(j) $\hat{y} = 1.279x + 10.451$

4. (a) $\hat{y} = 0.086(180) + 21.923 = 37.403$

(b) $\hat{y} = 1.026(100) - 15.323 = 87.277$

5. (weight, chest) $\rightarrow$ $r = 0.888$
(weight, hip) $r = 0.930$
(neck, wrist) $r = 0.849$
(chest, hip) $r = 0.953$
(chest, thigh) $r = 0.936$
(chest, knee) $r = 0.855$
(chest, ankle) $r = 0.908$
(abdom, thigh) $r = 0.863$
(abdom, knee) $r = 0.903$
(hip, thigh) $r = 0.894$
(hip, ankle) $r = 0.908$
(thigh, knee) $r = 0.954$
(thigh, ankle) $r = 0.874$
(ankle, knee) $r = 0.857$
(forearm, wrist) $r = 0.854$

CHAPTER 10

CASE STUDY: *FAST FOOD SURVEY*

Expected Frequencies:	Gender		
Response	Female	Male	Total
Somewhat Agree	272.214	127.786	400
Neither agree or disagree	91.192	42.808	134
Strong agree	55.123	25.877	81
Disagree	39.471	18.529	58
Total	458	215	673

1. Females exceeded the expected number of "somewhat agree" responses, males did not.

2. Females exceeded the expected number of neither agree nr disagree" responses, males did not.

3. H_0 : Response is independent of gender.

   H_a : Response is dependent on gender.

   $\alpha = 0.01$, d.f. $= (r-1)((c-1) = 3 \Rightarrow \chi_0^2 = 7.815$

O	E	$O - E$	$(O - E)^2$	$\dfrac{(O - E)^2}{E}$
286	272.214	13.786	190.053796	0.6982
114	127.786	−13.786	190.053796	1.4873
76	91.192	−15.192	230.796864	2.5309
58	42.808	15.192	230.796864	5.3914
62	55.123	6.877	47.293129	0.8580
19	25.877	−6.877	47.239129	1.8276
34	39.471	−5.471	29.931841	0,7583
24	18.529	5.471	29.931841	1.6154
24				15.1671

$\chi^2 \approx 15,167$

Reject H_0. There is enough evidence at the 1% level of significance to support the claim that response and gender are dependent.

4. H_0 : The distribution of responses of females is 5% "somewhat agree," 20% "neither agree or disagree," 12% "strongly agree," and 9% "disagree."

   H_a : The distribution of responses of females differs from the claimed or expected distribution.

   $\alpha = 0.05$, d.f. $= n - 1 = 3 \Rightarrow \chi_0^2 = 7.815$

Response	Distribution	O	E	$O-E$	$(O-E)^2$	$\dfrac{(O-E)^2}{E}$
Somewhat Agree	59%	286	270.22	15.78	249.0084	0.9215
Neither agree or disagree	20%	76	91.60	−15.60	243.3600	2.6568
Strong agree	12%	62	54.96	7.04	49.5616	0.9018
Disagree	9%	34	41.22	−7.22	52.1284	1.2646
Total						5.745

$\chi^2 \approx 5.745$

Fail to reject H_0. There is enough evidence at the 5% level of significance to that the distribution of female responses matches the national distribution.

5. H_0 : The distribution of responses of males is 59% "somewhat agree," 20% "neither agree or disagree," 12% "strongly agree," and 9% "disagree."

H_a : The distribution of responses of males differs from the claimed or expected distribution.

$\alpha = 0.05,\ \text{d.f.} = n - 1 = 3 \Rightarrow \chi_0^2 = 7.815$

Response	Distribution	O	E	$O-E$	$(O-E)^2$	$\dfrac{(O-E)^2}{E}$
Somewhat Agree	59%	114	126.85	15.78	249.00854	1.3017
Neither agree or disagree	20%	58	43.00	−15.60	243.3600	5.2326
Strong agree	12%	19	25.80	7.04	49.5616	1.7922
Disagree	9%	24	19.35	−7.22	52.1284	1.1174
Total						9.444

$\chi^2 \approx 9.444$

Reject H_0. There is enough evidence at the 5% level of significance to conclude that the distribution of male responses differs from the national distribution.

6. Answers will vary. *Sample answer:* Other variables that are important to consider when studying the distribution of U.S. consumers' attitudes about healthy fast food are age, frequency of fast food purchases, and region.

CHAPTER 11

CASE STUDY: *COLLEGE RANKS*

1. Using a technology, tool it appears the median freshman class size of North Carolina is different from the other states.

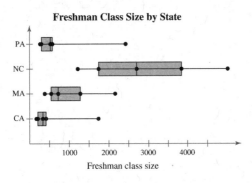

2. H_0: median ≤ 400 (claim); H_a: median > 400
   The critical value is 1.
   $x = 4$
   Fail to reject H_0. There is not enough evidence at the 5% level of significance to reject the claim that the median freshman class size at a California college is less than or equal to 400.

3. H_0: median ≥ 750 (claim); H_a: median < 750
   The critical value is 1.
   $x = 5$
   Fail to reject H_0. There is not enough evidence at the 5% level of significance to reject the claim that the median freshman class size at a Massachusetts college is greater than or equal to 750.

4. H_0: median $= 500$ (claim); H_a: median $\neq 500$
   The critical value is 1.
   $x = 5$
   Fail to reject H_0. There is not enough evidence at the 5% level of significance to reject the claim that the median freshman class size at a Pennsylvania college is 500.

5. H_0: median $= 2400$ (claim); H_a: median $\neq 2400$
   The critical value is 1.
   $x = 4$
   Fail to reject H_0. There is not enough evidence at the 5% level of significance to support the claim that the median freshman class size at a North Carolina college is different from 2400.

6. H_0: There is no difference between freshman class sizes for Pennsylvania colleges and California colleges. (claim)

H_a: There is a difference between freshman class sizes for Pennsylvania colleges and California colleges.

$z_0 = \pm 2.575$

Ordered Data	Sample	Rank
202	CA	1.5
202	CA	1.5
236	CA	3
252	CA	4
320	CA	5
327	PA	6
366	PA	7
372	PA	8
382	CA	9
399	PA	10
453	PA	11
458	CA	12
467	CA	13
574	CA	14
588	PA	15
601	PA	16
613	PA	17
957	PA	18
1703	CA	19
2400	PA	20

R = sum ranks of California = 82

$$\mu_R = \frac{n_1(n_1 + n_2 + 1)}{2} = \frac{10(10 + 10 + 1)}{2} = 105$$

$$\sigma_R = \sqrt{\frac{n_1 n_2 (n_1 + n_2 + 1)}{12}} = \sqrt{\frac{(10)(10)(10 + 10 + 1)}{12}} \approx 13.229$$

$$z = \frac{R - \mu_R}{\sigma_R} \approx \frac{82 - 105}{13.229} \approx -1.739$$

Fail to reject H_0. There is not enough evidence at the 1% level of significance to reject the claim that there is no difference between freshman class sizes for Pennsylvania colleges and California colleges.

7. H_0: There is no difference between freshman class sizes for Massachusetts colleges and North Carolina colleges.

   H_a: There is a difference between freshman class sizes for Massachusetts colleges and North Carolina colleges. (claim)

   $z_0 = \pm 2.575$

Ordered Data	Sample	Rank
439	MA	1
518	MA	2
540	MA	3
596	MA	4
643	MA	5
754	MA	6
1048	MA	7
1201	NC	8
1291	NC	9
1297	MA	10
1666	MA	11
1699	NC	12
2073	NC	13
2167	MA	14
2492	NC	15
2781	NC	16
3090	NC	17
3865	NC	18
4538	NC	19
4804	NC	20

R = sum ranks of Massachusetts = 63

$$\mu_R = \frac{n_1(n_1 + n_2 + 1)}{2} = \frac{10(10 + 10 + 1)}{2} = 105$$

$$\sigma_R = \sqrt{\frac{n_1 n_2 (n_1 + n_2 + 1)}{12}} = \sqrt{\frac{(10)(10)(10 + 10 + 1)}{12}} \approx 13.229$$

$$z = \frac{R - \mu_R}{\sigma_R} \approx \frac{63 - 105}{13.229} \approx -3.17$$

Reject H_0. There is enough evidence at the 1% level of significance to support the claim that there is a difference between freshman class sizes for Massachusetts colleges and North Carolina colleges.

CHAPTER 1

USES AND ABUSES

1. Answers will vary.

2. Answers will vary.

CHAPTER 2

USES AND ABUSES

1. Answers will vary.

2. No, it is not ethical because it misleads the consumer to believe that oatmeal is more effective at lowering cholesterol than it may actually be.

CHAPTER 3

USES AND ABUSES

1. (a) $P(\text{winning Tuesday and Wednesday}) = P(\text{winning Tuesday}) \cdot P(\text{winning Wednesday})$

$$= \left(\frac{1}{1000}\right) \cdot \left(\frac{1}{1000}\right)$$
$$= 0.000001$$

(b) $P(\text{winning Wednesday give won Tuesday}) = P(\text{winning Wednesday})$

$$= \frac{1}{1000}$$
$$= 0.001$$

(c) $P(\text{winning Wednesday give didn't win Tuesday}) = P(\text{winning Wednesday})$

$$= \frac{1}{1000}$$
$$= 0.001$$

2. Answers will vary.

$P(\text{pickup or SUV}) \le 0.55$ because $P(\text{pickup}) = 0.25$ and $P(\text{SUV}) = 0.30$, but a person may own both a pickup and an SUV (i.e. not mutually exclusive events). So, $P(\text{pickup and SUV}) \ge 0$ and this probability would have to be subtracted from 0.55.

If the events were mutually exclusive, the value of the probability would be 0.55. Otherwise, the probability will be less then 0.55 (not 0.60).

CHAPTER 4

USES AND ABUSES

1. 40

$$P(40) \approx 0.081.$$

2. Using the binomial distribution, $P(35 \leq x \leq 45) = P(35) + P(36) + \cdots + P(45) \approx 0.739$

3. Using the binomial distribution, the probability of finding 36 adults out of 100 who prefer Brand A is 0.059. So the manufacturer's claim is believable because it is not an unusual event.

4. Using the binomial distribution, the probability of finding 25 adults out of 100 who prefer Brand A is 0.000627. So the manufacturer's claim is not believable because it is a usual event.

CHAPTER 5

USES AND ABUSES

1. $\mu = 100$

$\sigma = 15$

(a) $z = \dfrac{\overline{x} - \mu}{\dfrac{\sigma}{\sqrt{n}}} = \dfrac{115 - 100}{\dfrac{15}{\sqrt{3}}} \approx 1.73$

$\overline{x} = 115$ is not an unusual sample mean.

(b) $z = \dfrac{\overline{x} - \mu}{\dfrac{\sigma}{\sqrt{n}}} = \dfrac{105 - 100}{\dfrac{15}{\sqrt{20}}} \approx 1.49$

$\overline{x} = 105$ is not an unusual sample mean.

2. The problem does not state the population of ages is normally distributed.

3. Answers will vary.

CHAPTER 6

USES AND ABUSES

1. Answers will vary

2. Answers will vary.

CHAPTER 7

USES AND ABUSES

1. Randomly sample airports and gather data necessary to answer question. (Answers will vary.)

2. $H_0: p = 0.57$
    We cannot prove that $p = 0.73$. We can only show that there is not enough evidence in our sample to reject $H_0: p = 0.73$. (Answers will vary.)

3. If we gather enough evidence to reject the null hypothesis when it is really true, then a Type I error would occur. (Answers will vary.)

4. If we fail to gather enough evidence to reject the null hypothesis when it is really false, then a Type II error would occur. (Answers will vary.)

CHAPTER 8

USES AND ABUSES

1. Age and health. (Answers will vary.)

2. Blind: The patients do not know which group (medicine or placebo) they belong to.

    Double Blind: Both the researcher and patient do not know which group (medicine or placebo) that the patient belongs to.

CHAPTER 9

USES AND ABUSES

1. Answers will vary.

2. Answers will vary. Sample answer: One example would be temperature and output of sulfuric acid. When sulfuric acid is manufactured, the amount of acid that is produced depends on the temperature at which the industrial process is run. As the temperature increases, so does the output of acid, up to a point. Once the temperature passes that point, the output begins to decrease.

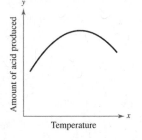

CHAPTER 10

USES AND ABUSES

1. Answers will vary. Sample answer: An example would be a biologist who is analyzing effectiveness of three types of pesticides. The biologist sprays one pesticide on five different acres during week one. At the end of week one, he calculates the mean number of insects in the acres. He sprays the second pesticide on the same five acres during week two. At the end of week two, he calculates the mean number of insects in the acres. He follows a similar procedure with the third pesticide during week three. He wants to determine whether there is a difference in the mean number of insects per acre. Since the same five acres are treated each time, it is unclear as to the effectiveness of each of the pesticides.

2. Answers will vary. *Sample answer:* An example would be another biologist who is analyzing the effectiveness of three types of pesticides. He has fifteen acres to test. He randomly assigns each pesticide to five acres and treats all of the acres for three weeks. At the end of three weeks, the biologist calculates the mean number of insects for each of the pesticides. He wants to determine whether there is a difference in the mean number of insects per acres.

   Rejecting the null hypothesis would mean that at least one of the means differs from the others.

   In this example, rejecting the null hypothesis means that there is at least one pesticide whose mean number of insects per acre differs from the other pesticides.

CHAPTER 11

USES AND ABUSES

1. Answers will vary. *Sample answer:*

   H_0: median ≥ 10
   H_a: median < 10

   Using the sign test with $n = 8$ and $\alpha = 0.05$, the critical value is 0. Thus. every item in the sample would have to be less than 10 in order to reject the H_0. (In other words, 100% if the sample would need to be less than 10.)
   However, using $n = 20$ and $\alpha = 0.05$, the critical value is 5. Not only 5 items (or 75%) of the sample would need to be less than 10 in order to reject H_0.

2. *Nonparametric test*   *Parametric test*

   (a) Sign test z-test or t-test
   (b) Paired sample sign test t-test
   (c) Wilcoxon signed-rank test   paired t-test
   (d) Wilcoxon rank sum test   two-sample t-test
   (e) Kruskal-Wallis test   one-way ANOVA
   (f) Spearman rank correlation coefficient   Pearson correlation coefficient

CHAPTER 1

REAL STATISTICS–REAL DECISIONS

1. (a) Answers will vary.

   (b) Yes

   (c) Use surveys

   (d) You may take too large a percentage of your sample from a subgroup of the population that is relatively small.

2. (a) Both, because questions will ask for demographics (qualitative) as well as cost (quantitative)

   (b) Gender, business/recreational: Nominal
   Cost of ticket: Ratio
   Comfort, safety: Ordinal

   (c) Sample

   (d) Statistics

3. (a) Answers will vary.

   (b) Answers will vary.

CHAPTER 2

REAL STATISTICS–REAL DECISIONS

1. (a) Find the average cost of renting an apartment for each area and do a comparison.

   (b) The mean would best represent the data sets for the four areas of the city.

   (c) Area A: $\bar{x} = \$1005.50$
   Area B: $\bar{x} = \$887.00$
   Area C: $\bar{x} = \$881.00$
   Area D: $\bar{x} = \$945.50$

2. (a) Construct a Pareto chart, because the data are quantitative and a Pareto chart positions data in order of decreasing height, with the tallest bar positioned at the left.

(b)

Cost of Monthly Rent per Area

(c) Yes. From the Pareto chart you can see that Area A has the highest average cost of monthly rent, followed by Area D, Area B, and Area C.

3. (a) You could use the range and sample standard deviation for each area.

   (b) Area A: $s \approx \$123.07$
            range = $415.00

        Area B: $s \approx \$144.91$
            range = $421.00

        Area C: $s \approx \$146.21$
            range = $460.00

        Area D: $s \approx \$138.70$
            range = $497.00

   (c) No. Area A has the lowest range and standard deviation so the rents in Areas B-D are more spread out. There could be one or two inexpensive rents that lower the means for these areas. It is possible that the population means of Areas B-D are close to the population mean of Area A.

4. (a) Answers will vary.

   (b) Location, weather, population

CHAPTER 3

REAL STATISTICS–REAL DECISIONS

1. (a) Answers will vary. Investigate the probability of not matching any of the 5 white balls selected.
   (b) You could use the Multiplication Rule, the Fundamental Counting Principle, and combinations.

2. If you played only the red ball, the probability of matching it is $\frac{1}{39}$. However, because you must pick five white balls, you must get the white balls wrong. So, using the Multiplication Rule, you get

P(matching only the red ball and not matching any of the 5 white balls)

= P(matching red ball) $\cdot$ P(not matching any white balls)

$= \frac{1}{39} \cdot \frac{54}{59} \cdot \frac{53}{59} \cdot \frac{52}{57} \cdot \frac{51}{56} \cdot \frac{50}{55}$

$= 0.016$

$= \frac{1}{62}$

3. The overall probability of winning a prize is determined by calculating the number of ways to win and dividing by the total number of outcomes.
To calculate the number of ways to win something, you must use combinations.

CHAPTER 4

REAL STATISTICS–REAL DECISIONS

1. (a) Answers will vary. For instance, calculate the probability of obtaining 0 clinical pregnancies out of 10 randomly selected ART cyclos.

   (b) Binomial. The distribution is discrete because the number of clinical pregnancies is countable.

2. $n = 10$, $p = 0.349$, $P(0) = 0.014$

x	$P(x)$
0	0.01367
1	0.07329
2	0.17681
3	0.25277
4	0.23714
5	0.15256
6	0.06815
7	0.02088
8	0.00420
9	0.00050
10	0.00003

Answers will vary. Sample answer: Because $P(0) = 0.014$, this event is unusual but not impossible.

3. (a) Suspicious, because the probability is very small.

   (b) Not suspicious, because the probability is not that small.

CHAPTER 5

REAL STATISTICS–REAL DECISIONS

1. $n = 60$, $p = 0.75$

    $np = 45 \geq 5$, $nq = 15 \geq 5$

    Can use normal distribution.

    $\mu = np = 45$, $\sigma = \sqrt{npq} \approx 3.35$

    (a) $P(x = 35) \approx P(34.5 < x < 35.5) = P(-3.13 < z < -2.84) = 0.0023 - 0.0009 = 0.0014$

    (b) $P(x \geq 40) \approx P(x > 39.5) = P(z > -1.64) = 0.9495$

    (c) $P(x < 20) \approx P(x < 19.5) = P(z < -7.61) \approx 0$

    (d) There is a very high probability that at least 40 out of 60 employees will participate, and the probability that fewer than 20 will participate is almost 0.

2. (a) $z = \dfrac{x - \mu}{\sigma} = \dfrac{5 - 6}{1.5} \approx -0.67$

    $P(x < 5) = P(z < -0.67) = 0.2514$

    (b) $z = \dfrac{x - \mu}{\sigma} = \dfrac{5 - 6}{1.5} \approx -0.67$

    $z = \dfrac{x - \mu}{\sigma} = \dfrac{7 - 6}{1.5} \approx 0.67$

    $P(5 < x < 7) = P(-0.67 < z < 0.67) = 0.7486 - 0.2514 = 0.4972$

    (c) $z = \dfrac{x - \mu}{\sigma} = \dfrac{7 - 6}{1.5} \approx 0.67$

    $P(x < 7) = P(z > 0.67) = 0.2514$

3. (a) 3; The line of symmetry occurs at $x = 3$.
    (b) Yes
    (c) Answers will vary.

CHAPTER 6

REAL STATISTICS–REAL DECISIONS

1. (a) Yes, there has been a change in the mean concentration level because the confidence interval for Year 1 does not overlap the confidence interval for Year 2.

    (b) No, there has not been a change in the mean concentration level because the confidence interval for Year 2 overlaps the confidence interval for Year 3.

    (c) Yes, there has been a change in the mean concentration level because the confidence interval for Year 1 does not overlap the confidence interval for Year 3.

2. Due to the fact the CIs from Years 2 and 3 do not overlap the CI from Year 1, it is very likely that concentrations of cyanide in the drinking water have increased over the three-year period.

3. The width of the confidence interval for Year 2 may have been caused by greater variation in the levels of cyanide than in other years, which may be the result of outliers.

4. (a) The sampling distribution of the sample means was used because the "mean concentration" was used. The sample mean is the most unbiased point estimate of the population mean.

   (b) No, because typically σ is unknown. They could have used the sample standard deviation.

CHAPTER 7

REAL STATISTICS–REAL DECISIONS

1. (a)-(c) Answers will vary.

2. $H_0 : p \leq 0.50$; $H_a : p > 0.50$ (claim)

$$\hat{p} = \frac{x}{n} = \frac{280}{560} = 0.5$$

$z_0 = 1.645$; Rejection region: $z > 1.645$

$$z = \frac{\hat{p} - p}{\sqrt{\dfrac{pq}{n}}} = \frac{0.5 - 0.5}{\sqrt{\dfrac{(0.5)(0.5)}{560}}} = 0$$

Fail to reject H_0. There is not enough evidence at the 5% level of significance to support the claim that more than 50% of cola drinkers prefer Pepsi over Coca-Cola.

3. Knowing the brand may influence participants' decisions.

4. (a)-(c) Answers will vary.

CHAPTER 8

REAL STATISTICS–REAL DECISIONS

1. (a) Answers will vary. *Sample answer:* Divide the records into groups according to the inpatients' ages, and then randomly select records from each group.

   (b) Answers will vary. *Sample answers:* Divide the records into groups according to geographic regions, and then randomly select several groups and examine all the records in the selected groups.

   (c) Answer will vary. *Sample answer:* Assign a different number to each record, randomly choose a starting number, and then select every 50th record.

   (d) Answers will vary. Sample answer: Assign a different number to each record and then use a table of random numbers to generate a sample of numbers.

2. (a) Answers will vary.

(b) Answers will vary.

3. Use a *t*-test because n_1 and n_2 are less than 30.

The samples are independent because both samples are randomly selected.

Yes, you need to know if the population's distribution is normal so you can use a *t*-test.

No, you do not need to know if the population variances are equal to you can use a *t*-test.

4. The claim is "there is a difference in the mean length of hospital stays for inpatients."

$$H_0 : \mu_1 = \mu_2 ; H_a : \mu_1 \neq \mu_2 \text{ (claim)}$$

$$\text{d.f.} = \min\{n_1 - 1, \ n_2 - 1\} = 25$$

$$t_0 = \pm 1.708; \ \text{Rejection region:} \ t < -1.708, \ t > 1.708$$

$$t = \frac{(\bar{x}_1 - \bar{x}_2) - (\mu_1 - \mu_2)}{\sqrt{\dfrac{s_1^2}{n_1} + \dfrac{s_2^2}{n_2}}} = \frac{(5.38 - 4.79) - (0)}{\sqrt{\dfrac{(1.65)^2}{26} + \dfrac{(1.26)^2}{28}}} \approx 1.469$$

Fail to reject H_0.

There is not enough evidence at the 10% level of significance to support the claim that there is a difference in the mean length of hospital stays for inpatients.

This decision does not support the claim.

CHAPTER 9

REAL STATISTICS–REAL DECISIONS

1. (a)

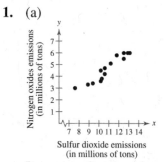

It appears that there is a positive linear correlation. As the sulfur dioxide emissions increase, the nitrogen oxide emissions increase.

(b) $r \approx 0.947$; There is a strong positive linear correlation.

(c) critical value $= 0.532$

$|r| \approx 0.947 > 0.532 \Rightarrow$ There is enough evidence at the 5% level of significance to conclude there is a significant linear correlation between sulfur dioxide emissions and nitrogen oxides emissions.

(d) $\hat{y} = 0.652x - 2.438$

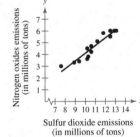

Yes, the line appears to be a good fit.

(e) Yes, for x-values that are within the range of the data set.

(f) $r^2 \approx 0.898$; About 89.8% of the variation in nitrogen oxides emissions can be explained by the variation in sulfur dioxide emissions, and about 10.2% of the variation is unexplained.
$s_e \approx 0.368$; The standard error of the estimate of nitrogen oxides emissions for a specific sulfur dioxide emissions is about 368,000 tons.

2. $1.358 < y < 3.286$

You can be 95% confident that the nitrogen oxides emissions will be between 1.358 and 3.286 million tons when the sulfur dioxide emissions are $17.3 - 10 = 7.3$ million tons.

CHAPTER 10

REAL STATISTICS–REAL DECISIONS

1.

Age	Distribution	Observed	Expected	$\dfrac{(O-E)^2}{E}$
Under 20	1%	30	10	40.000
20–39	13%	200	130	37.692
30–39	16%	300	160	122.500
40–49	19%	270	190	33.684
50–59	16%	150	160	0.625
60–69	13%	40	130	62.308
70+	22%	10	220	200.645
				$\chi^2 = 497.264$

H_0 : The distribution of ages is as shown in the table above. (claim)

H_a : The distribution of ages differs from the claimed distribution.

d.f. $= n - 1 = 6$

$\chi_0^2 = 16.812$

Reject H_0. There is enough evidence at the 1% level of significance to conclude the distribution of ages of telemarketing fraud victims differs form the survey.

CHAPTER 11

REAL STATISTICS–REAL DECISIONS

1. (a) Answers will vary.

   (b) Answers will vary.

   (c) Answers will vary.

2. (a) Answers will vary. For example, ask "Is the data a random sample?" and "Is the data normally distributed?"

   (b) Sign test; You need to use the nonparametric test because nothing is known about the shape of the population.

   (c) H_0: median ≥ 4.1; H_0: median < 4.1 (claim)

   (d) $\alpha = 0.05$

   $n = 20$

   The critical value is 5.

   $x = 7$

   Fail to reject H_0. There is not enough evidence at the 5% level of significance to support the claim that the median tenure is less than 4.1 years.

3. (a) Because the data from each sample appears non-normal, the Wilcoxon rank sum test should be used.

   (b) H_0: There is no difference between the median tenures for male workers and female workers.
   H_a: There is a difference between the median tenures for male workers and female workers.

(c)

Ordered data	Sample	Rank
0.9	M	1
1.3	F	2
1.8	F	3
2.2	F	4
2.3	M	5
3	F	6
3.3	F	7
3.6	M	8
3.8	M	9
3.9	M	10
4	F	11.5
4	F	11.5
4.3	M	13.5
4.3	F	13.5
4.4	M	15.5
4.4	F	15.5
4.7	M	17.5
4.7	M	17.5
4.9	M	19.5
4.9	F	19.5
5.1	M	22
5.1	F	22
5.1	F	22
5.2	F	24
5.4	F	25
6.5	M	26

R = sum ranks of male workers = 164.5

$$\mu_R = \frac{n_1(n_1 + n_2 + 1)}{2} = \frac{12(12 + 14 + 1)}{2} = 162$$

$$\sigma_R = \sqrt{\frac{n_1 n_2 (n_1 + n_2 + 1)}{12}} = \sqrt{\frac{(12)(14)(12 + 14 + 1)}{12}} \approx 19.442$$

$$z = \frac{R - \mu_R}{\sigma_R} \approx \frac{164.5 - 162}{19.442} \approx 0.129$$

Using $\alpha = 0.05$, $z_0 = \pm 1.96$.

Fail to reject H_0. There is not enough evidence at the 5% level of significance to conclude that there is a difference between the median tenures for male workers and female workers.

TECHNOLOGY: *USING TECHNOLOGY IN STATISTICS*

1. From a list of numbers ranging from 1 to 86, randomly select eight of them. Answers will vary.

2. From a list of numbers ranging from 1 to 300, randomly select 25 of them.

3. From a list of numbers ranging from 0 to 9, randomly select five of them. Repeat this two times. Average these three numbers and compare with the population average of 4.5. Answers will vary.

4. The average of the numbers 0 to 40 is 20. From a list of numbers ranging from 0 to 40, randomly select seven of them. Repeat this three times. Average these three numbers and compare with the population average of 20. Answers will vary.

5. Answers will vary.

6. No, we would anticipate 10-1's, 10-2's, 10-3's, 10-4's, 10-5's, and 10-6's. An inference that we might draw from the results is that the die is not a fair die.

7. Answers will vary.

8. No, we would anticipate 50 heads and 50 tails. An inference that we might draw from the results is that the coin is not fair.

9. The analyst could survey 10 counties by assigning each county a number from 1 to 47 and using a random number generator to find 10 numbers that correspond to certain counties.

CHAPTER 2

TECHNOLOGY: *MONTHLY MILK PRODUCTION*

1. $\bar{x} = 2270.5$

2. $s = 653.2$

3.

Lower limit	Upper limit	Frequency
1147	1646	7
1647	2146	15
2147	2646	13
2647	3146	11
3147	3646	3
3647	4146	0
4147	4646	1

4.

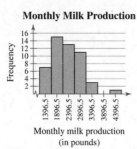

Monthly Milk Production

The distribution does not appear to be bell-shaped.

5. 74% of the entries were within one standard deviation of the mean (1617.3, 2923.7). 98% of the entries were within two standard deviations of the mean (964.1, 3576.9).

6. $\bar{x} = 2316.5$

7. $s \approx 641.75$

8. Answers will vary.

CHAPTER 3

TECHNOLOGY: *SIMULATION: COMPOSING MOZART VARIATIONS WITH DICE*

1. $2 + 11 = 13$ phrases were written.

2. $(11)^7 \cdot 2 \cdot (11)^7 \cdot 2 = 1.518999334333 \times 10^{15}$

3. (a) $\dfrac{1}{11} \approx 0.091$ (b) Results will vary.

4. (a) $P(\text{option 6, 7, or 8 for 1st bar}) = \dfrac{3}{11} = 0.273$

$P(\text{option 6, 7, or 8 for all 14 bars}) = \left(\dfrac{3}{11}\right)^{14} \approx 0.000000012595$

(b) Results will vary.

5. (a) $P(1) = \dfrac{1}{36}$ $P(2) = \dfrac{2}{36}$ $P(3) = \dfrac{3}{36}$ $P(4) = \dfrac{4}{36}$

$P(5) = \dfrac{5}{36}$ $P(6) = \dfrac{6}{36}$ $P(7) = \dfrac{5}{36}$ $P(8) = \dfrac{4}{36}$

$P(9) = \dfrac{3}{36}$ $P(10) = \dfrac{2}{36}$ $P(1) = \dfrac{1}{36}$

(b) Results will vary.

6. (a) $P(\text{option } 6, 7, \text{ or } 8 \text{ for 1st bar}) = \dfrac{15}{36} \approx 0.417$

$P(\text{option } 6, 7, \text{ or } 8 \text{ for all 14 bats}) = \left(\dfrac{15}{36}\right)^{14} \approx 0.00000475$

(b) Results will vary.

CHAPTER 4

TECHNOLOGY: *USING POISSON DISTRIBUTIONS AS QUEUING MODELS*

1.

x	$P(x)$
0	0.0183
1	0.0733
2	0.1465
3	0.1954
4	0.1954
5	0.1563
6	0.1042
7	0.0595
8	0.0298
9	0.0132
10	0.0053
11	0.0019
12	0.0006
13	0.0002
14	0.0001
15	0.0000
16	0.0000
17	0.0000
18	0.0000
19	0.0000
20	0.0000

2. (a) (See part b) 1, 2, 4, 7

(b)

Minute	Customers at Checkout	Total Customers at Checkout	Customers Serviced	Customers Remaining
1	3	3	3	0
2	3	3	3	0
3	3	3	3	0
4	3	3	3	0
5	5	5	4	1
6	5	6	4	2
7	6	8	4	4
8	7	11	4	7
9	3	10	4	6
10	6	12	4	8
11	3	11	4	7
12	5	12	4	8
13	6	14	4	10
14	3	13	4	9
15	4	13	4	9
16	6	15	4	11
17	2	13	4	9
18	2	11	4	7
19	4	11	4	7
20	1	8	4	4

3. Answers will vary.

4. 20 customers (an additional 1 customer would be forced to wait in line/minute)

5. Answers will vary.

6. $P(10) \approx 0.0181$

7. (a) It makes no difference if the customers were arriving during the 1st minute or the 3rd minute. The mean number of arrivals will still be 4 customers per minute.

   $P(3 \le x \le 5) = P(3) + P(4) + P(5) \approx 0.1954 + 0.1954 + 0.1563 = 0.5471$

   (b) $P(x > 4) = 1 - P(x \le 4) = 1 - \left[P(0) + P(1) + P(2) + P(3) + P(4) \right] = 1 - [0.6289] = 0.3711$

   (c) $P(x > 4$ during each of the first four minutes$) = (0.3711)^4 = 0.019$.

CHAPTER 5

TECHNOLOGY: *AGE DISTRIBUTION IN THE UNITED STATES*

1. $\mu \approx 37.06$

2. $\overline{x}$ of the 36 sample means ≈ 36.209
    This agrees with the Central Limit Theorem.

3. No, the distribution of ages appears to be positively skewed.

4.

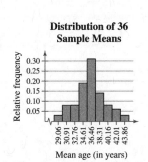

The distribution is approximately bell-shaped and symmetrical. This agrees with the Central Limit Theorem.

5. $\sigma \approx 22.729$

6. σ of the 36 sample means $= 3.552$
$$\frac{\sigma}{\sqrt{n}} = \frac{22.729}{\sqrt{36}} \approx 3.788$$
    This agrees with the Central Limit Theorem.

CHAPTER 6

TECHNOLOGY: *MOST ADMIRED POLLS*

1. $\hat{p} = 0.30$

$$\hat{p} \pm z_c \sqrt{\frac{\hat{p}\hat{q}}{n}} = 0.30 \pm 1.96 \sqrt{\frac{0.30(0.70)}{1025}}$$
$$\approx 0.30 \pm 0.028$$
$$= (0.272, \ 0.328)$$

2. $\hat{p} = 0.16$

$$\hat{p} \pm z_c \sqrt{\frac{\hat{p}\hat{q}}{n}} = 0.16 \pm 1.96 \sqrt{\frac{0.16(0.84)}{1025}}$$
$$\approx 0.16 \pm 0.022$$
$$= (0.138, \ 0.182)$$

3. No, the margins of error are ± 0.028 and ± 0.022.

4. $\hat{p} = 0.15$

$$\hat{p} \pm z_c \sqrt{\frac{\hat{p}\hat{q}}{n}} = 0.15 \pm 1.96 \sqrt{\frac{0.15(0.85)}{1025}}$$
$$\approx 0.15 \pm 0.022$$
$$= (0.128, \ 0.172)$$

5. Answers will vary.

6. No, because the 95% CI does not contain 18%.

CHAPTER 7

TECHNOLOGY: *THE CASE OF THE VANISHING WOMEN*

1. Reject H_0 with a P-value less than 0.01.

2. Type I error

3. Sampling process was non-random.

4. (a) $H_0 : p = 0.2914$ (claim); $H_a : p \neq 0.2914$
   (b) **Test and CI for One Proportion**
       Test of p = 0.2914 vs p not = 0.2914

Sample	X	N	Sample p	99% CI	Z-Value	P-Value
1	9	100	0.090000	(0.016284, 0.163716)	−4.43	0.000

   Using the normal approximation.
   (c) Reject H_0.
   (d) It was highly unlikely that random selection produced a sample of size 100 that contained only 9 women.

CHAPTER 8

TECHNOLOGY: *TAILS OVER HEADS*

1. CI for One Proportion

   Test of p = 0.5 vs. p not = 0.5

Sample	X	N	Sample p	99% CI	P-Value
1	5772	11902	0.484961	(0.473161m 0.496760)	0.001

   Reject H_0.

2. Yes, obtaining 5772 heads very uncommon occurrence (see sampling distribution). The coins might not be fair.

3. $\dfrac{1}{500} = 0.002 = 0.2\%$

4. $z = 8.802 \rightarrow$ Reject $H_0 : \mu_1 = \mu_2$ There is enough evidence at the 5% level of significance to support the claim that there is a difference in the mint dates of coins minted in Philadelphia and Denver.

5. $z = 1.010 \rightarrow$ Fail to reject $H_0 : \mu_1 = \mu_2$ There is not enough evidence at the 5% level of significance to support the claim that there is a difference in the value of coins minted in Philadelphia and Denver.

CHAPTER 9

TECHNOLOGY: *NUTRIENTS IN BREAKFAST CEREALS*

1. (a)   (b)   (c)

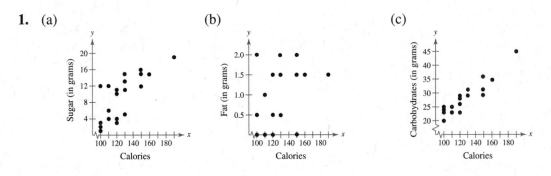

(d) (e) (f)

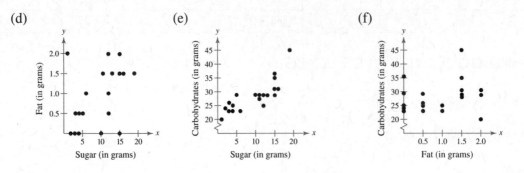

2. (calories, sugar), (calories, carbohydrates), (sugar, carbohydrates)

3. (calories, sugar): $r \approx 0.766$
   (calories, fat): $r \approx 0.415$
   (calories, carbohydrates): $r \approx 0.913$
   (sugar, fat): $r \approx 0.461$
   (sugar, carbohydrates): $r \approx 0.793$
   (fat, carbohydrates): $r \approx 0.230$

   Largest r: (calories, carbohydrates)

4. (a) $\hat{y} = -12.836 + 0.177x$
   (b) $\hat{y} = 1.072 + 0.213x$

5. (a) $\hat{y} = -12.836 + 0.177(120) = 8.404$ grams
   (b) $\hat{y} = 1.072 + 0.213(120) = 26.632$ grams

6. (a) $C = 12.929 - 0.268S + 7.567F + 3.886R$
   (b) $C = 23.279 + 0.496S + 3.518R$

7. $C = 12.929 - 0.268(7) + 7.567(0.5) + 3.886(31) \approx 135.303$ calories

CHAPTER 10

TECHNOLOGY: *TEACHER SALARIES*

1. Yes, because the salaries are from different states, it is safe to assume that the samples are independent.

2. Using a technology tool, it appears that all three samples were taken from approximately normal populations.

3. $H_0 : \sigma_1^2 = \sigma_2^2, H_a : \sigma_1^2 \neq \sigma_2^2 \, (F_0 = 2.86)$

(CA, OH) $\rightarrow F \approx 0.954 \rightarrow$ Fail to reject H_0.

(CA, TX) $\rightarrow F \approx 2.123 \rightarrow$ Fail to reject H_0.

(CA, TX) $\rightarrow F \approx 2.226 \rightarrow$ Fail to reject H_0.

4.   The three conditions for a one-way ANOVA test are satisfied.

$H_0 : \mu_1 = \mu_2 = \mu_3$ (claim)

H_a : At least one mean is different from the others.

Variation	Sum of squares	Degrees of Freedom	Mean squares	F
Between	2,663,311,122	2	1,331,655,561	26.992
Within	2,220,121,453	45	49,336,032.3	

$F \approx 26.992$

Reject H_0. There is not enough evidence at the 5% level of significance to rejects the claim that the mean salaries are the same.

5.   The sampleS are independent.

$H_0 : \sigma_1^2 = \sigma_2^2, H_a : \sigma_1^2 \neq \sigma_2^2 \, (F_0 = 2.86)$

(AK, NV) $\rightarrow F \approx 1.227 \rightarrow$ Fail to reject H_0.

(AK, NY) $\rightarrow F \approx 0.266 \rightarrow$ Fail to reject H_0.

(NV, NY) $\rightarrow F \approx 0.217 \rightarrow$ Fail to reject H_0.

The sample from the New York shows some sign of being drawn from a non-normal population. The three conditions for one-way ANOVA are not satisfied.

CHAPTER 11

TECHNOLOGY: *U.S. INCOME AND ECONOMIC RESEARCH*

1.

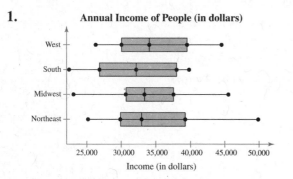

The median annual incomes do not appear to differ between regions.

2. H_0: median $\leq 30{,}000$

H_a: median $> 30{,}000$ (claim)

The critical value is 2.

$x = 2.$

Reject H_0. There is enough evidence at the 5% level of significance to support the claim that the median annual income in the Midwest is greater than \$30,000.

3. H_0: There is no difference in incomes in the Northeast and South. (claim)

H_a: There is a difference in incomes in the Northeast and South.

The critical values are $z_0 = \pm 1.96$.

$R = 162$

$$\mu_R = \frac{n_1(n_1 + n_2 + 1)}{2} = \frac{12(12 + 12 + 1)}{2} = 150$$

$$\sigma_R = \sqrt{\frac{n_1 n_2(n_1 + n_2 + 1)}{12}} = \sqrt{\frac{(12)(12)(12 + 12 + 1)}{12}} \approx 17.3$$

$$z = \frac{R - \mu_R}{\sigma_R} \approx \frac{162 - 150}{17.3} \approx 0.693$$

Fail to reject H_0. There is not enough evidence at the 5% level of significance to reject the claim that the median annual incomes in the Northeast and South are the same.

4. H_0: There is no difference in the incomes for all four regions.

H_a: There is a difference in the incomes for all four regions. (claim)

$\chi_0^2 = 7.815$

$H \approx 0.904$

Fail to reject H_0. There is not enough evidence at the 5% level of significance to reject the claim that the distributions of annual incomes for all four regions are the same.

5. H_0: There is no difference in the incomes for all four regions. (claim)

H_a: There is a difference in the incomes for all four regions. (claim)

Analysis of Variance

Variation	Sum of squares	Degrees of freedom	Mean squares	F	P
Between	69,265,161	3	23,088,387	0.53	0.664
Within	1.917×10^9	44	43,556,858		

$F \approx 0.53 \rightarrow P\text{-value} = 0.664$

Fail to reject H_0. There is not enough evidence at the 5% level of significance to reject the claim that the average annual incomes for all four regions are the same.

6. *(Box-and-whisker plot)*

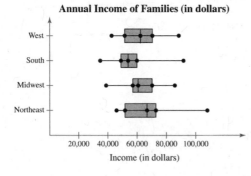

The median family incomes appear to be higher in the Northeast and lower in the South.

(Wilcoxon rank sum test)

H_0: There is no difference in incomes in the Northeast and South. (claim)
H_a: There is a difference in incomes in the Northeast and South.

The critical values are $z_0 = \pm 1.96$.

$$\mu_R = \frac{n_1(n_1 + n_2 + 1)}{2} = \frac{15(15 + 15 + 1)}{2} = 232.5$$

$$\sigma_R = \sqrt{\frac{n_1 n_2 (n_1 + n_2 + 1)}{12}} = \sqrt{\frac{(15)(15)(15 + 15 + 1)}{12}} \approx 24.1$$

$$z = \frac{R - \mu_R}{\sigma_R} \approx \frac{271 - 232.5}{24.1} \approx 1.598$$

Fail to reject H_0. There is not enough evidence at the 5% level of significance to reject the claim that the median annual incomes in the Northeast and South are the same.

(Kruskal-Wallis test)

H_0: There is no difference in incomes in all four regions. (claim)

H_a: There is a difference in incomes in all four regions.

$\chi_0^2 = 7.815$

$H = 4.38$

Fail to reject H_0. There is not enough evidence at the 5% level of significance to reject the claim that the distributions of annual incomes four all four regions are the same.

(ANOVA test)

H_0: There is no difference in the incomes for all four regions. (claim)

H_a: There is a difference in the incomes for all four regions. (claim)

Analysis of Variance

Variation	Sum of squares	Degrees of freedom	Mean squares	F	P
Between	810,166,455	3	270,055,485	1.26	0.297
Within	1.200×10^{10}	56	214,332,060		

$F \approx 1.26 \rightarrow P\text{-value} = 0.297$

Fail to reject H_0. There is not enough evidence at the 5% level of significance to reject the claim that the average annual incomes for all four regions are the same.